Mary Bell Hinshaw.
8-10-'49.

A TREASURY OF BRITISH HUMOR

A Treasury of

BRITISH HUMOR

Edited, with an Introduction,

BY

MORRIS BISHOP

COWARD-McCANN, INC., NEW YORK

MANUFACTURED IN THE UNITED STATES OF AMERICA

Van Rees Press • New York

12115

Editor's Note

A number of people have taken a helpful interest in this book before it was a book. But for Mrs. John C. Adams of Ithaca I should never have heard of Agnes Hunt, and I might well have overlooked Walter Raleigh. Harry Taber of Wilmington, Delaware, contributed generously from his store of learning and judgment. George Herbert Clarke of Kingston, Ontario, made many searching comments, and brought me A. Neil Lyons' *Cottage Pie* tenderly, on a piece of old Spode. William Strunk of Ithaca had many happy thoughts, the A. E. Housman verses among others. M. L. W. Laistner of Ithaca remembered, for our benefit, Kinglake's *Interview with a Pasha*. Angela Thirkell's description of the evacuees was the idea of Mrs. Clark McBurney of Ithaca. There were many others who took fire at the idea of a collection of British humor, and who gave lavish advice and criticism. I cannot mention all, but I should like to render especial thanks to Peter Monro Jack, Earle H. Balch, and Mrs. Fred T. Marsh of New York, Maurice Gorham of London, John C. Schroeder of New Haven, Romeyn Berry of Jacksonville, N. Y., and Mrs. Roy Harris and Miss Julia Eaton of Ithaca. And also to the courageous publisher, and to his indomitable aide, Miss Rose Dobbs. And to my wife, whose critical motto is *castigare ridendo Morris*.

M. B.

ACKNOWLEDGMENTS

The editor is grateful to the many authors who have allowed their work to be reprinted in this book. Every care has been taken to obtain permission from the owners to reprint material which is in copyright; any errors are unintentional and will be gladly corrected in future printings if notification is sent to the publishers, Coward-McCann, Inc., who wish to acknowledge with thanks the courtesy of the following for permission to reprint as indicated:

Mrs. Bambridge (the author's daughter), Doubleday, Doran & Company, Inc., and The Macmillan Company, Ltd., Canada, for "My Rival" and "Natural Theology" from *Verse, Definitive Edition,* by Rudyard Kipling.

Major the Hon. Maurice Baring and William Heinemann Ltd. Publishers, London, for "King Lear's Daughter" from *Dead Letters* and "Catherine Parr" from *Diminutive Dramas.*

Blackie & Son Ltd., London, and G. P. Putnam's Sons, New York, for "Mother" from *This Is My Life* (published in England under the title of *Reminiscences*) by Dame Agnes Hunt.

Geoffrey Bles, London, for a selection from *Mr. Thake* by J. B. Morton.

Brandt & Brandt, agents, for "At Grips with the Subway" from *Britisher On Broadway* by Anthony Armstrong, published by Methuen & Co. Ltd., London; also for "A Visit From Azania" from *Black Mischief,* copyright, 1932 by Evelyn Waugh, published by Farrar & Rinehart, Inc., and Chapman & Hall, London.

Roy Campbell and Faber & Faber Ltd., London, for "Home Thoughts in Bloomsbury" and "On Some South African Novelists" from *Adamastor.*

Jonathan Cape Ltd., London, and the authors for "Advice to the Reader" from *Variety* by Peter Fleming; "The Lion Roars" from *Sagittarius Rhyming* by "Sagittarius"; and "Willie Waugh" from *Fishmonger's Fiddle* and "Alas, Poor Bollington!" from *The Black Dog and Other Stories,* both by A. E. Coppard. Thanks are also due Jonathan Cape and Laurance Housman for permission to reprint from

A.E.H. "When Adam Day by Day" and "Amelia Mixed the Mustard" by A. E. Housman.

Covici Friede, Inc. for a selection from William Van Wyck's translation of *The Canterbury Tales of Geoffrey Chaucer.*

E. M. Delafield and The Macmillan Company Ltd., London, for "With the Difficult Guest," "Discussing the Fiancee," and "The Unselfish Hostess" from *As Others Hear Us.*

J. M. Dent & Sons Ltd., London, for the essays "The Vice of Punctuality from *Searchlights and Nightingales* by Robert Lynd and "A Walk with Papa" from *The Birdikin Family,* by A. Marshall, illustrated by George Morrow.

Dodd, Mead & Company, the Executrix of G. K. Chesterton and Burns, Oates & Washburne Ltd., London, for "The Perfect Game" from *Tremendous Trifles,* and "A Ballade of Suicide" and "The Song Against Grocers" from *The Collected Poems* of G. K. Chesterton; also to Dodd, Mead & Company for "The Vanderflints and the Vanderphants" from *The Polyglots* by William Gerhardi; "The Adventure of the Kind Mr. Smith" from *The Joyous Adventures of Aristide Pujol* by William J. Locke; and "A Naturalist" and "Jenner" from *Cottage Pie* by A. Neil Lyons; and Dodd, Mead & Company and Stephen Leacock for "Soaked In Seaweed" from *Nonsense Novels* and "With the Photographer" from *Laugh Parade.*

Doubleday, Doran & Company, Inc. for "Weatherwise" from *Collected Sketches and Lyrics* by Noel Coward; selections from *Trivia* by Logan Pearsall Smith; a selection from *The Young Visiters* by Daisy Ashford; and "God Save the King" from *Adventures of Dr. Whitty* by George A. Birmingham. Thanks are also due to Chatto & Windus, London, and to Methuen & Co. Ltd., London, for permission to reprint the last two selections, respectively.

Norman Douglas for "Trouble on Nepenthe" from his *South Wind.*

The Estate of William Henry Drummond for "M'Sieu Smit'; The Adventures of an Englishman in the Canadian Woods."

E. P. Dutton & Company for "The Bishop's Comedy" from *The Man Who Understood Women* by Leonard Merrick, and selections from *1066 And All That* by Walter Carruthers Sellar and Robert Julian Yeatman, published and copyrighted by E. P. Dutton & Co. Inc., New York.

Lord Dunsany for "The True History of the Hare and the Tortoise" from his *Fifty-One Tales.*

Herbert Farjeon for "Our British Pastimes" from his *Omnibus*.

Nathaniel Gubbins for "Fun in a Nursing Home" from his *Diary of a Worm*, published by Hutchinson and Co. Ltd., London.

Harcourt, Brace & Company for selections by Logan Pearsall Smith from *More Trivia*, 1921; *Afterthoughts*, 1931; *All Trivia* (containing *Last Words*) 1934; all copyrighted by Harcourt, Brace & Company; and "The Eve of the Shoot" and "Christmas Shopping" from *Mrs. Miniver* by Jan Struther.

Harper & Bros. for "Jonah" and "The Fifth Philosopher's Song" from *Leda*, and a selection from *Crome Yellow*, both by Aldous Huxley; and a selection from *The Flying Yorkshireman* by Eric Knight. Thanks are also due the Musson Book Company, Canada, for permission to reprint the latter selection.

A. P. Herbert and the Proprietors of *Punch* for "Mrs. Mole" and "I Can't Think What He Sees in Her" from *A Book of Ballads*.

The Hogarth Press, London, for "Headline History" from *The Family Tree* by William Plomer.

Henry Holt & Co. and William Heinemann Ltd., London, for a selection from *Joseph Vance* by William De Morgan.

Miss Rowena Jerome and J. W. Arrowsmith (London) Ltd. for "Harris Sings a Comic Song" from *Three Men in a Boat*, and "Overhauling a Bicycle" from *Three Men on the Bummel*, both by Jerome K. Jerome.

Alfred A. Knopf, Inc. for "A Stitch in Time, or Pride Prevents a Fall" from *Ladies' Mistakes* by James Laver; "The Brewer's Man" and "Jesse Welch" from *Selected Poems* by L. A. G. Strong; "Germans at Meat" and "The Modern Soul" from *In a German Pension* by Katherine Mansfield; "Evacuees in Barsetshire" from *Cheerfulness Breaks In* by Angela Thirkell; and "Charles Augustus Fortescue" from *Cautionary Verses* by Hilaire Belloc. Thanks are also due to The Macmillan Company, Ltd., Canada, Hamish Hamilton Ltd., London, and Duckworth & Co. Ltd., London, for permission to reprint the last three selections, respectively.

John Lane, The Bodley Head Ltd., London, for "A Good Prince" from *Works* and "A Home-Coming" from *Yet Again*, both by Max Beerbohm; and "Abdallah the Adite" from *The Twilight of the Gods* by Richard Garnett. Thanks are also due to the Executors of the late Richard Garnett for permission to use the selection from his book.

D. B. Wyndham Lewis and Andrew Melrose and Cecil Palmer,

London, for "The Case of the Village Blacksmith" from *At the Sign of the Blue Moon,* and "Mainly Musical" and "A Balkan Lyric" from *A London Farrago.*

Longmans, Green & Company for "Cambridge Dons" from *As We Were* by E. F. Benson; "Morning in Cold Comfort Farm" from *Cold Comfort Farm* by Stella Gibbons; and "Poisson d'Avril" from *Further Experiences of an Irish R. M.* by E. Œ. Somerville and Martin Ross.

Rose Macaulay for "The Continental Boat Train."

Robert M. McBride Inc. for selections from *Sonnets and Verse* by Hilaire Belloc.

The Macmillan Company for "The Ruined Maid" from *Poems of the Past and Present* and "Epitaph on a Pessimist" from *Human Shows—Far Phantasies* by Thomas Hardy; selections from *The Letters of Sir Walter Raleigh;* and "From Sense to Sensibility" from *The Decline and Fall of the Romantic Ideal* by F. L. Lucas. Thanks are also due the Cambridge University Press, London, for permission to reprint the last selection.

The Macmillan Company, Ltd., Canada, for "Andrey Satchel and the Parson and Clerk" from *A Few Crusted Characters* by Thomas Hardy.

Bruce Marshall for "Conversation in an Edinburgh Bar" from his *Father Malachy's Miracle.*

Matson & Duggan, agents, for "Country Idyll" from *Morton's Folly* by J. B. Morton; also A. D. Peters, London, agent, for this and selections from *I Do Not Think So* by J. B. Morton, published by Burns, Oates and Washburne, London.

Methuen & Co. Ltd., London, for "Take Me in Your Arms, Miss Moneypenny-Wilson" from *Songs of a Sub-Man* by Patrick Barrington; "The Lion and the Sheep" from *Both Sides of the Road* by Robert Lynd; "Mrs. Murphy on Honesty" from *Barry Pain* by Barry Pain; and "How I Brought the Good News from Aix to Ghent" from *Horse Nonsense* by R. J. Yeatman and W. C. Sellar.

John Murray Ltd., London, John Betjeman for "Distant View of a Provincial Town" from *Continual Dew.*

Nelson & Co. Ltd., London, for "The Drinking Song of Pelagius" from *The Four Men* by Hilaire Belloc.

The *New Statesman and Nation* and Eliot Crawshay-Williams for "Bombed."

Oxford University Press, Oxford, for "The Motor Bus" from *Fifty Poems* by A. D. Godley.

Adrian Porter and Messrs. W. Collins Sons & Co. Ltd., London, for "The Perfect Child" from *The Perfect Pest*.

The Proprietors of *Punch* and the authors for "Burglar Bill" from *Mr. Punch's Young Reciter;* "Jungle English" from *What a Word!* and *"Rex vs. Haddock, Is a Golfer a Gentleman?"* from *Uncommon Law* by A. P. Herbert; "White Sox vs. Giants," "The Old Silent House," and "A Polite Protest" by E. V. Knox; "Entertaining in War Time" by Angela Milne; "Correspondence of a Censor" by Daniel Pettiward; and the selections printed under the general title of "Kultur" by R. A. A. Robertson.

G. P. Putnam's Sons and T. H. White for "Encounter with a Medieval Witch" from *The Sword in the Stone* and for selections from *More Ruthless Rhymes from Heartless Homes* by Harry Graham.

Lady Raleigh and Constable & Co. Ltd., London, for "The Wishes of an Elderly Man" from *Laughter From A Cloud* by Walter Raleigh.

Paul R. Reynolds & Son, agents, for "Tried in the Furnace" from *The Crime Wave at Blandings,* copyright 1937, by P. G. Wodehouse.

The Richards Press, London, and Ernest Bramah for "The Story of Yung Chang" from *The Wallet of Kai-Lung*.

George Bernard Shaw for "Boiled Heroine" from his *Dramatic Opinions and Essays*.

Charles Scribner's Sons and W. W. Jacobs for "The Persecution of Bob Pretty" from *Odd Craft;* "The Writer" from *Satires* by John Galsworthy; a selection from *The Wind in the Willows* by Kenneth Grahame, illustrated by E. H. Shepard; and "Kipps in the Royal Grand Hotel" from *Kipps* by H. G. Wells.

The Viking Press for "The Frog Prince" and "Night! Youth! Paris! And the Moon!" from *Presenting Moonshine* by John Collier; and "Tea" and "The Reticence of Lady Anne" from *The Short Stories of Saki (H. H. Munro)*. Thanks are also due John Lane, The Bodley Head Ltd., London, for permission to reprint the Saki stories.

INTRODUCTION

Before we undertake the wearisome task of analyzing British humor, it would be well to define our terms. What is humor? What is British? In fact, what is a definition?

A definition has been satisfactorily defined by Samuel Butler, in his *Note-Books*. "Definitions," he says, "are a kind of scratching, and generally leave a sore place more sore than it was before."

"British" is easy. Anyone who has lived and done his significant work within the Empire is British. You will find in these pages a good number of Scots and Irish, four Canadians, two South Africans, one New Zealander, one Barbadoan, and one American domiciled in England.

But "humor" is the hard one. Humor has been much and laboriously defined. I think that after all the best rule is that humor is what makes people laugh, or experience a muscular quake premonitory of laughter. This is philosophically and psychologically unsatisfactory, but so are the conclusions of the philosophers and psychologists.

Man has been defined as the laughing animal, because he is the only animal that laughs, except the hyena. But if man is a laughing animal, may we conclude that all men laugh? Evidently not. Saint Ignatius Loyola urged his followers to abstain from all laughter and from words which might provoke a laugh. Certain Indians of the Texas coast were known as "weepers"; on meeting, they would sit speechless for half an hour, shedding mutual tears. Gaiety shuns the temple, the tomb, the cells of the condemned. Laughter has its places; it has also its times. The Elizabethan age was loud with laughter, of a snorting, thigh-slapping sort, and the Cavaliers carried on the tradition. Sir Thomas Urquhart, the great translator of Rabelais, died in a laughing fit when he heard that Charles II was restored to the English throne. It is true that seventeenth-century humors rouse in us more wonder than sympathetic mirth. I choose a curious example of the comic sense of those days, from the autobiography of William Taswell. This country clergyman visited, in 1675, Wilton House, the seat of the Earl of Pembroke. "In the gardens of this were very curious waterworks. There was a rock with a bird sitting on it on one side; on the other side were some waters conveyed through pipes, which on its rising and falling resembled the warbling of birds. In another place there was a looking-glass, in which, if any lady beheld her face, a pipe under her feet was sure to convey the water to her thighs. If a man was curious in that way too, a pipe constructed behind him would convey the water into his breeches."

In the eighteenth century such high humors ceased, at least among the polite. Our contributor, Professor F. L. Lucas (*vide post*, p. 647), notes that Lord Chesterfield never laughed in the course of his adult life. And when Fontenelle was asked if he ever laughed, he pondered a moment and replied: "No; I never go 'Hah! Hah! Hah!'" I see old Fontenelle, opening his mouth wide to bare his rare yellow eighteenth-century teeth, laboriously heaving his diaphragm, and expelling a harsh, spasmodic breath.

Thus social pressure may still the laughter in our throats. You will grant, however, that most people laugh, and that what they laugh at is humor. You will grant, too, that there are differences in humor. People are proud of laughing when others are silent, and to every chorused roar there is a silvery murmur of "I don't see what there is to laugh at in that." Happily married couples develop a family sense of humor; the unhappily married laugh separately. Every nation has its body of comic tradition and comic literature. As each particular culture progresses, historians arise who define and limit their national humor and sneer at the national humor of their neighbors.

Thus it is commonly accepted that humor is evanescent and variable. It is accepted further that our nation and our time possess true humor, and that our neighbors laugh, if at all, in the wrong places. For example, the extraordinary belief is current in America that the English are unhumorous, that they do not understand a joke.

Certainly there are variations in humor. But the remarkable thing, I think, is not that humor varies, but that the variations are so small. We have dwelt enough on the localism and particularity of humor; let us rather dwell on its universality. A good joke rises above space and time into the infinite.

Here is a Greek joke: The orator Isocrates was making a speech in Athens. His rival, in spite, climbed on a soapbox at the rear of the crowd and silently held up a dead fish. One or two people turned around and stared. They nudged their neighbors. Soon the audience was abuzz. All faced about and looked at the mute sage holding aloft the dead fish. Isocrates faltered and was silent. And the rival proclaimed: "See how a dead fish is more interesting than Isocrates!"

How modern! How American!

Here is a Latin joke: A friend said to Cato the Elder: "It's a scandal that no statue has been erected to you in Rome! I am going to form a committee..."—"No," said Cato, "I would rather have people ask, 'Why isn't there a statue to Cato?' than 'Why is there one?'"

How modern! How middle-western! How Joe Cannon!

Rabelais, Molière, and Voltaire make American college students bellow with laughter. Dostoevski's description of Yulia Mihailovna's fête in *The Possessed* is one of the funniest sustained bits of broad comedy in literature. There is a sixteenth-century Chinese novel called *Chin P'ing Mei* which is terrific, and if you haven't read it (there is a fine translation by Bernard Miall) I urge you to get a copy as soon as you finish this book. A witty German, Dutchman, or Swede is witty in the narrowest American sense, and a lot of his anecdotes about the town character of Rothenburg or Upsala are the same anecdotes we tell about our uncle in Sandy Creek. A music-hall comic travels from country to country, setting his audiences in a monotonous roar. Laurel and Hardy wow them in Bolivia, Charles Chaplin in Chinese Turkestan.

The several national traditions of humor are variations, relatively minute, on the great species of universal humor. American humor is a minute variation on British humor.

With all the current hurly-burly about Americanism there has been a tendency, amounting almost to a trend, to regard American literature as something separate from European literature, and a like tendency to regard American humor as something individual and distinct. I think this is a mistake. In my reading of the humorous literature of Britain, I have been constantly impressed by the identity of the Britons' humorous devices with those of the Americans. If you want to make a classification of humor, you had better make it horizontally, and not vertically. That is, don't say Jokes: British; and Jokes: American; but Jokes: Mother-in-Law; and Jokes: Cheese. A cheese joke is the same on both sides of the Atlantic, except that Limburger substitutes for Stilton; it evokes the same hoarse blood-curdling glee on the BBC and on your favorite radio station. The cheese joke may represent the lower level of humor. The upper level, which may be called the "refined," or "super-cheese," level, is likewise independent of national boundaries. We laugh with Dickens, the English laugh with Mark Twain. The *New Yorker* has an important clientele in England; it is more read and relished in London, I suspect, than in Kansas City. The English subscriber to the *New Yorker* never sees *Tit-Bits*. Similarly, or contrariwise, *Punch* is more enjoyed in a Boston club or a Long Island country house than it is in a Lancashire mill town.

We befool ourselves, I fear, by our habit of taking what is most admirable and exceptional in our civilization and calling it "typically American" (as the English call the corresponding thing "characteristically English," and the Germans, *"echt deutsch"*). Take our great, unique American master, Mark Twain. No one could be more typically American, certainly? He was endowed, evidently by Nature, with a rare intelligence, which was shaped by his contacts with the people of the frontier and by his reading of English literature. But suppose that by some bizarre fate Mark Twain's family had transported him, at the age of sixteen, to an English village. My guess is that Mark Twain, or Samuel Clemens, would have become a great English humorous writer. We should not have had *Roughing It,* or *Innocents Abroad;* but we should have had some superb pictures of raffish life on the English roads, and an immortal characterization of a carefree tinker's boy named, perhaps, Whortleberry Finn. Samuel Clemens, eventually Sir Samuel Clemens, though formed in America, would have been known as "typically English" because his subject matter was typically English. But the mind of Mark Twain would have revealed itself in forms essentially similar to those we know.

No one writes more typically English humor than Logan Pearsall Smith, who left America for England at the age of twenty-three. No one is more typically American, in his sense of absurdity, his genial satire, his artful manipulation of the English language, than Ludwig Bemelmans in his magical tales of the Hotel Splendide. Bemelmans came here from Germany when he was about sixteen, and went to work as a bus boy in a New York hotel.

The fact is—or I think the fact is—that the truly humorous mind is superior to its moment and milieu. Literary critics have been making a great deal recently of the influences of a given period upon a writer. Maybe they have made too much of the influences and not enough of the writer. Certainly the comics of the past who are still comic are rare. Ordinary humor represents the humor of the times; the great humorists are those who forecast future humor—our own. These great humorists are few, and they appear strangely isolated. Chaucer, for instance. You would naturally think that a society which could produce so accomplished, so complete a humorist as Chaucer must have produced a lot of little Chaucers. But if so, they are lost beyond the reach of even the most dogged researcher. And don't go muttering "Hoccleve" and "Lydgate" in your beard, please. Too much beard-muttering around here, anyway. Too many beards, in fact.

Usually the people of any time recognized their great comics, but did not recognize their uniqueness. Take the Rev. Sydney Smith. Almost everything Sydney said was good, and some of his things were wonderful. But try to read the witticisms of his contemporaries, of equal fame in their day! For example:

"I know you, Mr. Jerrold, but you shall not make a butt of me!" said a stranger to the great wit, Douglas Jerrold. "Then don't bring your *hog's head* in here," was the prompt reply.... The conversation at Holland House turning on first love, Thomas Moore compared it to a potato, because "it shoots from the eyes." "Or rather," exclaimed Lord Byron, "because it becomes less by *pairing*." ...And this is wonderful: "When Foote was on his way to France, for a change of air, he went into the kitchen at the inn at Dover, to order a particular dish for dinner. The true English cook boasted that she had never set foot out of her country. On this, the invalid gravely observed: 'Why, cookey, that is very extraordinary, as they tell me upstairs that you have been several times *all over grease!*' 'They may tell you what they please above or below stairs,' replied the cook, 'but I was never ten miles from Dover in my life.' 'Nay, now, that must be a *fib*,' says Foote, 'for I have myself seen you at *Spithead!*' The next day (October 21, 1777) the exhausted wit 'shuffled off this mortal coil.' "

(As I interpret the jest which crowned and concluded a life devoted to double meanings, Foote wished to imply that cookey had been at the town of "Spithead," distant more than ten miles from Dover, because she had been seen at the *head* of a roasting-*spit!* Get it?)

These examples are intended to prove merely that the average humor of the late eighteenth and early nineteenth centuries inspires in us something between a kindly shudder and actual nausea. But not because the examples are British. One has only to examine the humorous products of America in the same age to recognize that American wit was positively emetic. My distinguished colleagues, E. B. and Katharine White, found no one of this period except Franklin and Irving to put in their monumental *Subtreasury of American Humor.*

I maintain, therefore, that the differences between American and British humor are slight. But I do not go so far as to say that there are no differences at all.

Harold Nicolson, in a shrewd article in his *Small Talk,* alleges that "the tendency of the best British humor is to render the rational ridiculous, whereas the tendency of the best American humor is to render the ridiculous rational." This is excellent, but I suspect that the proof must lie in the examples one chooses to admit as "the best." What fits Mr. Nicolson's thesis is "the best"; what does not, is not. I should say that Lewis Carroll, W. S. Gilbert, and John Collier render the ridiculous rational, while Frank Moore Colby, Cornelia Otis Skinner, Clarence Day render the rational ridiculous.

My erudite and subtle friend, Harry P. Taber, of Wilmington, Delaware, writes me on this theme:

Sympathy is the motivation of humor, and humor in and of itself is not necessarily laughable. In it there is no corrosive bitterness as there is in wit—of which acridity is an essential part. . . .

Quoting one bit of British humor may better explain what I'm driving at. It is a part of Lewis Carroll's introduction to *The Hunting of the Snark:*

"If—and the thing is wildly possible—the charge of writing nonsense were ever brought against the author of this brief but instructive poem, it would be based, I feel convinced, on the line, 'Then the bowsprit got mixed with the rudder sometimes.' In view of this painful possibility, I will not (as I might) appeal indignantly to my other writings as a proof that I am incapable of such a deed: I will not (as I might) point to the strong moral purpose of this poem itself, to the arithmetical principles so cautiously inculcated in it, or to its noble teachings in Natural History—I will take the more prosaic course of simply explaining how it happened.

"The Bellman, who was almost morbidly sensitive about appearances, used to have the bowsprit unshipped once or twice a week to be revarnished; and it more than once happened, when the time came for replacing it, that no one on board could remember which end of the ship it belonged to. They knew it was not of the slightest use to appeal to the Bellman about it—he would only refer to his Naval Code, and read out in pathetic tones Admiralty Instructions which none of them had ever been able to understand—so it generally ended in its being fastened on, anyhow, across the rudder. The helmsman used to stand by with tears in his eyes: *he* knew it was all wrong, but alas! Rule 42 of the Code, *'No one shall speak to the Man at the Helm,'* had been completed by the Bellman himself with the words 'and the Man at the Helm shall speak to no one.' So remonstrance was impossible, and no steering could be done till the next varnishing day. During these bewildering intervals the ship usually sailed backwards."

And there [continues the admirable Taber] you have as perfect an example of British humor as you'll find in many a long day's journey. The word "humor" does not explain its peculiar appeal; nor does "facetious" or "funny"; not even "laughable," and most certainly not "wit" or "witticism," for these latter imply disparagement. I shall have to go back to the Priestley phrase: "odd pathos," and that does not completely satisfy me. One word which means "perfect sympathetic understanding" is what I want, and it must, too, contain some element suggesting pity.... In her introduction to her *Letters of Edward Lear,* Lady Strachey quotes Carlyle: "True humor is sensibility in the most catholic and deepest sense; but it is the sport of sensibility; wholesome and perfect therefore." And Lady Strachey continues: "It is said that humor is allied to sadness, and it is this quality which defines it from its kindred quality, wit...."

All this is well said. The odd pathos is indeed a frequent component of humor, tears hide in laughter, tragedy puts on the comic mask. But I don't see that pathos is a necessary or even a usual component of humor. And I don't see that it is specifically British. How about Cervantes? And Musset? And Karel Capek?

Another frequent distinction between the two humors, an impressive after-dinner antithesis, is the statement that British humor depends on understatement, American humor on overstatement. The best thing about this distinction is that it permits the distinguisher to tell some of his favorite jokes. Thus Harry Taber chooses this "indirect, solemn, effective" bit from an old *Punch:* The picture shows the exterior of the United Service Clubs on a snowy, windy night. A fiercely medaled general approaches a waiting cab. GENERAL: "Nasty night, what?" CABBY: "I give you my word, sir, I 'aven't seen a butterfly orl day."

And I would cite this, also from an old *Punch:* Picture of a crowded omnibus. The conductor has obviously been thrown on a well-dressed passenger by a lurch of the bus. WELL-DRESSED PASSENGER: "I say, conductor, can't you keep off a person's feet?" CONDUCTOR: "Wot d'yer expect for a penny fare? Pavlover?"

In illustration of American humor by exaggeration, one may allege the Paul Bunyan saga, or the tall stories of the West, some of which filtered into Mark Twain's juvenilia. I like the story of Singleshot Johnson, as reported by Desmond Powell of Colorado College. Singleshot Johnson was hoeing his corn patch when he was attacked by a horned snake. Using his hoe as a pole, he vaulted out of danger; the snake buried his horn in the hoe handle. Singleshot dispatched the snake with a single shot from his forty-four. Then the hoe handle began to swell. When it stopped swelling, Singleshot sawed enough boards out of it to build a fair-sized smokehouse. Something in the snake's venom conveyed a miraculous flavor to the hams cured in that smokehouse. It was something like hog crossed with wood pigeon; old Doc Schmuck, a learned neighbor, compared it rather to the flesh of the phoenix or the gumperz. A restaurant man came from San Francisco, and immediately took an option on all the ham Singleshot could smoke. But unfortunately Singleshot incurred the enmity of old Doc Schmuck by proving, in response to a challenge, that with a single shot he could raise a furrow of dust on top of the Doc's silk hat without injuring the hat. The Doctor, his dignity ruffled, sneaked over to the smokehouse one night and poured over it a bottle of his famous liniment which would wizen a wen or take the pride out of a senator. And in the morning the smokehouse had shrunk to a pile of match-sticks.

That story, like the rest of the tall tales, certainly depends on overstatement. But it is not essentially American. It is related in style and technique to the Gargantua cycle of France and to all the tall stories of the European folk tradition. It is simply a folk story. And if the folk story and its method of overstatement have been regarded as typically American, no doubt the reason is that a half century ago such stories were closer to the literary surface than they were in England. But to the average American today they are as piquantly strange as they are to the average Englishman.

As overstatement is not typically American, no more is understatement exclusively English. If you will take your copy of *A Subtreasury of American Humor* in hand, you will find that the device of understatement is constantly used, by Frank R. Stockton, Anita Loos, Dorothy Parker, etc., etc. There is some overstatement too, but it is employed mostly by the older group, Washington Irving, Mark Twain, George Ade.

It is our duty to examine one more distinction between the two humors. It is frequently said in England that the English joker makes his jokes short, snappy, and to the point, whereas the American's jokes seem to last forever, winding sluggishly through lush marshlands toward the Point, a lighthouse long glimpsed and desired from afar.

But this distinction is based on a misconception. The English joke is compared, not with the American joke, which is snappy enough for any taste, but with the Story. The Story, perhaps a native American *genre,* is a giant anecdote. It should be told only by a skilled raconteur. Its virtue consists not so much in the Point as in the decorative detail with which the raconteur adorns its innumerable convolutions. In its literary aspect, it is the American Short Story, of which O. Henry was the great practitioner. It is not to be confused nor compared with the Joke.

No, we aren't going to find any valid distinction between the two humors here. In fact (not to waste any more time about it) we aren't going to find any valid distinction. We are going to reach this sounding conclusion:

The substance and technique of British and American humor are essentially the same. What difference there is lies, naturally, in the subject matter. It lies also in the point of view which the humorist adopts, in order to assure the sympathy of his reader. British humorists have commonly adopted an aristocratic attitude, while the Americans have been usually anti-aristocratic.

Typically, the elder British humorist was, or pretended to be, an Etonian or Harrovian and a Senior Wrangler in the Big Little Greats at Oxford or Cambridge. He nearly died laughing at the bounder who used a false quantity in quoting his Horace, or who passed the port counterclockwise, or who wore a gray bowler instead of a cocked hat on the hunting field, or who shouted "Yoicks" instead of "Tally-ho" when the hare sprang out of its covert in the paddock at Epsom. British humorists are forever stepping into their billiard rooms for a quiet game after dinner. Billiard rooms indeed! I'll wager most of them step into the local for a game of darts.

Almost until our own times British humorists would not admit that they or their readers could be anything less than landed gentry. Even Dickens, who went to work in a blacking warehouse at the age of nine, treats his lower-class characters as quaint and laughable figures in an upper-class world. For all his sympathy with certain of the virtuous poor, he did not identify himself with them, nor permit his readers to make such an identification. Most of his commoners, with their freakish physique, dress, mannerisms, and language, were intended to amuse readers who were pleasantly conscious of having no peculiarities at all. You and I always pass the port clockwise.

This genteel point of view was normal also among American humorists of the earlier nineteenth century. Oliver Wendell Holmes, Nathaniel P. Willis, John G. Saxe, assumed that their readers possessed breeding and an income. The same assumption was made by the editors of the popular magazines. The aristocratic attitude persists today, especially in scholarly humor. Curiously, it is visible, I should say, in the *New Yorker,* which presumes that its readers are well educated, traveled, comfortably well off, and intelligently skeptical. Its readers like that.

But from the time of the American Revolution, the anti-aristocratism of the people began to express itself in mockery of the well dressed and the well educated, and this anti-aristocratism became the characteristic attitude of American humor. The humorist, from Seba Smith through Will Rogers, pretended that he and his readers were powerful countrymen in cowhide boots, possessed of a heart of gold and a penetrating intelligence—David Harums, in short, or at least the city-dwelling sons of David Harum. (True, Will Rogers revealed a certain distrust by chewing gum instead of tobacco.) Though much of our democratic wit was directed against the English, it was relished by the English themselves. One need only recall the great vogue of Artemus Ward, Mark Twain, and Will Rogers himself in England.

In England, however, the aristocratic tradition of humor remained dominant. Today *Punch* represents this tradition. *Punch* has, to be sure, lost or hidden some of its hoity-toity airs. But at least until the current war it laughed at profiteers, Jews, Americans, musicians, the commoner who attempts to hunt and who always comes a cropper on stone walls which gentlemen clear, the provincial in a restaurant which is too good for him, the charwoman trying to use language which is too good for her, the pert parlormaid who is getting above herself. These are all fine comic figures. I for one find *Punch* very funny. I keep it in the gun room, with the heads I brought home from Africa.

But you can't base a theory of British humor on *Punch,* any more than you can take the *New Yorker* as a miniature of American humor. The interesting thing is that there has been in England a rebellion against *Punch* and against aristocratic humor in general.

Naturally this is not new. Democratic English humor goes back at least to the Norman Conquest, which introduced into England a ruling class identical with a ruling race. "When Adam delved and Eve span, Who was then the gentleman?" sang the churls. You will find in this collection some curious examples of the anti-aristocratic humor of Robert B. Brough (b. 1828). But by and large the mockery of the gentleman did not find much humorous expression until the time of H. G. Wells (b. 1866). And the tendency became clearly defined immediately after the first World War. On the high literary level Aldous Huxley and Evelyn Waugh and all the disintegrators derided the vanity, futility, and vice of the well born and gently bred. P. G. Wodehouse, certainly without any social purpose, draws a picture of genteel inanity which will some day be the subject of horrifying sociological studies.

On the lower literary level the revolution has been most visible. In the music halls the idiot gentleman is the audience's favorite butt. The Old School Tie, the Straight Bat, Play the Game, Cads, are always good for a laugh. Low's Colonel Blimp was a symbol and an omen, and Low's announcement of his death is another symbol. The great popular newspapers, the *Daily Mail,* the *Express,* the *Herald,* have developed their New Humor. Those incomparable comics, J. B. Morton ("Beachcomber"), D. B. Wyndham Lewis, and Nathaniel Gubbins, are anti-aristocrat, anti-Punch, anti-Tory. I don't know about their politics, but their rise has coincided with the rise of the Labour Party as an intellectual force. They may represent, on the plane of humor, something new and very important. They are the expression of a new England, strange to Americans who have known, from visits abroad or from their reading, the old England. They may represent, even, the England that is to be, the England of the coming millennium.

In choosing the examples of British humor in this volume, I have had a few guiding principles, which I have followed in a fidgety way: (1) Every selection must have made me (a) laugh out loud; (b) chuckle; (c) smile broadly. No item which failed to pass this requirement could be admitted, no matter how famous its author.

(2) Among an author's various works, I have chosen the less known in preference to the well known.

(3) The old standard comic pieces that everyone knows have been omitted.

(4) The mere joke and the anecdote have been banned, also unconscious humor, and also the parody, in the strict sense. Parodists, says Salvador de Madariaga, are literary cockroaches, and, while I think this is a little harsh, I find most of them painful, like horrible children doing "imitations."

(5) Indecency has been eschewed, except in a few rare examples from privileged authors. Ed Wynn is right—indecency is usually the recourse of the comic who can't get a laugh by other means.

These rules have got me into a good deal of trouble. There are omissions which will astound and grieve nice judges. A snarl will be heard in the colleges: "Where is Laurence Sterne? And Tobias Smollett? And Charles Lamb? And Surtees? And Lever and Lover? And *The Diary of a Nobody?* And that wonderful story in the *Strand Magazine* in 1888?"

I am sorry. I felt that I must have the courage of my sense of humor. I read Sterne without a smile; his famous sly digs leave me black and blue. I dislike Charles Lamb personally; he breathes on me; he stutters on purpose to make people listen to his silly jokes. I thought that I would put in a lot of the minor Elizabethans, but there wasn't a laugh in a barrel of them, except some bits of Thomas Heywood. They just didn't seem funny to me. I am sorry.

Some of the glaring omissions are not to be blamed on my perverse sense of humor. Fielding, for instance; I think Fielding is marvelous, but his comedy depends on character and situation, and on the tone of the whole, which needs the build-up of the novel. Thackeray, again. I have gone through all Thackeray's works, without finding a humorous prose selection that fitly represents him. His casual papers for *Punch* are too casual; and I found nothing in the great novels that would lift out without bruising. Read, for instance, Becky Sharp's letter to Amelia, describing her arrival at Queen's Crawley. It is a humorous masterpiece when you are already acquainted with the characters. But if you don't know them, you don't quite see what the fuss is about. So much humor in novels and plays is cumulative.

As I just remarked, I have omitted passages that are too well known. It seemed a pity to give up my precious pages to *Alice in Wonderland,* or Dogberry and the Watch, or the opening pages of *Pickwick.* And yet there are some things I couldn't bear to leave out, well known as they are: Falstaff, for instance, and Calverley's *Lovers and a Reflection,* and Gilbert's *Etiquette.* This is inconsistent, you will object. You are right. This is inconsistent.

I haven't begun to answer your objections. However, I think I have good reason for all of my selections. As for my omission of something you would have included, either (1) I didn't think it was funny; or (2) I thought it was funny, but too long, or short, or indecent, or cruel, or something; or (3) the author or publisher made trouble about reproducing it; or (4) I never heard of it.

If you are dissatisfied, I can only suggest, with all good will, that you make your own anthology. You will find it a delightful occupation, and a shield against the world's woe and evil. Everyone should make his own anthology. Indeed, everyone is, in a way, an Anthology.

M. B.

Contents

A TREASURY OF BRITISH HUMOR

Anonymous

There must have been plenty of British humor during the Middle Ages. On the Continent there was comedy enough, in Latin and the various vernaculars, and some of it very funny too. But the English apparently were ashamed of their own laughter. They had the reputation of making merry sadly. "Ils se réjouissaient tristement selon la coutume de leur pays," said Froissart in the fourteenth century. At any rate, most specimens of medieval English humor amuse only antiquaries, who have very hollow laughs at best.

But the Irish were lads for a joke. Here is a curious bit about the Great Bardic Association, which flourished in the seventh century. According to its editor, Owen Connellan, it was probably written in the same century, by an enemy of the Great Bardic Association. From my own knowledge of bards, I should say that the author had probably been blackballed by the Association.

THE PROCEEDINGS OF THE GREAT BARDIC ASSOCIATION (Selection)

A noble, worthy king ruled Oirgiall at one time whose name was Hugh, son of Duach the Dark. Contemporaneous with him was Hugh the Fair, son of Fergus, son of Muredagh Mal, King of Brefney, and these two were at strife. In every good act performed by one, the other would endeavour to excel him; yet both were not equally circumstanced; for one was a hundred fold more wealthy, just, and prosperous, namely Hugh the Fair; whilst the other was valiant and warlike, namely Hugh the son of Duach the Dark, King of Oirgiall. It was, indeed, far easier for him to be the more warlike of the two, for he had a shield, and the name of the shield was Duv-Gilla, and one of its properties was this, that whosoever was opposed to it in the field of battle became as enfeebled as an old woman, and all fled before it in every conflict it entered into, even when there was present but the shield itself and its bearer.

It was at this very period and time that Eohy the Chief Professor

3

of the Great Bardic Association was staying with Hugh the Fair, and this was Dallan Forguil. He was accompanied by a numerous professional body, and the quarter he liked best was Brefney, for numerous were its flocks and cattle herds....

[Hugh the Fair sends Dallan Forguil, the Chief Professor, to obtain the shield from Hugh the Dark.]

"I will not stay," says Dallan to Hugh the Dark, "till I know whether I shall obtain my request." "What is the request?" asked the King. "Thy shield," replied Dallan, "namely Duv-Gilla." "That is not the request of a truly learned man," said the King, "and if it were thou shouldst obtain it." "I have brought you a poem for it," said Dallan. "I would like to hear your poem," said the King. He then recited the poem as follows:

> A hero of fortune art thou, O Hugh,
> Thou daring, determined foe;
> Thy goodness is as the great ocean.
> Thou canst not be subdued,
> Thou canst not be impeded,
> O Hugh, son of Duach the Dark.
> Good and great is his substance,
> Without censure, and without reproach,
> Thou sun after leaving its stars,
> Which is awful to me,
> Thou white chessboard.
> We will return, O hero.

"That is a good poem," says the King, "whoever could understand it. But I will not give you the shield." "I will satirize you," said Dallan. "Nothing will save you from being satirized by me; and it is no satisfaction to me to satirize you except I do so in your presence." And this is what he said:

> O Hugh, son of Duach the Dark,
> Thou pool not permanent;
> Thou pet of the mild cuckoos;
> Thou quick chafferer of a blackbird;
>
> Thou sour green berry;
> Swarms of bees will suck the herbs;

Thou green crop like fine clothes,
A candlestick without light;

Thou cold wooden boat,
Thou bark that will give dissatisfaction,
Thou disgusting black chafer;
Thou art more disgusting, O Hugh.

"We must confess," said Hugh, "that we do not know whether that is better or worse than the first poem you composed." "No wonder for a man of your intellect to say so," said Dallan. "Be done, O Dallan," said the King, "do not satirize me any more in my presence, for I will now excuse you from further professional attendance." . . .

[Dallan and the professors leave; Dallan dies. The Great Bardic Association elects Seanchan Chief Bard. The entire Association goes to visit Guaire, son of Colman, who had never been reproached or satirized for illiberality.]

Seanchan continued for a day and night without food or drink. Bridget, the daughter of Onithcerne, desired her maidservant to give Seanchan her spare food. "What leavings hast thou?" enquired Seanchan. "A hen egg," replied Bridget. "It is almost enough for me," said Seanchan, "and it will suffice for the present." The maidservant went for the egg, Beaidgill was her name, and she searched for the remnant of the food a long time and did not find it. Seanchan said, "I believe it is thyself that art eating the leavings." "Not I, O Chief Bard," replied Beaidgill, "but the nimble race that have eaten it, namely the mice." "That was not proper for them," said Seanchan; "nevertheless there is not a king or chief, be he ever so great, but these mice would wish to leave the traces of their own teeth in his food, and in that they err, for food should not be used by any person after the prints of their teeth, and I will satirize them," said Seanchan; and he began to satirize them, and he said:

The mice, though sharp are their beaks,
Are not powerful in the battles of warriors.
Venomous death I'll deal out to the tribe
In avengement of Bridget's leavings.

MOUSE: Small were the leavings you left,
It was not abundance you retired from;

Receive payment from us, receive compensation,
Don't satirize us all, O learned bard.

BRIDGET: Thou mouse that art in the hole,
Whose utterance is opposition,
'Twas thou, whose claws are not short,
That ate my leavings in your ambling.

MOUSE: My own son Bianan of the white breast,
Thou art the non-observer of ordinances;
To the mighty and luxurious bardic body
Is the knowledge of it, thou little doomed being.

SEANCHAN: Clear ye out of your spacious abodes,
As we are prepared to convict you,
Come ye all out of the hole, or burrow,
And lie down here, O ye mice!

And it is stated that ten mice fell dead in the presence of Seanchan;
and Seanchan said unto them, "It is not you that I ought to have
satirized but the party whose duty it is to suppress you, namely the
tribe of cats; and now I will satirize them effectually."

[Transactions of the Ossianic Society for the year 1857]

Geoffrey Chaucer

Chaucer knew practically every trick of the humorist; indeed, practically every device of the storyteller and the poet. Then why didn't others learn with him or from him? Why wasn't fourteenth-century England a nest of mocking birds? I do not know why.

Since many cultivated readers go through hell trying to pronounce Chaucer in the original, I quote the spirited translation by William Van Wyck.

THE WIFE OF BATH'S FIFTH HUSBAND

... "At the next month's end,
This Jenkin, whom gay Love to me did send,
Wedded me with a great solemnity.
I gave him all the land, and every fee
That ever had been given me before.
But later I repented me, and sore.
He never suffered me to have my way.
By God, he struck me on the ear, one day,
For taking from his book a little page!
And I grew deaf, thereon, for his wild rage.
But I was stubborn as a lioness,
And something of a chatterbox I guess.
I visited as I had done before,
From house to house, although my Jenkin swore
He'd break me of it. How that chap would preach
At me! And Roman tales he tried to teach
Against my will. How Gallus left his wife
Alone for the remainder of his life;
Because she was bareheaded when he saw
Her one day gazing from the cottage door.

"Another Roman (I forget his name)
Who, when his wife went to the summer-game
Without his knowledge, let the woman go,

And proved as just and right, her pain and woe,
And sought a saying from Ecclesiastes
That tells us that a wife must ever haste to please
And do her man's command nor gad about.
He would have spoken thus without a doubt:

> *'Who-so would build his house of sallows* [1]
> *Or jump a blind horse over fallows,*
> *Or let his wife go seeking hallows* [2]
> *Should be hanged on the highest gallows.'*

But all for naught, I didn't care a haw
For either his old proverb or his saw.
Nor would I let myself be thus corrected,
Or told of vices or be disrespected.
No woman will allow this for displeasure.
And he was wild with me and beyond measure.
And I would tolerate him in no way.
  "Now by Saint Thomas it's the truth I say!
That's why I went and took a little leaf
From out his book, and why he struck me deaf.
This damned book he was reading night and day.
It was his only pleasure, I would say.
I think the thing was called Valerius.
About the book he made a dreadful fuss.
It seems there was one time, a clerk of Rome,
A cardinal that was called Saint Jerome.
He wrote opposing good Jovinian.
His book included old Tertullian,
Chrysippus, Trotula, and Héloïse,
An abbess nigh to Paris if you please.
Also there were the works of Solomon,
And Ovid's *Art*. And books, a many a one.
And all of these were bound in one great tome,
Which he read every night when he came home
And had the leisure when on his vacation
From all his other worldly occupation.
He loved to read his work on wicked wives.

---

[1] Willows.
[2] Hallowed things; pilgrimages.

He knew more legends and he knew more lives
Of them than can be found in Holy Writ.
But you know too that not one little bit
Of good will any clerk tell you of wives.
Concerning holy saints they write their lives.
But not of women will they ever say.
As conqueror, who paints the lion, pray?
By God, if women had writ half the stories
That clerks do in their musty oratories,
They would have written of more wickedness,
Than all the men from Adam could redress.
Venus's child, and that of Mercury,
Are as contrary as they well may be.
Mercury ever seeks for wisdom's level,
And Venus loves all luxury and revel.
Although each of them has a different station,
Each falls into the other's exaltation.
And God knows Mercury is desolate
In Pisces wherein Venus is in state.
When Venus falls, then Mercury arises.
A clerk, therefore, no kind of woman prizes.
And when a clerk is old, he cannot do
For Venus what is worth a worn-out shoe.
Then down he sits and writes, when he is old,
Because in bed no woman can he hold.
    "But now I'll tell you, Sirs, the reason why
I was so beaten, till I thought I'd die.
One night, my Jenkin had a great desire
To read his book as he sat by the fire.
He read of Eve, who for her wickedness,
Brought every one of us to great distress,
For which Lord Jesus Christ Himself was slain,
That He redeem us with His blood again.
Within this vile and stinking book you'll find
That woman's the perdition of mankind.
    "Then he read me how Samson lost his hair,
Which was cut off by his false wench and fair.
And for this treason he lost both his eyes.
    "He read to me, I swear I tell no lies,

Of Hercules and lovely Deianir
Who caused the wretch to set himself on fire.
"Nor did he fail to tell the pain and woe
Of Socrates, who found much hurt also,
When his Xantippe ——'d upon his head.
This simple man sat quiet as one dead,
And wiped his skull, and nothing did he say,
Save: 'After thunder, rain must come alway.'
Then he told of the evil queen of Crete,
As though this doleful tale were very sweet.
I'll say no more. It is a grisly thing,
For her desire had a frightful sting.
He spoke of Clytemnestra's lechery
Who falsely caused her husband not to be.
And this he read with great devotion too.
"He told me for some reason, I tell you,
Of Theban Amphiaraus, when his life
Was blotted out forever by his wife
Eriphylë and for a brooch of gold.
In private, to the Greeks, she went and told
Where he was hidden in a certain place.
Therefore, at Thebes he found but little grace.
"Of Lucia and Livia, I learned
How hate came to the one; the other yearned.
Both of them killed their husbands, let me state.
Livia on an evening, very late,
Killed her good man. She was his dire foe.
Passionate Lucia loved her husband so,
In order that he'd love as hot as she,
Gave him a philtre, and then rapidly
The man was dead, indeed, before the morrow.
And so it is that husbands have much sorrow.
"And then he told me how Latumeus
Complained unto his fellow, Arrius,
That in his garden grew a certain tree
On which (he told him) that his wives, all three,
Had hanged themselves because of pain and woe.
'O my dear brother,' Arrius spoke so,
'Give me a cut of this same blessed tree,

And in my garden, planted it will be.'
"Of wives of latter days, he also read.
How one had slain the husband that she wed,
And let her lover lie with her that night.
The corpse lay on the floor, a fearful sight.
Another drove a nail into the brain
Of her poor sleeping husband. He was slain.
And some were given poison in a drink.
He told more instances than mind could think,
And knew more proverbs, did this cheerful one,
Than there is grass beneath a summer sun.
'It's better that your habitation be
With lions or with dragons foul,' quoth he,
'Than that with angry jade a life be spent.
Better,' he said, 'an attic or a tent
Than the best room shared with an angry wife,
Who's wicked and contrary, on my life!
Women hate husbands who love them, I claim.'
He said: 'A woman casts away her shame,
Casting her smock away. And this I know,
A lovely woman, if she's chaste also,
Is like a golden ring in some sow's nose.'
And none of you could in the least suppose
What pain and sorrow lay within my heart.
"And when I saw that he would never part
From his old book which was a frightful bore;
Then suddenly, three of the leaves I tore
Out of the thing, although my heart went weak.
And with my fist, I took him on the cheek.
Backwards into the fire fell the lad,
And then he started like a lion mad,
And with his fist he whacked me on the head.
I lay upon the floor, a woman dead.
And when he saw how white and ill I lay,
He was aghast and would have run away.
I came out of my swoon, to his relief,
And cried out: 'You have killed me, you false thief!
It's for my land, I think, you've bashed my head.
Give me one little kiss ere I be dead.'

"He knelt down by my side when he came near,
And said: 'So help me God, my sister dear,
No more against you will I lift my hand,
As I have done. This you must understand.
Forgive me, darling. Speak, I beg you, speak.'
But once again I banged him on the cheek,
And said he was a thief to do to me
Such harm; that I might die, maybe.
And finally, but with much care and woe,
We made it up between ourselves. And so
He put the reins and bridle in my hand,
And bade me run his house and all his land.
I ran his tongue and hand, in this our home,
And made him burn his rotten, filthy tome.
At last when I had gotten unto me
The mastership and all the sovereignty,
He said to me: 'My own, my darling wife,
Do as you will with me for all your life.
You hold my honour, you keep my estate.'
From that day, we were never at debate.
So help me God, 1 was as good and kind
As any wife could be from Wales to Ind.
And I was true to him. And true to me
He was, by God Who sits in majesty!
And may God bless him through His mercy dear.
Now, I shall tell my tale, if you will hear."

[From *The Canterbury Tales*]

Anonymous

THE RIVERS TILL AND TWEED

Says Tweed to Till:
    "What gars ye rin sae still?"
Says Till to Tweed:
    "Though ye rin with speed
      And I rin slaw,
For ae man that ye droon
      I droon twa."

William Shakespeare

I put in one of the tremendous Falstaff passages because I could hardly leave out the greatest comic creation in English literature, and the Thersites passages because most people never get around to reading Troilus and Cressida. Elizabethan humor consisted largely of abuse, which was elevated to a kind of lyrical drama. Notice that when an Elizabethan was called, for instance, a "whoreson indistinguishable cur," he did not reply with fist or sword; he was too busy preparing his rebuttal: "thou green sarcenet flap for a sore eye," and so forth. Thersites is also a wonderful study of the man mishandled by Nature, who turns jealous and vindictive; but that is by the way.

FALSTAFF REPORTS TO PRINCE HENRY

SCENE: *The Boar's Head Tavern in Eastcheap.* PRINCE HENRY *and* POINS, *one of his low companions, are on the stage. Enter* SIR JOHN FALSTAFF *and his mates,* GADSHILL, BARDOLPH, *and* PETO. FRANCIS, *the inn servant, follows with wine.*

POINS: Welcome, Jack: where hast thou been?

FALSTAFF: A plague of all cowards, I say, and a vengeance too! marry, and amen! Give me a cup of sack, boy. Ere I lead this life long, I'll sew nether stocks and mend them and foot them too. A plague of all cowards! Give me a cup of sack, rogue. Is there no virtue extant? (*He drinks.*)

PRINCE: Didst thou never see Titan[1] kiss a dish of butter—pitiful-hearted Titan—that melted at the sweet tale of the sun's? if thou didst, then behold that compound.

FALSTAFF: You rogue, here's lime in this sack too: there is nothing but roguery to be found in villainous man: yet a coward is worse than a cup of sack with lime in it. A villainous coward! Go thy ways, old Jack; die when thou wilt, if manhood, good manhood, be not forgot upon the face of the earth, then am I a shotten herring.

[1] Titan: the sun.

There lives not three good men unhanged in England; and one
of them is fat, and grows old: God help the while! a bad world,
I say. I would I were a weaver; I could sing psalms or any thing.
A plague of all cowards, I say still.

PRINCE: How, now, wool-sack! what mutter you?

FALSTAFF: A king's son! If I do not beat thee out of thy kingdom with
a dagger of lath, and drive all thy subjects afore thee like a flock
of wild geese, I'll never wear hair on my face more. You Prince
of Wales!

PRINCE: Why, you whoreson round man, what's the matter?

FALSTAFF: Are not you a coward? answer me to that: and Poins there?

POINS: 'Zounds, ye fat paunch, an ye call me coward, by the Lord, I'll
stab thee.

FALSTAFF: I call thee coward! I'll see thee damned ere I call thee
coward: but I would give a thousand pound I could run as fast
as thou canst. You are straight enough in the shoulders, you care
not who sees your back: call you that backing of your friends?
A plague upon such backing! give me them that will face me. Give
me a cup of sack: I am a rogue, if I drunk today.

PRINCE: O villain! thy lips are scarce wiped since thou drunkest last.

FALSTAFF: All's one for that. (*He drinks.*) A plague of all cowards,
still say I.

PRINCE: What's the matter?

FALSTAFF: What's the matter! there be four of us here have ta'en a
thousand pound this day morning.

PRINCE: Where is it, Jack? where is it?

FALSTAFF: Where is it! taken from us it is: a hundred upon poor four
of us.

PRINCE: What, a hundred, man?

FALSTAFF: I am a rogue, if I were not at half-sword with a dozen of
them two hours together. I have 'scaped by miracle. I am eight
times thrust through the doublet, four through the hose; my
buckler cut through and through; my sword hacked like a hand-
saw—*ecce signum!* I never dealt better since I was a man: all
would not do. A plague of all cowards! Let them speak: if they
speak more or less than truth, they are villains and the sons of
darkness.

PRINCE: Speak, sirs; how was it?

GADSHILL: We four set upon some dozen—

FALSTAFF: Sixteen at least, my lord.

GADSHILL: And bound them.

PETO: No, no, they were not bound.

FALSTAFF: You rogue, they were bound, every man of them; or I am a Jew else, an Ebrew Jew.

GADSHILL: As we were sharing, some six or seven fresh men set upon us—

FALSTAFF: And unbound the rest, and then come in the other.

PRINCE: What, fought you with them all?

FALSTAFF: All! I know not what you call all; but if I fought not with fifty of them, I am a bunch of radish; if there were not two or three and fifty upon poor old Jack, then am I no two-legged creature.

PRINCE: Pray God you have not murdered some of them.

FALSTAFF: Nay, that's past praying for; I have peppered two of them; two I am sure I have paid, two rogues in buckram suits. I tell thee what, Hal, if I tell thee a lie, spit in my face, call me horse. Thou knowest my old ward; here I lay, and thus I bore my point. Four rogues in buckram let drive at me—

PRINCE: What, four? thou saidst but two even now.

FALSTAFF: Four, Hal; I told thee four.

POINS: Ay, ay, he said four.

FALSTAFF: These four came all a-front, and mainly thrust at me. I made me no more ado but took all their seven points in my target, thus.

PRINCE: Seven? why, there were but four even now.

FALSTAFF: In buckram?

POINS: Ay, four, in buckram suits.

FALSTAFF: Seven, by these hilts, or I am a villain else.

PRINCE: Prithee, let him alone; we shall have more anon.

FALSTAFF: Dost thou hear me, Hal?

PRINCE: Ay, and mark thee too, Jack.

FALSTAFF: Do so, for it is worth the listening to. These nine in buckram that I told thee of—

PRINCE: So, two more already.

FALSTAFF: Their points being broken—

POINS: Down fell their hose.

FALSTAFF: Began to give me ground: but I followed me close, came in foot and hand; and with a thought [2] seven of the eleven I paid.

[2] With a thought: in an instant.

PRINCE: O monstrous! eleven buckram men grown out of two!

FALSTAFF: But, as the devil would have it, three misbegotten knaves in Kendal green came at my back and let drive at me: for it was so dark, Hal, that thou couldst not see thy hand.

PRINCE: These lies are like their father that begets them: gross as a mountain, open, palpable. Why, thou clay-brained guts, thou knotty-pated fool, thou whoreson, obscene, greasy tallow-catch—

FALSTAFF: What, art thou mad? art thou mad? is not the truth the truth?

PRINCE: Why, how couldst thou know these men in Kendal green, when it was so dark thou couldst not see thy hand? come, tell us your reason; what sayest thou to this?

POINS: Come, your reason, Jack, your reason.

FALSTAFF: What, upon compulsion? 'Zounds, an I were at the strappado, or all the racks in the world, I would not tell you on compulsion. Give you a reason on compulsion! if reasons [3] were as plentiful as blackberries, I would give no man a reason upon compulsion, I.

PRINCE: I'll be no longer guilty of this sin; this sanguine coward, this bedpresser, this horseback-breaker, this huge hill of flesh—

FALSTAFF: 'Sblood, you starveling, you elf-skin, you dried neat's tongue, you bull's pizzle, you stock-fish! O for breath to utter what is like thee? you tailor's-yard, you sheath, you bow-case, you vile standing-tuck [4]—

PRINCE: Well, breathe a while, and then to it again: and when thou hast tired thyself in base comparisons, hear me speak but this.

POINS: Mark, Jack.

PRINCE: We two saw you four set on four and bound them, and were masters of their wealth. Mark now, how a plain tale shall put you down. Then did we two set on you four; and, with a word, out-faced you from your prize, and have it; yea, and can show it you here in the house: and, Falstaff, you carried your guts away as nimbly, with as quick dexterity, and roared for mercy, and still run and roared, as ever I heard bull-calf. What a slave art thou, to hack thy sword as thou hast done, and then say it was in fight! What trick, what device, what starting-hole, canst thou now find out to hide thee from this open and apparent shame?

[3] Reasons: a pun on "raisins." The two words were pronounced the same.
[4] Standing-tuck: small rapier on end.

POINS: Come, let's hear, Jack; what trick hast thou now?

FALSTAFF: By the Lord, I knew ye as well as he that made ye. Why, hear you, my masters: was it for me to kill the heir-apparent? should I turn upon the true prince? why, thou knowest I am as valiant as Hercules; but beware instinct; the lion will not touch the true prince. Instinct is a great matter; I was now a coward on instinct. I shall think the better of myself and thee during my life; I for a valiant lion, and thou for a true prince. But, by the Lord, lads, I am glad you have the money. Hostess, clap to the doors: watch tonight, pray tomorrow. Gallants, lads, boys, hearts of gold, all the titles of good fellowship come to you! What, shall we be merry? shall we have a play extempore?

PRINCE: Content; and the argument shall be thy running away.

FALSTAFF: Ah, no more of that, Hal, an thou lovest me!

   (*Enter* HOSTESS.)

HOSTESS: O Jesu, my lord the prince!

PRINCE: How now, my lady the hostess! what sayest thou to me?

HOSTESS: Marry, my lord, there is a nobleman of the court at door would speak with you; he says he comes from your father.

PRINCE: Give him as much as will make him a royal man, and send him back again to my mother.

FALSTAFF: What manner of man is he?

HOSTESS: An old man.

FALSTAFF: What doth gravity out of his bed at midnight? Shall I give him his answer?

PRINCE: Prithee, do, Jack.

FALSTAFF: Faith, and I'll send him packing.

   (*Exit.*)

PRINCE: Now, sirs: by'r lady, you fought fair; so did you, Peto; so did you, Bardolph: you are lions, too, you ran away upon instinct, you will not touch the true prince; no, fie!

BARDOLPH: Faith, I ran when I saw others run.

PRINCE: Faith, tell me now in earnest, how came Falstaff's sword so hacked?

PETO: Why, he hacked it with his dagger, and said he would swear truth out of England but he would make you believe it was done in fight, and persuaded us to do the like.

BARDOLPH: Yea, and to tickle our noses with spear-grass to make them bleed, and then to beslubber our garments with it and swear it was the blood of true men. I did that I did not this seven year before, I blushed to hear his monstrous devices.

PRINCE: O villain, thou stolest a cup of sack eighteen years ago, and wert taken with the manner, and ever since thou hast blushed extempore. Thou hadst fire and sword on thy side, and yet thou rannest away: what instinct hadst thou for it?

BARDOLPH: My lord, do you see these meteors? do you behold these exhalations?

PRINCE: I do.

BARDOLPH: What think you they portend?

PRINCE: Hot livers and cold purses.

BARDOLPH: Choler, my lord, if rightly taken.

PRINCE: No, if rightly taken, halter. (*Re-enter* FALSTAFF.) Here comes lean Jack, here comes bare-bone. How now, my sweet creature of bombast! How long is't ago, Jack, since thou sawest thine own knee?

FALSTAFF: My own knee! When I was about thy years, Hal, I was not an eagle's talon in the waist; I could have crept into any alderman's thumb-ring: a plague of sighing and grief; it blows a man up like a bladder. There's villainous news abroad: here was Sir John Bracy from your father; you must to the court in the morning. That same mad fellow of the north, Percy, and he of Wales, that gave Amamon the bastinado, and made Lucifer cuckold, and swore the devil his true liegeman upon the cross of a Welsh hook—what a plague call you him?

POINS: Oh, Glendower.

FALSTAFF: Owen, Owen, the same; and his son-in-law Mortimer, and old Northumberland, and that sprightly Scot of Scots, Douglas, that runs o' horseback up a hill perpendicular—

PRINCE: He that rides at high speed and with his pistol kills a sparrow flying.

FALSTAFF: You have hit it.

PRINCE: So did he never the sparrow.

FALSTAFF: Well, that rascal hath good mettle in him; he will not run.

PRINCE: Why, what a rascal art thou then, to praise him so for running!

FALSTAFF: O' horseback, ye cuckoo; but afoot he will not budge a foot.

PRINCE: Yes, Jack, upon instinct.

FALSTAFF: I grant ye, upon instinct. Well, he is there too, and one
Mordake, and a thousand bluecaps more: Worcester is stolen away
tonight; thy father's beard is turned white with the news: you
may buy land now as cheap as stinking mackerel.

PRINCE: Why, then, it is like, if there come a hot June and this civil
buffeting hold, we shall buy maidenheads as they buy hobnails,
by the hundreds.

FALSTAFF: By the mass, lad, thou sayest true; it is like we shall have
good trading that way. But tell me, Hal, art not thou horrible
afeard? thou being heir-apparent, could the world pick thee out
three such enemies again as that fiend Douglas, that spirit Percy,
and that devil Glendower? art thou not horribly afraid? doth
not thy blood thrill at it?

PRINCE: Not a whit, i' faith; I lack some of thy instinct.

FALSTAFF: Well, thou wilt be horribly chid tomorrow when thou
comest to thy father; if thou love me, practise an answer.

PRINCE: Do thou stand for my father, and examine me upon the particulars of my life.

FALSTAFF: Shall I? content: this chair shall be my state, this dagger
my sceptre, and this cushion my crown.

PRINCE: Thy state is taken for a joined-stool, thy golden sceptre for a
leaden dagger, and thy precious rich crown for a pitiful bald
crown!

FALSTAFF: Well, an the fire of grace be not quite out of thee, now shalt
thou be moved. Give me a cup of sack to make my eyes look red,
that it may be thought I have wept; for I must speak in passion,
and I will do it in King Cambyses' vein.

PRINCE: Well, here is my leg.

FALSTAFF: And here is my speech. Stand aside, nobility.

HOSTESS: O Jesu, this is excellent sport, i' faith!

FALSTAFF: Weep not, sweet queen; for trickling tears are vain.

HOSTESS: O, the father, how he holds his countenance!

FALSTAFF: For God's sake, lords, convey my tristful queen;
For tears do stop the flood-gates of her eyes.

HOSTESS: O Jesu, he doth it as like one of these harlotry players as
ever I see!

FALSTAFF: Peace, good pint-pot; peace, good tickle-brain. Harry, I do
not only marvel where thou spendest thy time, but also how thou
art accompanied: for though the camomile, the more it is trodden

on, the faster it grows, yet youth, the more it is wasted, the sooner
it wears. That thou art my son, I have partly thy mother's word,
partly my own opinion, but chiefly a villainous trick of thine eye,
and a foolish hanging of thy nether lip, that doth warrant me.
If then thou be son to me, here lies the point: why, being son to
me, art thou so pointed at? Shall the blessed sun of heaven prove
a micher [5] and eat blackberries? a question not to be asked. Shall
the son of England prove a thief and take purses? a question to
be asked. There is a thing, Harry, which thou hast often heard of,
and it is known to many in our land by the name of pitch: this
pitch, as ancient writers do report, doth defile; so doth the company thou keepest: for, Harry, now I do not speak to thee in
drink but in tears, not in pleasure but in passion, not in words
only, but in woes also: and yet there is a virtuous man whom
I have often noted in thy company, but I know not his name.

PRINCE: What manner of man, an it like your majesty?

FALSTAFF: A goodly portly man, i' faith, and a corpulent; of a cheerful
look, a pleasing eye, and a most noble carriage; and, as I think,
his age some fifty, or, b'r lady, inclining to three score; and now
I remember me, his name is Falstaff: if that man should be lewdly
given, he deceiveth me; for, Harry, I see virtue in his looks. If
then the tree may be known by the fruit, as the fruit by the tree,
then, peremptorily I speak it, there is virtue in that Falstaff: him
keep with, the rest banish. And tell me now, thou naughty varlet,
tell me, where hast thou been this month?

PRINCE: Dost thou speak like a king? Do thou stand for me, and I'll
play my father.

FALSTAFF: Depose me? if thou dost it half so gravely, so majestically,
both in word and matter, hang me up by the heels for a rabbit-
sucker or a poulter's hare.

PRINCE: Well, here I am set.

FALSTAFF: And here I stand: judge, my masters.

PRINCE: Now, Harry, whence come you?

FALSTAFF: My noble lord, from Eastcheap.

PRINCE: The complaints I hear of thee are grievous.

FALSTAFF: 'Sblood, my lord, they are false: nay, I'll tickle ye for a
young prince, i' faith.

[5] Micher: truant.

PRINCE: Swearest thou, ungracious boy? henceforth ne'er look on me. Thou art violently carried away from grace: there is a devil haunts thee in the likeness of an old fat man; a tun of man is thy companion. Why dost thou converse with that trunk of humours, that bolting-hutch of beastliness, that swollen parcel of dropsies, that huge bombard of sack, that stuffed cloak-bag of guts, that roasted Manningtree ox with the pudding in his belly, that reverend vice, that grey iniquity, that father ruffian, that vanity in years? Wherein is he good, but to taste sack and drink it? wherein neat and cleanly, but to carve a capon and eat it? wherein cunning, but in craft? wherein crafty, but in villainy? wherein villainous, but in all things? wherein worthy, but in nothing?

FALSTAFF: I would your grace would take me with you: whom means your grace?

PRINCE: That villainous abominable misleader of youth, Falstaff, that old white-bearded Satan.

FALSTAFF: My lord, the man I know.

PRINCE: I know thou dost.

FALSTAFF: But to say I know more harm in him than in myself, were to say more than I know. That he is old, the more the pity, his white hairs do witness it; but that he is, saving your reverence, a whoremaster, that I utterly deny. If sack and sugar be a fault, God help the wicked! if to be old and merry be a sin, then many an old host that I know is damned: if to be fat be to be hated, then Pharaoh's lean kine are to be loved. No, my good lord; banish Peto, banish Bardolph, banish Poins: but for sweet Jack Falstaff, kind Jack Falstaff, true Jack Falstaff, valiant Jack Falstaff, and therefore more valiant, being, as he is, old Jack Falstaff, banish not him thy Harry's company, banish not him thy Harry's company: banish plump Jack, and banish all the world.

PRINCE: I do, I will.

(*A knocking heard. Exeunt* HOSTESS, FRANCIS, *and* BARDOLPH. *Re-enter* BARDOLPH, *running.*)

BARDOLPH: O my lord, my lord! the sheriff with a most monstrous watch is at the door.

FALSTAFF: Out, ye rogue! Play out the play: I have much to say in the behalf of that Falstaff.

(*Re-enter* HOSTESS.)

HOSTESS: O Jesu, my lord, my lord!—

PRINCE: Heigh, heigh! the devil rides upon a fiddlestick: what's the matter?

HOSTESS: The sheriff and all the watch are at the door: they are come to search the house. Shall I let them in?

FALSTAFF: Dost thou hear, Hal? never call a true piece of gold a counterfeit: thou art essentially mad, without seeming so.

PRINCE: And thou a natural coward, without instinct.

FALSTAFF: I deny your major: if you will deny the sheriff, so; if not, let him enter: if I become not a cart as well as another man, a plague on my bringing up! I hope I shall as soon be strangled with a halter as another.

PRINCE: Go, hide thee behind the arras: the rest walk up above. Now, my masters, for a true face and good conscience.

FALSTAFF: Both which I have had: but their date is out, and therefore I'll hide me.

PRINCE: Call in the sheriff. (*Exeunt all except the* PRINCE *and* PETO. *Enter* SHERIFF *and the* CARRIER.) Now, master sheriff, what is your will with me?

SHERIFF: First, pardon me, my lord. A hue and cry
Hath follow'd certain men unto this house.

PRINCE: What men?

SHERIFF: One of them is well known, my gracious lord,
A gross fat man.

CARRIER: As fat as butter.

PRINCE: The man, I do assure you, is not here;
For I myself at this time have employ'd him.
And, sheriff, I will engage my word to thee
That I will, by tomorrow dinner-time,
Send him to answer thee, or any man,
For anything he shall be charged withal:
And so let me entreat you leave the house.

SHERIFF: I will, my lord. There are two gentlemen
Have in this robbery lost three hundred marks.

PRINCE: It may be so: if he have robb'd these men,
He shall be answerable; and so farewell.

SHERIFF: Good night, my noble lord.

PRINCE: I think it is good morrow, is it not?

SHERIFF: Indeed, my lord, I think it be two o'clock.
(*Exeunt* SHERIFF *and* CARRIER.)

PRINCE: This oily rascal is known as well as Paul's.
Go, call him forth.

PETO: Falstaff!—Fast asleep behind the arras, and snorting like a horse.

PRINCE: Hark, how hard he fetches breath. Search his pockets. (*He
searcheth his pockets, and findeth certain papers.*) What hast thou
found?

PETO: Nothing but papers, my lord.

PRINCE: Let's see what they be: read them.

PETO (*reads*): Item, A capon,   2s. 2d.
           Item, Sauce   4d.
           Item, Sack, two gallons   5s. 8d.
           Item, Anchovies and sack after supper   2s. 6d.
           Item, Bread   ob.[6]

PRINCE: O monstrous! but one half-pennyworth of bread to this intolerable deal of sack! What there is else, keep close; we'll read it at
more advantage; there let him sleep till day. I'll to the court in
the morning. We must all to the wars, and thy place shall be
honourable. I'll procure this fat rogue a charge of foot; and I
know his death will be a march of twelve-score. The money shall
be paid back again with advantage. Be with me betimes in the
morning; and so, good morrow, Peto.

PETO: Good morrow, good my lord.
(*Exeunt.*)

[From *Henry IV;* Part One, Act II, Scene iv]

THERSITES

SCENE: *The Grecian camp. Enter* AJAX *and* THERSITES.

AJAX: Thersites!

THERSITES: Agamemnon—how if he had boils—full, all over, generally?

AJAX: Thersites!

THERSITES: And those boils did run?—Say so,—did not the general run
then? were not that a botchy core?

[6] Ob.: obolus, a halfpenny.

Ajax: Dog!

Thersites: Then would come some matter from him; I see none now.

Ajax: Thou bitch-wolf's son, canst thou not hear? Feel then. (*Strikes him.*)

Thersites: The plague of Greece upon thee, thou mongrel beef-witted lord!

Ajax: Speak then, thou vinewed'st [7] leaven, speak: I will beat thee into handsomeness.

Thersites: I shall sooner rail thee into wit and holiness: but, I think, thy horse will sooner con an oration than thou learn a prayer without book. Thou canst strike, canst thou? a red murrain o' thy jade's tricks!

Ajax: Toadstool, learn me the proclamation.

Thersites: Dost thou think I have no sense, thou strikest me thus?

Ajax: The proclamation!

Thersites: Thou art proclaimed a fool, I think.

Ajax: Do not, porpentine, do not; my fingers itch.

Thersites: I would thou didst itch from head to foot, and I had the scratching of thee; I would make thee the loathsomest scab in Greece. When thou art forth in the incursions, thou strikest as slow as another.

Ajax: I say, the proclamation!

Thersites: Thou grumblest and railest every hour on Achilles, and thou art as full of envy at his greatness as Cerberus is at Proserpina's beauty, ay, that thou barkest at him.

Ajax: Mistress Thersites!

Thersites: Thou shouldst strike him.

Ajax: Cobloaf!

Thersites: He would pun thee into shivers with his fist, as a sailor breaks a biscuit.

Ajax (*beating him*): You whoreson cur!

Thersites: Do, do.

Ajax: Thou stool for a witch!

Thersites: Ay, do, do; thou sodden-witted lord! thou hast no more brain than I have in mine elbows; an assinego [8] may tutor thee: thou scurvy-valiant ass! thou art here but to thrash Trojans; and thou art bought and sold among those of any wit, like a barbarian

---

[7] Vinewed'st: most mouldy.
[8] Assinego: donkey.

slave. If thou use to beat me, I will begin at thy heel and tell what thou art by inches, thou thing of no bowels, thou!

AJAX: You dog!

THERSITES: You scurvy lord!

AJAX (*beating him*): You cur!

THERSITES: Mars his idiot! do, rudeness; do, camel, do, do.

(*Enter* ACHILLES *and* PATROCLUS.)

ACHILLES: Why, how now, Ajax! Wherefore do ye thus? How now, Thersites! what's the matter, man?

THERSITES: You see him there, do you?

ACHILLES: Ay; what's the matter?

THERSITES: Nay, look upon him.

ACHILLES: So I do: what's the matter?

THERSITES: Nay, but regard him well.

ACHILLES: "Well!" why, so I do.

THERSITES: But yet you look not well upon him; for, whosoever you take him to be, he is Ajax.

ACHILLES: I know that, fool.

THERSITES: Ay, but that fool knows not himself.

AJAX: Therefore I beat thee.

THERSITES: Lo, lo, lo, lo, what modicums of wit he utters! his evasions have ears thus long. I have bobbed his brain more than he has beat my bones: I will buy nine sparrows for a penny, and his *pia mater* is not worth the ninth part of a sparrow. This lord, Achilles, Ajax, who wears his wit in his belly and his guts in his head, I'll tell you what I say of him.

ACHILLES: What?

THERSITES: I say, this Ajax— (AJAX *offers to strike him.*)

ACHILLES: Nay, good Ajax.

THERSITES: Has not so much wit—

ACHILLES: Nay, I must hold you.

THERSITES: As will stop the eye of Helen's needle, for whom he comes to fight.

ACHILLES: Peace, fool!

THERSITES: I would have peace and quietness, but the fool will not: he there: that he: look you there!

AJAX: O thou damned cur! I shall—

ACHILLES: Will you set your wit to a fool's?

THERSITES: No, I warrant you; for a fool's will shame it.

PATROCLUS: Good words, Thersites.

ACHILLES: What's the quarrel?

AJAX: I bade the vile owl go learn me the tenour of the proclamation, and he rails upon me.

THERSITES: I serve thee not.

AJAX: Well, go to, go to.

THERSITES: I serve here voluntary.

ACHILLES: Your last service was sufferance, 'twas not voluntary; no man is beaten voluntary: Ajax was here the voluntary, and you as under an impress.

THERSITES: E'en so; a great deal of your wit too lies in your sinews, or else there be liars. Hector shall have a great catch, if he knock out either of your brains: a' were as good crack a fusty nut with no kernel.

ACHILLES: What, with me too, Thersites?

THERSITES: There's Ulysses and old Nestor, whose wit was mouldy ere your grandsires had nails on their toes, yoke you like draught-oxen, and make you plough up the wars.

ACHILLES: What? what?

THERSITES: Yes, good sooth: to, Achilles! to, Ajax, to!

AJAX: I shall cut out your tongue.

THERSITES: 'Tis no matter; I shall speak as much as thou afterwards.

PATROCLUS: No more words, Thersites; peace!

THERSITES: I will hold my peace when Achilles' brooch bids me, shall I?

ACHILLES: There's for you, Patroclus.

THERSITES: I will see you hanged, like clotpoles, ere I come any more to your tents: I will keep where there is wit stirring, and leave the faction of fools. (*Exit.*)

[From *Troilus and Cressida;* Act II, Scene 1]

SCENE: *The Grecian camp. Before Achilles' tent. Enter* ACHILLES *and* PATROCLUS.

ACHILLES: I'll heat his blood with Greekish wine tonight,
Which with my scimitar I'll cool tomorrow.
Patroclus, let us feast him to the height.

PATROCLUS: Here comes Thersites.
>   (*Enter* THERSITES.)
ACHILLES: How now, thou core of envy!
>   Thou crusty batch of nature, what's the news?
THERSITES: Why, thou picture of what thou seemest, an idol of idiot-worshippers, here's a letter for thee.
ACHILLES: From whence, fragment?
THERSITES: Why, thou full dish of fool, from Troy.
PATROCLUS: Who keeps the tent now?
THERSITES: The surgeon's box, or the patient's wound.
PATROCLUS: Well said, adversity! and what need these tricks?
THERSITES: Prithee, be silent, boy; I profit not by thy talk; thou art thought to be Achilles' male varlet.
PATROCLUS: Male varlet, you rogue! what's that?
THERSITES: Why, his masculine whore. Now, the rotten diseases of the south, the guts-griping, ruptures, catarrhs, loads o' gravel i' the back, lethargies, cold palsies, raw eyes, dirt-rotten livers, wheezing lungs, bladders full of imposthume, sciaticas, limekilns i' the palm, incurable bone-ache, and the rivelled fee-simple of the tetter, take and take again such preposterous discoveries!
PATROCLUS: Why, thou damnable box of envy, thou, what mean'st thou to curse thus?
THERSITES: Do I curse thee?
PATROCLUS: Why, no, you ruinous butt; you whoreson indistinguishable cur, no.
THERSITES: No! why art thou then exasperate, thou idle immaterial skein of sleave silk, thou green sarcenet flap for a sore eye, thou tassel of a prodigal's purse, thou? Ah, how the poor world is pestered with such waterflies, diminutives of nature!
PATROCLUS: Out, gall!
THERSITES: Finch-egg!
ACHILLES: My sweet Patroclus, I am thwarted quite
>   From my great purpose in tomorrow's battle.
>   Here is a letter from Queen Hecuba,
>   A token from her daughter, my fair love,
>   Both taxing me and gaging me to keep
>   An oath that I have sworn. I will not break it:
>   Fall Greeks; fail fame; honour or go or stay;
>   My major vow lies here, this I'll obey.

Come, come, Thersites, help to trim my tent:
This night in banqueting must all be spent.
Away, Patroclus!

 (*Exeunt* ACHILLES *and* PATROCLUS.)

THERSITES: With too much blood and too little brain, these two may run mad; but, if with too much brain and too little blood they do, I'll be a curer of madmen. Here's Agamemnon, an honest fellow enough and one that loves quails; but he has not so much brain as ear-wax: and the goodly transformation of Jupiter there, his brother, the bull, the primitive statue and oblique memorial of cuckolds; a thrifty shoeing-horn in a chain, hanging at his brother's leg—to what form but that he is, should wit larded with malice and malice forced with wit turn him to? To an ass, were nothing; he is both ass and ox: to an ox, were nothing; he is both ox and ass. To be a dog, a mule, a cat, a fitchew, a toad, a lizard, an owl, a puttock, or a herring without a roe, I would not care; but to be Menelaus! I would conspire against destiny. Ask me not what I would be, if I were not Thersites; for I care not to be the louse of a lazar, so I were not Menelaus. Hoy-day! spirits and fires!

[From *Troilus and Cressida;* Act V, Scene 1]

John Davies

GULLING SONNET

The sacred muse that first made love divine
Hath made him naked and without attire;
But I will clothe him with this pen of mine,
That all the world his fashion shall admire:
His hat of hope, his band of beauty fine,
His cloak of craft, his doublet of desire;
Grief, for a girdle, shall about him twine;
His points of pride, his eyelet-holes of ire,
His hose of hate, his codpiece of conceit,
His stockings of stern strife, his shirt of shame,
His garters of vainglory gay and slight,
His pantofles of passion I will frame;
Pumps of presumption shall adorn his feet,
And socks of sullenness exceeding sweet.

Robert Herrick

TO THE SOUR READER

If thou dislik'st the piece thou light'st on first,
Think that, of all that I have writ, the worst;
But if thou read'st my book unto the end,
And still dost this and that verse reprehend,
O perverse man! if all disgustful be,
The extreme scab take thee and thine, for me.

Thomas Randolph

STRAPHYLA'S LULLABY

Quiet sleep, or I will make
Erinnys whip thee with a snake,
And cruel Rhadamanthus take
Thy body to the boiling lake,
Where fire and brimstone never slake.
Thy heart shall burn; thy head shall ache,
And every joint about thee quake.
And therefore dare not yet to wake.

Quiet sleep, or thou shalt see
The horrid hags of Tartary,
Whose tresses ugly serpents be;
And Cerberus shall bark at thee,
And all the furies that are three,
The worst is call'd Tisiphone,
Shall lash thee to eternity.
And therefore sleep thou peacefully.

Alexander Brome

THE MAD LOVER

I have been in love, and in debt, and in drink,
 This many and many a year;
And those three are plagues enough, one would think,
 For one poor mortal to bear.
'Twas drink made me fall into love,
 And love made me run into debt,
And though I have struggled and struggled and strove,
 I cannot get out of them yet.
 There's nothing but money can cure me,
 And rid me of all my pain;
 'Twill pay all my debts,
 And remove all my lets,
 And my mistress, that cannot endure me,
 Will love me and love me again,—
Then I'll fall to loving and drinking amain.

John Aubrey

BISHOP RICHARD CORBET

After he was Doctor of Divinity, he sang ballads at the Cross at Abingdon on a market-day. He and some of his comrades were at the tavern by the Cross (which, by the way, was then the finest of England. I remember it when I was a freshman; it was admirable curious Gothic architecture, and fine figures in the niches, 'twas one of those built by a king for his queen). The ballad-singer complained he had no custom; he could not put off his ballads. The jolly Doctor puts off his gown, and puts on the ballad-singer's leathern jacket, and being a handsome man, and had a rare full voice, he presently vended a great many, and had a great audience. . . .

His conversation was extreme pleasant. Dr. Stubbins was one of his cronies; he was a jolly fat Doctor and a very good housekeeper; parson in Oxfordshire. As Dr. Corbet and he were riding in Lob Lane in wet weather ('tis an extraordinary deep, dirty lane), the coach fell; and Dr. Corbet said that Dr. Stubbins was up to the elbows in mud, he was up to the elbows in Stubbins.

He was made Bishop of Oxford, and I have heard that he had an admirable, grave, and venerable aspect.

One time, as he was confirming, the country people pressing in to see the ceremony, said he: "Bear off there, or I'll confirm ye with my staff!" Another time, being to lay his hand on the head of a man very bald, he turns to his chaplain, Lushington, and said: "Some dust, Lushington!" (To keep his hand from slipping.) There was a man with a great venerable beard; said the Bishop: "You, behind the beard!"

His chaplain, Dr. Lushington, was a very learned and ingenious man, and they loved one another. The Bishop sometimes would take the key of the wine cellar, and he and his chaplain would go and lock themselves in and be merry. Then first he lays down his episcopal hat—"There lies the Doctor." Then he puts off his gown—"There lies the Bishop." Then 'twas: "Here's to thee, Corbet!" and "Here's to thee, Lushington!" The last words he said were: "Good night, Lushington."

[From *Brief Lives*]

Matthew Prior

To Matt Prior and to the eighteenth century in general, the amorous misdemeanor was the one really funny thing on earth. The nineteenth century looked deeper, and grieved for the tears succeeding joy. The twentieth century, looking still deeper, coolly explores love's monstrous psychology. However we may deplore the light view of the eighteenth century, there may be something in it.

FATAL LOVE

Poor Hal caught his death standing under a spout,
Expecting till midnight when Nan would come out,
But fatal his patience, as cruel the dame,
And curs'd was the weather that quench'd the man's flame.

Whoe'er thou art, that read'st these moral lines,
Make love at home, and go to bed betimes.

A BETTER ANSWER

Dear Chloe, how blubbered is that pretty face!
 Thy cheek all on fire, and thy hair all uncurled!
Prithee quit this caprice, and (as old Falstaff says)
 Let us e'en talk a little like folks of this world.

How canst thou presume thou hast leave to destroy
 The beauties which Venus but lent to thy keeping?
Those looks were designed to inspire love and joy;
 More ordinary eyes may serve people for weeping.

To be vexed at a trifle or two that I writ,
 Your judgment at once and my passion you wrong;

34

You take that for fact which will scarce be found wit:
  Od's life! must one swear to the truth of a song?

What I speak, my fair Chloe, and what I write, shows
  The difference there is betwixt nature and art:
I court others in verse, but I love thee in prose;
  And they have my whimsies, but thou hast my heart.

The god of us verse-men (you know, child), the sun,
  How after his journeys he sets up his rest;
If at morning o'er earth 'tis his fancy to run,
  At night he reclines on his Thetis's breast.

So when I am wearied with wandering all day,
  To thee, my delight, in the evening I come:
No matter what beauties I saw on my way,
  They were but my visits, but thou art my home.

Then finish, dear Chloe, this pastoral war,
  And let us like Horace and Lydia agree;
For thou art a girl as much brighter than her
  As he was a poet sublimer than me.

AN EPITAPH

   Interred beneath this marble stone
   Lie sauntering Jack and idle Joan.
   While rolling threescore years and one
   Did round this world their courses run,
   If human things went well or ill,
   If changing empires rose or fell,
   The morning passed, the evening came,
   And found this couple just the same.
   They walked and ate, good folks. What then?
   Why, then they walked and ate again.
   They soundly slept the night away;

They did just nothing all the day.
And having buried children four,
Would not take pains to try for more.
Nor sister either had, nor brother;
They seemed just tallied for each other.

Their moral and economy
Most perfectly they made agree.
Each virtue kept its proper bound,
Nor trespassed on the other's ground.
Nor fame nor censure they regarded;
They neither punished nor rewarded.
He cared not what the footmen did;
Her maids she neither praised nor chid;
So every servant took his course,
And, bad at first, they all grew worse.
Slothful disorder filled his stable,
And sluttish plenty decked her table.
Their beer was strong, their wine was port;
Their meal was large, their grace was short.
They gave the poor the remnant meat,
Just when it grew not fit to eat.

They paid the church and parish rate,
And took, but read not, the receipt,
For which they claimed their Sunday's due
Of slumbering in an upper pew.

No man's defects they sought to know,
So never made themselves a foe.
No man's good deeds did they commend,
So never raised themselves a friend.
Nor cherished they relations poor,
That might decrease their present store.
Nor barn nor house did they repair:
That might oblige their future heir.
They neither added nor confounded;
They neither wanted nor abounded.
Each Christmas they accounts would clear;

And wound their bottom round the year.
Nor tear nor smile did they employ
At news of public grief or joy.
When bells were rung and bonfires made,
If asked, they ne'er denied their aid;
Their jug was to the ringers carried,
Whoever either died or married.
Their billet at the fire was found,
Whoever was deposed or crowned.

Nor good, nor bad, nor fools, nor wise,
They would not learn, nor could advise.
Without love, hatred, joy, or fear,
They led—a kind of—as it were;
Nor wished, nor cared, nor laughed, nor cried.
And so they lived, and so they died.

———

EPIGRAM

"My Lord, there's a christening," the officer said;
"The gossips are ready, the cushions are laid."
"What? Without my leave asked?" said the prelate, inflamed;
"Go lock up my font; let the infant be damned!"

Jonathan Swift

Dean Swift's persistent scatology pleases few moderns, besides D. H. Lawrence. And much of his famous wit is cruel and repellent. I had thought of printing his admired proposal for ending Ireland's distresses by fattening the surplus babies for food. But it is really painful. Strange; the British, a squeamish and decorous race, love to jest about cannibalism and seasickness. They overdo it, to our taste. No doubt most humor has a core of horror, the bitters in the cocktail, the civet in the sweet perfume. But Swift really puts in too much civet.

Of course, he was witty. Here are a few examples, relatively unfamiliar.

GOD'S REVENGE AGAINST PUNNING

Showing the Miserable Fates of Persons Addicted to This Crying Sin, in Court and Town

Manifold have been the judgments, which heaven, from time to time, for the chastisement of a sinful people, has inflicted on whole nations. For when the degeneracy becomes common, 'tis but just the punishment should be general. Of this kind, in our own unfortunate country, was that destructive pestilence, whose mortality was so fatal, as to sweep away, if Sir William Petty may be believed, five millions of Christian souls, besides women and Jews.

Such also was that dreadful conflagration ensuing, in this famous metropolis of London, which consumed, according to the computation of Sir Samuel Morland, one hundred thousand houses, not to mention churches and stables.

Scarce had this unhappy nation recovered these *funeste* disasters, when the abomination of playhouses rose up in the land; from hence hath an inundation of obscenity flowed from the court and overspread the kingdom; even infants disfigured the walls of holy temples with exorbitant representations of the members of generation; nay, no sooner had they learnt to spell, but they had wickedness enough to

38

write the names thereof in large capitals: an enormity observed by travellers to be found in no country but England.

But when whoring and popery were driven hence by the happy Revolution, still the nation so greatly offended, that Socinianism, Arianism, and Whistonism triumphed in our streets, and were in a manner become universal.

And yet still, after all these visitations, it has pleased Heaven to visit us with a contagion more epidemical, and of consequence more fatal: this was foretold to us, first, by that unparalleled eclipse in 1714: secondly, by the dreadful coruscation in the air this present year: and thirdly, by the nine comets seen at once over Soho Square, by Mrs. Katharine Wadlington and others; a contagion that first crept in among the first quality, descended to their footmen, and infused itself into their ladies: I mean the woful practice of PUNNING. This does occasion the corruption of our language, and therein of the word of God translated into our language, which certainly every sober Christian must tremble at.

Now such is the enormity of this abomination, that our very nobles not only commit punning over tea, and in taverns, but even on the Lord's day, and in the king's chapel: therefore, to deter men from this evil practice, I shall give some true and dreadful examples of God's revenge against punsters.

The right honourable ——, but it is not safe to insert the name of an eminent nobleman in this paper, yet I will venture to say that such a one has been seen; which is all we can say, considering the largeness of his sleeves: this young nobleman was not only a flagitious punster himself, but was accessory to the punning of others, by consent, by provocation, by connivance, and by defence of the evil committed; for which the Lord mercifully spared his neck, but as a mark of reprobation wryed his nose.

Another nobleman of great hopes, no less guilty of the same crime, was made the punisher of himself with his own hand, in the loss of five hundred pounds at box and dice; whereby this unfortunate young gentleman incurred the heavy displeasure of his aged grandmother.

A third of no less illustrious extraction, for the same vice, was permitted to fall into the hands of a Delilah, who may one day cut off his curious hair and deliver him up to the Philistines.

Colonel F——, an ancient gentleman of grave deportment, gave in to this sin so early in his youth, that whenever his tongue endeavours to speak common sense, he hesitates so, as not to be understood.

Thomas Pickle, gentleman, for the same crime banished to Minorca.

Muley Hamet, from a healthy and hopeful officer in the army, turned a miserable invalid at Tilbury Fort.

—— Eustace, Esq., for the murder of much of the king's English in Ireland is quite deprived of his reason, and now remains a lively instance of emptiness and vivacity.

Poor Daniel Button [1] for the same offence deprived of his wits.

One Samuel an Irishman, for his forward attempt to pun, was stunted in his stature, and hath been visited all his life after with bulls and blunders.

George Simmons, shoemaker at Turnstile in Holborn, was so given to this custom, and did it with so much success, that his neighbours gave out he was a wit. Which report coming among his creditors, nobody would trust him; so that now he is a bankrupt, and his family in a miserable condition.

Divers eminent clergymen of the university of Cambridge, for having propagated this vice, became great drunkards and Tories.

A Devonshire man of wit, for only saying in a jesting manner *I get up pun a horse,* instantly fell down, and broke his snuff-box and neck, and lost the horse.

"From which calamities, the Lord in his mercy defend us all, &c. &c." So prayeth the punless and pennyless J. Baker, knight.[2]

MARY THE COOK-MAID'S LETTER TO DOCTOR SHERIDAN

Well; if ever I saw such another man, since my mother bound my head,
You a gentleman! Marry come up, I wonder where you were bred?
I am sure such words do not become a man of your cloth,

---

[1] The keeper of the celebrated Wits' Coffee-house.
[2] Sir James Baker was a noted gambler. Americans will do well to note that "pun" is the colloquial pronunciation of "pound."

I would not give such language to a dog, faith and troth.
Yes, you called my master a knave. Fie, Mr. Sheridan, 'tis a shame
For a parson, who should know better things, to come out with such
  a name.
Knave in your teeth, Mr. Sheridan, 'tis both a shame and a sin,
And the dean my master is an honester man than you and all your
  kin:
He has more goodness in his little finger, than you have in your whole
  body,
My master is a parsonable man, and not a spindle-shanked hoddy
  doddy.
And now whereby I find you would fain make an excuse,
Because my master one day in anger called you goose.
Which, and I am sure I have been his servant four years since October,
And he never called me worse than sweetheart drunk or sober:
Not that I know his Reverence was ever concerned to my knowledge,
Though you and your come-rogues keep him out so late in your
  College.

You say you will eat grass on his grave: a Christian eat grass!
Whereby you now confess yourself to be a goose or an ass:
But that's as much as to say, that my master should die before ye,
Well, well, that's as God pleases, and I don't believe that's a true story,
And so say I told you so, and you may go tell my master; what care I?
And I don't care who knows it, 'tis all one to Mary.
Everybody knows, that I love to tell truth and shame the Devil,
I am but a poor servant, but I think gentlefolks should be civil.
Besides, you found fault with our vittles one day that you was here,
I remember it was upon a Tuesday, of all days in the year.
And Saunders the man says, you are always jesting and mocking,
Mary (said he, one day as I was mending my master's stocking),
My master is so fond of that minister that keeps the school;
I thought my master a wise man, but that man makes him a fool.
Saunders, said I, I would rather than a quart of ale,
He would come into our kitchen, and I would pin a dishclout to his
  tail.

And now I must go, and get Saunders to direct this letter,
For I write but a sad scrawl, but my sister Marget she writes better.

Well, but I must run and make the bed before my master comes from
   prayers,
And see now, it strikes ten, and I hear him coming upstairs:
Whereof I could say more to your verses, if I could write written hand,
And so I remain in a civil way, your servant to command,

MARY

A COPY OF A COPY OF VERSES

From Thomas Sheridan, Clerk, to
George-Nim-Dan-Dean, Esq.

Written July 15, 1721, at night.

I'd have you t'know, George, Dan, Dean, 'nd Nim,
That I've learn'd how verse t'compose trim,
Much better b'half th'n you, n'r you, n'r him,
And th't I'd rid'cule their 'nd your flam-flim.
Ay b't then, p'rhaps, says you, t's a merry whim,
With 'bundance of mark'd notes i'th'rim.
So th't I oughtn't for t'be morose 'nd t'look grim,
Think n't your 'p'stle put m'in a megrim;
Though 'n Rep't't'on Day, I 'ppear ver' slim,
Th' last bowl 't Helsham's did m' head t' swim,
So th't I h'd man' aches 'n 'v'ry scrubb'd limb,
'Cause th' top of th' bowl I h'd oft us'd t' skim;
And b'sides D'lan swears th't I h'd swall'w'd s'v'r'l brim—
Mers, 'nd that my vis'ge's cov'r'd o'er with r'd pim—
Ples; m'r'o'er though m' skull were ('s 'tisn't) 's strong's tim—
Ber, 't must have ach'd. Th' clans of th' c'llege Sanh'drim
Pres'nt the'r humbl' and 'fect'nate respects; that's t' say, D'ln', 'chlin,
   P. Ludl', Dic' St'wart, H'lsham, Capt'n P'rr Walmsl', 'nd Long-
   sh'nks Timm.

Richard Steele

SIR ROGER DE COVERLEY'S AMOURS

Tuesday, July 10, 1711

—Haerent infixi pectore vultus. [Virg. Aen. iv. ver. 4]
"Her looks were deep imprinted in his heart."

In my first description of the company in which I pass most of my time, it may be remembered that I mentioned a great affliction which my friend Sir Roger had met with in his youth; which was no less than a disappointment in love. It happened this evening, that we fell into a very pleasing walk at a distance from his house. As soon as we came into it, "It is," quoth the good old man, looking round him with a smile, "very hard, that any part of my land should be settled upon one who has used me so ill as the perverse widow did; and yet I am sure I could not see a sprig of any bough of this whole walk of trees, but I should reflect upon her and her severity. She has certainly the finest hand of any woman in the world. You are to know, this was the place wherein I used to muse upon her: and by that custom I can never come into it, but the same tender sentiments revive in my mind, as if I had actually walked with that beautiful creature under these shades. I have been fool enough to carve her name on the bark of several of these trees; so unhappy is the condition of men in love, to attempt the removing of their passion by the methods which serve only to imprint it deeper. She has certainly the finest hand of any woman in the world."

Here followed a profound silence: and I was not displeased to observe my friend falling so naturally into a discourse, which I had ever before taken notice he industriously avoided. After a very long pause, he entered upon an account of this great circumstance in his life with an air which I thought raised my idea of him above what I had ever had before; and gave me the picture of that cheerful mind of his, before it received that stroke which has ever since affected his words and actions. But he went on as follows:

43

"I came to my estate in my twenty-second year, and resolved to follow the steps of the most worthy of my ancestors who have inhabited this spot of earth before me, in all the methods of hospitality and good neighbourhood, for the sake of my fame; and in country sports and recreations, for the sake of my health. In my twenty-third year I was obliged to serve as sheriff of the county; and in my servants, officers, and whole equipage, indulged the pleasure of a young man (who did not think ill of his own person) in taking that public occasion of shewing my figure and behaviour to advantage. You may easily imagine to yourself what appearance I made, who am pretty tall, ride well, and was very well dressed, at the head of a whole county, with music before me, a feather in my hat, and my horse well bitted. I can assure you, I was not a little pleased with the kind looks and glances I had from all the balconies and windows as I rode to the hall where the assizes were held. But when I came there, a beautiful creature in a widow's habit sat in court to hear the event of a cause concerning her dower. This commanding creature (who was born for the destruction of all who beheld her) put on such a resignation in her countenance, and bore the whispers of all around the court with such a pretty uneasiness, I warrant you, and then recovered herself from one eye to another, until she was perfectly confused by meeting something so wistful in all she encountered, that at last, with a murrain to her, she cast her bewitching eye upon me. I no sooner met it but I bowed like a great surprised booby; and knowing her cause to be the first which came on, I cried like a captivated calf as I was, 'Make way for the defendant's witnesses.' This sudden partiality made all the county immediately see the sheriff also was become a slave to the fine widow. During the time her cause was upon trial, she behaved herself, I warrant you, with such a deep attention to her business, took opportunities to have little billets handed to her counsel, then would be in such a pretty confusion, occasioned, you must know, by acting before so much company, that not only I but the whole court was prejudiced in her favour; and all that the next heir to her husband had to urge, was thought so groundless and frivolous, that when it came to her counsel to reply, there was not half so much said as every one besides in the court thought he could have urged to her advantage. You must understand, Sir, this perverse woman is one of those unaccountable creatures that secretly rejoice in the admiration of men, but indulge themselves in no farther consequences. Hence it is that she has ever had a train

of admirers, and she removes from her slaves in town to those in the
country, according to the seasons of the year. She is a reading lady,
and far gone in the pleasures of friendship. She is always accompanied
by a confidant, who is witness to her daily protestations against our
sex, and consequently a bar to her first steps towards love, upon the
strength of her own maxims and declarations.

"However, I must needs say, this accomplished mistress of mine has
distinguished me above the rest, and has been known to declare Sir
Roger de Coverley was the tamest and most humane of all the brutes
in the country. I was told she said so, by one who thought he rallied
me; but upon the strength of this slender encouragement of being
thought least detestable, I made new liveries, new-paired my coach-
horses, sent them all to town to be bitted, and taught to throw their
legs well, and move all together, before I pretended to cross the country, and wait upon her. As soon as I thought my retinue suitable to the
character of my fortune and youth, I set out from hence to make my
addresses. The particular skill of this lady has ever been to enflame
your wishes, and yet command respect. To make her mistress of this
art, she has a greater share of knowledge, wit, and good sense, than
is usual even among men of merit. Then she is beautiful beyond the
race of women. If you will not let her go on with a certain artifice
with her eyes, and the skill of beauty, she will arm herself with her
real charms, and strike you with admiration instead of desire. It is certain, that if you were to behold the whole woman, there is that dignity
in her aspect, that composure in her motion, that complacency in her
manner, that if her form makes you hope, her merit makes you fear.
But then again, she is such a desperate scholar, that no country gentleman can approach her without being a jest. As I was going to tell you,
when I came to her house I was admitted to her presence with great
civility; at the same time she placed herself to be first seen by me in
such an attitude, as I think you call the posture of a picture, that she
discovered new charms, and I at last came towards her with such an
awe as made me speechless. This she no sooner observed but she made
her advantage of it, and began a discourse to me concerning love and
honour, as they both are followed by pretenders, and the real votaries
to them. When she discussed these points in a discourse, which I
verily believe was as learned as the best philosopher in Europe could
possibly make, she asked me whether she was so happy as to fall in
with my sentiments on these important particulars. Her confidant sat

by her, and upon my being in the last confusion and silence, this malicious aid of hers, turning to her, says, 'I am very glad to observe Sir Roger pauses upon this subject, and seems resolved to deliver all his sentiments upon the matter when he pleases to speak.' They both kept their countenances, and after I had sat half an hour meditating how to behave before such profound casuists, I rose up and took my leave. Chance has since that time thrown me very often in her way, and she as often has directed a discourse to me which I do not understand. This barbarity has kept me ever at a distance from the most beautiful object my eyes ever beheld. It is thus also she deals with all mankind, and you must make love to her, as you would conquer the sphinx, by posing her. But were she like other women, and that there were any talking to her, how constant must the pleasure of that man be, who would converse with a creature— But, after all, you may be sure her heart is fixed on some one or other; and yet I have been credibly informed—but who can believe half that is said! after she had done speaking to me, she put her hand to her bosom, and adjusted her tucker. Then she cast her eyes a little down, upon my beholding her too earnestly. They say she sings excellently; her voice in her ordinary speech has something in it inexpressibly sweet. You must know I dined with her at a public table the day after I first saw her, and she helped me to some tansy in the eye of all the gentlemen in the county. She has certainly the finest hand of any woman in the world. I can assure you, Sir, were you to behold her, you would be in the same condition; for as her speech is music, her form is angelic. But I find I grow irregular while I am talking of her; but indeed it would be stupidity to be unconcerned at such perfection. Oh, the excellent creature! she is as inimitable to all women, as she is inaccessible to all men."

I found my friend begin to rave, and insensibly led him towards the house, that we might be joined by some other company; and am convinced that the widow is the secret cause of all that inconsistency which appears in some parts of my friend's discourse; though he has so much command of himself as not directly to mention her, yet according to that of Martial, which one knows not how to render into English, *Dum tacet hanc loquitur.* I shall end this paper with that whole epigram, which represents with much humour my honest friend's condition:

Quicquid agit Rufus, nihil est, nisi Naevia Rufo,
Si gaudet, si flet, si tacet, hanc loquitur;
Coenat, propinat, poscit, negat, annuit, una est
Naevia; si non sit Naevia, mutus erit.
Scriberet hesterna, patri cum luce salutem,
Naevia lux, inquit, Naevia numen ave.

[*Epig.* I, 68.]

"Let Rufus weep, rejoice, stand, sit, or walk,
Still he can nothing but of Naevia talk;
Let him eat, drink, ask questions, or dispute,
Still he must speak of Naevia, or be mute.
He writ to his father, ending with this line,
'I am, my lovely Naevia, ever thine.'"

[From *The Spectator*]

John Gay

John Gay, author of The Beggar's Opera, *obviously always hummed as he wrote. One should hum, or even sing, the work of authors who hum as they write.*

MOLLY MOG

Says my uncle: "I pray you, discover
    What hath been the cause of your woes,
Why you pine and you whine like a lover?"
    "I have seen Molly Mog of the Rose."

"O nephew! Your grief is but folly!
    In town you may find better prog;
Half a crown there will get you a Molly,
    A Molly much better than Mog."

"I know that by wits 'tis recited
    That women at best are a clog,
But I'm not so easily frighted
    From loving of sweet Molly Mog.

"The schoolboy's desire is a play-day,
    The schoolmaster's joy is to flog;
The milkmaid's delight is on May Day,
    But mine is on sweet Molly Mog.

"Will-a-wisp leads the Trav'ler a-gadding
    Thro' ditch and thro' quagmire and bog;
But no light can set me a-madding
    Like the eyes of my sweet Molly Mog.

"For guineas in other men's breeches
    Your gamesters will palm and will cog;
But I envy them none of their riches
    So I may win sweet Molly Mog.

"The heart, when half wounded, is changing,
  It here and there leaps like a frog;
But my heart can never be ranging,
  'Tis so fixed upon sweet Molly Mog.

"I feel I'm in love to distraction,
  My senses all lost in a fog;
And nothing can give satisfaction
  But thinking of sweet Molly Mog.

"A letter when I am inditing,
  Comes Cupid and gives me a jog,
And I fill all the paper with writing
  Of nothing but sweet Molly Mog.

"If I would not give up the three Graces,
  I wish I were hang'd like a dog,
And at Court all the drawing-room faces
  For a glance of my sweet Molly Mog.

"Those faces want Nature and Spirit,
  And seem as cut out of a log;
Juno, Venus, and Pallas's merit
  Unite in my sweet Molly Mog.

"Were Virgil alive with his Phillis,
  And writing another eclogue,
Both his Phillis and fair Amaryllis
  He'd give up for sweet Molly Mog.

"When she smiles on each guest, like her liquor,
  Then jealousy sets me agog.
To be sure she's a bit for the Vicar,
  And so I shall lose Molly Mog."

Alexander Pope

ON CERTAIN LADIES

When other fair ones to the shades go down,
Still Chloe, Flavia, Delia, stay in town:
Those ghosts of beauty wandering here reside,
And haunt the places where their honour died.

Isaac Bickerstaffe

AN EXPOSTULATION

When late I attempted your pity to move,
  What made you so deaf to my prayers?
Perhaps it was right to dissemble your love,
  But—why did you kick me downstairs?

James Boswell

SALLIES OF SAMUEL JOHNSON

A lady once asked him how he came to define *Pastern* the *knee* of a horse: instead of making an elaborate defence, as she expected, he at once answered, "Ignorance, Madam, pure ignorance."

He said, "No man will be a sailor who has contrivance enough to get himself into a jail: for being in a ship is being in a jail, with the chance of being drowned."

"When I was running about this town a very poor fellow, I was a great arguer for the advantages of poverty; but I was, at the same time, very sorry to be poor. Sir, all the arguments which are brought to represent poverty as no evil, shew it to be evidently a great evil. You never find people labouring to convince you that you may live very happily upon a plentiful fortune."

When I called upon Dr. Johnson next morning, I found him highly satisfied with his colloquial prowess the preceding evening. "Well, (said he,) we had good talk." BOSWELL: "Yes, Sir; you tossed and gored several persons."

Lord Eldon (at that time Mr. John Scott) has the following reminiscences of a visit of Dr. Johnson to Oxford:—"I had a walk in New Inn Hall Garden with Dr. Johnson and Sir Robert Chambers (Principal of the Hall). Sir Robert was gathering snails, and throwing them over the wall into his neighbour's garden. The Doctor reproached him very roughly, and stated to him that this was unmannerly and unneighbourly. "Sir," said Sir Robert, "my neighbour is a Dissenter." "Oh!" said the Doctor, "if so, Chambers, toss away, toss away, as hard as you can."

[Note by George Birkbeck Hill]

Our conversation turned on a variety of subjects. He thought portrait painting an improper employment for a woman. "Publick practice of any art, (he observed,) and staring in men's faces, is very indelicate in a female."

When I expressed an earnest wish for his remarks on Italy, he said, "I do not see that I could make a book upon Italy; yet I should be glad to get two hundred pounds, or five hundred pounds, by such a work." This shewed both that a journal of his Tour upon the Continent was not wholly out of his contemplation, and that he uniformly adhered to that strange opinion, which his indolent disposition made him utter: "No man but a blockhead ever wrote, except for money."

He observed, that a gentleman of eminence in literature had got into a bad style of poetry of late. "He puts (said he) a very common thing in a strange dress till he does not know it himself, and thinks other people do not know it." BOSWELL: "That is owing to his being so much versant in old English poetry." JOHNSON: "What is that to the purpose, Sir? If I say a man is drunk, and you tell me that it is owing to his taking much drink, the matter is not mended. No, Sir, —— has taken to an odd mode. For example; he'd write thus:

> Hermit hoar, in solemn cell,
> Wearing out life's evening gray.

Gray evening is common enough! but *evening gray* he'd think fine.—Stay;—we'll make out the stanza:

> Hermit hoar, in solemn cell,
> Wearing out life's evening gray;
> Smite thy bosom, sage, and tell,
> What is bliss? and which the way?"

BOSWELL: "But why smite his bosom, Sir?" JOHNSON: "Why, to shew he was in earnest" (smiling).—He at an after period added the following stanza:

> Thus I spoke; and speaking sigh'd;
> —Scarce repress'd the starting tear;—
> When the smiling sage reply'd—
> —Come, my lad, and drink some beer.

In our way, Johnson strongly expressed his love of driving fast in a post-chaise. "If (said he) I had no duties, and no reference to futurity,

I would spend my life in driving briskly in a post-chaise with a pretty woman; but she should be one who could understand me, and would add something to the conversation."

I suggested a doubt, that if I were to reside in London, the exquisite zest with which I relished it in occasional visits might go off, and I might grow tired of it. JOHNSON: "Why, Sir, you find no man, at all intellectual, who is willing to leave London. No, Sir, when a man is tired of London, he is tired of life; for there is in London all that life can afford."

As he opened a note which his servant brought to him, he said, "An odd thought strikes me: we shall receive no letters in the grave."

Richard Brinsley Sheridan

THE CRITIC (Act II)

SCENE I: *The Theatre, before the Curtain*
(*Enter* DANGLE, PUFF, *and* SNEER)

PUFF: No, no, sir; what Shakspeare says of actors may be better applied to the purpose of plays; they ought to be *the abstract and brief chronicles of the time*. Therefore when history, and particularly the history of our own country, furnishes anything like a case in point, to the time in which an author writes, if he knows his own interest, he will take advantage of it; so, sir, I call my tragedy *The Spanish Armada;* and have laid the scene before Tilbury Fort.

SNEER: A most happy thought, certainly!

DANGLE: Egad it was—I told you so. But pray now, I don't understand how you have contrived to introduce any love into it.

PUFF: Love! oh, nothing so easy! for it is a received point among poets, that where history gives you a good heroic outline for a play, you may fill up with a little love at your own discretion: in doing which, nine times out of ten, you only make up a deficiency in the private history of the times. Now I rather think I have done this with some success.

SNEER: No scandal about Queen Elizabeth, I hope?

PUFF: O lud! no, no;—I only suppose the governor of Tilbury Fort's daughter to be in love with the son of the Spanish admiral.

SNEER: Oh, is that all!

DANGLE: Excellent, i'faith! I see at once. But won't this appear rather improbable?

PUFF: To be sure it will—but what the plague! a play is not to show occurrences that happen every day, but things just so strange, that though they never did, they might happen.

SNEER: Certainly nothing is unnatural, that is not physically impossible.

PUFF: Very true—and for that matter Don Ferolo Whiskerandos, for that's the lover's name, might have been over here in the train of the Spanish Ambassador; or Tilburina, for that is the lady's name,

54

might have been in love with him, from having heard his character, or seen his picture; or from knowing that he was the last man in the world she ought to be in love with—or for any other good female reason.—However, sir, the fact is, that though she is but a knight's daughter, egad! she is in love like any princess!

DANGLE: Poor young lady! I feel for her already! for I can conceive how great the conflict must be between her passion and her duty; her love for her country, and her love for Don Ferolo Whiskerandos!

PUFF: Oh, amazing!—her poor susceptible heart is swayed to and fro by contending passions like—

(*Enter* UNDER PROMPTER)

UNDER PROMPTER: Sir, the scene is set, and everything is ready to begin, if you please.

PUFF: Egad, then we'll lose no time.

UNDER PROMPTER: Though, I believe, sir, you will find it very short, for all the performers have profited by the kind permission you granted them.

PUFF: Hey! what?

UNDER PROMPTER: You know, sir, you gave them leave to cut out or omit whatever they found heavy or unnecessary to the plot, and I must own they have taken very liberal advantage of your indulgence.

PUFF: Well, well.—They are in general very good judges, and I know I am luxuriant.—Now, Mr. Hopkins, as soon as you please.

UNDER PROMPTER (*to the Orchestra*): Gentlemen, will you play a few bars of something, just to—

PUFF: Ay, that's right; for as we have the scenes and dresses, egad, we'll go to't, as if it was the first night's performance;—but you need not mind stopping between the acts—(*Exit* UNDER PROMPTER. —*Orchestra plays—then the bell rings.*) So! stand clear, gentlemen. Now you know there will be a cry of Down! down!—Hats off!— Silence!—Then up curtain, and let us see what our painters have done for us. (*Curtain rises.*)

"SCENE II: *Tilbury Fort*
(*Two* SENTINELS *discovered asleep*)"

DANGLE: Tilbury Fort—very fine indeed!

PUFF: Now, what do you think I open with?

SNEER: Faith, I can't guess—

PUFF: A clock.—Hark!—(*Clock strikes*) I open with a clock striking, to beget an awful attention in the audience: it also marks the time, which is four o'clock in the morning, and saves a description of the rising sun, and a great deal about gilding the eastern hemisphere.

DANGLE: But pray, are the sentinels to be asleep?

PUFF: Fast as watchmen.

SNEER: Isn't that odd though at such an alarming crisis?

PUFF: To be sure it is,—but smaller things must give way to a striking scene at the opening; that's a rule. And the case is, that two great men are coming to this very spot to begin the piece: now, it is not to be supposed they would open their lips, if these fellows were watching them; so, egad, I must either have sent them off their posts, or set them asleep.

SNEER: Oh, that accounts for it.—But tell us, who are these coming?

PUFF: These are they—Sir Walter Raleigh, and Sir Christopher Hatton. You'll know Sir Christopher by his turning out his toes—famous, you know, for his dancing. I like to preserve all the little traits of character.—Now attend.

> "(*Enter* SIR WALTER RALEIGH *and* SIR CHRISTOPHER HATTON)
> SIR CHRISTOPHER: True, gallant Raleigh!"—

DANGLE: What, they had been talking before?

PUFF: Oh, yes; all the way as they came along.—(*To the Actors*): I beg pardon, gentlemen, but these are particular friends of mine, whose remarks may be of great service to us.—(*To* SNEER *and* DANGLE): Don't mind interrupting them whenever any thing strikes you.

> "SIR CHRISTOPHER: True, gallant Raleigh!
> But oh, thou champion of thy country's fame,
> There is a question which I yet must ask:
> A question which I never ask'd before—
> What mean these mighty armaments?
> This general muster? and this throng of chiefs?"

SNEER: Pray, Mr. Puff, how came Sir Christopher Hatton never to ask that question before?

PUFF: What, before the play began?—how the plague could he?

DANGLE: That's true, i'faith!

PUFF: But you will hear what he thinks of the matter.

"SIR CHRISTOPHER: Alas! my noble friend, when I behold
       Yon tented plains in martial symmetry
       Array'd; when I count o'er yon glittering lines
       Of crested warriors, where the proud steeds' neigh,
       And valour-breathing trumpet's shrill appeal,
       Responsive vibrate on my listening ear;
       When virgin majesty herself I view,
       Like her protecting Pallas, veil'd in steel,
       With graceful confidence exhort to arms!
       When, briefly, all I hear or see bears stamp
       Of martial vigilance and stern defence,
       I cannot but surmise—forgive, my friend,
       If the conjecture's rash—I cannot but
       Surmise the state some danger apprehends!"

SNEER: A very cautious conjecture that.

PUFF: Yes, that's his character; not to give an opinion but on secure
  grounds.—Now then.

"SIR WALTER: O most accomplish'd Christopher!"—

PUFF: He calls him by his Christian name, to show that they are on
  the most familiar terms.

"SIR WALTER: O most accomplish'd Christopher! I find
        Thy staunch sagacity still tracks the future,
        In the fresh print of the o'ertaken past."

PUFF: Figurative!

"SIR WALTER: Thy fears are just.
SIR CHRISTOPHER: But where? whence? when? and what
        The danger is,—methinks I fain would learn.
SIR WALTER: You know, my friend, scarce two revolving suns,
        And three revolving moons, have closed their course,
        Since haughty Philip, in despite of peace,
        With hostile hand hath struck at England's trade.
SIR CHRISTOPHER: I know it well.
SIR WALTER: Philip, you know, is proud Iberia's king!
SIR CHRISTOPHER: He is.
SIR WALTER: His subjects in base bigotry
        And Catholic oppression held;—while we,
        You know, the Protestant persuasion hold.

SIR CHRISTOPHER: We do.
SIR WALTER: You know, beside, his boasted armament,
                   The famed Armada, by the Pope baptized,
                   With purpose to invade these realms—
SIR CHRISTOPHER: Is sailed,
                   Our last advices so report.
SIR WALTER: While the Iberian admiral's chief hope,
                   His darling son—
SIR CHRISTOPHER: Ferolo Whiskerandos hight—
SIR WALTER: The same—by chance a prisoner hath been ta'en,
                   And in this fort of Tilbury—
SIR CHRISTOPHER: Is now
                   Confined—'tis true, and oft from yon tall turret's top
                   I've mark'd the youthful Spaniard's haughty mien—
                   Unconquer'd, though in chains.
SIR WALTER: You also know"—

DANGLE: Mr. Puff, as he knows all this, why does Sir Walter go on telling him?

PUFF: But the audience are not supposed to know anything of the matter, are they?

SNEER: True; but I think you manage ill: for there certainly appears no reason why Sir Walter should be so communicative.

PUFF: 'Fore Gad, now, that is one of the most ungrateful observations I ever heard!—for the less inducement he has to tell all this, the more, I think, you ought to be obliged to him; for I am sure you'd know nothing of the matter without it.

DANGLE: That's very true, upon my word.

PUFF: But you will find he was not going on.

"SIR CHRISTOPHER: Enough, enough—'tis plain—and I no more
                   Am in amazement lost!"—

PUFF: Here, now you see, Sir Christopher did not in fact ask any one question for his own information.

SNEER: No, indeed: his has been a most distinterested curiosity!

DANGLE: Really, I find, we are very much obliged to them both.

PUFF: To be sure you are. Now then for the commander-in-chief, the Earl of Leicester, who, you know, was no favourite but of the queen's.—We left off—*in amazement lost!*

"SIR CHRISTOPHER: Am in amazement lost.
But, see where noble Leicester comes! supreme
In honours and command.
SIR WALTER: And yet, methinks,
At such a time, so perilous, so fear'd,
That staff might well become an abler grasp.
SIR CHRISTOPHER: And so, by Heaven! think I; but soft, he's here!"

PUFF: Ay, they envy him!

SNEER: But who are these with him?

PUFF: Oh! very valiant knights: one is the governor of the fort, the other the master of the horse. And now, I think, you shall hear some better language: I was obliged to be plain and intelligible in the first scene, because there was so much matter of fact in it; but now, i'faith, you have trope, figure, and metaphor, as plenty as noun-substantives.

"(*Enter* EARL OF LEICESTER, GOVERNOR, MASTER OF THE HORSE, KNIGHTS, &c.)

LEICESTER: How's this, my friends! is't thus your new-fledged zeal
And plumèd valour moulds in roosted sloth?
Why dimly glimmers that heroic flame,
Whose reddening blaze, by patriot spirit fed,
Should be the beacon of a kindling realm?
Can the quick current of a patriot heart
Thus stagnate in a cold and weedy converse,
Or freeze in tideless inactivity?
No! rather let the fountain of your valour
Spring through each stream of enterprise,
Each petty channel of conducive daring,
Till the full torrent of your foaming wrath
O'erwhelm the flats of sunk hostility!"

PUFF: There it is—followed up!

"SIR WALTER: No more!—the freshening breath of thy rebuke
Hath fill'd the swelling canvas of our souls!
Aud thus, though fate should cut the cable of
          (*All take hands*)
Our topmost hopes, in friendship's closing line
We'll grapple with despair, and if we fall,
We'll fall in glory's wake!
LEICESTER: There spoke old England's genius!
Then, are we all resolved?

ALL: We are—all resolved.
LEICESTER: To conquer—or be free?
ALL: To conquer, or be free.
LEICESTER: All?
ALL: All."

DANGLE: *Nem. con.*[1] egad!

PUFF: Oh, yes!—where they do agree on the stage, their unanimity is wonderful!

"LEICESTER: Then let's embrace—and now— (*kneels*)."

SNEER: What the plague, is he going to pray?

PUFF: Yes; hush!—in great emergencies, there is nothing like a prayer.

"LEICESTER: O mighty Mars!"

DANGLE: But why should he pray to Mars?

PUFF: Hush!

"LEICESTER: If in thy homage bred,
                        Each point of discipline I've still observed;
                        Nor but by due promotion, and the right
                        Of service, to the rank of major-general
                        Have risen; assist thy votary now!
GOVERNOR: Yet do not rise—hear me! (*Kneels.*)
MASTER: And me! (*Kneels*)
KNIGHT: And me! (*Kneels*)
SIR WALTER: And me! (*Kneels*)
SIR CHRISTOPHER: And me! (*Kneels*)"

PUFF: Now pray altogether.

"ALL: Behold thy votaries submissive beg,
                        That thou wilt deign to grant them all they ask;
                        Assist them to accomplish all their ends,
                        And sanctify whatever means they use
                        To gain them!"

SNEER: A very orthodox quintetto!

PUFF: Vastly well, gentlemen!—Is that well managed or not? Have you such a prayer as that on the stage?

---

[1] "Nemine contradicente": "no one contradicting."

SNEER: Not exactly.

LEICESTER (*to* PUFF): But, sir, you haven't settled how we are to get off here.

PUFF: You could not go off kneeling, could you?

SIR WALTER (*to Puff*): Oh, no, sir; impossible!

PUFF: It would have a good effect, i'faith, if you could exeunt praying! —Yes, and would vary the established mode of springing off with a glance at the pit.

SNEER: Oh, never mind, so as you get them off!—I'll answer for it, the audience won't care how.

PUFF: Well, then, repeat the last line standing, and go off the old way.

"ALL: And sanctify whatever means we use
               To gain them. (*Exeunt*)"

DANGLE: Bravo! a fine exit.

SNEER: Well, really, Mr. Puff—

PUFF: Stay a moment!

"(*The* SENTINELS *get up*)

1 SENTINEL: All this shall to Lord Burleigh's ear.
2 SENTINEL: 'Tis meet it should. (*Exeunt*)"

DANGLE: Hey!—why, I thought those fellows had been asleep?

PUFF: Only a pretence; there's the art of it: they were spies of Lord Burleigh's.

SNEER: But isn't it odd they never were taken notice of, not even by the commander-in-chief?

PUFF: O lud, sir! if people who want to listen or overhear, were not always connived at in a tragedy, there would be no carrying on any plot in the world.

DANGLE: That's certain!

PUFF: But take care, my dear Dangle! the morning-gun is going to fire. (*Cannon fires*)

DANGLE: Well, that will have a fine effect!

PUFF: I think so, and helps to realise the scene.—(*Cannon twice*) What the plague! three morning-guns! there never is but one!—Ay, this is always the way at the theatre: give these fellows a good thing, and they never know when to have done with it.—You have no more cannon to fire?

UNDER PROMPTER (*within*): No, sir.

PUFF: Now, then, for soft music.

SNEER: Pray, what's that for?

PUFF: It shows that Tilburina is coming;—nothing introduces you a heroine like soft music. Here she comes!

DANGLE: And her confidant, I suppose?

PUFF: To be sure! Here they are—inconsolable to the minuet in Ariadne! (*Soft music*)

"(*Enter* TILBURINA *and* CONFIDANT)

TILBURINA: Now has the whispering breath of gentle morn
Bid Nature's voice and Nature's beauty rise;
While orient Phœbus, with unborrow'd hues,
Clothes the waked loveliness which all night slept
In heavenly drapery! Darkness is fled.
Now flowers unfold their beauties to the sun,
And, blushing, kiss the beam he sends to wake them—
The striped carnation, and the guarded rose,
The vulgar wallflower, and smart gillyflower,
The polyanthus mean—the dapper daisy,
Sweet-william—and sweet marjoram—and all
The tribe of single and of double pinks!
Now, too, the feather'd warblers tune their notes
Around, and charm the listening grove. The lark!
The linnet! chaffinch! bullfinch! goldfinch! greenfinch!
But O, to me no joy can they afford!
Nor rose, nor wallflower, nor smart gillyflower,
Nor polyanthus mean, nor dapper daisy,
Nor William sweet, nor marjoram—nor lark,
Linnet, nor all the finches of the grove!"

PUFF: Your white handkerchief, madam!—

TILBURINA: I thought, sir, I wasn't to use that till *heart-rending woe.*

PUFF: Oh, yes, madam, at *the finches of the grove,* if you please.

"TILBURINA: Nor lark,
Linnet, nor all the finches of the grove! (*weeps*)."

PUFF: Vastly well, madam!

DANGLE: Vastly well, indeed!

"TILBURINA: For, oh, too sure, heart-rending woe is now
The lot of wretched Tilburina!"

DANGLE: Oh!—'tis too much!
SNEER: Oh!—it is indeed!

"CONFIDANT: Be comforted, sweet lady; for who knows,
                      But Heaven has yet some milk-white day in store?
TILBURINA: Alas! my gentle Nora,
                      Thy tender youth as yet hath never mourn'd
                      Love's fatal dart. Else wouldst thou know, that when
                      The soul is sunk in comfortless despair,
                      It cannot taste of merriment."

DANGLE: That's certain!

"CONFIDANT: But see where your stern father comes:
                      It is not meet that he should find you thus."

PUFF: Hey, what the plague!—what a cut is here! Why, what is become of the description of her first meeting with Don Whiskerandos—his gallant behaviour in the sea fight—and the simile of
the canary-bird?
TILBURINA: Indeed, sir, you'll find they will not be missed.
PUFF: Very well, very well!
TILBURINA (to CONFIDANT): The cue, ma'am, if you please.

"CONFIDANT: It is not meet that he should find you thus.
TILBURINA: Thou counsel'st right; but 'tis no easy task
                      For barefaced grief to wear a mask of joy.

(*Enter* GOVERNOR)

GOVERNOR: How's this!—in tears?—O Tilburina, shame!
                      Is this a time for maudling tenderness,
                      And Cupid's baby woes?—Hast thou not heard
                      That haughty Spain's pope-consecrated fleet
                      Advances to our shores, while England's fate,
                      Like a clipp'd guinea, trembles in the scale?
TILBURINA: Then is the crisis of my fate at hand!
                      I see the fleets approach—I see—"

PUFF: Now, pray, gentlemen, mind. This is one of the most useful
figures we tragedy writers have, by which a hero or heroine, in
consideration of their being often obliged to overlook things that
are on the stage, is allowed to hear and see a number of things that
are not.

SNEER: Yes; a kind of poetical second-sight!

PUFF: Yes.—Now then, madam.

"TILBURINA: I see their decks
> Are clear'd!—I see the signal made!
> The line is form'd!—a cable's length asunder!—
> I see the frigates station'd in the rear;
> And now, I hear the thunder of the guns!
> I hear the victor's shouts!—I also hear
> The vanquished groan!—and now 'tis smoke—and now
> I see the loose sails shiver in the wind!
> I see—I see—what soon you'll see—

GOVERNOR: Hold, daughter! peace! this love hath turn'd thy brain:
> The Spanish fleet thou canst not see—because
> —It is not yet in sight!"

DANGLE: Egad, though, the governor seems to make no allowance for this poetical figure you talk of.

PUFF: No, a plain matter-of-fact man;—that's his character.

"TILBURINA: But will you then refuse his offer?

GOVERNOR: I must—I will—I can—I ought—I do.

TILBURINA: Think what a noble price.

GOVERNOR: No more—you urge in vain.

TILBURINA: His liberty is all he asks."

SNEER: All who asks, Mr. Puff? Who is—

PUFF: Egad, sir, I can't tell! Here has been such cutting and slashing, I don't know where they have got to myself.

TILBURINA: Indeed, sir, you will find it will connect very well.

"—And your reward secure."

PUFF: Oh, if they hadn't been so devilish free with their cutting here, you would have found that Don Whiskerandos has been tampering for his liberty, and has persuaded Tilburina to make this proposal to her father. And now, pray observe the conciseness with which the argument is conducted. Egad, the *pro* and *con* goes as smart as hits in a fencing-match. It is indeed a sort of small-sword logic, which we have borrowed from the French.

"TILBURINA: A retreat in Spain!

GOVERNOR: Outlawry here!

TILBURINA: Your daughter's prayer?

GOVERNOR: Your father's oath.

TILBURINA:	My lover!
GOVERNOR:	My country!
TILBURINA:	Tilburina!
GOVERNOR:	England!
TILBURINA:	A title!
GOVERNOR:	Honour!
TILBURINA:	A pension!
GOVERNOR:	Conscience!
TILBURINA:	A thousand pounds!
GOVERNOR:	Ha! thou hast touch'd me nearly!"

PUFF: There you see—she threw in *Tilburina*. Quick, party quarte with *England!*—Ha! thrust in tierce *a title!*—parried by *honour*. Ha! *a pension* over the arm!—put by by *conscience*. Then flankonade with *a thousand pounds*—and a palpable hit, egad!

| "TILBURINA: | Canst thou—
Reject the suppliant, and the daughter too? |
| GOVERNOR: | No more; I would not hear thee plead in vain:
The father softens—but the governor
Is fix'd! (*Exit*)" |

DANGLE: Ay, that antithesis of persons is a most established figure.

"TILBURINA:	'Tis well,—hence then, fond hopes,—fond passion, hence; Duty, behold I am all over thine—
WHISKERANDOS	(*without*): Where is my love—my—
TILBURINA:	Ha!

(*Enter* DON FEROLO WHISKERANDOS)

| WHISKERANDOS: | My beauteous enemy!—" |

PUFF: Oh, dear, ma'am, you must start a great deal more than that! Consider, you had just determined in favour of duty—when, in a moment, the sound of his voice revives your passion—overthrows your resolution—destroys your obedience. If you don't express all that in your start, you do nothing at all.

TILBURINA: Well, we'll try again!

DANGLE: Speaking from within has always a fine effect.

SNEER: Very.

| "WHISKERANDOS: | My conquering Tilburina! How! is't thus
We meet? why are thy looks averse? what means
That falling tear—that frown of boding woe? |

Ha! now indeed I am a prisoner!
Yes, now I feel the falling weight of these
Disgraceful chains—which, cruel Tilburina!
Thy doating captive gloried in before.—
But thou art false, and Whiskerandos is undone!

TILBURINA: O no! how little dost thou know thy Tilburina!

WHISKERANDOS: Art thou then true?—Begone cares, doubts, and fears,
I make you all a present to the winds;
And if the winds reject you—try the waves."

PUFF: The wind, you know, is the established receiver of all stolen sighs, and cast-off griefs and apprehensions.

"TILBURINA: Yet must we part!—stern duty seals our doom:
Though here I call yon conscious clouds to witness,
Could I pursue the bias of my soul,
All friends, all right of parents, I'd disclaim,
And thou, my Whiskerandos, shouldst be father
And mother, brother, cousin, uncle, aunt,
And friend to me!

WHISKERANDOS: Oh, matchless excellence! and must we part?
Well, if—we must—we must—and in that case
The less is said the better."

PUFF: Heyday! here's a cut!—What, are all the mutual protestations out?

TILBURINA: Now, pray, sir, don't interrupt us just here: you ruin our feelings.

PUFF: Your feelings!—but zounds, my feelings, ma'am!

SNEER: No; pray don't interrupt them.

"WHISKERANDOS: One last embrace.

TILBURINA: Now,—farewell, for ever.

WHISKERANDOS: For ever!

TILBURINA: Ay, for ever! (*Going*)"

PUFF: 'Sdeath and fury!—Gad's life!—sir! madam! if you go out without the parting look, you might as well dance out. Here, here!

CONFIDANT: But pray, sir, how am I to get off here?

PUFF: You! pshaw! what the devil signifies how you get off! edge away at the top, or where you will—(*Pushes the* CONFIDANT *off*). Now, ma'am, you see—

TILBURINA: We understand you, sir.

"Ay, for ever.

BOTH: Oh! (*Turning back, and exeunt*).—Scene closes."

DANGLE: Oh, charming!

PUFF: Hey!—'tis pretty well, I believe: you see I don't attempt to strike out any thing new—but I take it I improve on the established modes.

SNEER: You do, indeed! But, pray, is not Queen Elizabeth to appear?

PUFF: No, not once—but she is to be talked of for ever; so that, egad, you'll think a hundred times that she is on the point of coming in.

SNEER: Hang it, I think it's a pity to keep her in the green-room all the night.

PUFF: Oh, no, that always has a fine effect—it keeps up expectation.

DANGLE: But are we not to have a battle?

PUFF: Yes, yes, you will have a battle at last; but, egad, it's not to be by land, but by sea—and that is the only quite new thing in the piece.

DANGLE: What, Drake at the Armada, hey?

PUFF: Yes, i'faith—fire-ships and all; then we shall end with the procession. Hey, that will do, I think?

SNEER: No doubt on't.

PUFF: Come, we must not lose time; so now for the under-plot.

SNEER: What the plague, have you another plot?

PUFF: O Lord, yes; ever while you live have two plots to your tragedy. The grand point in managing them is only to let your under-plot have as little connection with your main-plot as possible.—I flatter myself nothing can be more distinct than mine; for as in my chief plot the characters are all great people, I have laid my under-plot in low life; and as the former is to end in deep distress, I make the other end as happy as a farce.—Now, Mr. Hopkins, as soon as you please.

(*Enter* UNDER PROMPTER)

UNDER PROMPTER: Sir, the carpenter says it is impossible you can go to the park scene yet.

PUFF: The park scene! no! I mean the description scene here, in the wood.

UNDER PROMPTER: Sir, the performers have cut it out.

PUFF: Cut it out!

UNDER PROMPTER: Yes, sir.

PUFF: What! the whole account of Queen Elizabeth?

UNDER PROMPTER: Yes, sir.

PUFF: And the description of her horse and side-saddle?

UNDER PROMPTER: Yes, sir.

PUFF: So, so; this is very fine indeed!—Mr. Hopkins, how the plague could you suffer this?

MR. HOPKINS (*within*): Sir, indeed the pruning-knife—

PUFF: The pruning-knife—zounds!—the axe! Why, here has been such lopping and topping, I shan't have the bare trunk of my play left presently!—Very well, sir—the performers must do as they please; but, upon my soul, I'll print it every word.

SNEER: That I would, indeed.

PUFF: Very well, sir; then we must go on.—Zounds! I would not have parted with the description of the horse!—Well, sir, go on.—Sir, it was one of the finest and most laboured things.—Very well, sir; let them go on.—There you had him and his accoutrements, from the bit to the crupper.—Very well, sir; we must go to the park scene.

UNDER PROMPTER: Sir, there is the point: the carpenters say, that unless there is some business put in here before the drop, they shan't have time to clear away the fort, or sink Gravesend and the river.

PUFF: So! this is a pretty dilemma, truly!—Gentlemen, you must excuse me—these fellows will never be ready, unless I go and look after them myself.

SNEER: Oh, dear, sir, these little things will happen.

PUFF: To cut out this scene!—but I'll print it—egad, I'll print it every word! (*Exeunt*)

William Blake

LONG JOHN BROWN AND LITTLE MARY BELL

Little Mary Bell had a Fairy in a Nut,
Long John Brown had the Devil in his Gut;
Long John Brown lov'd Little Mary Bell,
And the Fairy drew the Devil into the Nut-shell.

Her Fairy Skip'd out & her Fairy Skip'd in;
He laugh'd at the Devil saying "Love is a Sin."
The Devil he raged and the Devil he was wroth,
And the Devil enter'd into the Young Man's broth.

He was soon in the Gut of the loving Young Swain,
For John eat & drank to drive away Love's pain;
But all he could do he grew thinner & thinner,
Tho' he eat & drank as much as ten Men for his dinner.

Some said he had a Wolf in his stomach day & night,
Some said he had the Devil & they guess'd right;
The Fairy skip'd about in his Glory, Joy & Pride,
And he laugh'd at the Devil till poor John Brown died.

Then the Fairy skip'd out of the old Nut-shell,
And woe & alack for Pretty Mary Bell!
For the Devil crept in when the Fairy skip'd out,
And there goes Miss Bell with her fusty old Nut.

TWO EPIGRAMS

Her whole Life is an Epigram, smart, smooth, & neatly pen'd,
Platted quite neat to catch applause with a sliding noose at the end.

A petty Sneaking Knave I knew—
O Mr. Cromek, how do ye do?

Robert Burns

HOLY WILLIE'S PRAYER

Mr. Gavin Hamilton, the friend and patron of Burns, had fallen under the censure of the Church for alleged Sabbath desecration. Mr. Fisher, a farmer near Mauchline, one of the Rev. Mr. Auld's session, had taken a prominent part in the prosecution of Mr. Hamilton, and Burns therefore sought to revenge his patron by this satire. Its subject well merited the merciless shafts directed against him. A great pretender to sanctity, and a stickler for outward observance, he scrupled not to "get fou [drunk]"; and when he left Mr. Auld's session for a neighbouring one, it was discovered that he had made too free with the money for the poor. Returning drunk from Mauchline one night, he fell into a ditch, and died from exposure.

O Thou wha in the heav'ns does dwell,
Wha, as it pleases best Thysel',
Sends ane to heaven and ten to hell,
  A' for Thy glory,
And no for ony guid or ill
  They've done afore Thee!

I bless and praise Thy matchless might,
Whan thousands Thou hast left in night,
That I am here, afore Thy sight,
  For gifts an' grace,
A burnin' an' a shinin' light
  To a' this place.

What was I, or my generation,
That I should get sic exaltation—
I, wha deserve sic just damnation
  For broken laws
Five thousand years 'fore my creation,
  Through Adam's cause?

When frae my mither's womb I fell,
Thou might ha'e plungèd me in hell,
To gnash my gums, to weep and wail,
      In burnin' lake,
Whare damnèd devils roar and yell
      Chained to a stake.

Yet I am here, a chosen sample,
To show Thy grace is great and ample;
I'm here a pillar in Thy temple,
      Strong as a rock,
A guide, a buckler, an example,
      To a' Thy flock.

O L—d, Thou kens what zeal I bear,
When drinkers drink, and swearers swear,
And singing there, and dancing here,
      Wi' great and sma';
For I am keepit by Thy fear
      Free frae them a'.

But yet, O L—d, confess I must,
At times I'm fashed wi' fleshly lust;
And sometimes, too, wi' wardly trust,
      Vile self gets in;
But thou remembers we are dust,
      Defiled in sin.

O L—d, yestreen, Thou kens, wi' Meg—
Thy pardon I sincerely beg;
Oh, may it ne'er be a livin' plague
      To my dishonour!
And I'll ne'er lift a lawless leg
      Again upon her.

Besides, I further maun allow,
Wi' Lizzie's lass three times I trow—
But, L—d, that Friday I was fou'
      When I came near her,
Or else, Thou kens, Thy servant true
      Wad ne'er ha'e steered her.

Maybe Thou lets this fleshly thorn
Beset Thy servant e'en and morn,
Lest he owre high and proud should turn,
    'Cause he's sae gifted!
If sae, Thy han' maun e'en be borne
    Until Thou lift it.

L—d, bless Thy chosen in this place,
For here Thou hast a chosen race;
But G—d confound their stubborn face,
    And blast their name,
Wha bring Thy elders to disgrace
    And public shame!

L—d, mind Gawn Hamilton's deserts!
He drinks, and swears, and plays at cartes,
Yet has sae mony takin' arts
    Wi' grit and sma'
Frae G—d's ain priests the people's hearts
    He steals awa'.

An' whan we chastened him therefor,
Thou kens how he bred sic a splore [1]
As set the warld in a roar
    O' laughin' at us;
Curse Thou his basket and his store,
    Kail and potatoes!

L—d, hear my earnest cry and prayer,
Against the Presbyt'ry of Ayr;
Thy strong right hand, L—d, mak' it bare
    Upo' their heads!
L—d, weigh it down, and dinna spare,
    For their misdeeds!

O L—d my G—d, that glib-tongued Aiken—
My very heart and soul are quakin',
To think how we stood groanin', shakin',
    And swat wi' dread,
While he wi' hinging lip and snakin'
    Held up his head.

[1] Splore: uproar.

L—d, in the day of vengeance try him!
L—d, visit them wha did employ him!
And pass not in Thy mercy by 'em,
   Nor hear their prayer;
But, for Thy people's sake, destroy 'em,
   And dinna spare!

But, L—d, remember me and mine
Wi' mercies temp'ral and divine,
That I for gear and grace may shine,
   Excelled by nane,
An' a' the glory shall be Thine.
   Amen, amen!

ON A WAG IN MAUCHLINE

Lament him, Mauchline husbands a'—
 He aften did assist ye;
For had ye staid whole weeks awa',
 Your wives they ne'er had missed ye.

Ye Mauchline bairns, as on ye pass
 To school in bands thegither,
Oh, tread ye lightly on his grass—
 Perhaps he was your father.

GUDE'EN TO YOU, KIMMER

Tune: "We're a' noddin'"

Gude'en to you, kimmer,
 And how do ye do?
Hiccup, quo' kimmer,

The better that I'm fou.
We're a' noddin', nid, nid, noddin',
We're a' noddin' at our house at hame.

Kate sits i' the neuk,
    Suppin' hen broo; [2]
De'il tak' Kate
    An' she be na noddin' too!

How's a' wi' you, kimmer,
    And how do ye fare?
A pint o' the best o't,
    And twa pints mair.

How's a' wi' you, kimmer,
    And how do ye thrive?
How mony bairns ha'e ye?
    Quo' kimmer, I ha'e five.

Are they a' Johnny's?
    Eh! atweel na; [3]
Twa o' them were gotten
    When Johnny was awa'.

Cats like milk,
    And dogs like broo,
Lads like lasses weel,
    And lasses lads too.
        We're a' noddin', nid, nid, noddin',
        We're a' noddin' at our house at hame.

[2] Hen broo: chicken broth.
[3] Atweel na: indeed not.

Maria Edgeworth

Maria Edgeworth was the first of that great line of British women writers who have pictured the humdrum life they themselves have lived with gaiety, humor, and love. Castle Rackrent appeared in 1800, and inspired Walter Scott to write novels about Scotland. I suppose people still read Castle Rackrent, since it is included in Everyman's Library; but they certainly don't read it enough. Try reading this one aloud, with a slight brogue. Rackrent, by the way, means an exorbitant rent, nearly equal to the full annual value of the land.

SIR KIT AND HIS JEWISH WIFE

Having, out of friendship for the family, upon whose estate, praised be Heaven! I and mine have lived rent-free, time out of mind, voluntarily undertaken to publish the Memoirs of the Rackrent Family, I think it my duty to say a few words, in the first place, concerning myself. My real name is Thady Quirk, though in the family I have always been known by no other than *"honest Thady,"*—afterward, in the time of Sir Murtagh, deceased, I remember to hear them calling me *"old Thady,"* and now I'm come to "poor Thady"; for I wear a long great coat winter and summer, which is very handy, as I never put my arms into the sleeves; they are as good as new, though come Holantide next I've had it these seven years; it holds on by a single button round my neck, cloak fashion.

[Sir Kit succeeds to the estate, but gambles away his money in Bath.]

Then, in a private postscript, he condescended to tell us, that all would be speedily settled to his satisfaction, and we should turn over a new leaf, for he was going to be married in a fortnight to the grandest heiress in England, and had only immediate occasion at present for 200*l.*, as he would not choose to touch his lady's fortune for travelling expenses home to Castle Rackrent, where he intended to be, wind and weather permitting, early in the next month; ...

I never shall forget the day he came home: we had waited and waited all day long till eleven o'clock at night, and I was thinking of sending the boy to lock the gates, and giving them up for that night, when there came the carriages thundering up to the great hall door. I got the first sight of the bride; for when the carriage door opened, just as she had her foot on the steps, I held the flam [1] full in her face to light her, at which she shut her eyes, but I had a full view of the rest of her, and greatly shocked I was, for by that light she was little better than a blackamoor, and seemed crippled, but that was only sitting so long in the chariot. . . .

The short and the long of it was, I couldn't tell what to make of her; so I left her to herself, and went straight down to the servants' hall to learn something for certain about her. Sir Kit's own man was tired, but the groom set him a-talking at last, and we had it all out before ever I closed my eyes that night. The bride might well be a great fortune—she was a *Jewish* by all accounts, who are famous for their great riches. I had never seen any of that tribe or nation before, and could only gather, that she spoke a strange kind of English of her own, that she could not abide pork or sausages, and went neither to church or mass. Mercy upon his honour's poor soul, thought I; what will become of him and his, and all of us, with his heretic blackamoor at the head of the Castle Rackrent estate! I never slept a wink all night for thinking of it: but before the servants I put my pipe in my mouth, and kept my mind to myself; for I had a great regard for the family; and after this, when strange gentlemen's servants came to the house, and would begin to talk about the bride, I took care to put the best foot foremost, and passed her for a nabob in the kitchen, which accounted for her dark complexion and everything.

The very morning after they came home, however, I saw plain enough how things were between Sir Kit and my lady, though they were walking together arm in arm after breakfast, looking at the new building and improvements. "Old Thady," said my master, just as he used to do, "how do you do?" "Very well, I thank your honour's honour," said I; but I saw he was not well pleased, and my heart was in my mouth as I walked along after him. "Is the large room damp, Thady?" said his honour. "Oh, damp, your honour! how should it but be as dry as a bone," says I, "after all the fires we have kept in it day and night? It's the barrack-room your honour's talking on." "And

[1] Flam: flambeau, torch.

what is a barrack-room, pray, my dear?" were the first words I ever heard out of my lady's lips. "No matter, my dear!" said he, and went on talking to me, ashamed like I should witness her ignorance. To be sure, to hear her talk one might have taken her for an innocent, for it was, "What's this, Sir Kit? and what's that, Sir Kit?" all the way we went. To be sure, Sir Kit had enough to do to answer her. "And what do you call that, Sir Kit?" said she, "That, that looks like a pile of black bricks, pray, Sir Kit?" "My turf stack, my dear," said my master, and bit his lip. Where have you lived, my lady, all your life, not to know a turf stack when you see it? thought I, but I said nothing. Then, by-and-by, she takes out her glass, and begins spying over the country. "And what's all that black swamp out yonder, Sir Kit?" says she. "My bog, my dear," says he, and went on whistling. "It's a very ugly prospect, my dear," says she. "You don't see it, my dear," says he, "for we've planted it out, when the trees grow up in summer time," says he. "Where are the trees," said she, "my dear?" still looking through her glass. "You are blind, my dear," says he. "What are these under your eyes?" "These shrubs," said she. "Trees," said he. "May be they are what you call trees in Ireland, my dear," said she; "but they are not a yard high, are they?" "They were planted out but last year, my lady," says I, to soften matters between them, for I saw she was going the way to make his honour mad with her; "they are very well grown for their age, and you'll not see the bog of Allyballycarricko'shaughlin at-all-at-all through the screen, when once the leaves come out. But, my lady, you must not quarrel with any part or parcel of Allybally-carricko'shaughlin, for you don't know how many hundred years that same bit of bog has been in the family; we would not part with the bog of Allyballycarricko'shaughlin upon no account at all; it cost the late Sir Murtagh two hundred good pounds to defend his title to it and boundaries against the O'Learys, who cut a road through it." Now one would have thought this would have been hint enough for my lady, but she fell to laughing like one out of their right mind, and made me say the name of the bog over for her to get it by heart, a dozen times—then she must ask me how to spell it, and what was the meaning of it in English—Sir Kit standing by whistling all the while; I verily believed she laid the corner stone of all her future misfortunes at that very instant; but I said no more, only looked at Sir Kit.

There were no balls, no dinners, no doings; the country was all disappointed—Sir Kit's gentleman said in a whisper to me, it was all my lady's own fault, because she was so obstinate about the cross. "What cross?" says I; "is it about her being a heretic?" "Oh, no such matter," says he; "my master does not mind her heresies, but her diamond cross, it's worth I can't tell you how much; and she has thousands of English pounds concealed in diamonds about her, which she as good as promised to give up to my master before he married, but now she won't part with any of them, and she must take the consequences."

Her honey-moon, at least her Irish honey-moon, was scarcely well over, when his honour one morning said to me, "Thady, buy me a pig!" and then the sausages were ordered, and here was the first open breaking-out of my lady's troubles. My lady came down herself into the kitchen, to speak to the cook about the sausages, and desired never to see them more at her table. Now my master had ordered them, and my lady knew that. The cook took my lady's part, because she never came down into the kitchen, and was young and innocent in housekeeping, which raised her pity; besides, said she, at her own table, surely, my lady should order and disorder what she pleases; but the cook soon changed her note, for my master made it a principle to have the sausages, and swore at her for a Jew herself, till he drove her fairly out of the kitchen; then, for fear of her place, and because he threatened that my lady should give her no discharge without the sausages, she gave up, and from that day forward always sausages, or bacon, or pig meat in some shape or other, went up to table; upon which my lady shut herself up in her own room, and my master said she might stay there, with an oath; and to make sure of her, he turned the key in the door, and kept it ever after in his pocket. We none of us ever saw or heard her speak for seven years after that: he carried her dinner himself. Then his honour had a great deal of company to dine with him, and balls in the house, and was as gay and gallant, and as much himself as before he was married; and at dinner he always drank my Lady Rackrent's good health, and so did the company, and he sent out always a servant, with his compliments to my Lady Rackrent, and the company was drinking her ladyship's health, and begged to know if there was anything at table he might send her; and the man came back, after the sham errand, with my Lady Rackrent's compliments, and she was very much obliged to Sir Kit—she did not wish for anything, but drank the company's health. The country, to be sure, talked and wondered at my lady's being shut up, but nobody chose to interfere or ask any impertinent questions, for they knew my master was a man very apt to give a short answer himself, and likely to call a man out for it afterwards; he was a famous shot; had killed his man before he came of age, and nobody scarce dared look at him whilst at Bath. Sir Kit's character was so well known in the country, that he lived in peace and quietness ever after, and was a great favourite with the ladies, especially when in process of time, in the fifth year of her confinement, my Lady Rackrent fell ill, and took entirely to her bed, and he gave out that she was now skin and bone, and could not last through the winter. In this he had two physicians' opinions to back him (for now he called in two physicians for her), and tried all his arts to get the diamond cross from her on her death-bed, and to get her to make a will in his favour of her separate possessions; but there she was too tough for him. He used to swear at her behind her back, after kneeling to her to her face, and call her in the presence of his gentleman his stiff-necked Israelite, though before he married her, that same gentleman told me he used to call her (how he could bring it out, I don't know) "my pretty Jessica!" To be sure, it must have been hard for her to guess what sort of a husband he reckoned to make her. When she was lying, to all expectation, on her death-bed of a broken heart, I could not but pity her, though she was a Jewish; and considering too it was no fault of hers to be taken with my master so young as she was at the Bath, and so fine a gentleman as Sir Kit was when he courted her; and considering too, after all they had heard and seen of him as a husband, there were now no less than three ladies in our county talked of for his second wife, all at daggers drawn with each other, as his gentleman swore, at the balls, for Sir Kit for their partner,—I could not but think them bewitched; but they all reasoned with themselves, that Sir Kit would make a good husband to any Christian but a Jewish, I suppose, and especially as he was now a reformed rake; and it was not known how my lady's fortune was settled in her will, nor how the Castle Rackrent estate was all mortgaged, and bonds out against him, for he was never cured of his gaming tricks; but that was the only fault he had, God bless him!

My lady had a sort of fit, and it was given out she was dead, by mistake; this brought things to a sad crisis for my poor master,—one of the three ladies showed his letters to her brother, and claimed his promises, whilst another did the same. I don't mention names. Sir Kit, in his defence, said he would meet any man who dared to question his conduct, and as to the ladies, they must settle it amongst them who was to be his second, and his third, and his fourth, whilst his first was still alive, to his mortification and theirs. Upon this, as upon all former occasions, he had the voice of the country with him, on account of the great spirit and propriety he acted with. He met and shot the first lady's brother; the next day he called out the second, who had a wooden leg; and their place of meeting by appointment being in a new-ploughed field, the wooden-leg man stuck fast in it. Sir Kit, seeing his situation, with great candour fired his pistol over his head; upon which the seconds interposed, and convinced the parties there had been a slight misunderstanding between them; thereupon they shook hands cordially, and went home to dinner together. This gentleman, to show the world how they stood together, and by the advice of the friends of both parties, to re-establish his sister's injured reputation, went out with Sir Kit as his second, and carried his message next day to the last of his adversaries: I never saw him in such fine spirits as that day he went out—sure enough he was within ames-ace of getting quit handsomely of all his enemies; but unluckily, after hitting the tooth-pick out of his adversary's finger and thumb, he received a ball in a vital part, and was brought home, in little better than an hour after the affair, speechless on a hand-barrow, to my lady. We got the key out of his pocket the first thing we did, and my son Jason ran to unlock the barrack-room, where my lady had been shut up for seven years, to acquaint her with the fatal accident. The surprise bereaved her of her senses at first, nor would she believe but we were putting some new trick upon her, to entrap her out of her jewels, for a great while, till Jason bethought himself of taking her to the window, and showed her the men bringing Sir Kit up the avenue upon the hand-barrow, which had immediately the desired effect; for directly she burst into tears, and pulling her cross from her bosom, she kissed it with as great devotion as ever I witnessed; and lifting up her eyes to heaven, uttered some ejaculation, which none present heard; but I take the sense of it to be, she returned thanks for this unexpected interposition in her favour when she had least reason to expect it. My master was greatly lamented: there was no life in him when we lifted him off the barrow, so he was laid out immediately, and *waked* the same night. The country was all in an uproar about him, and not a soul but cried shame upon his murderer; who would have been hanged surely, if he could have been brought to his trial, whilst the gentlemen in the country were up about it; but he very prudently withdrew himself to the continent before the affair was made public. As for the young lady, who was the immediate cause of the fatal accident, however innocently, she could never show her head after at the balls in the county or any place; and by the advice of her friends and physicians, she was ordered soon after to Bath, where it was expected, if anywhere on this side of the grave, she would meet with the recovery of her health and lost peace of mind. As a proof of his great popularity, I need only add, that there was a song made upon my master's untimely death in the newspapers, which was in everybody's mouth, singing up and down through the country, even down to the mountains, only three days after his unhappy exit. He was also greatly bemoaned at the Curragh, where his cattle were well known; and all who had taken up his bets were particularly inconsolable for his loss to society. His stud sold at the cant at the greatest price ever known in the county; his favourite horses were chiefly disposed of amongst his particular friends, who would give any price for them for his sake; but no ready money was required by the new heir, who wished not to displease any of the gentlemen of the neighborhood just upon his coming to settle amongst them; so a long credit was given where requisite, and the cash has never been gathered in from that day to this.

But to return to my lady:—She got surprisingly well after my master's decease. No sooner was it known for certain that he was dead, than all the gentlemen within twenty miles of us came in a body, as it were, to set my lady at liberty, and to protest against her confinement, which they now for the first time understood was against her own consent. The ladies too were as attentive as possible, striving who should be foremost with their morning visits; and they that saw the diamonds spoke very handsomely of them, but thought it a pity they were not bestowed, if it had so pleased God, upon a lady who would have become them better. All these civilities wrought little with my lady, for she had taken an unaccountable prejudice against the country, and everything belonging to it, and was so partial to her native land, that after parting with the cook, which she did immediately upon my master's decease, I never knew her easy one instant, night or day, but when she was packing up to leave us. Had she meant to make any stay in Ireland, I stood a great chance of being a great favourite with her; for when she found I understood the weathercock, she was always finding some pretence to be talking to me, and asking me which way the wind blew, and was it likely, did I think, to continue fair for England. But when I saw she had made up her mind to spend the rest of her days upon her own income and jewels in England, I considered her quite as a foreigner, and not at all any longer as part of the family. She gave no vails to the servants at Castle Rackrent at parting, notwithstanding the old proverb of *"as rich as a Jew,"* which she being a Jewish, they built upon with reason. But from first to last she brought nothing but misfortunes amongst us; and if it had not been all along with her, his honour, Sir Kit, would have been now alive in all appearance. Her diamond cross was, they say, at the bottom of it all; and it was a shame for her, being his wife, not to show more duty, and to have given it up when he condescended to ask so often for such a bit of a trifle in his distresses, especially when he all along made it no secret he married for money. But we will not bestow another thought upon her. This much I thought it lay upon my conscience to say, in justice to my poor master's memory.

[From *Castle Rackrent*]

George Canning, George Ellis, and John Hookham Frere

George Canning, the eminent statesman and friend of South American freedom, was the principal author of The Rovers. *It appeared in his paper, the* Anti-Jacobin, *in 1798. It is said to be a bitter satire on French revolutionary principles, but don't let that put you off. The Progress of Man is by Canning alone.*

THE ROVERS (Act I)

SCENE I: *Represents a room at an Inn, at Weimar—On one side of the stage the bar-room, with jellies, lemons in nets, syllabubs, and part of a cold roast fowl, etc.—On the opposite side a window looking into the street, through which persons (inhabitants of Weimar) are seen passing to and fro in apparent agitation.—*MATILDA *appears in a greatcoat and riding habit, seated at the corner of the dinner-table, which is covered with a clean huckaback cloth.—Plates and napkins, with buck's-horn-handled knives and forks, are laid as if for four persons.*

MATILDA: Is it impossible for me to have dinner sooner?

LANDLADY: Madam, the Brunswick post-waggon is not yet come in, and the ordinary is never before two o'clock.

MATILDA (*with a look expressive of disappointment, but immediately recomposing herself*): Well, then, I must have patience. (*Exit* LANDLADY) Oh, Casimere! How often have the thoughts of thee served to amuse these moments of expectation! What a difference, alas! Dinner—it is taken away as soon as over, and we regret it not! It returns again with the return of appetite. The beef of tomorrow will succeed to the mutton of today, as the mutton of today succeeded to the veal of yesterday. But when once the heart has been occupied by a beloved object, in vain would we attempt to supply the chasm by another. How easily are our desires transferred from dish to dish! Love only, dear, delusive, delightful love,

83

restrains our wandering appetites, and confines them to a particular gratification! ...

(Post-horn blows.—Re-enter LANDLADY)

LANDLADY: Madam, the post-waggon is come in with only a single gentlewoman.

MATILDA: Then show her up—and let us have dinner instantly; (LANDLADY *going*) and remember—(*after a moment's recollection, and with great eagerness*)—remember the toasted cheese.

(*Exit* LANDLADY. CECILIA *enters, in a brown cloth riding-dress, as if just alighted from the post-waggon.*)

MATILDA: Madam, you seem to have had an unpleasant journey, if I may judge from the dust on your riding-habit.

CECILIA: The way was dusty, madam, but the weather was delightful. It recall'd to me those blissful moments when the rays of desire first vibrated through my soul.

MATILDA (*aside*): Thank Heaven! I have at last found a heart which is in unison with my own. (*To* CECILIA): Yes, I understand you— the first pulsation of sentiment—the silver tones upon the yet unsounded harp ...

CECILIA: The dawn of life—when this blossom (*putting her hand upon her heart*) first expanded its petals to the penetrating dart of love!

MATILDA: Yes—the time—the golden time, when the first beams of the morning meet and embrace one another! The blooming blue upon the yet unplucked plum! ...

CECILIA: Your countenance grows animated, my dear madam.

MATILDA: And yours too is glowing with illumination.

CECILIA: I had long been looking out for a congenial spirit! My heart was withered, but the beams of yours have rekindled it.

MATILDA: A sudden thought strikes me; let us swear an eternal friendship.

CECILIA: Let us agree to live together!

MATILDA: Willingly. (*With rapidity and earnestness*)

CECILIA: Let us embrace. (*They embrace.*)

MATILDA: Yes; I too have loved!—you, too, like me, have been forsaken! (*Doubtingly and as if with a desire to be informed*)

CECILIA: Too true!

BOTH: Ah, these men! these men!

(LANDLADY *enters, and places a leg of mutton on the table, with sour kraut and prune sauce—then a small dish of black puddings.* CECILIA *and* MATILDA *appear to take no notice of her.*)

MATILDA: Oh, Casimere!

CECILIA (*aside*): Casimere! that name! Oh, my heart, how it is distracted with anxiety.

MATILDA: Heavens! Madam, you turn pale.

CECILIA: Nothing—a slight megrim—with your leave, I will retire.

MATILDA: I will attend you.

> (*Exeunt* MATILDA *and* CECILIA. *Manent* LANDLADY *and* WAITER *with the dinner on the table.*)

LANDLADY: Have you carried the dinner to the prisoner in the vaults of the abbey?

WAITER: Yes. Pease-soup, as usual—with the scrag-end of a neck of mutton—the emissary of the Count was here again this morning, and offered me a large sum of money if I would consent to poison him.

LANDLADY: Which you refused? (*With hesitation and anxiety*)

WAITER: Can you doubt it? (*With indignation*)

LANDLADY (*recovering herself, and drawing up with an expression of dignity*): The conscience of a poor man is as valuable to him as that of a prince.

WAITER: It ought to be still more so, in proportion as it is generally more pure.

LANDLADY: Thou say'st truly, Job.

WAITER (*with enthusiasm*): He who can spurn at wealth when proffer'd as the price of crime, is greater than a prince.

> (*Post-horn blows. Enter* CASIMERE, *in a travelling dress—a light blue great-coat with large metal buttons—his hair in a long queue, but twisted at the end; a large Kevenhuller hat; a cane in his hand.*)

CASIMERE: Here, waiter, pull off my boots, and bring me a pair of slippers. (*Exit* WAITER.) And heark'ye, my lad, a basin of water (*rubbing his hands*) and a bit of soap—I have not washed since I began my journey.

WAITER (*answering from behind the door*): Yes, sir.

CASIMERE: Well, landlady, what company are we to have?

LANDLADY: Only two gentlewomen, sir. They are just stepp'd into the next room—they will be back again in a minute.

CASIMERE: Where do they come from?

(*All this while the* WAITER *re-enters with the basin and water,* CASIMERE *pulls off his boots, takes a napkin from the table, and washes his face and hands.*)

LANDLADY: There is one of them, I think, comes from Nuremburgh.

CASIMERE (*aside*): From Nuremburgh; (*with eagerness*) her name?

LANDLADY: Matilda.

CASIMERE (*aside*): How does this idiot woman torment me! (*Aloud*): What else?

LANDLADY: I can't recollect.

CASIMERE: Oh, agony! (*in a paroxysm of agitation*).

WAITER: See here, her name upon the travelling trunk—Matilda Pottingen.

CASIMERE: Ecstasy! ecstasy! (*embracing the* WAITER).

LANDLADY: You seem to be acquainted with the lady—shall I call her?

CASIMERE: Instantly—instantly—tell her, her loved, her long lost—tell her—

LANDLADY: Shall I tell her dinner is ready?

CASIMERE: Do so—and in the meanwhile I will look after my portmanteau.

(*Exeunt severally.*

*Scene changes to a subterraneous vault in the Abbey of Quedlinburgh, with coffins, scutcheons, Death's heads and cross-bones.—Toads, and other loathsome reptiles are seen traversing the obscurer parts of the stage.—*ROGERO *appears in chains, in a suit of rusty armour, with his beard grown, and a cap of a grotesque form upon his head.—Beside him a crock, or pitcher, supposed to contain his daily allowance of sustenance.—A long silence, during which the wind is heard to whistle through the caverns.—*ROGERO *rises, and comes slowly forward, with his arms folded.*)

ROGERO: Eleven years! it is now eleven years since I was first immured in this living sepulchre—the cruelty of a minister—the perfidy of a monk—yes, Matilda! for thy sake—alive amidst the dead—chained —coffined—confined—cut off from the converse of my fellow-men.

Soft! what have we here? (*stumbles over a bundle of sticks*). This cavern is so dark, that I can scarcely distinguish the objects under my feet! Oh! the register of my captivity. Let me see, how stands the account? (*Takes up the sticks and turns them over with a melancholy air; then stands silent for a few moments, as if absorbed in calculation.*) Eleven years and fifteen days! Hah! the twenty-eighth of August! How does the recollection of it vibrate on my heart! It was on this day that I took my last leave of my Matilda. It was a summer evening—her melting hand seemed to dissolve in mine, as I press'd it to my bosom. Some demon whispered me that I should never see her more. I stood gazing on the hated vehicle which was conveying her away for ever. The tears were petrified under my eyelids. My heart was crystallized with agony. Anon, I looked along the road. The diligence seemed to diminish every instant. I felt my heart beat against its prison, as if anxious to leap out and overtake it. My soul whirled round as I watched the rotation of the hinder wheels. A long trail of glory followed after her, and mingled with the dust—it was the emanation of Divinity, luminous with love and beauty, like the splendour of the setting sun; but it told me that the sun of my joys was sunk for ever. Yes, here in the depths of an eternal dungeon— in the nursing cradle of hell—the suburbs of perdition—in a nest of demons, where despair, in vain, sits brooding over the putrid eggs of hope; where agony woos the embrace of death; where patience, beside the bottomless pool of despondency, sits angling for impossibilities. Yet even *here,* to behold her, to embrace her—yes, Matilda, whether in this dark abode, amidst toads and spiders, or in a royal palace, amidst the more loathsome reptiles of a Court, would be indifferent to me. Angels would shower down their hymns of gratulation upon our heads—while fiends would envy the eternity of suffering love. . . . Soft, what air was that? it seemed a sound of more than human warblings. Again (*listens attentively for some minutes*)—only the wind. It is well, however; it reminds me of that melancholy air which has so often solaced the hours of my captivity. Let me see whether the damps of this dungeon have not yet injured my guitar. (*Takes his guitar, tunes it, and begins the following air, with a full accompaniment of violins from the orchestra.*)

(Air, *Lanterna Magica*)

Song

By Rogero

Whene'er with haggard eyes I view
This dungeon that I'm rotting in,
I think of those companions true
Who studied with me at the U—
—niversity of Gottingen,—
—niversity of Gottingen.

(*Weeps, and pulls out a blue kerchief, with which he wipes his
eyes; gazing tenderly at it, he proceeds—*)

Sweet kerchief, check'd with heavenly blue,
Which once my love sat knotting in!—
Alas! Matilda *then* was true!—
At least I thought so at the U—
—niversity of Gottingen—
—niversity of Gottingen.

(*At the repetition of this line,* Rogero *clanks his chains in
cadence.*)

Barbs! barbs! alas! how swift you flew,
Her neat post-waggon trotting in!
Ye bore Matilda from my view;
Forlorn I languish'd at the U—
—niversity of Gottingen—
—niversity of Gottingen.

This faded form! this pallid hue!
This blood my veins is clotting in,
My years are many—they were few
When first I entered at the U—
—niversity of Gottingen—
—niversity of Gottingen.

There first for thee my passion grew,
Sweet! sweet Matilda Pottingen!
Thou wast the daughter of my tu—
tor, Law Professor at the U—
—niversity of Gottingen—
—niversity of Gottingen.

Sun, moon, and thou, vain world, adieu,
    That kings and priests are plotting in:
Here doom'd to starve on water gru—
    el, never shall I see the U—
        —niversity of Gottingen—
        —niversity of Gottingen.

(*During the last stanza,* ROGERO *dashes his head repeatedly against the walls of his prison; and, finally, so hard as to produce a visible contusion. He then throws himself on the floor in an agony. The curtain drops—the music still continuing to play till it is wholly fallen.*)

THE PROGRESS OF MAN
(Selection)

Let us a plainer, steadier theme pursue—
Mark the grim savage scoop his light canoe;
Mark the dark rook, on pendant branches hung,
With anxious fondness feed her cawing young.—
Mark the fell leopard through the desert prowl,
Fish prey on fish, and fowl regale on fowl;
How Lybian tigers' chawdrons love assails,
And warms, midst seas of ice, the melting whales;—
Cools the crimpt cod, fierce pangs to perch imparts,
Shrinks shrivell'd shrimps, but opens oysters' hearts;—
Then say, how all these things together tend
To one great truth, prime object, and good end?
    First—to each living thing, whate'er its kind,
Some lot, some part, some station is assign'd.
The feather'd race with pinions skim the *air*—
Not so the mackerel, and still less the bear;
This roams the *wood,* carniv'rous, for its prey;
That with soft roe, pursues his *watery* way:—
This slain by hunters yields his shaggy hide;
That, caught by fishers, is on *Sundays* cried.—

But each contented with his humble sphere,
Moves unambitious through the circling year;
Nor e'er forgets the fortune of his race,
Nor pines to quit, or strives to change his place.
Ah! who has seen the mailèd lobster rise,
Clap her broad wings, and soaring claim the skies?
When did the owl, descending from her bow'r,
Crop, 'midst the fleecy flocks, the tender flower;
Or the young heifer plunge, with pliant limb,
In the salt wave, and fish-like strive to swim?

The same with plants—potatoes 'tatoes breed—
Uncostly cabbage springs from cabbage seed;
Lettuce to lettuce, leeks to leeks succeed;
Nor e'er did cooling cucumbers presume
To flow'r like myrtle, or like violets bloom.
—Man, only—rash, refined, presumptuous Man,
Starts from his rank, and mars creation's plan.
Born the free heir of Nature's wide domain,
To art's strict limits bounds his narrow reign;
Resigns his native rights for meaner things,
For Faith and Fetters—Laws, and Priests, and Kings.

Sydney Smith

The Reverend Sydney Smith was the perfect diner-out. He could always be depended upon to say two or three good things, which the gentlemen present would note down for their memoirs. Diner-out humour, to be at its best, requires perfect phrasing, perfect timing, and a perfect dinner. Its greatest representative today is Logan Pearsall Smith.

Sydney Smith wrote several volumes of serious essays, which are well spoken of.

GOOD THINGS

"Tell Murray that I was much struck with the politeness of Miss Markham the day after he went. In carving a partridge I splashed her with gravy from head to foot; and though I saw three distinct rills of animal juice trickling down her cheek, she had the complaisance to swear that not a drop had reached her. Such circumstances are the triumphs of civilised life."

"Macaulay," he said, "was a book in breeches; he not only overflowed with learning but stood in the slops; he was laying society waste with his waterspouts of talk; people in his company burst for want of an opportunity of dropping in a word; he confounded soliloquy and colloquy. The great use of the raised centre, revolving on a round table, would be to put Macaulay on it and distribute his talk fairly to the company." Smith called on Macaulay and found him ill in bed. He was "more agreeable than I have ever seen him. There were some gorgeous flashes of silence."

He described the country as "a kind of healthy grave," spoke of "the serious apoplexy of a country life," and of "the delusions of flowers, green turf, and birds; they all afford slight gratification, but not worth an hour of rational conversation: and rational conversation in sufficient quantities is only to be had from the congregation of a million people in one spot.... You may depend upon it, all lives out of London are mistakes, more or less grievous—but mistakes."

"Luttrell is remarkably well, considering that he has been remarkably well for so many years."

"Philosopher Malthus came here last week. I got an agreeable party for him of unmarried people. There was only one lady who had a child; but he is a good-natured man, and, if there are no appearances of approaching fertility, is civil to every lady."

"What is real piety? What is true attachment to the Church? How are these fine feelings best evinced? The answer is plain: by sending strawberries to a clergyman. Many thanks."

"When a man is a fool, in England we only trust him with the immortal concerns of human beings."

"The observances of the Church concerning feasts and fasts are tolerably well kept upon the whole, since the rich keep the feasts and the poor the fasts."

"I must believe in the Apostolic Succession, there being no other way of accounting for the descent of the Bishop of Exeter from Judas Iscariot."

"My idea of Heaven is, eating *pâtés de foie gras* to the sound of trumpets."

"What a pity it is that we have no amusements in England but vice and religion!"

In a friend's house, he was watching a child stroke the shell of a pet turtle. "Why are you doing that?" asked Sydney. "To please the turtle." "Why, you might as well stroke the dome of St. Paul's to please the Dean and Chapter."

A lady spoke of the oppressive heat of the preceding week. "Heat, ma'am! It was so dreadful here that I found there was nothing left for it but to take off my flesh and sit in my bones."

"I don't like dogs; I always expect them to go mad. A lady asked me once for a motto for her dog Spot. I proposed 'Out, damned Spot!' but strange to say she did not think it sentimental enough."

He was riding with Leslie, the philosopher, and Lord Jeffrey. Leslie mentioned the North Pole. "Oh, damn the North Pole!" shouted Jeffrey, spurring his horse and galloping off. Leslie complained to his companion of Jeffrey's behaviour. "Oh, my dear fellow," said Smith, "never mind. No one cares what Jeffrey says. He is a privileged person; he respects nothing, absolutely nothing. Why, you will scarcely credit it, but, strictly between ourselves, it is not more than a week ago that I heard him speak disrespectfully of the Equator."

"The sloth, in its wild state, spends its life in trees, and never leaves them but from force or accident. The eagle to the sky, the mole to the ground, the sloth to the tree; but what is most extraordinary, he lives not *upon* the branches, but *under* them. He moves suspended, rests suspended, sleeps suspended, and passes his life in suspense—like a young clergyman distantly related to a bishop."

Francis Jeffrey

ON PETER ROBINSON

Here lies the preacher, judge, and poet, Peter,
Who broke the laws of God, and man, and metre.

Jane Austen

A VISIT TO NORTHANGER ABBEY

[Catherine Morland, taking the waters at Bath, makes the acquaintance of Isabella Thorpe.]

The following conversation, which took place between the two friends in the Pump-room one morning, after an acquaintance of eight or nine days, is given as a specimen of their very warm attachment, and of the delicacy, discretion, originality of thought, and literary taste which marked the reasonableness of that attachment.

They met by appointment; and as Isabella had arrived nearly five minutes before her friend, her first address naturally was: "My dearest creature, what can have made you so late? I have been waiting for you at least this age!"

"Have you, indeed?—I am very sorry for it; but really I thought I was in very good time. It is but just one. I hope you have not been here long?"

"Oh! these ten ages at least. I am sure I have been here this half hour. But now, let us go and sit down at the other end of the room, and enjoy ourselves. I have an hundred things to say to you. In the first place, I was so afraid it would rain this morning, just as I wanted to set off; it looked very showery, and that would have thrown me into agonies! Do you know, I saw the prettiest hat you can imagine, in a shop window in Milsom Street just now—very like yours, only with coquelicot ribbons instead of green; I quite longed for it. But, my dearest Catherine, what have you been doing with yourself all this morning?—Have you gone on with Udolpho?"

"Yes, I have been reading it ever since I woke; and I am got to the black veil."

"Are you, indeed? How delightful! Oh! I would not tell you what is behind the black veil for the world! Are not you wild to know?"

"Oh! yes, quite; what can it be?—But do not tell me—I would not be told upon any account. I know it must be a skeleton. I am sure it is Laurentina's skeleton. Oh! I am delighted with the book! I should like to spend my whole life in reading it. I assure you, if it had not been to meet you, I would not have come away from it for all the world."

"Dear creature! how much I am obliged to you; and when you have finished Udolpho, we will read the Italian together; and I have made out a list of ten or twelve more of the same kind for you."

"Have you, indeed! How glad I am!—What are they all?"

"I will read you their names directly; here they are, in my pocket-book. Castle of Wolfenbach, Clermont, Mysterious Warnings, Necromancer of the Black Forest, Midnight Bell, Orphan of the Rhine, and Horrid Mysteries. Those will last us some time."

"Yes, pretty well; but are they all horrid, are you sure they are all horrid?"

"Yes, quite sure; for a particular friend of mine, a Miss Andrews, a sweet girl, one of the sweetest creatures in the world, has read every one of them. I wish you knew Miss Andrews, you would be delighted with her. She is netting herself the sweetest cloak you can conceive. I think her as beautiful as an angel, and I am so vexed with the men for not admiring her!—I scold them all amazingly about it."

"Scold them! Do you scold them for not admiring her?"

"Yes, that I do. There is nothing I would not do for those who are really my friends. I have no notion of loving people by halves, it is not my nature. My attachments are always excessively strong. I told Captain Hunt at one of our assemblies this winter, that if he was to tease me all night, I would not dance with him, unless he would allow Miss Andrews to be as beautiful as an angel. The men think us incapable of real friendship, you know, and I am determined to shew them the difference. Now, if I were to hear anybody speak slightingly of you, I should fire up in a moment:—but that is not at all likely, for you are just the kind of girl to be a great favourite with the men."

"Oh! dear," cried Catherine, colouring, "how can you say so?"

"I know you very well; you have so much animation, which is exactly what Miss Andrews wants, for I must confess there is something amazingly insipid about her. Oh! I must tell you, that just after we parted yesterday, I saw a young man looking at you so earnestly—I am sure he is in love with you." Catherine coloured, and disclaimed again. Isabella laughed. "It is very true, upon my honour; but I see how it is: you are indifferent to everybody's admiration, except that of one gentleman, who shall be nameless. Nay, I cannot blame you—

(speaking more seriously)—your feelings are easily understood. Where the heart is really attached, I know very well how little one can be pleased with the attention of anybody else. Everything is so insipid, so uninteresting, that does not relate to the beloved object! I can perfectly comprehend your feelings."

"But you should not persuade me that I think so very much about Mr. Tilney, for perhaps I may never seen him again."

"Not see him again! My dearest creature, do not talk of it. I am sure you would be miserable if you thought so."

"No, indeed, I should not. I do not pretend to say that I was not very much pleased with him; but while I have Udolpho to read, I feel as if nobody could make me miserable. Oh! the dreadful black veil! My dear Isabella, I am sure there must be Laurentina's skeleton behind it."

"It is so odd to me, that you should never have read Udolpho before; but I suppose Mrs. Morland objects to novels."

"No, she does not. She very often reads Sir Charles Grandison herself; but new books do not fall in our way."

"Sir Charles Grandison! That is an amazing horrid book, is it not? —I remember Miss Andrews could not get through the first volume."

"It is not like Udolpho at all; but yet I think it is very entertaining."

"Do you indeed!—you surprise me; I thought it had not been readable."

[Catherine Morland is invited to General Tilney's seat of Northanger Abbey.]

The bustle of going was not pleasant.—The clock struck ten while the trunks were carrying down, and the General had fixed to be out of Milsom Street by that hour. His great coat, instead of being brought for him to put on directly, was spread out in the curricle in which he was to accompany his son. The middle seat of the chaise was not drawn out, though there were three people to go in it, and his daughter's maid had so crowded it with parcels, that Miss Morland would not have room to sit; and, so much was he influenced by this apprehension when he handed her in, that she had some difficulty in saving her own new writing-desk from being thrown out into the street.—At last, however, the door was closed upon the three females, and they set off at the sober pace in which the handsome, highly-fed four horses of a gentleman usually perform a journey of thirty miles: such was the distance of Northanger from Bath, to be now divided into two equal stages. Catherine's spirits revived as they drove from the door; for with Miss Tilney she felt no restraint; and, with the interest of a road entirely new to her, of an abbey before, and a curricle behind, she caught the last view of Bath without any regret, and met with every mile-stone before she expected it. The tediousness of a two hours' wait at Petty-France, in which there was nothing to be done but to eat without being hungry, and loiter about without anything to see, next followed—and her admiration of the style in which they travelled, of the fashionable chaise-and-four, postillions handsomely liveried, rising so regularly in their stirrups, and numerous outriders properly mounted, sunk a little under this consequent inconvenience. Had their party been perfectly agreeable, the delay would have been nothing; but General Tilney, though so charming a man, seemed always a check upon his children's spirits, and scarcely anything was said but by himself; the observation of which, with his discontent at whatever the inn afforded, and his angry impatience at the waiters, made Catherine grow every moment more in awe of him, and appeared to lengthen the two hours into four.—At last, however, the order of release was given; and much was Catherine then surprized by the General's proposal of her taking his place in his son's curricle for the rest of the journey:—"the day was fine, and he was anxious for her seeing as much of the country as possible."

The remembrance of Mr. Allen's opinion, respecting young men's open carriages, made her blush at the mention of such a plan, and her first thought was to decline it; but her second was of greater deference for General Tilney's judgment; he could not propose anything improper for her; and, in the course of a few minutes, she found herself with Henry in the curricle, as happy a being as ever existed. A very short trial convinced her that a curricle was the prettiest equipage in the world; the chaise-and-four wheeled off with some grandeur, to be sure, but it was a heavy and troublesome business, and she could not easily forget its having stopped two hours at Petty-France. Half the time would have been enough for the curricle; and so nimbly were the light horses disposed to move, that, had not the General chosen to have his own carriage lead the way, they could have passed it with ease in half a minute. But the merit of the curricle did not all belong to the horses;—Henry drove so well,—so quietly—without making any disturbance, without parading to her, or swearing at them; so different from the only gentleman-coachman whom it was in her power to compare him with!—And then his hat sat so well, and the innumerable capes of his great coat looked so becomingly important!—To be driven by him, next to being dancing with him, was certainly the greatest happiness in the world. In addition to every other delight, she had now that of listening to her own praise; of being thanked, at least on his sister's account, for her kindness in thus becoming her visitor; of hearing it ranked as real friendship, and described as creating real gratitude. His sister, he said, was uncomfortably circumstanced—she had no female companion—and, in the frequent absence of her father, was sometimes without any companion at all.

"But how can that be?" said Catherine, "are not you with her?"

"Northanger is not more than half my home; I have an establishment at my own house in Woodston, which is nearly twenty miles from my father's, and some of my time is necessarily spent there."

"How sorry you must be for that!"

"I am always sorry to leave Eleanor."

"Yes; but besides your affection for her, you must be so fond of the abbey!—After being used to such a home as the abbey, an ordinary parsonage-house must be very disagreeable."

He smiled and said, "You have formed a very favourable idea of the abbey."

"To be sure I have. Is not it a fine old place, just like what one reads about?"

"And are you prepared to encounter all the horrors that a building such as 'what one reads about' may produce?—Have you a stout heart?—Nerves fit for sliding panels and tapestry?"

"Oh! yes—I do not think I should be easily frightened, because there would be so many people in the house—and besides, it has never been uninhabited and left deserted for years, and then the family come back to it unawares, without giving any notice, as generally happens."

"No, certainly.—We shall not have to explore our way into a hall dimly lighted by the expiring embers of a wood fire—nor be obliged to spread our beds on the floor of a room without windows, doors, or furniture. But you must be aware that when a young lady is (by whatever means) introduced into a dwelling of this kind, she is always lodged apart from the rest of the family. While they snugly repair to their own end of the house, she is formally conducted by Dorothy, the ancient housekeeper, up a different staircase, and along many gloomy passages, into an apartment never used since some cousin or kin died in it about twenty years before. Can you stand such a ceremony as this? Will not your mind misgive you, when you find yourself in this gloomy chamber—too lofty and extensive for you, with only the feeble rays of a single lamp to take in its size—its walls hung with tapestry exhibiting figures as large as life, and the bed, of dark green stuff or purple velvet, presenting even a funereal appearance. Will not your heart sink within you?"

"Oh! but this will not happen to me, I am sure."

"How fearfully will you examine the furniture of your apartment! —And what will you discern?—Not tables, toilettes, wardrobes, or drawers, but on one side perhaps the remains of a broken lute, on the other a ponderous chest which no efforts can open, and over the fireplace the portrait of some handsome warrior, whose features will so incomprehensively strike you, that you will not be able to withdraw your eyes from it. Dorothy meanwhile, no less struck by your appearance, gazes on you in great agitation, and drops a few unintelligible hints. To raise your spirits, moreover, she gives you reason to suppose that the part of the abbey you inhabit is undoubtedly haunted, and informs you that you will not have a single domestic within call. With this parting cordial she curtseys off—you listen to the sound of her receding footsteps as long as the last echo can reach you—and when, with fainting spirits, you attempt to fasten your door, you discover, with increased alarm, that it has no lock."

"Oh! Mr. Tilney, how frightful.—This is just like a book!—But it cannot really happen to me. I am sure your housekeeper is not really Dorothy.—Well, what then?"

"Nothing further to alarm perhaps may occur the first night. After surmounting your *unconquerable* horror of the bed, you will retire to rest, and get a few hours' unquiet slumber. But on the second, or at farthest the *third* night after your arrival, you will probably have a violent storm. Peals of thunder so loud as to seem to shake the edifice to its foundation will roll round the neighbouring mountains—and during the frightful gusts of wind which accompany it, you will probably think you discern (for your lamp is not extinguished) one part of the hanging more violently agitated than the rest. Unable, of course, to repress your curiosity in so favourable a moment for indulging it, you will instantly arise, and throwing your dressing-gown around you, proceed to examine this mystery. After a very short search, you will discover a division in the tapestry so artfully constructed as to defy the minutest inspection, and on opening it, a door will immediately appear —which door being only secured by massy bars and a padlock, you will, after a few efforts, succeed in opening,—and, with your lamp in your hand, will pass through it into a small vaulted room."

"No, indeed; I should be too much frightened to do any such thing."

"What! not when Dorothy has given you to understand that there is a secret subterraneous communication between your apartment and the chapel of St. Anthony, scarcely two miles off— Could you shrink from so simple an adventure? No, no, you will proceed into this small vaulted room, and through this into several others, without perceiving anything very remarkable in either. In one perhaps there may be a dagger, in another a few drops of blood, and in a third the remains of some instrument of torture; but there being nothing in all this out of the common way, and your lamp being nearly exhausted, you will return towards your own apartment. In repassing through the small vaulted room, however, your eyes will be attracted towards a large, old-fashioned cabinet of ebony and gold, which, though narrowly examining the furniture before, you had passed unnoticed. Impelled by an irresistible presentiment, you will eagerly advance to it, unlock its folding doors, and search into every drawer;—but for some time without discovering anything of importance—perhaps nothing but a considerable hoard of diamonds. At last, however, by touching a secret spring, an inner compartment will open—a roll of paper appears:— you seize it—it contains many sheets of manuscript—you hasten with the precious treasure into your own chamber, but scarcely have you been able to decipher 'Oh! thou—whomsoever thou mayst be, into whose hands these memoirs of the wretched Matilda may fall'—when your lamp suddenly expires in the socket, and leaves you in total darkness."

"Oh! no, no—do not say so. Well, go on."

But Henry was too much amused by the interest he had raised, to be able to carry it farther; he could no longer command solemnity either of subject or voice, and was obliged to entreat her to use her own fancy in the perusal of Matilda's woes. Catherine, recollecting herself, grew ashamed of her eagerness, and began earnestly to assure

him that her attention had been fixed without the smallest apprehension of really meeting with what he related. "Miss Tilney, she
was sure, would never put her into such a chamber as he had described!—She was not at all afraid."

As they drew near the end of their journey, her impatience for a
sight of the abbey—for some time suspended by his conversation on
subjects very different—returned in full force, and every bend in the
road was expected with solemn awe to afford a glimpse of its massy
walls of grey stone, rising amidst a grove of ancient oaks, with the
last beams of the sun playing in beautiful splendour on its high Gothic
windows. But so low did the building stand, that she found herself
passing through the great gates of the lodge, into the very grounds
of Northanger, without having discerned even an antique chimney.

She knew not that she had any right to be surprised, but there was
a something in this mode of approach which she certainly had not
expected. To pass between lodges of a modern appearance, to find herself with such ease in the very precincts of the abbey, and driven so
rapidly along a smooth, level road of fine gravel, without obstacle,
alarm or solemnity of any kind, struck her as odd and inconsistent. She
was not long at leisure, however, for such considerations. A sudden
scud of rain driving full in her face, made it impossible for her to
observe anything further, and fixed all her thoughts on the welfare of
her new straw bonnet:—and she was actually under the abbey walls,
was springing, with Henry's assistance, from the carriage, was beneath
the shelter of the old porch, and had even passed on to the hall, where
her friend and the General were waiting to welcome her, without feeling one aweful foreboding of future misery to herself, or one moment's
suspicion of any past scenes of horror being acted within the solemn
edifice. The breeze had not seemed to waft the sighs of the murdered
to her; it had wafted nothing worse than a thick mizzling rain; and
having given a good shake to her habit, she was ready to be shewn into
the common drawing-room, and capable of considering where she was.

An abbey!—yes, it was delightful to be really in an abbey!—but she
doubted, as she looked round the room, whether anything within her
observation, would have given her the consciousness. The furniture
was in all the profusion and elegance of modern taste. The fireplace,
where she had expected the ample width and ponderous carving of
former times, was contracted to a Rumford, with slabs of plain though
handsome marble, and ornaments over it of the prettiest English

china. The windows, to which she looked with peculiar dependence, from having heard the General talk of his preserving them in their Gothic form with reverential care, were yet less what her fancy had portrayed. To be sure, the pointed arch was preserved—the form of them was Gothic, they might be even casements—but every pane was so large, so clear, so light! To an imagination which had hoped for the smallest divisions, and the heaviest stone-work, for painted glass, dirt and cobwebs, the difference was very distressing.

The General, perceiving how her eye was employed, began to talk of the smallness of the room and simplicity of the furniture, where everything being for daily use, pretended only to comfort, &c., flattering himself, however, that there were some apartments in the Abbey not unworthy her notice—and was proceeding to mention the costly gilding of one in particular, when taking out his watch, he stopped short, to pronounce it with surprize within twenty minutes of five! This seemed the word of separation, and Catherine found herself hurried away by Miss Tilney, in such a manner as convinced her that the strictest punctuality to the family hours would be expected at Northanger.

Returning through the large and lofty hall, they ascended a broad staircase of shining oak, which, after many flights and many landing-places, brought them upon a long wide gallery. On one side it had a range of doors, and it was lighted on the other by windows which Catherine had only time to discover looked into a quadrangle, before Miss Tilney led the way into a chamber, and scarcely staying to hope she would find it comfortable, left her with an anxious entreaty that she would make as little alteration as possible in her dress.

A moment's glance was enough to satisfy Catherine that her apartment was very unlike the one which Henry had endeavoured to alarm her by the description of.—It was by no means unreasonably large, and contained neither tapestry nor velvet.—The walls were papered, the floor was carpeted; the windows were neither less perfect nor more dim than those of the drawing-room below; the furniture, though not of the latest fashion, was handsome and comfortable, and the air of the room altogether far from uncheerful. Her heart instantaneously at ease on this point, she resolved to lose no time in particular examination of anything, as she greatly dreaded disobliging the General by any delay. Her habit therefore was thrown off with all possible haste, and she was preparing to unpin the linen package, which the chaise-seat had conveyed for her immediate accommodation, when her eye suddenly fell on a large high chest, standing back in a deep recess on one side of the fireplace. The sight of it made her start; and, forgetting everything else, she stood gazing on it in motionless wonder, while these thoughts crossed her:—

"This is strange, indeed! I did not expect such a sight as this!—An immense heavy chest!—What can it hold?—Why should it be placed here?—Pushed back too, as if meant to be out of sight!—I will look into it—cost me what it may, I will look into it—and directly too—by daylight.—If I stay till evening my candle may go out." She advanced and examined it closely: it was of cedar, curiously inlaid with some darker wood, and raised, about a foot from the ground, on a carved stand of the same. The lock was silver, though tarnished from age; at each end were the imperfect remains of handles also of silver, broken perhaps prematurely by some strange violence; and, on the centre of the lid, was a mysterious cypher, in the same metal. Catherine bent over it intently, but without being able to distinguish anything with certainty. She could not, in whatever direction she took it, believe the last letter to be a *T;* and yet that it should be anything else in that house was a circumstance to raise no common degree of astonishment. If not originally theirs, by what strange events could it have fallen into the Tilney family?

Her fearful curiosity was every moment growing greater; and seizing, with trembling hands, the hasp of the lock, she resolved at all hazards to satisfy herself at least as to its contents. With difficulty, for something seemed to resist her efforts, she raised the lid a few inches; but at that moment a sudden knocking at the door of the room made her, starting, quit her hold, and the lid closed with alarming violence. This ill-timed intruder was Miss Tilney's maid, sent by her mistress to be of use to Miss Morland; and though Catherine immediately dismissed her, it recalled her to the sense of what she ought to be doing, and forced her, in spite of her anxious desire to penetrate this mystery, to proceed in her dressing without further delay. Her progress was not quick, for her thoughts and her eyes were still bent on the object so well calculated to interest and alarm; and though she dared not waste a moment upon a second attempt, she could not remain many paces from the chest. At length, however, having slipped one arm into her gown, her toilet seemed so nearly finished, that the impatience of her curiosity might safely be indulged. One moment surely might be spared; and, so desperate should be the exertion of her strength, that, unless secured by supernatural means, the lid in one moment should be thrown back. With this spirit she sprang forward, and her confidence did not deceive her. Her resolute effort threw back the lid, and gave to her astonished eyes the view of a white cotton counterpane, properly folded, reposing at one end of the chest in undisputed possession!

She was gazing on it with the first blush of surprize, when Miss Tilney, anxious for her friend's being ready, entered the room, and to the rising shame of having harboured for some minutes an absurd expectation, was then added the shame of being caught in so idle a search. "That is a curious old chest, is not it?" said Miss Tilney, as Catherine hastily closed it and turned away to the glass. "It is impossible to say how many generations it has been here. How it came to be first put in this room I know not, but I have not had it moved, because I thought it might sometimes be of use in holding hats and bonnets. The worst of it is that its weight makes it difficult to open. In that corner, however, it is at least out of the way."

Catherine had no leisure for speech, being at once blushing, tying her gown, and forming wise resolutions with the most violent dispatch. Miss Tilney gently hinted her fear of being late; and in half a minute they ran down stairs together, in an alarm not wholly unfounded, for General Tilney was pacing the drawing-room, his watch in his hand, and having, on the very instant of their entering, pulled the bell with violence, ordered, "Dinner to be on table *directly!*"

Catherine trembled at the emphasis with which he spoke, and sat pale and breathless, in a most humble mood, concerned for his children, and detesting old chests; and the General recovering his politeness as he looked at her, spent the rest of his time in scolding his daughter, for so foolishly hurrying her fair friend, who was absolutely out of breath from haste, when there was not the least occasion for hurry in the world: but Catherine could not at all get over the double distress of having involved her friend in a lecture and been a great simpleton herself, till they were happily seated at the dinner-table, when the General's complacent smiles, and a good appetite of her own, restored her to peace. The dining-parlour was a noble room, suitable in its dimensions to a much larger drawing-room than the one in common use, and fitted up in a style of luxury and expense which was almost lost on the unpractised eye of Catherine, who saw little more than its spaciousness and the number of their attendants. Of the former, she spoke aloud her admiration; and the General, with a very gracious countenance, acknowledged that it was by no means an ill-sized room; and further confessed, that, though as careless on such subjects as most people, he did look upon a tolerably large eating-room as one of the necessaries of life; he supposed, however, "that she must have been used to much better sized apartments at Mr. Allen's?"

"No, indeed," was Catherine's honest assurance; "Mr. Allen's dining-parlour was not more than half as large": and she had never seen so large a room as this in her life. The General's good-humour increased. —Why, as he *had* such rooms, he thought it would be simple not to make use of them; but, upon his honour, he believed there might be more comfort in rooms of only half their size. Mr. Allen's house, he was sure, must be exactly of the true size for rational happiness.

The evening passed without any further disturbance, and, in the occasional absence of General Tilney, with much positive cheerfulness. It was only in his presence that Catherine felt the smallest fatigue from her journey; and even then, even in moments of languor or restraint, a sense of general happiness preponderated, and she could think of her friends in Bath without one wish of being with them.

The night was stormy; the wind had been rising at intervals the whole afternoon; and by the time the party broke up, it blew and rained violently. Catherine, as she crossed the hall, listened to the tempest with sensations of awe; and, when she heard it rage round a corner of the ancient building and close with sudden fury a distant door, felt for the first time that she was really in an Abbey.—Yes, these were characteristic sounds;—they brought to her recollection a count-less variety of dreadful situations and horrid scenes which such build-ings had witnessed, and such storms ushered in; and most heartily did she rejoice in the happier circumstances attending her entrance within walls so solemn!—*She* had nothing to dread from midnight assassins or drunken gallants. Henry had certainly been only in jest in what he had told her that morning. In a house so furnished, and so guarded, she could have nothing to explore or to suffer; and might go to her bedroom as securely as if it had been her own chamber at Fullerton. Thus wisely fortifying her mind, as she proceeded up stairs, she was enabled, especially on perceiving that Miss Tilney slept only two doors from her, to enter her room with a tolerably stout heart; and her spirits were immediately assisted by the cheerful blaze of a wood fire. "How much better is this," said she, as she walked to the fender—"how much better to find a fire ready lit, than to have to wait shivering in the cold till all the family are in bed, as so many poor girls have been obliged to do, and then to have a faithful old servant frightening one by coming in with a faggot! How glad I am that Northanger is what it is! If it had been like some other places, I do not know that, in such a night as this, I could have answered for my courage:—but now, to be sure, there is nothing to alarm one."

She looked round the room. The window curtains seemed in motion. It could be nothing but the violence of the wind penetrating through the divisions of the shutters; and she stept boldly forward, carelessly humming a tune, to assure herself of its being so, peeped courageously behind each curtain, saw nothing on either low window seat to scare her, and on placing a hand against the shutter, felt the strongest conviction of the wind's force. A glance at the old chest, as she turned away from this examination, was not without its use; she scorned the causeless fears of an idle fancy, and began with a most happy indifference to prepare herself for bed. "She should take her time; she should not hurry herself; she did not care if she were the last person up in the house. But she would not make up her fire; *that* would seem cowardly, as if she wished for the protection of light after she were in bed." The fire, therefore, died away, and Catherine, having spent the best part of an hour in her arrangements, was beginning to think of stepping into bed, when, on giving a parting glance round the room, she was struck by the appearance of a high old-fashioned black cabinet, which, though in a situation conspicuous enough, had never caught her notice before. Henry's words, his description of the ebony cabinet which was to escape her observation at first, immediately rushed across her; and though there could be nothing really in it, there was something whimsical, it was certainly a very remarkable coincidence! She took her candle and looked closely at the cabinet. It was not absolutely ebony and gold; but it was Japan, black and yellow Japan of the handsomest kind; and as she held her candle, the yellow had very much the effect of gold. The key was in the door, and she had a strange fancy to look into it; not, however, with the smallest expectation of finding anything, but it was so very odd, after what Henry had said. In short, she could not sleep till she had examined it. So, placing the candle with great caution on a chair, she seized the key with a very tremulous hand and tried to turn it; but it resisted her utmost strength. Alarmed, but not discouraged, she tried it another way; a bolt flew, and she believed herself successful; but how strangely mysterious!—the door was still immoveable. She paused a moment in breathless wonder. The wind roared down the chimney, the rain beat in torrents against the windows, and everything seemed to speak the awfulness of her situation. To retire to bed, however, unsatisfied on such a point, would be vain, since sleep must be impossible with the consciousness of a cabinet so mysteriously closed in her immediate vicinity. Again, therefore, she applied herself to the key, and after moving it in every possible way for some instants with the determined celerity of hope's last effort, the door suddenly yielded to her hand: her heart leaped with exultation at such a victory, and having thrown open each folding door, the second being secured only by bolts of less wonderful construction than the lock, though in that her eye could not discern anything unusual, a double range of small drawers appeared in view, with some larger drawers above and below them, and in the centre, a small door, closed also with lock and key, secured in all probability a cavity of importance.

Catherine's heart beat quick, but her courage did not fail her. With a cheek flushed by hope, and an eye straining with curiosity, her fingers grasped the handle of a drawer and drew it forth. It was entirely empty. With less alarm and greater eagerness she seized a second, a third, a fourth; each was equally empty. Not one was left unsearched, and in not one was anything found. Well read in the art of concealing a treasure, the possibility of false linings to the drawers did not escape her, and she felt round each with anxious acuteness in vain. The place in the middle alone remained now unexplored; and though she had "never from the first had the smallest idea of finding anything in any part of the cabinet, and was not in the least disappointed at her ill success thus far, it would be foolish not to examine it thoroughly while she was about it." It was some time, however, before she could unfasten the door, the same difficulty occurring in the management of this inner lock as of the outer; but at length it did open; and not vain, as hitherto, was her search; her quick eyes directly fell on a roll of paper pushed back into the further part of the cavity, apparently for concealment, and her feelings at that moment were indescribable. Her heart fluttered, her knees trembled, and her cheeks grew pale. She seized, with an unsteady hand, the precious manuscript, for half a glance sufficed to ascertain written characters; and while she acknowledged with awful sensations this striking exemplification of what Henry had foretold, resolved instantly to peruse every line before she attempted to rest.

The dimness of the light her candle emitted made her turn to it with alarm; but there was no danger of its sudden extinction, it had yet some hours to burn; and that she might not have any greater difficulty in distinguishing the writing than what its ancient date might occasion, she hastily snuffed it. Alas! it was snuffed and extinguished in one. A lamp could not have expired with more awful effect. Catherine, for a few moments, was motionless with horror. It was done completely; not a remnant of light in the wick could give hope to the rekindling breath. Darkness impenetrable and immoveable filled the room. A violent gust of wind, rising with sudden fury, added fresh horror to the moment. Catherine trembled from head to foot. In the pause which succeeded, a sound like receding footsteps and the closing of a distant door struck on her affrighted ear. Human nature could support no more. A cold sweat stood on her forehead, the manuscript fell from her hand, and groping her way to the bed, she jumped hastily in, and sought some suspension of agony by creeping far underneath the clothes. To close her eyes in sleep that night, she felt must be entirely out of the question. With a curiosity so justly awakened, and feelings in every way so agitated, repose must be absolutely impossible. The storm too abroad so dreadful! She had not been used to feel alarm from wind, but now every blast seemed fraught with awful intelligence. The manuscript so wonderfully found, so wonderfully accomplishing the morning's prediction, how was it to be accounted for?—What could it contain?—to whom could it relate?—by what means could it have been so long concealed?—and how singularly strange that it should fall to her lot to discover it! Till she had made herself mistress of its contents, however, she could have neither repose nor comfort; and with the sun's first rays she was determined to peruse it. But many were the tedious hours which must yet intervene. She shuddered, tossed about in her bed, and envied every quiet sleeper. The storm still raged, and various were the noises, more terrific even than the wind, which struck at intervals on her startled ear. The very curtains of her bed seemed at one moment in motion, and at another

the lock of her door was agitated, as if by the attempt of somebody
to enter. Hollow murmurs seemed to creep along the gallery, and
more than once her blood was chilled by the sound of distant moans.
Hour after hour passed away, and the wearied Catherine had heard
three proclaimed by all the clocks in the house, before the tempest
subsided, or she unknowingly fell fast asleep.

The housemaid's folding back her window-shutters at eight o'clock
the next day was the sound which first roused Catherine; and she
opened her eyes, wondering that they could ever have been closed, on
objects of cheerfulness; her fire was already burning, and a bright
morning had succeeded the tempest of the night. Instantaneously with
the consciousness of existence, returned her recollection of the manuscript; and springing from the bed in the very moment of the maid's
going away, she eagerly collected every scattered sheet which had burst
from the roll on its falling to the ground, and flew back to enjoy the
luxury of their perusal on her pillow. She now plainly saw that she
must not expect a manuscript of equal length with the generality of
what she had shuddered over in books, for the roll, seeming to consist
entirely of small disjointed sheets, was altogether but of trifling size,
and much less than she had supposed it to be at first.

Her greedy eye glanced rapidly over a page. She started at its im-
port. Could it be possible, or did not her senses play her false?—An
inventory of linen, in coarse and modern characters, seemed all that
was before her! If the evidence of sight might be trusted, she held a
washing-bill in her hand. She seized another sheet, and saw the same
articles with little variation; a third, a fourth, and a fifth presented
nothing new. Shirts, stockings, cravats and waistcoats faced her in each.
Two others, penned by the same hand, marked an expenditure scarcely
more interesting, in letters, hair-powders, shoe-string, and breeches-
ball. And the larger sheet, which had enclosed the rest, seemed by its
first cramp line, "To poultice chestnut mare," a farrier's bill! Such was
the collection of papers (left perhaps, as she could then suppose, by
the negligence of a servant in the place whence she had taken them)
which had filled her with expectation and alarm, and robbed her of
half her night's rest! She felt humbled to the dust. Could not the adventure of the chest have taught her wisdom? A corner of it catching
her eye as she lay, seemed to rise up in judgment against her. Nothing

could now be clearer than the absurdity of her recent fancies. To suppose that a manuscript of many generations back could have remained undiscovered in a room such as that, so modern, so habitable!—or that she should be the first to possess the skill of unlocking a cabinet, the key of which was open to all!

[From *Northanger Abbey*]

John Galt

John Galt (who spent some time in Canada and who had the city of Galt, Ontario, named after him) was a pre-Walter Scott depicter of Scottish life and manners. Scottish humor is called pawky.

ANNALS OF THE PARISH
(Selection)

The An. Dom. one thousand seven hundred and sixty was remarkable for three things in the parish of Dalmailing. First and foremost, there was my placing; then, the coming of Mrs. Malcolm with her five children to settle among us; and next, my marriage upon my own cousin, Miss Betty Lanshaw:—by which the account of this year naturally divides itself into three heads or portions.

First, of the placing. It was a great affair; for I was put in by the patron, and the people knew nothing whatsoever of me, and their hearts were stirred into strife on the occasion, and they did all that lay within the compass of their power to keep me out, insomuch that there was obliged to be a guard of soldiers to protect the presbytery; and it was a thing that made my heart grieve when I heard the drum beating and the fife playing as we were going to the kirk. The people were really mad and vicious, and flung dirt upon us as we passed, and reviled us all, and held out the finger of scorn at me; but I endured it with a resigned spirit, compassionating their wilfulness and blindness. Poor old Mr. Kilfuddy of the Braehill got such a clash of glar [1] on the side of his face that his eye was almost extinguished.

When we got to the kirk door it was found to be nailed up, so as by no possibility to be opened. The sergeant of the soldiers wanted to break it; but I was afraid that the heritors would grudge and complain of the expense of a new door, and I supplicated him to let it be as it was. We were, therefore, obligated to go in by a window, and the crowd followed us in the most unreverent manner, making

---

[1] Clash of glar: lump of mud.

the Lord's house like an inn on a fair day with their grievous yelly-hooing. During the time of the psalm and the sermon they behaved themselves better; but when the induction came on their clamour was dreadful, and Thomas Thorl, the weaver, a pious zealot in that time, got up and protested, and said, "Verily, verily, I say unto you, he that entereth not by the door into the sheepfold, but climbeth up some other way, the same is a thief and a robber." And I thought I would have a hard and sore time of it with such an outstrapolous people. Mr. Given that was then the minister of Lugton was a jocose man, and would have his joke even at a solemnity. When the laying of the hands upon me was adoing, he could not get near enough to put on his, but he stretched out his staff and touched my head, and said, to the great diversion of the rest, "This will do well enough: timber to timber"; but it was an unfriendly saying of Mr. Given, considering the time and the place, and the temper of my people.

After the ceremony, we then got out at the window, and it was a heavy day to me; but we went to the manse, and there we had an excellent dinner, which Mrs. Watts of the new inns of Irville prepared at my request and sent her chaise-driver to serve (for he was likewise her waiter, she having then but one chaise, and that no often called for).

But, although my people received me in this unruly manner, I was resolved to cultivate civility among them, and, therefore, the very next morning I began a round of visitations; but, oh! it was a steep brae that I had to climb, and it needed a stout heart. For I found the doors in some places barred against me; in others, the bairns, when they saw me coming, ran crying to their mothers, "Here's the feckless Mess-John!" and then, when I went into the houses, their parents wouldna ask me to sit down, but with a scornful way said, "Honest man, what's your pleasure here?" . . .

[By the year 1764 his wife has died.]

So I often walked in the fields, and held communion with nature, and wondered at the mysteries thereof. On one of these occasions, as I was sauntering along the edge of Eaglesham-wood, looking at the industrious bee going from flower to flower, and at the idle butterfly that layeth up no store but perisheth ere it is winter, I felt as it were a spirit from on high descending upon me, a throb at my heart, and a thrill in my brain; and I was transported out of myself, and seized with the notion of writing a book. But what it should be about, I could not settle to my satisfaction. Sometimes I thought of an orthodox poem, like *Paradise Lost* by John Milton, wherein I proposed to treat more at large of Original Sin, and of the great mystery of Redemption. At others, I fancied that a connect treatise on the efficacy of Free Grace would be more taking. But, although I made divers beginnings in both subjects, some new thought ever came into my head, and the whole summer passed away and nothing was done. I therefore postponed my design of writing a book till the winter, when I would have the benefit of the long nights. Before that, however, I had other things of more importance to think about. My servant lasses, having no eye of a mistress over them, wastered everything at such a rate, and made such a galravitching in the house, that, long before the end of the year, the year's stipend was all spent, and I did not know what to do. At lang and length I mustered courage to send for Mr. Auld, who was then living, and an elder. He was a douce and discreet man, fair and well-doing in the world, and had a better handful of strong common sense than many even of the heritors. So I told him how I was situated, and conferred with him. He advised me, for my own sake, to look out for another wife, as soon as decency would allow, which, he thought, might very properly be after the turn of the year, by which time the first Mrs. Balwhidder would be dead more than twelve months; and when I mentioned my design to write a book, he said (and he was a man of good discretion) that the doing of the book was a thing that would keep, but wasteful servants were a growing evil. So, upon his counselling, I resolved not to meddle with the book till I was married again, but employ the interim, between then and the turn of the year, in looking out for a prudent woman to be my second wife, strictly intending (as I did perform) not to mint a word about my choice, if I made one, until the whole twelve months and a day, from the date of the first Mrs. Balwhidder's interment, had run out.

In this the hand of Providence was very visible, and lucky for me it was that I had sent for Mr. Auld when I did send. The very week following, a sound began to spread in the parish that one of my lassies had got herself with bairn,—which was an awful thing to think had happened in the house of her master, and that master a minister of the gospel. Some there were,—for backbiting appertaineth to all conditions,—that jealoused and wondered if I had not a finger in the pie: which when Mr. Auld heard, he bestirred himself in such a manful and godly way in my defence as silenced the clash, telling that I was utterly incapable of any such thing, being a man of a guileless heart, and a spiritual simplicity, that would be ornamental in a child. We then had the latheron summoned before the Session, and was not long in making her confess that the father was Nichol Snipe, Lord Glencairn's gamekeeper. Both she and Nichol were obligated to stand in the kirk; but Nichol was a graceless reprobate, for he came with two coats,—one buttoned behind him, and another buttoned before him—, and two wigs of my lord's, lent him by the valet-de-chamer,—the one over his face, and the other in the right way—; and he stood with his face to the church wall. When I saw him from the poopit, I said to him, "Nichol, you must turn your face towards me!" At the which he turned round, to be sure; but there he presented the same show as his back. I was confounded, and did not know what to say, but cried out with a voice of anger, "Nichol, Nichol! If ye had been a' back, ye wouldna hae been there this day;"— which had such an effect on the whole congregation that the poor fellow suffered afterwards more derision than if I had rebuked him in the manner prescribed by the Session.

Lord Byron

IN PRAISE OF THE TURK

He was a Turk, the colour of mahogany;
　And Laura saw him, and at first was glad,
Because the Turks so much admire philogyny,
　Although their usage of their wives is sad;
'Tis sad they use no better than a dog any
　Poor woman, whom they purchase like a pad:
They have a number, though they ne'er exhibit 'em,
Four wives by law, and concubines "ad libitum."

They lock them up, and veil, and guard them daily,
　They scarcely can behold their male relations,
So that their moments do not pass so gaily
　As is supposed the case with northern nations;
Confinement, too, must make them look quite palely:
　And as the Turks abhor long conversations,
Their days are either pass'd in doing nothing,
Or bathing, nursing, making love, and clothing.

They cannot read, and so don't lisp in criticism;
　Nor write, and so they don't affect the muse;
Were never caught in epigram or witticism,
　Have no romances, sermons, plays, reviews,—
In harems learning soon would make a pretty schism.
　But luckily these beauties are no "Blues";
No bustling Botherbys have they to show 'em
"That charming passage in the last new poem,"

No solemn, antique gentleman of rhyme,
　Who having angled all his life for fame,
And getting but a nibble at a time,
　Still fussily keeps fishing on, the same

115

Small "Triton of the minnows," the sublime
Of mediocrity, the furious tame,
The echo's echo, usher of the school
Of female wits, boy bards—in short, a fool!

. . . .

Oh, Mirth and Innocence! Oh, Milk and Water!
Ye happy mixtures of more happy days!
In these sad centuries of sin and slaughter,
Abominable Man no more allays
His thirst with such pure beverage. No matter,
I love you both, and both shall have my praise:
Oh, for old Saturn's reign of sugar-candy!—
Meantime I drink to your return in brandy.

[From *Beppo*]

DON JUAN ADOLESCENT

Silent and pensive, idle, restless, slow,
His home deserted for the lonely wood,
Tormented with a wound he could not know,
His, like all deep grief, plunged in solitude:
I'm fond myself of solitude or so,
But then, I beg it may be understood,
By solitude I mean a Sultan's, not
A hermit's, with a harem for a grot.

"O Love! in such a wilderness as this,
Where transport and security entwine,
Here is the empire of thy perfect bliss,
And here thou art a god indeed divine."
The bard I quote from does not sing amiss,
With the exception of the second line,
For that same twining "transport and security"
Are twisted to a phrase of some obscurity.

The poet meant, no doubt, and thus appeals
  To the good sense and senses of mankind,
The very thing which everybody feels,
  As all have found on trial, or may find,
That no one likes to be disturb'd at meals
  Or love.—I won't say more about "entwined"
Or "transport," as we knew all that before,
But beg "Security" will bolt the door.

Young Juan wander'd by the glassy brooks,
  Thinking unutterable things; he threw
Himself at length within the leafy nooks
  Where the wild branch of the cork forest grew;
There poets find materials for their books,
  And every now and then we read them through,
So that their plan and prosody are eligible,
Unless, like Wordsworth, they prove unintelligible.

He, Juan (and not Wordsworth), so pursued
  His self-communion with his own high soul,
Until his mighty heart, in its great mood,
  Had mitigated part, though not the whole
Of its disease; he did the best he could
  With things not very subject to control,
And turn'd, without perceiving his condition,
Like Coleridge, into a metaphysician.

He thought about himself, and the whole earth,
  Of man the wonderful, and of the stars,
And how the deuce they ever could have birth;
  And then he thought of earthquakes, and of wars,
How many miles the moon might have in girth,
  Of air-balloons, and of the many bars
To perfect knowledge of the boundless skies;—
And then he thought of Donna Julia's eyes.

In thoughts like these true wisdom may discern
  Longings sublime, and aspirations high,
Which some are born with, but the most part learn
  To plague themselves withal, they know not why:

'Twas strange that one so young should thus concern
His brain about the action of the sky;
If *you* think 'twas philosophy that this did,
I can't help thinking puberty assisted.

[From *Don Juan,* Canto I]

DON JUAN'S ARRIVAL IN ENGLAND

Don Juan now saw Albion's earliest beauties,
Thy cliffs, *dear* Dover! harbour, and hotel;
Thy custom-house, with all its delicate duties;
Thy waiters running mucks at every bell;
Thy packets, all whose passengers are booties
To those who upon land or water dwell;
And last, not least, to strangers uninstructed,
Thy long, long bills, whence nothing is deducted.

Juan, though careless, young, and magnifique,
And rich in rubles, diamonds, cash, and credit,
Who did not limit much his bills per week,
Yet stared at this a little, though he paid it—
(His Maggior Duomo, a smart, subtle Greek,
Before him summ'd the awful scroll and read it):
But, doubtless, as the air, though seldom sunny,
Is free, the respiration's worth the money.

On with the horses! Off to Canterbury!
Tramp, tramp o'er pebble, and splash, splash
through puddles;
Hurrah! how swiftly speeds the post so merry!
Not like slow Germany, wherein they muddle
Along the road, as if they want to bury
Their fare; and also pause besides, to fuddle,
With "schnapps"—sad dogs! whom "Hundsfot,"
or "Verflucter,"
Affect no more than lightning a conductor.

Now there is nothing gives a man such spirits,
　　Leavening his blood as cayenne doth a curry,
As going at full speed—no matter where its
　　Direction be, so 'tis but in a hurry,
And merely for the sake of its own merits;
　　For the less cause there is for all this flurry,
The greater is the pleasure in arriving
And the great *end* of travel—which is driving.

They saw at Canterbury the cathedral;
　　Black Edward's helm, and Becket's bloody stone,
Were pointed out as usual by the bedral,
　　In the same quaint, uninterested tone:—
There's glory again for you, gentle reader! All
　　Ends in a rusty casque and dubious bone,
Half-solved into these sodas or magnesias,
Which form that bitter draught, the human species.

[From *Don Juan,* Canto X]

Richard Barham

NELL COOK
A Legend of the "Dark Entry"

SCENE—A back parlour in Mr. John Ingoldsby's house in the Precinct, Canterbury.—A blazing fire.—Mine Uncle is seated in a high-backed easy-chair, twirling his thumbs, and contemplating his list shoe.—Little Tom, the "King's Scholar," on a stool opposite.—Mrs. John Ingoldsby at the table, busily employed in manufacturing a cabbage-rose [cauliflower?] in many-coloured worsteds.—Mine Uncle's meditations are interrupted by the French clock on the mantelpiece. He prologizeth with vivacity.

"Hark! listen, Mrs. Ingoldsby,—the clock is striking nine!
Give Master Tom another cake, and half a glass of wine,
And ring the bell for Jenny Smith, and bid her bring his coat,
And a warm bandanna handkerchief to tie about his throat.

"And bid them go the nearest way, for Mr. Birch has said
That nine o'clock's the hour he'll have his boarders all in bed;
And well we know when little boys their coming home delay,
They often seem to walk and sit uneasily next day!"

"—Now nay, dear Uncle Ingoldsby, now send me not, I pray,
Back by that Entry dark, for that you know's the nearest way;
I dread that Entry dark with Jane alone at such an hour,
It fears me quite—it's Friday night!—and then Nell Cook hath pow'r!"

"And who's Nell Cook, thou silly child?—and what's Nell Cook to
    thee?
That thou shouldst dread at night to tread with Jane that dark entrée?"
—"Nay, list and hear, mine Uncle dear! such fearsome things they tell
Of Nelly Cook, that few may brook at night to meet with Nell!

"It was in bluff King Harry's days,—and Monks and Friars were then,
You know, dear Uncle Ingoldsby, a sort of Clergymen.
They'd coarse stuff gowns, and shaven crowns,—no shirts,—and no
    cravats,
And a cord was placed about their waist—they had no shovel hats!

"It was in bluff King Harry's days, while yet he went to shrift,
And long before he stamp'd and swore, and cut the Pope adrift;
There lived a portly Canon then, a sage and learned clerk;
He had, I trow, a goodly house, fast by that Entry dark!

"The Canon was a portly man—of Latin and of Greek
And learned lore, he had good store,—yet health was on his cheek.
The Priory fare was scant and spare, the bread was made of rye,
The beer was weak, yet he was sleek—he had a merry eye.

"For though within the Priory the fare was scant and thin,
The Canon's house it stood without;—he kept good cheer within;
Unto the best he prest each guest with free and jovial look,
And Ellen Bean ruled his *cuisine.*—He called her 'Nelly Cook.'

"For soups, and stews, and choice *ragoûts,* Nell Cook was famous still!
She'd make them even of old shoes, she had such wondrous skill:
Her manchets fine were quite divine, her cakes were nicely brown'd,
Her boil'd and roast, they were the boast of all the 'Precinct' round;

"And Nelly was a comely lass, but calm and staid her air,
And earthward bent her modest look—yet was she passing fair;
And though her gown was russet brown, their heads grave people
    shook:
—They all agreed no Clerk had need of such a pretty Cook.

"One day, 'twas on a Whitsun Eve—there came a coach and four;—
It pass'd the 'Green-Court' gate, and stopp'd before the Canon's door;
The travel-stain on wheel and rein bespoke a weary way,—
Each panting steed relax'd its speed—out stept a Lady gay.

" 'Now, welcome! welcome! dearest Niece!'—the Canon then did cry,
And to his breast the Lady prest—he had a merry eye,—
'Now, welcome! welcome! dearest Niece! in sooth, thou'rt welcome
    here,
'Tis many a day since we have met—how fares my Brother dear?'—

" 'Now thanks, my loving Uncle,' that Lady gay replied:
'Gramercy for thy benison!'—then 'Out, alas!' she sigh'd;
'My father dear he is not near; he seeks the Spanish Main;
He prays thee give me shelter here till he return again!'—

" 'Now, welcome! welcome! dearest Niece; come lay thy mantle by!'
The Canon kiss'd her ruby lip—he had a merry eye,—
But Nelly Cook askew did look,—it came into her mind
They were a little less than 'kin,' and rather more than 'kind.'

.   .   .   .   .

"Three weeks are gone and over—full three weeks and a day,
Yet still within that Canon's house doth dwell that Lady gay;
On capons fine they daily dine, rich cates and sauces rare,
And they quaff good store of Bordeaux wine,—so dainty is their fare.

"And fine upon the virginals is that gay Lady's touch,
And sweet her voice unto the lute, you'll scarce hear any such;
But is it 'O Sanctissima!' she sings in dulcet tone?
Or 'Angels ever bright and fair?'—Ah, no!—it's 'Bobbing Joan!'

.   .   .   .   .

"The Canon's house is lofty and spacious to the view;
The Canon's cell is order'd well—yet Nelly looks askew;
The Lady's bower is in the tower,—yet Nelly shakes her head—
She hides the poker and the tongs in that gay Lady's bed!

.   .   .   .   .

"Six weeks are gone and over—full six weeks and a day,
Yet in that bed the poker and the tongs unheeded lay!
From which, I fear, it's pretty clear that Lady rest had none;
Or, if she slept in any bed—it was not in her own.

"But where that Lady pass'd her night, I may not well divine,
Perhaps in pious oraisons at good St. Thomas' shrine,
And for her father far away breathed tender vows and true—
It may be so—I cannot say—but Nelly look'd askew.

"And still at night, by fair moonlight, when all were lock'd in sleep,
She'd listen at the Canon's door,—she'd through the keyhole peep—
I know not what she heard or saw, but fury fill'd her eye—
—She bought some nasty Doctor's stuff, and she put it in a pie!

        .   .   .

"It was a glorious summer's eve—with beams of rosy red,
The Sun went down—all Nature smiled—but Nelly shook her head!
Full softly to the balmy breeze rang out the Vesper bell—
—Upon the Canon's startled ear it sounded like a knell!

" 'Now, here's to thee, mine Uncle! a health I drink to thee!
Now, pledge me back in Sherris sack, or a cup of Malvoisie!'—
The Canon sigh'd—but, rousing, cried, 'I answer to thy call,
And a Warden-pie's a dainty dish to mortify withall!'

" 'Tis early dawn—the matin chime rings out for morning pray'r—
And Prior and Friar is in his stall—the Canon is not there!
Nor in the small Refect'ry hall, nor cloister'd walk is he—
All wonder—and the Sacristan says, 'Lauk-a-daisy-me!'

"They've searched the aisles and Baptistry—they've searched above—
     around—
The 'Sermon House'—the 'Audit Room'—the Canon is not found.
They only find that pretty Cook concocting a *ragoût,*
They ask her where her master is—but Nelly looks askew.

"They call for crow-bars—'jemmies' is the modern name they bear—
They burst through lock, and bolt, and bar—but what a sight is there!—
The Canon's head lies on the bed—his Niece lies on the floor!
—They are as dead as any nail that is in any door!

"The livid spot is on his breast, the spot is on his back!
His portly form, no longer warm with life, is swoln and black!—
The livid spot is on her cheek,—it's on her neck of snow,
And the Prior sighs, and sadly cries, 'Well, here's a pretty Go!'

        .   .   .   .

"All at the silent hour of night a bell is heard to toll,
A knell is rung, a *requiem's* sung as for a sinful soul,
And there's a grave within the Nave; it's dark, and deep, and wide,
And they bury there a Lady fair, and a Canon by her side!

"An Uncle—so 'tis whisper'd now throughout the sacred Fane,—
And a Niece—whose father's far away upon the Spanish Main.—
The Sacristan, he says no word that indicates a doubt,
But he puts his thumb unto his nose, and spreads his fingers out!

"And where doth tarry Nelly Cook, that staid and comely lass?
Ay, where?—for ne'er from forth that door was Nelly known to pass.
Her coif and gown of russet brown were lost unto the view,
And if you mention'd Nelly's name—the Monks all look'd askew!

.   .   .   .   .   .

"There is a heavy paving-stone fast by the Canon's door,
Of granite grey, and it may weigh a half a ton or more,
And it is laid deep in the shade within that Entry dark,
Where sun or moon-beam never play'd, or e'en one starry spark.

"That heavy granite stone was moved that night, 'twas darkly said,
And the mortar round its sides next morn seem'd fresh and newly laid,
But what within the narrow vault beneath that stone doth lie,
Or if that there be vault or no—I cannot tell—not I!

"But I've been told that moan and groan, and fearful wail and shriek,
Came from beneath that paving-stone for nearly half a week—
For three long days and three long nights came forth those sounds
    of fear;
Then all was o'er—they never more fell on the listening ear.

.   .   .   .   .   .

"A hundred years were gone and past since last Nell Cook was seen,
When worn by use, that stone got loose, and they went and told the
    Dean.—
—Says the Dean, says he, 'My Masons three! now haste and fix it tight';
And the Masons three peep'd down to see, and they saw a fearsome
    sight.

"Beneath that heavy paving-stone a shocking hole they found—
It was not more than twelve feet deep, and barely twelve feet round;
—A fleshless, sapless skeleton lay in that horrid well!
But who the deuce 'twas put it there those Masons could not tell.

"And near this fleshless skeleton a pitcher small did lie,
And a mouldy piece of 'kissing-crust,' as from a Warden-pie!
And Doctor Jones declared the bones were female bones, and 'Zooks!
I should not be surprised,' said he, 'if these were Nelly Cook's!'

"It was in good Dean Bargrave's days, if I remember right,
Those fleshless bones beneath the stones these Masons brought to light;
And you may well in the 'Dean's Chapelle' Dean Bargrave's portrait
     view,
'Who died one night,' says old Tom Wright, 'in sixteen forty-two!'

"And so two hundred years have pass'd since that these Masons three,
With curious looks, did set Nell Cook's unquiet spirit free;
That granite stone had kept her down till then—so some suppose,—
—Some spread their fingers out, and put their thumb unto their nose.

"But one thing's clear, that all the year, on every Friday night,
Throughout that Entry dark doth roam Nell Cook's unquiet Sprite:
On Friday was that Warden-pie all by that Canon tried;
On Friday died he, and that tidy Lady by his side!

"And though two hundred years have flown, Nell Cook doth still pursue
Her weary walk, and they who cross her path the deed may rue;
Her fatal breath is fell as death—The Simoom's blast is not
More dire—(a wind in Africa that blows uncommon hot).

"But all unlike the Simoom's blast, her breath is deadly cold,
Delivering quivering, shivering shocks upon both young and old,
And whoso in that Entry dark doth feel that fatal breath,
He ever dies within the year some dire untimely death!

"No matter who—no matter what condition, age, or sex,
But some 'get shot,' and some 'get drown'd,' and some 'get' broken
     necks;
Some 'get run over' by a coach;—and one beyond the seas
'Got' scraped to death with oyster-shells among the Caribbees!

"Those Masons three, who set her free, fell first!—it is averr'd
That two were hang'd on Tyburn tree for murdering of the third:
Charles Storey, too, his friend who slew, had ne'er, if truth they tell,
Been gibbeted on Chatham Downs, had they not met with Nell!

"Then send me not, mine Uncle dear, oh! send me not, I pray,
Back through that Entry dark tonight, but round some other way!
I will not be a truant boy, but good, and mind my book,
For Heaven forfend that ever I forgather with Nell Cook!"

The class was call'd at morning tide, and Master Tom was there;
He look'd askew, and did eschew both stool, and bench, and chair.
He did not talk, he did not walk, the tear was in his eye,—
He had not e'en that sad resource, to sit him down and cry.

Hence little boys may learn, when they from school go out to dine,
They should not deal in rigmarole, but still be back by nine;
For if when they've their greatcoat on, they pause, before they part,
To tell a long and prosy tale,—perchance their own may smart.

———————

MORAL

—A few remarks to learned Clerks in country and in town—
Don't keep a pretty serving-maid, though clad in russet brown!—
Don't let your Niece sing "Bobbing Joan!"—don't, with a merry eye,
Hob-nob in Sack and Malvoisie,—and don't eat too much pie!!

And oh! beware that Entry dark,—Especially at night,—
And don't go there with Jenny Smith all by the pale moonlight!
So bless the Queen and her Royal Weans,—And the Prince whose hand
    she took,—
And bless us all, both great and small,—and keep us from Nell Cook!

[From *The Ingoldsby Legends*]

Frederick Marryat

A NURSE FOR JACK EASY

The reader may observe that, in general, all my first chapters are very short, and increase in length as the work advances. I mention this as a proof of my modesty and diffidence. At first, I am like a young bird just out of its mother's nest, pluming my little feathers and taking short flights. By degrees I obtain more confidence, and wing my course over hill and dale.

It is very difficult to throw any interest into a chapter on childhood. There is the same uniformity in all children until they develop. We cannot, therefore, say much relative to Jack Easy's earliest days; he sucked and threw up his milk while the nurse blessed it for a pretty dear, slept, and sucked again. He crowed in the morning like a cock, screamed when he was washed, stared at the candle, and made wry faces with the wind. Six months passed in these innocent amusements, and then he was put into shorts. But I ought here to have remarked, that Mrs. Easy did not find herself equal to nursing her own infant, and it was necessary to look out for a substitute.

Now a common-place person would have been satisfied with the recommendation of the medical man, who looks but to the one thing needful, which is a sufficient and wholesome supply of nourishment for the child; but Mr. Easy was a philosopher, and had latterly taken to craniology, and he descanted very learnedly with the Doctor upon the effect of his only son obtaining his nutriment from an unknown source. "Who knows," observed Mr. Easy, "but that my son may not imbibe with his milk the very worst passions of human nature."

"I have examined her," replied the Doctor, "and can safely recommend her."

"That examination is only preliminary to one more important," replied Mr. Easy. "I must examine her."

"Examine who, Mr. Easy?" exclaimed his wife, who had lain down again on the bed.

"The nurse, my dear."

127

"Examine what, Mr. Easy?" continued the lady.

"Her head, my dear," replied the husband. "I must ascertain what her propensities are."

"I think you had better leave her alone, Mr. Easy. She comes this evening, and I shall question her pretty severely. Dr. Middleton, what do you know of this young person?"

"I know, madam, that she is very healthy and strong, or I should not have selected her."

"But is her character good?"

"Really, madam, I know little about her character; but you can make any inquiries you please. But at the same time I ought to observe, that if you are too particular in that point, you will have some difficulty in providing yourself."

"Well, I shall see," replied Mrs. Easy.

"And I shall feel," rejoined the husband.

This parleying was interrupted by the arrival of the very person in question, who was announced by the housemaid, and was ushered in. She was a handsome, florid, healthy-looking girl, awkward and naïve in her manner, and apparently not over wise; there was more of the dove than of the serpent in her composition.

Mr. Easy, who was very anxious to make his own discoveries, was the first who spoke. "Young woman, come this way, I wish to examine your head."

"Oh! dear me, sir, it's quite clean, I assure you," cried the girl, dropping a curtsey.

Doctor Middleton, who sat between the bed and Mr. Easy's chair, rubbed his hands and laughed.

In the meantime, Mr. Easy had untied the string and taken off the cap of the young woman, and was very busy putting his fingers through her hair, during which the face of the young woman expressed fear and astonishment.

"I am glad to perceive that you have a large portion of benevolence."

"Yes," replied the young woman, dropping a curtsey.

"And veneration also."

"Thanky, sir."

"And the organ of modesty is strongly developed."

"Yes, sir," replied the girl with a smile.

"That's quite a new organ," thought Dr. Middleton.

"Philo-progenitiveness very powerful."

"If you please, sir, I don't know what that is," answered Sarah with a curtsey.

"Nevertheless you have given us a practical illustration. Mrs. Easy, I am satisfied. Have you any questions to ask? But it is quite unnecessary."

"To be sure I have, Mr. Easy. Pray, young woman, what is your name?"

"Sarah, if you please, ma'am."

"How long have you been married?"

"Married, ma'am?"

"Yes, married."

"If you please, ma'am, I had a misfortune, ma'am," replied the girl, casting down her eyes.

"What, have you not been married?"

"No, ma'am, not yet."

"Good heavens! Dr. Middleton, what can you mean by bringing this person here?" exclaimed Mrs. Easy. "Not a married woman, and she has a child!"

"If you please, ma'am," interrupted the young woman, dropping a curtsey, "it was a very little one."

"A very little one!" exclaimed Mrs. Easy.

"Yes, ma'am, very small indeed, and died soon after it was born."

"Oh, Dr. Middleton!—what could you mean, Dr. Middleton?"

"My dear madam," exclaimed the Doctor, rising from his chair, "this is the only person that I could find suited to the wants of your child, and if you do not take her, I cannot answer for its life. It is true, that a married woman might be procured; but married women, who have a proper feeling, will not desert their own children; and as Mr. Easy asserts, and you appear to imagine, the temper and disposition of your child may be affected by the nourishment it receives, I think it more likely to be injured by the milk of a married woman who will desert her own child for the sake of gain. The misfortune which has happened to this young woman is not always a proof of a bad heart, but of strong attachment, and the overweening confidence of simplicity."

"You are correct, Doctor," replied Mr. Easy, "and her head proves that she is a modest young woman, with strong religious feeling, kindness of disposition, and every other requisite."

"The head may prove it all for what I know, Mr. Easy, but her conduct tells another tale."

"She is well fitted for the situation, ma'am," continued the Doctor.

"And if you please, ma'am," rejoined Sarah, "it was such a little one."

"Shall I try the baby, ma'am?" said the monthly nurse, who had listened in silence. "It is fretting so, poor thing, and has its dear little fist right down its throat."

Dr. Middleton gave the signal of assent, and in a few seconds Master John Easy was fixed to Sarah as tight as a leech.

"Lord love it, how hungry it is!—there, there, stop it a moment, it's choking, poor thing!"

Mrs. Easy, who was lying on her bed, rose up, and went to the child. Her first feeling was that of envy, that another should have such a pleasure which was denied to herself; the next, that of delight, at the satisfaction expressed by the infant. In a few minutes the child fell back in a deep sleep. Mrs. Easy was satisfied; maternal feelings conquered all others, and Sarah was duly installed.

To make short work of it, we have said that Jack Easy in six months was in shorts. He soon afterwards began to crawl and show his legs; indeed, so indecorously, that it was evident that he had imbibed no modesty with Sarah's milk, neither did he appear to have gained veneration or benevolence, for he snatched at everything, squeezed the kitten to death, scratched his mother, and pulled his father by the hair; notwithstanding all which, both his father and mother and the whole household declared him to be the finest and sweetest child in the universe. But if we were to narrate all the wonderful events of Jack's childhood from the time of his birth up to the age of seven years, as chronicled by Sarah, who continued his dry nurse after he had been weaned, it would take at least three volumes folio. Jack was brought up in the way that every only child usually is—that is, he was allowed to have his own way.

[From *Mr. Midshipman Easy*]

John Keats

THERE WAS A NAUGHTY BOY

There was a naughty Boy,
And a naughty Boy was he,
He ran away to Scotland
The people for to see—

Then he found
That the ground
Was as hard,
That a yard
Was as long,
That a song
Was as merry,
That a cherry
Was as red—
That lead
Was as weighty,
That fourscore
Was as eighty,
That a door
Was as wooden
As in England—

So he stood in his shoes
And he wonder'd,
He wonder'd,
He stood in his shoes
And he wonder'd.

[From a letter to Fanny Keats]

Thomas Hood

Thomas Hood (1799-1845) is the first professional humorist to appear in our pages; that is, the first who made his living chiefly by writing humor. There were, perhaps, a few stray professional humorists before him, such as the seventeenth-century Tom Brown, of whose wit you will find no examples here, please God. But Hood marks a date in the sociological history of humor. By working hard and fast, the humorist is now able to keep alive. How fortunate this is!

A FEW LINES ON COMPLETING FORTY-SEVEN

When I reflect with serious sense,
   While years and years run on,
How soon I may be summoned hence—
   There's cook a-calling John.

Our lives are built so frail and poor,
   On sand and not on rocks,
We're hourly standing at Death's door—
   There's someone double-knocks.

All human days have settled terms,
   Our fates we cannot force;
This flesh of mine will feed the worms—
   They're come to lunch, of course.

And when my body's turned to clay,
   And dear friends hear my knell,
Oh, let them give a sigh and say--
   I hear the upstairs bell.

A NOCTURNAL SKETCH

Even is come; and from the dark Park, hark,
The signal of the setting sun—one gun!
And six is sounding from the chime, prime time
To go and see the Drury-Lane Dane slain,—
Or hear Othello's jealous doubt spout out,—
Or Macbeth raving at that shade-made blade,
Denying to his frantic clutch much touch;—
Or else to see Ducrow with wide stride ride
Four horses as no other man can span;
Or in the small Olympic Pit, sit split
Laughing at Liston, while you quiz his phiz.

Anon Night comes, and with her wings brings things
Such as, with his poetic tongue, Young sung;
The gas up-blazes with its bright white light,
And paralytic watchmen prowl, howl, growl,
About the streets and take up Pall-Mall Sal,
Who, hasting to her nightly jobs, robs fobs.
Now thieves to enter for your cash, smash, crash,
Past drowsy Charley, in a deep sleep, creep,
But frightened by Policeman B 3, flee,
And while they're going, whisper low, "No go!"

Now puss, while folks are in their beds, treads leads.
And sleepers waking, grumble—"Drat that cat!"
Who in the gutter caterwauls, squalls, mauls
Some feline foe, and screams in shrill ill-will.

Now Bulls of Bashan, of a prize size, rise
In childish dreams, and with a roar gore poor
Georgy, or Charley, or Billy, willy-nilly;—
But Nursemaid, in a nightmare rest, chest-pressed,
Dreameth of one of her old flames, James Games,
And that she hears—what faith is man's!—Ann's banns

And his, from Reverend Mr. Rice, twice, thrice:
White ribbons flourish, and a stout shout out,
That upward goes, shows Rose knows those bows' woes!

LOVE LANGUAGE OF A MERRY YOUNG SOLDIER

(From the German, *"Ach Gretchen, mein Täubchen"*)

O Gretel, my Dove, my heart's Trumpet,
My Cannon, my Big Drum, and also my Musket,
Oh, hear me, my mild little Dove,
In your still little room.

Your portrait, my Gretel, is always on guard,
Is always attentive to Love's parole and watchword;
Your picture is always going the rounds,
My Gretel, I call at every hour!

My heart's Knapsack is always full of you;
My looks, they are quartered with you;
And when I bite off the top end of a cartridge,
Then I think I give you a kiss.

You alone are my Word of Command and orders,
Yea, my Right-face, Left-face, Brown Tommy, and wine,
And at the word of command "Shoulder Arms!"
Then I think you say, "Take me in your arms."

Your eyes sparkle like a Battery,
Yea, they wound like Bombs and Grenades;
As black as Gunpowder is your hair,
Your hand as white as Parading Breeches!

Yes, you are the Match and I am the Cannon;
Have pity, my love, and give quarter,
And give the word of command, "Wheel round
Into my heart's Barrack Yard."

Alexander W. Kinglake

INTERVIEW WITH A PASHA

Unless you can contrive to learn a little of the language of the Ottoman
Turks, you will be rather bored by your visits of ceremony; the inter-
vention of the Dragoman is fatal to the spirit of conversation. I think
I should mislead you if I were to attempt to give the substance of any
particular conversation with Orientals. A traveller may write and say
that, "the Pasha of So-and-So was particularly interested in the vast
progress which has been made in the application of steam, and appeared to understand the structure of our machinery—that he remarked
upon the gigantic results of our manufacturing industry—showed that
he possessed considerable knowledge of our Indian affairs, and of the
constitution of the Company, and expressed a lively admiration of
the many sterling qualities for which the people of England are distinguished." But the heap of commonplaces thus quietly attributed to
the Pasha will have been founded perhaps on some such talking
as this:—

PASHA: The Englishman is welcome; most blessed among hours is this,
the hour of his coming.

DRAGOMAN (*to the* TRAVELLER): The Pasha pays you his compliments.

TRAVELLER: Give him my best compliments in return, and say I'm delighted to have the honour of seeing him.

DRAGOMAN (*to the* PASHA): His Lordship, this Englishman, Lord of
London, Scorner of Ireland, Suppressor of France, has quitted his
governments, and left his enemies to breathe for a moment, and
has crossed the broad waters in strict disguise, with a small but
eternally faithful retinue of followers, in order that he might look
upon the bright countenance of the Pasha among Pashas—the
Pasha of the everlasting Pashalik of Karagholookoldour.

TRAVELLER (*to his* DRAGOMAN): What on earth have you been saying
about London? The Pasha will be taking me for a mere cockney.
Have not I told you *always* to say, that I am from a branch of the

135

family of Mudcombe Park, and that I am to be a magistrate for the county of Bedfordshire, only I've not qualified, and that I should have been a Deputy-Lieutenant, if it had not been for the extraordinary conduct of Lord Mountpromise, and that I was a candidate for Boughton-Soldborough at the last election, and that I should have won easy if my committee had not been bribed? I wish to heaven that if you *do* say anything about me, you'd tell the simple truth.

DRAGOMAN (*is silent*)

PASHA: What says the friendly Lord of London? is there aught that I can grant him within the Pashalik of Karagholookoldour?

DRAGOMAN (*growing sulky and literal*): This friendly Englishman— this branch of Mudcombe—this head purveyor of Boughton-Soldborough—this possible policeman of Bedfordshire is recounting his achievements and the number of his titles.

PASHA: The end of his honours is more distant than the ends of the earth, and the catalogue of his glorious deeds is brighter than the firmament of heaven!

DRAGOMAN (*to the* TRAVELLER): The Pasha congratulates your Excellency.

TRAVELLER: About Boughton-Soldborough? The deuce he does!—but I want to get at his views in relation to the present state of the Ottoman Empire; tell him the Houses of Parliament have met, and that there has been a speech from the throne pledging England to maintain the integrity of the Sultan's dominions.

DRAGOMAN (*to the* PASHA): This branch of Mudcombe, this possible policeman of Bedfordshire, informs your Highness that in England the talking houses have met, and that the integrity of the Sultan's dominions has been assured for ever and ever by a speech from the velvet chair.

PASHA: Wonderful chair! Wonderful houses!—whirr! whirr! all by wheels!—whiz! whiz! all by steam!—wonderful chair! wonderful houses! wonderful people!—whirr! whirr! all by wheels!—whiz! whiz! all by steam!

TRAVELLER (*to the* DRAGOMAN): What does the Pasha mean by that whizzing? he does not mean to say, does he, that our government will ever abandon their pledges to the Sultan?

DRAGOMAN: No, your Excellency, but he says the English talk by wheels and by steam.

TRAVELLER: That's an exaggeration; but say that the English really
have carried machinery to great perfection; tell the Pasha (he'll
be struck with that) that whenever we have any disturbances to
put down, even at two or three hundred miles from London, we
can send troops by the thousand to the scene of action in a few
hours.

DRAGOMAN (*recovering his temper and freedom of speech*): His Excellency, this Lord of Mudcombe, observes to your Highness, that
whenever the Irish, or the French, or the Indians rebel against the
English, whole armies of soldiers and brigades of artillery are
dropped into a mighty chasm called Euston Square, and, in the
biting of a cartridge, they rise up again in Manchester, or Dublin,
or Paris, or Delhi, and utterly exterminate the enemies of England
from the face of the earth.

PASHA: I know it—I know all—the particulars have been faithfully
related to me, and my mind comprehends locomotives. The armies
of the English ride upon the vapours of boiling cauldrons, and
their horses are flaming coals!—whirr! whirr! all by wheels!—whiz!
whiz! all by steam!

TRAVELLER (*to his* DRAGOMAN): I wish to have the opinion of an unpreju-
diced Ottoman gentleman as to the prospects of our English commerce and manufactures; just ask the Pasha to give me his views
on the subject.

PASHA (*after having received the communication of the* DRAGOMAN):
The ships of the English swarm like flies; their printed calicoes
cover the whole earth, and by the side of their swords the blades
of Damascus are blades of grass. All India is but an item in the
Ledger-books of the Merchants whose lumber-rooms are filled with
ancient thrones! whirr! whirr! all by wheels!—whiz! whiz! all
by steam!

DRAGOMAN: The Pasha compliments the cutlery of England, and also
the East India Company.

TRAVELLER: The Pasha's right about the cutlery: I tried my scimitar with
the common officers' swords belonging to our fellows at Malta,
and they cut it like the leaf of a Novel. Well (*to the* DRAGOMAN),
tell the Pasha I am exceedingly gratified to find that he entertains
such a high opinion of our manufacturing energy, but I should
like him to know, though, that we have got something in England
besides that. These foreigners are always fancying that we have

nothing but ships and railways, and East India Companies; do just tell the Pasha, that our rural districts deserve his attention, and that even within the last two hundred years there has been an evident improvement in the culture of the turnip; and if he does not take any interest about that, at all events you can explain that we have our virtues in the country—that we are a truth-telling people, and, like the Osmanlees, are faithful in the performance of our promises. Oh! and by the by, whilst you are about it, you may as well just say at the end that the British yeoman is still, thank God! the British yeoman.

PASHA (*after hearing the* DRAGOMAN): It is true, it is true:—through all Feringhistan the English are foremost and best, for the Russians are drilled swine, and the Germans are sleeping babes, and the Italians are the servants of Songs, and the French are the sons of Newspapers, and the Greeks are the weavers of lies, but the English and the Osmanlees are brothers together in righteousness; for the Osmanlees believe in one only God, and cleave to the Koran, and destroy idols; so do the English worship one God, and abominate graven images, and tell the truth, and believe in a book, and though they drink the juice of the grape, yet to say that they worship their prophet as God, or to say that they are eaters of pork, these are lies—lies born of Greeks and nursed by Jews!

DRAGOMAN: The Pasha compliments the English.

TRAVELLER (*rising*): Well, I've had enough of this. Tell the Pasha I am greatly obliged to him for his hospitality, and still more for his kindness in furnishing me with horses, and say that now I must be off.

PASHA (*after hearing the* DRAGOMAN, *and standing up on his Divan*): Proud are the sires, and blessed are the dams of the horses, that shall carry his Excellency to the end of his prosperous journey. May the saddle beneath him glide down to the gates of the happy city like a boat swimming on the third river of Paradise. May he sleep the sleep of a child, when his friends are around him; and the while that his enemies are abroad may his eyes flame red through the darkness—more red than the eyes of ten tigers!—farewell!

DRAGOMAN: The Pasha wishes your Excellency a pleasant journey.

So ends the visit.

[From *Eothen*]

A TREASURY OF BRITISH HUMOR

Elizabeth C. Gaskell

OLD LETTERS

I have often noticed that almost everyone has his own individual small economies—careful habits of saving fractions of pennies in some one peculiar direction—any disturbance of which annoys him more than spending shillings or pounds on some real extravagance. An old gentleman of my acquaintance, who took the intelligence of the failure of a Joint-Stock Bank, in which some of his money was invested, with stoical mildness, worried his family all through a long summer's day, because one of them had torn (instead of cutting) out the written leaves of his now useless bank-book; of course, the corresponding pages at the other end came out as well; and this little unnecessary waste of paper (his private economy) chafed him more than all the loss of his money. Envelopes fretted his soul terribly when they first came in; the only way in which he could reconcile himself to such waste of his cherished article was by patiently turning inside out all that were sent to him, and so making them serve again. Even now, though tamed by age, I see him casting wistful glances at his daughters when they send a whole instead of a half sheet of note-paper, with the three lines of acceptance to an invitation, written on only one of the sides. I am not above owning that I have this human weakness myself. String is my foible. My pockets get full of little hanks of it, picked up and twisted together, ready for uses that never come. I am seriously annoyed if anyone cuts the string of a parcel, instead of patiently and faithfully undoing it fold by fold. How people can bring themselves to use India-rubber rings, which are a sort of deification of string, as lightly as they do, I cannot imagine. To me an India-rubber ring is a precious treasure. I have one which is not new; one that I picked up off the floor, nearly six years ago. I have really tried to use it; but my heart failed me, and I could not commit the extravagance.

Small pieces of butter grieve others. They cannot attend to conversation, because of the annoyance occasioned by the habit which some people have of invariably taking more butter than they want. Have you not seen the anxious look (almost mesmeric) which such persons fix on the article? They would feel it a relief if they might bury it out of their sight by popping it into their own mouths, and swallowing it down; and they are really made happy if the person on whose plate it lies unused, suddenly breaks off a piece of toast (which he does not want at all) and eats up his butter. They think that this is not waste.

Now Miss Matty Jenkyns was chary of candles. We had many devices to use as few as possible. In the winter afternoons she would sit knitting for two or three hours; she could do this in the dark, or by firelight; and when I asked if I might not ring for candles to finish stitching my wristbands, she told me to "keep blind man's holiday." They were usually brought in with tea; but we only burnt one at a time. As we lived in constant preparation for a friend who might come in any evening (but who never did), it required some contrivance to keep our two candles of the same length, ready to be lighted, and to look as if we burnt two always. The candles took it in turns; and, whatever we might be talking about or doing, Miss Matty's eyes were habitually fixed upon the candle, ready to jump up and extinguish it, and to light the other before they had become too uneven in length to be restored to equality in the course of the evening.

One night, I remember this candle economy particularly annoyed me. I had been very much tired of my compulsory "blind man's holiday,"— especially as Miss Matty had fallen asleep, and I did not like to stir the fire and run the risk of awakening her; so I could not even sit on the rug, and scorch myself with sewing by firelight, according to my usual custom. I fancied Miss Matty must be dreaming of her early life; for she spoke one or two words, in her uneasy sleep, bearing reference to persons who were dead long before. When Martha brought in the lighted candle and tea, Miss Matty started into wakefulness, with a strange bewildered look around, as if we were not the people she expected to see about her. There was a little sad expression that shadowed her face as she recognised me; but immediately afterwards she tried to give me her usual smile. All through tea-time her talk ran upon the days of her childhood and youth. Perhaps this reminded her of the desirableness of looking over all the old family letters, and destroying such as ought not to be allowed to fall into the hands of strangers; for she had often spoken of the necessity of this task, but had always shrunk from it, with a timid dread of something painful. To-night, however, she rose up after tea and went for them—in the dark;

for she piqued herself on the precise neatness of all her chamber arrangement, and used to look uneasily at me when I lighted a bedcandle to go to another room for anything. When she returned, there was a faint smell of Tonquin beans in the room. I had always noticed this scent about any of the things which had belonged to her mother; and many of the letters were addressed to her—yellow bundles of loveletters, sixty or seventy years old.

Miss Matty undid the packet with a sigh; but she stifled it directly, as if it were hardly right to regret the flight of time, or of life either. We agreed to look them over separately, each taking a different letter out of the same bundle, and describing its contents to the other, before destroying it. I never knew what sad work the reading of old letters was before that evening, though I could hardly tell why. The letters were as happy as letters could be—at least those early letters were. There was in them a vivid and intense sense of the present time, which seemed so strong and full, as if it could never pass away, and as if the warm, living hearts that so expressed themselves could never die, and be as nothing to the sunny earth. I should have felt less melancholy, I believe, if the letters had been more so. I saw the tears stealing down the well-worn furrows of Miss Matty's cheeks, and her spectacles often wanted wiping. I trusted at last that she would light the other candle, for my own eyes were rather dim, and I wanted more light to see the pale, faded ink; but no—even through her tears, she saw and remembered her little economical ways.

The earliest set of letters were two bundles tied together, and ticketed (in Miss Jenkyns's handwriting), "Letters interchanged between my ever-honoured father and my dearly-beloved mother, prior to their marriage, in July, 1774." I should guess that the Rector of Cranford was about twenty-seven years of age when he wrote those letters; and Miss Matty told me that her mother was just eighteen at the time of her wedding. With my idea of the Rector, derived from a picture in the dining-parlour, stiff and stately, in a huge full bottomed wig, with gown, cassock, and bands, and his hand upon a copy of the only sermon he ever published—it was strange to read these letters. They were full of eager, passionate ardour; short homely sentences, right fresh from the heart—(very different from the grand Latinised, Johnsonian style of the printed sermon, preached before some judge at assize time). His letters were a curious contrast to those of his girl-bride. She was evidently rather annoyed at his demands upon her for expressions of love, and could not quite understand what he meant by repeating the same thing over in so many different ways; but what she was quite clear about was her longing for a white "Paduasoy"—whatever that might be; and six or seven letters were principally occupied in asking her lover to use his influence with her parents (who evidently kept her in good order) to obtain this or that article of dress, more especially the white "Paduasoy." He cared nothing how she was dressed; she was always lovely enough for him, as he took pains to assure her when she begged him to express in his answers a predilection for particular pieces of finery, in order that she might show what he said to her parents. But at length he seemed to find out that she would not be married till she had a "trousseau" to her mind; and then he sent her a letter, which had evidently accompanied a whole box full of finery, and in which he requested that she might be dressed in everything her heart desired. This was the first letter ticketed in a frail, delicate hand, "From my dearest John." Shortly afterwards they were married,—I suppose, from the intermission in their correspondence.

"We must burn them, I think," said Miss Matty, looking doubtfully at me. "No one will care for them when I am gone." And one by one she dropped them into the middle of the fire; watching each blaze up, die out, and rise away, in faint, white, ghostly semblance, up the chimney, before she gave another to the same fate. The room was light enough now; but I, like her, was fascinated into watching the destruction of those letters, into which the honest warmth of a manly heart had been poured forth.

The next letter, likewise docketed by Miss Jenkyns, was endorsed, "Letter of pious congratulation and exhortation from my venerable grandfather to my beloved mother, on occasion of my own birth. Also some practical remarks on the desirability of keeping warm the extremities of infants, from my excellent grandmother."

The first part was, indeed, a severe and forcible picture of the responsibilities of mothers, and a warning against the evils that were in the world, and lying in ghastly wait for the little baby of two days old. His wife did not write, said the old gentleman, because he had forbidden it, she being indisposed with a sprained ankle, which (he said) quite incapacitated her from holding a pen. However, at the foot of the page was a small "T.O.," and on turning it over, sure enough, there was a letter to "my dear, dearest Molly," begging her, when she left her room, whatever she did, to go *up* stairs before going *down*: and telling her to wrap her baby's feet up in flannel, and keep it warm by the fire, although it was summer, for babies were so tender.

It was pretty to see from the letters, which were evidently exchanged with some frequency, between the young mother and the grandmother, how the girlish vanity was being weeded out of her heart by love for her baby. The white "Paduasoy" figured again in the letters, with almost as much vigor as before. In one, it was being made into a christening cloak for the baby. It decked it when it went with its parents to spend a day or two at Arley Hall. It added to its charms when it was "the prettiest little baby that ever was seen. Dear mother, I wish you could see her! Without any parshality, I do think she will grow up a regular bewty!" I thought of Miss Jenkyns, grey, withered, and wrinkled; and I wondered if her mother had known her in the courts of heaven; and then I knew that she had, and that they stood there in angelic guise.

There was a great gap before any of the Rector's letters appeared. And then his wife had changed her mode of endorsement. It was no longer from "My dearest John"; it was from "My honoured Husband." The letters were written on the occasion of the publication of the same Sermon which was represented in the picture. The preaching before "My Lord Judge," and the "publishing by request," was evidently the culminating point—the event of his life. It had been necessary for him to go up to London to superintend it through the press. Many friends had to be called upon, and consulted, before he could decide on any printer fit for so onerous a task; and at length it was arranged that J. & J. Rivingtons were to have the honourable responsibility. The worthy Rector seemed to be strung up by the occasion to a high literary pitch, for he could hardly write a letter to his wife without cropping out into Latin. I remember the end of one of his letters ran thus: "I shall ever hold the virtuous qualities of my Molly in remembrance, *dum memor ipse mei, dum spiritus regit artus,*" which, considering that the English of his correspondent was sometimes at fault in grammar, and often in spelling, might be taken as a proof of how much he "idealised his Molly"; and, as Miss Jenkyns used to say, "People talk a great deal about idealising now-a-days, whatever that may mean." But this was nothing to a fit of writing classical poetry, which soon seized him; in which his Molly figured away as "Maria." The letter containing the *carmen* was endorsed by her, "Hebrew verses sent me by my honoured husband. I thowt to have had a letter about killing the pig, but must wait. Mem., to send the poetry to Sir Peter Arley, as my husband desires." And in a post-scriptum note in his handwriting, it was stated that the Ode had appeared in the *Gentleman's Magazine,* December, 1782.

Her letters back to her husband (treasured as fondly by him as if they had been *M. T. Ciceronis Epistolæ*) were more satisfactory to an absent husband and father than his could ever have been to her. She told him how Deborah sewed her seam very neatly every day, and read to her in the books he had set her; how she was a very "forrard" good child, but *would* ask questions her mother could not answer; but how she did not let herself down by saying she did not know, but took to stirring the fire, or sending the "forrard" child on an errand. Matty was now the mother's darling, and promised (like her sister at her age) to be a greaty beauty. I was reading this aloud to Miss Matty, who smiled and sighed a little at the hope, so fondly expressed, that "little Matty might not be vain, even if she were a bewty."

"I had very pretty hair, my dear," said Miss Matilda; "and not a bad mouth." And I saw her soon afterwards adjust her cap and draw herself up.

But to return to Mrs. Jenkyns's letters. She told her husband about the poor in the parish; what homely domestic medicines she had administered; what kitchen physic she had sent. She had evidently held his displeasure as a rod in pickle over the heads of all the ne'er-do-wells. She asked for his directions about the cows and pigs; and did not always obtain them, as I have shown before.

The kind old grandmother was dead when a little boy was born, soon after the publication of the Sermon; but there was another letter of exhortation from the grandfather, more stringent and admonitory than ever, now that there was a boy to be guarded from the snares of the world. He described all the various sins into which men might fall, until I wondered how any man ever came to a natural death. The gallows seemed as if it must have been the termination of the lives of most of the grandfather's friends and acquaintance; and I was not surprised at the way in which he spoke of this life being "a vale of tears."

It seemed curious that I should never have heard of this brother before; but I concluded that he had died young; or else surely his name would have been alluded to by his sisters.

By-and-by we came to   packets of Miss Jenkyns's letters. These, Miss Matty did regret to burn. She said all the others had been only interesting to those who loved the writers; and that it seemed as if it would have hurt her to allow them to fall into the hands of strangers, who had not known her dear mother, and how good she was, although she did not always spell quite in the modern fashion; but Deborah's letters were so very superior! Anyone might profit by reading them. It was a long time since she had read Mrs. Chapone, but she knew she used to think that Deborah could have said the same things quite as well; and as for Mrs. Carter! people thought a deal of her letters, just because she had written *Epictetus;* but she was quite sure Deborah would never have made use of such a common expression as "I canna be fashed!"

Miss Matty did grudge burning these letters, it was evident. She would not let them be carelessly passed over with any quiet reading, and skipping, to myself. She took them from me, and even lighted the second candle, in order to read them aloud with a proper emphasis, and without stumbling over the big words. Oh, dear! how I wanted facts instead of reflections, before those letters were concluded! They lasted us two nights; and I won't deny that I made use of the time to think of many other things, and yet I was always at my post at the end of each sentence.

The Rector's letters, and those of his wife and mother-in-law, had all been tolerably short and pithy, written in a straight hand, with the lines very close together. Sometimes the whole letter was contained on a mere scrap of paper. The paper was very yellow, and the ink very brown; some of the sheets were (as Miss Matty made me observe) the old original Post, with the stamp in the corner, representing a postboy riding for life and twanging his horn. The letters of Mrs. Jenkyns and her mother were fastened with a great round red wafer; for it was before Miss Edgeworth's "Patronage" had banished wafers from polite society. It was evident, from the tenor of what was said, that franks were in great request, and were even used as a means of paying debts by needy Members of Parliament. The Rector sealed his epistles with an immense coat of arms, and showed by the care with which he had performed this ceremony that he expected they should be cut open, not broken by any thoughtless or impatient hand. Now, Miss Jenkyns's letters were of a later date in form and writing. She wrote on the square sheet, which we have learned to call old-fashioned. Her hand was admirably calculated, together with her use of many-syllabled words, to fill up a sheet, and then came the pride and delight of crossing. Poor Miss Matty got sadly puzzled with this, for the words gathered size like snow-balls, and towards the end of her letter Miss Jenkyns used to become quite sesquipedalian. In one to her father, slightly theological and controversial in its tone, she had spoken of Herod, Tetrarch of Idumea. Miss Matty read it "Herod Petrarch of Etruria," and was just as well pleased as if she had been right.

I can't quite remember the date, but I think it was in 1805 that Miss Jenkyns wrote the longest series of letters; on occasion of her absence on a visit to some friends near Newcastle-upon-Tyne. These friends were intimate with the commandant of the garrison there, and heard from him of all the preparations that were being made to repel the invasion of Buonaparte, which some people imagined might take place at the mouth of the Tyne. Miss Jenkyns was evidently very much alarmed; and the first part of her letters was often written in pretty intelligible English, conveying particulars of the preparations which were made in the family with whom she was residing against the dreaded event; the bundles of clothes that were packed up ready for a flight to Alston Moor (a wild hilly piece of ground between Northumberland and Cumberland); the signal that was to be given for this flight, and for the simultaneous turning out of the volunteers under arms; which said signal was to consist (if I remember rightly) in ringing the church bells in a particular and ominous manner. One day, when Miss Jenkyns and her hosts were at a dinner-party in Newcastle, this warning summons was actually given (not a very wise proceeding, if there be any truth in the moral attached to the fable of the Boy and the Wolf; but so it was), and Miss Jenkyns, hardly recovered from her fright, wrote the next day to describe the sound, the breathless shock, the hurry and alarm; and then, taking breath, she added, "How trivial, my dear father, do all our apprehensions of the last evening appear, at the present moment, to calm and inquiring minds!" And here Miss Matty broke in with—

"But, indeed, my dear, they were not at all trivial or trifling at the time. I know I used to wake up in the night many a time, and think I heard the tramp of the French entering Cranford. Many people talked of hiding themselves in the salt-mines; and meat would have kept capitally down there, only perhaps we should have been thirsty. And my father preached a whole set of sermons on the occasion; one set in the mornings, all about David and Goliath, to spirit up the people to fighting with spades or bricks, if need were; and the other set in the afternoons, proving that Napoleon (that was another name for Bony, as we used to call him) was all the same as an Apollyon and Abaddon. I remember my father rather thought he should be asked to print this last set; but the parish had, perhaps, had enough of them with hearing."

Peter Marmaduke Arley Jenkyns ("poor Peter!" as Miss Matty began to call him) was at school at Shrewsbury by this time. The Rector took up his pen, and rubbed up his Latin, once more, to correspond with his boy. It was very clear that the lad's were what are called show-letters. They were of a highly mental description, giving an account of his studies, and his intellectual hopes of various kinds, with an occasional quotation from the classics; but, now and then, the animal nature broke out in such a little sentence as this, evidently written in a trembling hurry, after the letter had been inspected: "Mother, dear, do send me a cake, and put plenty of citron in." The "mother, dear," probably answered her boy in the form of cakes and "goody," for there were none of her letters among this set; but a whole collection of the Rector's, to whom the Latin in his boy's letters was like a trumpet to the old war-horse. I do not know much about Latin, certainly, and it is, perhaps, an ornamental language; but not very useful, I think—at least to judge from the bits I remember out of the Rector's letters. One was: "You have not got that town in your map of Ireland: but *Bonus Bernardus non videt omnia,* as the Proverbia say." Presently it became very evident that "poor Peter" got himself into many scrapes. There were letters of stilted penitence to his father, for some wrongdoing; and, among them all, was a badly-written, badly-sealed, badly-directed, blotted note—"My dear, dear, dear, dearest mother, I will be a better boy—I will, indeed; but don't, please, be ill for me; I am not worth it; but I will be good, darling mother."

Miss Matty could not speak for crying, after she had read this note. She gave it to me in silence, and then got up and took it to her sacred recesses in her own room, for fear, by any chance, it might get burnt. "Poor Peter!" she said; "he was always in scrapes; he was too easy. They led him wrong, and then left him in the lurch. But he was too fond of mischief. He could never resist a joke. Poor Peter!"

[From *Cranford*]

William Makepeace Thackeray

I feel very badly about not finding a proper bit of Thackeray's prose. The great passages from the great novels come out all ragged; his innumerable journalistic miscellanies do not show him at his best. I thought I would include his Rolandseck, *which is better than most; but on the whole, no.*

THE SORROWS OF WERTHER

Werther had a love for Charlotte
     Such as words could never utter;
Would you know how first he met her?
     She was cutting bread and butter.

Charlotte was a married lady,
     And a moral man was Werther,
And for all the wealth of Indies
     Would do nothing for to hurt her.

So he sigh'd and pined and ogled,
     And his passion boil'd and bubbled,
Till he blew his silly brains out,
     And no more was by it troubled.

Charlotte, having seen his body
     Borne before her on a shutter,
Like a well-conducted person,
     Went on cutting bread and butter.

THE LAMENTABLE BALLAD OF THE FOUNDLING OF SHOREDITCH
(Based on a News Report in *The Times* of February 14, 1850)

Come, all ye Christian people, and listen to my tail,
It is all about a doctor was travelling by the rail,
By the Heastern Counties Railway (vich the shares I don't desire)
From Ixworth town in Suffolk, vich his name did not transpire.

A travelling from Bury this Doctor was employed
With a gentleman, a friend of his, vich his name was Captain Loyd;
And on reaching Marks Tey Station, that is next beyond Colchest-
er, a lady entered into them most elegantly dressed.

She entered into the Carriage all with a tottering step,
And a pooty little Bayby upon her bussum slep;
The gentlemen received her with kindness and siwillaty,
Pitying this lady for her illness and debillaty.

She had a fust class ticket, this lovely lady said,
Because it was so lonesome she took a secknd instead.
Better to travel by secknd class, than sit alone in the fust,
And the pooty little Baby upon her breast she nust.

A seein of her cryin, and shiverin and pail,
To her spoke this young surging, the Ero of my tail;
Saysee you look unwell, Ma'am, I'll elp you if I can,
And you may tell your case to me, for I'm a meddicle man.

"Thank you, Sir," the lady said, "I ony look so pale
Because I ain't accustom'd to travelling on the Rale;
I shall be better presnly, when I've ad some rest":
And that pooty little Baby she squeeged it to her breast.

So in conwersation the journey they beguiled,
Capting Loyd and the medical man, and the lady and the child,
Till the warious stations along the line was passed,
For even the Heastern Counties' trains must come in at last.

When at Shoreditch tumminus at lenth stopped the train,
This kind meddicle gentleman proposed his aid again.
"Thank you, Sir," the lady said, "for your kyindness dear;
My carridge and my osses is probbibly come here.

"Will you old this baby, please, vilst I step and see?"
The Doctor was a famly man: "That I will," says he.
Then the little child she kist, kist it very gently,
Vich was sucking his little fist, sleeping innocently.

With a sigh from her art, as though she would have bust it,
Then she gave the Doctor the child—wery kind he nust it:
Hup then the lady jumped hoff the bench she sate from,
Tumbled down the carridge steps and ran along the platform.

Vile hall the other passengers vent upon their vays,
The Capting and the Doctor sate there in a maze;
Some vent in a Homminibus, some vent in a Cabby,
The Capting and the Doctor vaited vith the babby.

There they sate looking queer, for an hour or more,
But their feller passinger neather on 'em sore:
Never, never, back again did that lady come
To that pooty sleeping Hinfnt a suckin of his Thum!

What could this pore Doctor do, bein treated thus,
When the darling Baby woke, cryin for its nuss?
Off he drove to a female friend, vich she was both kind and mild,
And igsplained to her the circumstance of this year little child.

That kind lady took the child instantly in her lap.
And made it very comforable by giving it some pap;
And when she took its close off, what d'you think she found
A couple of ten pun notes sewn up, in its little gownd!

Also in its little close, was a note which did conwey,
That this little baby's parents lived in a handsome way:
And for its Headucation they reglarly would pay,
And sirtingly like gentlefolks would claim the child one day,
If the Christian people who'd charge of it would say,
Per adwertisement in the *Times,* where the baby lay.

Pity of this bayby many people took,
It had such pooty ways and such a pooty look;
And there came a lady forrard (I wish that I could see
Any kind lady as would do as much for me;

And I wish with all my art, some night in *my* night gownd,
I could find a note stitched for ten or twenty pound)—
There came a lady forrard, that most honourable did say,
She'd adopt this little baby, which her parents cast away.

While the Doctor pondered on this hoffer fair,
Comes a letter from Devonshire, from a party there,
Hordering the Doctor, at its Mar's desire,
To send the little Infant back to Devonshire.

Lost in apoplexity, this pore meddicle man,
Like a sensable gentleman, to the Justice ran;
Which his name was Mr. Hammill, a honorable beak,
That takes his seat in Worship Street four times a week.

"O Justice!" says the Doctor, "instrugt me what to do,
I've come up from the country, to throw myself on you;
My patients have no doctor to tend them in their ills
(There they are in Suffolk without their draffts and pills!).

"I've come up from the country, to know how I'll dispose
Of this pore little baby, and the twenty pun note, and the clothes,
And I want to go back to Suffolk, dear Justice, if you please,
And my patients wants their Doctor, and their Doctor wants his feez."

Up spoke Mr. Hammill, sittin at his desk,
"This year application does me much perplesk;
What I do adwise you, is to leave this babby
In the Parish where it was left, by its mother shabby."

The Doctor from his Worship sadly did depart—
He might have left the baby, but he hadn't got the heart,
To go for to leave that Hinnocent, has the law allows,
To the tender mussies of the Union House.

Mother, who left this little one on a stranger's knee,
Think how cruel you have been, and how good was he!
Think, if you've been guilty, innocent was she;
And do not take unkindly this little word of me:
Heaven be merciful to us all, sinners as we be!

POLICEMAN X

Charles Dickens

MR. MANTALINI VISITS RALPH NICKLEBY

"What a demnition long time you have kept me ringing at this confounded old cracked tea-kettle of a bell, every tinkle of which is enough to throw a strong man into blue convulsions, upon my life and soul, oh demmit," said Mr. Mantalini to Newman Noggs, scraping his boots, as he spoke, on Ralph Nickleby's scraper.

"I didn't hear the bell more than once," replied Newman.

"Then you are most immensely and outr*i*geously deaf," said Mr. Mantalini, "as deaf as a demnition post."

Mr. Mantalini had got by this time into the passage, and was making his way to the door of Ralph's office with very little ceremony, when Newman interposed his body; and hinting that Mr. Nickleby was unwilling to be disturbed, inquired whether the client's business was of a pressing nature.

"It is most demnebly particular," said Mr. Mantalini. "It is to melt some scraps of dirty paper into bright, shining, chinking, tinkling, demd mint sauce."

Newman uttered a significant grunt, and taking Mr. Mantalini's proffered card, limped with it into his master's office. As he thrust his head in at the door, he saw that Ralph had resumed the thoughtful posture into which he had fallen after perusing his nephew's letter, and that he seemed to have been reading it again, as he once more held it open in his hand. The glance was but momentary, for Ralph, being disturbed, turned to demand the cause of the interruption.

As Newman stated it, the cause himself swaggered into the room, and grasping Ralph's horny hand with uncommon affection, vowed that he had never seen him looking so well in all his life.

"There is quite a bloom upon your demd countenance," said Mr. Mantalini, seating himself unbidden, and arranging his hair and whiskers. "You look quite juvenile and jolly, demmit!"

"We are alone," returned Ralph, tartly. "What did you want with me?"

"Good!" cried Mr. Mantalini, displaying his teeth. "What did I want! Yes. Ha, ha! Very good. *What* did I want. Ha, ha. Oh dem!"

"What *do* you want, man?" demanded Ralph, sternly.

"Demnition discount," returned Mr. Mantalini, with a grin, and shaking his head waggishly.

"Money is scarce," said Ralph.

"Demd scarce, or I shouldn't want it," interrupted Mr. Mantalini.

"The times are bad, and one scarcely knows whom to trust," continued Ralph. "I don't want to do business just now, in fact I would rather not; but as you are a friend—how many bills have you there?"

"Two," returned Mr. Mantalini.

"What is the gross amount?"

"Demd trifling—five-and-seventy."

"And the dates?"

"Two months, and four."

"I'll do them for you—mind, for *you;* I wouldn't for many people—for five-and-twenty-pounds," said Ralph deliberately.

"Oh, demmit!" cried Mr. Mantalini, whose face lengthened considerably at this handsome proposal.

"Why, that leaves you fifty," retorted Ralph. "What would you have? Let me see the names."

"You are so demd hard, Nickleby," remonstrated Mr. Mantalini.

"Let me see the names," replied Ralph, impatiently extending his hand for the bills. "Well! They are not sure, but they are safe enough. Do you consent to the terms, and will you take the money? I don't want you to do so. I would rather you didn't."

"Demmit, Nickleby, can't you—" began Mr. Mantalini.

"No," replied Ralph, interrupting him. "I can't. Will you take the money—down, mind; no delay, no going into the City and pretending to negotiate with some other party who has no existence, and never had. Is it a bargain, or is it not?"

Ralph pushed some papers from him as he spoke, and carelessly rattled his cash-box, as though by mere accident. The sound was too much for Mr. Mantalini. He closed the bargain directly it reached his ears, and Ralph told the money out upon the table.

He had scarcely done so, and Mr. Mantalini had not yet gathered it all up, when a ring was heard at the bell, and immediately afterwards Newman ushered in no less a person than Madame Mantalini, at sight of whom Mr. Mantalini evinced considerable discomposure, and swept the cash into his pocket with remarkable alacrity.

"Oh, you *are* here," said Madame Mantalini, tossing her head.

"Yes, my life and soul, I am," replied her husband, dropping on his knees, and pouncing with kitten-like playfulness upon a stray sovereign. "I am here, my soul's delight, upon Tom Tidler's ground, picking up the demnition gold and silver."

"I am ashamed of you," said Madame Mantalini, with much indignation.

"Ashamed—of *me,* my joy? It knows it is talking demd charming sweetness, but naughty fibs," returned Mr. Mantalini. "It knows it is not ashamed of its own popolorum tibby."

Whatever were the circumstances which had led to such a result, it certainly appeared as though the popolorum tibby had rather miscalculated, for the nonce, the extent of his lady's affection. Madame Mantalini only looked scornful in reply; and, turning to Ralph, begged him to excuse her intrusion.

"Which is entirely attributable," said Madame, "to the gross misconduct and most improper behaviour of Mr. Mantalini."

"Of me, my essential juice of pine-apple?"

"Of you," returned his wife. "But I will not allow it. I will not submit to be ruined by the extravagance and profligacy of any man. I call Mr. Nickleby to witness the course I intend to pursue with you."

"Pray don't call me to witness anything, ma'am," said Ralph. "Settle it between yourselves, settle it between yourselves."

"No, but I must beg you as a favour," said Madame Mantalini, "to hear me give him notice of what it is my fixed intention to do—my fixed intention, sir," repeated Madame Mantalini, darting an angry look at her husband.

"Will she call me 'Sir?'" cried Mantalini. "Me who dote upon her with the demdest ardour! She, who coils her fascinations round me like a pure angelic rattlesnake! It will be all up with my feelings; she will throw me into a demd state."

"Don't talk of feelings, sir," rejoined Madame Mantalini, seating herself, and turning her back upon him. "You don't consider mine."

"I do not consider yours, my soul!" exclaimed Mr. Mantalini.

"No," replied his wife.

And notwithstanding various blandishments on the part of Mr. Mantalini, Madame Mantalini still said no, and said it too with such determination and resolute ill-temper, that Mr. Mantalini was clearly taken aback.

"His extravagance, Mr. Nickleby," said Madame Mantalini, addressing herself to Ralph, who leant against his easy-chair with his hands behind him, and regarded the amiable couple with a smile of the supremest and most unmitigated contempt,—"his extravagance is beyond all bounds."

"I should scarcely have supposed it," answered Ralph, sarcastically.

"I assure you, Mr. Nickleby, however, that it is," returned Madame Mantalini. "It makes me miserable! I am under constant apprehensions, and in constant difficulty. And even this," said Madame Mantalini, wiping her eyes, "is not the worst. He took some papers of value out of my desk this morning without asking my permission."

Mr. Mantalini groaned slightly, and buttoned his trousers pocket.

"I am obliged," continued Madame Mantalini, "since our late misfortunes, to pay Miss Knag a great deal of money for having her name in the business, and I really cannot afford to encourage him in all his wastefulness. As I have no doubt that he came straight here, Mr. Nickelby, to convert the papers I have spoken of, into money, and as you have assisted us very often before, and are very much connected with us in this kind of matters, I wish you to know the determination at which his conduct has compelled me to arrive."

Mr. Mantalini groaned once more from behind his wife's bonnet, and fitting a sovereign into one of his eyes, winked with the other at Ralph. Having achieved this performance with great dexterity, he whipped the coin into his pocket, and groaned again with increased penitence.

"I have made up my mind," said Madame Mantalini, as tokens of impatience manifested themselves in Ralph's countenance, "to allowance him."

"To do what, my joy?" inquired Mr. Mantalini, who did not seem to have caught the words.

"To put him," said Madame Mantalini, looking at Ralph, and prudently abstaining from the slightest glance at her husband, lest his many graces should induce her to falter in her resolution, "to put him upon a fixed allowance; and I say that if he has a hundred and twenty pounds a year for his clothes and pocket-money, he may consider himself a very fortunate man."

Mr. Mantalini waited, with much decorum, to hear the amount of the proposed stipend, but when it reached his ears, he cast his hat and cane upon the floor, and drawing out his pocket-handkerchief, gave vent to his feelings in a dismal moan.

"Demnition!" cried Mr. Mantalini, suddenly skipping out of his chair, and as suddenly skipping into it again, to the great discomposure of his lady's nerves. "But no. It is a demd horrid dream. It is not reality. No!"

Comforting himself with this assurance, Mr. Mantalini closed his eyes and waited patiently till such time as he should wake up.

"A very judicious arrangement," observed Ralph, with a sneer, "if your husband will keep within it, ma'am—as no doubt he will."

"Demmit!" exclaimed Mr. Mantalini, opening his eyes at the sound of Ralph's voice, "it is a horrid reality. She is sitting there before me. There is the graceful outline of her form; it cannot be mistaken— there is nothing like it. The two countesses had no outlines at all, and the dowager's was a demd outline. Why is she so excruciatingly beautiful that I cannot be angry with her, even now?"

"You have brought it upon yourself, Alfred," returned Madame Mantalini—still reproachfully, but in a softened tone.

"I am a demd villain!" cried Mr. Mantalini, smiting himself on the head. "I will fill my pockets with change for a sovereign in halfpence and drown myself in the Thames; but I will not be angry with her, even then, for I will put a note in the twopenny-post as I go along, to tell her where the body is. She will be a lovely widow. I shall be a body. Some handsome women will cry; she will laugh demnebly."

"Alfred, you cruel, cruel creature," said Madame Mantalini, sobbing at the dreadful picture.

"She calls me cruel—me—me—who for her sake will become a demd, damp, moist, unpleasant body!" exclaimed Mr. Mantalini.

"You know it almost breaks my heart, even to hear you talk of such a thing," replied Madame Mantalini.

"Can I live to be mistrusted?" cried her husband. "Have I cut my heart into a demd extraordinary number of little pieces, and given them all away, one after another, to the same little engrossing demnition captivater, and can I live to be suspected by her? Demmit, no I can't."

"Ask Mr. Nickleby whether the sum I have mentioned is not a proper one," reasoned Madame Mantalini.

"I don't want any sum," replied her disconsolate husband; "I shall require no demd allowance. I will be a body."

On this repetition of Mr. Mantalini's fatal threat, Madame Mantalini wrung her hands, and implored the interference of Ralph Nickleby; and after a great quantity of tears and talking, and several attempts on the part of Mr. Mantalini to reach the door, preparatory to straightway committing violence upon himself, that gentleman was prevailed upon, with difficulty, to promise that he wouldn't be a body. This great point attained, Madame Mantalini argued the question of the allowance, and Mr. Mantalini did the same, taking occasion to show that he could live with uncommon satisfaction upon bread and water, and go clad in rags, but that he could not support existence with the additional burden of being mistrusted by the object of his most devoted and disinterested affection. This brought fresh tears into Madame Mantalini's eyes, which having just begun to open to some few of the demerits of Mr. Mantalini, were only open a very little way, and could be easily closed again. The result was, that without quite giving up the allowance question, Madame Mantalini postponed its further consideration; and Ralph saw, clearly enough, that Mr. Mantalini had gained a fresh lease of his easy life, and that, for some time longer at all events, his degradation and downfall were postponed.

[From *Nicholas Nickleby*]

MR. CHADBAND ON TEREWTH

[Mr. Chadband is a layman, an amateur of righteousness, who preaches in parlors. Dickens indicates his pious unction with a lot of talk about the Oil Trade. Mrs. Snagsby admires and feeds him devoutly. Jo is a crossing-sweeper whom Mr. Snagsby has befriended; Mrs. Snagsby suspects he is her husband's son. Guster is Augusta, the servant.]

Tomorrow comes, the savoury preparations for the Oil Trade come, the evening comes. Comes, Mr. Snagsby in his black coat; come, the Chadbands; come (when the gorging vessel is replete), the 'prentices and Guster, to be edified; comes, at last, with his slouching head, and his shuffle backward, and his shuffle forward, and his shuffle to the right, and his shuffle to the left, and his bit of fur cap in his muddy hand, which he picks as if it were some mangy bird he had caught, and was plucking before eating raw, Jo, the very, very tough subject Mr. Chadband is to improve.

Mrs. Snagsby screws a watchful glance on Jo as he is brought into the little drawing-room by Guster. He looks at Mr. Snagsby the moment he comes in. Aha! Why does he look at Mr. Snagsby? Mr. Snagsby looks at him. Why should he do that, but that Mrs. Snagsby sees it all? Why else should that look pass between them, why else should Mr. Snagsby be confused, and cough a signal cough behind his hand? It is as clear as crystal that Mr. Snagsby is that boy's father.

"Peace, my friends!" says Chadband, rising and wiping the oily exudations from his reverend visage. "Peace be with us! My friends, why with us? Because," with his fat smile, "it cannot be against us, because it must be for us; because it is not hardening, because it is softening; because it does not make war like the hawk, but comes home unto us like the dove. Therefore, my friends, peace be with us! My human boy, come forward!"

Stretching forth his flabby paw, Mr. Chadband lays the same on Jo's arm, and considers where to station him. Jo, very doubtful of his reverend friend's intentions, and not at all clear but that something practical and painful is going to be done to him, mutters, "You let me alone. I never said nothink to you. You let me alone."

"No, my young friend," says Chadband smoothly, "I will not let you alone. And why? Because I am a harvest labourer, because I am a toiler and a moiler, because you are delivered over untoe me, and are become as a precious instrument in my hands. My friends, may I so employ this instrument as to use it toe your advantage, toe your profit, toe your gain, toe your welfare, toe your enrichment! My young friend, sit upon this stool."

Jo, apparently possessed with an impression that the reverend gentleman wants to cut his hair, shields his head with both arms, and is got into the required position with great difficulty, and every possible manifestation of reluctance.

When he is at last adjusted like a lay-figure, Mr. Chadband, retiring behind the table, holds up his bear's paw, and says, "My friends!" This is the signal for a general settlement of the audience. The 'prentices giggle internally, and nudge each other. Guster falls into a staring

and vacant state, compounded of a stunned admiration of Mr. Chadband and pity for the friendless outcast whose condition touches her
nearly. Mrs. Snagsby silently lays trains of gunpowder. Mrs. Chadband
composes herself grimly by the fire, and warms her knees: finding that
sensation favourable to the reception of eloquence.

It happens that Mr. Chadband has a pulpit habit of fixing some
member of his congregation with his eye, and fatly arguing his points
with that particular person; who is understood to be expected to be
moved to an occasional grunt, groan, gasp, or other audible expression

of inward working; which expression of inward working, being echoed
by some elderly lady in the next pew, and so communicated, like a
game of forfeits, through a circle of the more fermentable sinners
present, serves the purpose of parliamentary cheering, and gets Mr.
Chadband's steam up. From mere force of habit, Mr. Chadband, in
saying "My friends!" has rested his eye on Mr. Snagsby; and proceeds
to make that ill-starred stationer, already sufficiently confused, the
immediate recipient of his discourse.

"We have here among us, my friends," says Chadband, "a Gentile
and a Heathen, a dweller in the tents of Tom-all-Alone's, and a
mover-on upon the surface of the earth. We have here among us, my
friends,"—and Mr. Chadband, untwisting the point with his dirty
thumb-nail, bestows an oily smile on Mr. Snagsby, signifying that he

will throw him an argumentative back-fall presently, if he be not already down,—"a brother and a boy. Devoid of parents, devoid of relations, devoid of flocks and herds, devoid of gold and silver, and of precious stones. Now, my friends, why do I say he is devoid of these possessions? Why? Why is he?" Mr. Chadband states the question as if he were propounding an entirely new riddle, of much ingenuity and merit, to Mr. Snagsby, and entreating him not to give it up.

Mr. Snagsby, greatly perplexed by the mysterious look he received just now from his little woman—at about the period when Mr. Chadband mentioned the word parents—is tempted into modestly remarking, "I don't know, I'm sure, sir." On which interruption, Mrs. Chadband glares, and Mrs. Snagsby says, "For shame!"

"I hear a voice," says Chadband; "is it a still small voice, my friends? I fear not, though I fain would hope so—"

("Ah—h!" from Mrs. Snagsby.)

"Which says, I don't know. Then I will tell you why. I say this brother, present here among us, is devoid of parents, devoid of relations, devoid of flocks and herds, devoid of gold, of silver, and of precious stones, because he is devoid of the light that shines in upon some of us. What is that light? What is it? I ask you what is that light?"

Mr. Chadband draws back his head and pauses, but Mr. Snagsby is not to be lured on to his destruction again. Mr. Chadband, leaning forward over the table, pierces what he has got to follow, directly into Mr. Snagsby, with the thumb-nail already mentioned.

"It is," says Chadband, "the ray of rays, the sun of suns, the moon of moons, the star of stars. It is the light of Terewth."

Mr. Chadband draws himself up again, and looks triumphantly at Mr. Snagsby, as if he would be glad to know how he feels after that.

"Of Terewth," says Mr. Chadband, hitting him again. "Say not to me that it is *not* the lamp of lamps. I say to you, it is. I say to you, a million of times over, it is. It is! I say to you that I will proclaim it to you, whether you like it or not; nay, that the less you like it, the more I will proclaim it to you. With a speaking-trumpet! I say to you that, if you rear yourself against it, you shall fall, you shall be bruised, you shall be battered, you shall be flawed, you shall be smashed!"

The present effect of this flight of oratory—much admired for its general power by Mr. Chadband's followers—being not only to make

Mr. Chadband unpleasantly warm, but to represent the innocent Mr. Snagsby in the light of a determined enemy to virtue, with a forehead of brass and a heart of adamant, that unfortunate tradesman becomes yet more disconcerted; and is in a very advanced state of low spirits and false position, when Mr. Chadband accidentally finishes him.

"My friends," he resumes, after dabbing his fat head for some time—and it smokes to such an extent that he seems to light his pocket-handkerchief at it, which smokes, too, after every dab—"to pursue the subject we are endeavouring with our lowly gifts to improve, let us in a spirit of love inquire what is that Terewth to which I have alluded. For, my young friends," suddenly addressing the 'prentices and Guster, to their consternation, "if I am told by the doctor that calomel or castor oil is good for me, I may naturally ask what is calomel, and what is castor oil. I may wish to be informed of that, before I dose myself with either or with both. Now, my young friends, what is this Terewth, then? Firstly, (in a spirit of love) what is the common sort of Terewth—the working clothes—the everyday wear, my young friends? Is it deception?"

("Ah—h!" from Mrs. Snagsby.)

"Is it suppression?"

(A shiver in the negative from Mrs. Snagsby.)

"Is it reservation?"

(A shake of the head from Mrs. Snagsby—very long and very tight.)

"No, my friends, it is neither of these. Neither of these names belongs to it. When this young Heathen now among us—who is now, my friends, asleep, the seal of indifference and perdition being set upon his eyelids; but do not wake him, for it is right that I should have to wrestle, and to combat, and to struggle, and to conquer, for his sake—when this young hardened Heathen told us a story of a Cock, and of a Bull, and of a lady, and of a sovereign, was *that* the Terewth? No. Or, if it was partly, was it wholly, and entirely? No, my friends, no!"

If Mr. Snagsby could withstand his little woman's look, as it enters at his eyes, the windows of his soul, and searches the whole tenement, he were other than the man he is. He cowers and droops.

"Or, my juvenile friends," says Chadband, descending to the level of their comprehension, with a very obtrusive demonstration, in his greasily meek smile, of coming a long way downstairs for the purpose, "if the master of this house was to go forth into the city, and there see an eel, and was to come back, and was to call untoe him the mistress of this house, and was to say, 'Sarah, rejoice with me, for I have seen an elephant!' would *that* be Terewth?"

Mrs. Snagsby in tears.

"Or put it, my juvenile friends, that he saw an elephant, and returning said, 'Lo, the city is barren, I have seen but an eel,' would *that* be Terewth?"

Mrs. Snagsby sobbing loudly.

"Or put it, my juvenile friends," says Chadband, stimulated by the sound, "that the unnatural parents of this slumbering Heathen—for parents he had, my juvenile friends, beyond a doubt—after casting him forth to the wolves and the vultures, and the wild dogs and the young gazelles, and the serpents, went back to their dwellings, and had their pipes, and their pots, and their flutings and their dancings, and their malt liquors, and their butcher's meat and poultry, would *that* be Terewth?"

Mrs. Snagsby replies by delivering herself a prey to spasms; not an unresisting prey, but a crying and a tearing one, so that Cook's Court re-echoes with her shrieks. Finally, becoming cataleptic, she has to be carried up the narrow staircase like a grand piano. After unspeakable suffering, productive of the utmost consternation, she is pronounced, by expresses from the bedroom, free from pain, though much exhausted; in which state of affairs Mr. Snagsby, trampled and crushed in the piano-forte removal, and extremely timid and feeble, ventures to come out from behind the door in the drawing-room.

All this time Jo has been standing on the spot where he woke up, ever picking his cap, and putting bits of fur in his mouth. He spits them out with a remorseful air, for he feels that it is in his nature to be an unimprovable reprobate, and that it's no good *his* trying to keep awake, for *he* won't never know nothink. Though it may be, Jo, that there is a history so interesting and affecting even to minds as near the brutes as thine, recording deeds done on this earth for common men, that if the Chadbands, removing their own persons from the light, would but show it thee in simple reverence, would but leave it unimproved, would but regard it as being eloquent enough without their modest aid—it might hold thee awake, and thou might learn from it yet!

Jo never heard of any such book. Its compilers, and the Reverend

Chadband, are all one to him—except that he knows the Reverend Chadband, and would rather run away from him for an hour than hear him talk for five minutes. "It an't no good my waiting here no longer," thinks Jo. "Mr. Snagsby an't a-going to say nothink to me tonight." And down-stairs he shuffles.

[From *Bleak House*]

PODSNAPPERY

Mr. Podsnap was well to do, and stood very high in Mr. Podsnap's opinion. Beginning with a good inheritance, he had married a good inheritance, and had thriven exceedingly in the Marine Insurance way, and was quite satisfied. He never could make out why everybody was not quite satisfied, and he felt conscious that he set a brilliant social example in being particularly well satisfied with most things, and, above all other things, with himself.

Thus happily acquainted with his own merit and importance, Mr. Podsnap settled that whatever he put behind him he put out of existence. There was a dignified conclusiveness—not to add a great convenience—in this way of getting rid of disagreeables, which had done much towards establishing Mr. Podsnap in his lofty place in Mr. Podsnap's satisfaction. "I don't want to know about it; I don't choose to discuss it; I don't admit it!" Mr. Podsnap had even acquired a peculiar flourish of his right arm in often clearing the world of its most difficult problems, by sweeping them behind him (and consequently sheer away) with those words and a flushed face. For they affronted him.

Mr. Podsnap's world was not a very large world, morally; no, nor even geographically: seeing that, although his business was sustained upon commerce with other countries, he considered other countries, with that important reservation, a mistake, and of their manners and customs would conclusively observe, "Not English!" when, PRESTO! with a flourish of the arm, and a flush of the face, they were swept away. Elsewise, the world got up at eight, shaved close at a quarter past, breakfasted at nine, went to the City at ten, came home at half-past five, and dined at seven. Mr. Podsnap's notions of the Arts in their integrity might have been stated thus. Literature: large print, respectfully descriptive of getting up at eight, shaving close at a quarter past, breakfasting at nine, going to the City at ten, coming home at half-past five, and dining at seven. Painting and Sculpture: models and portraits representing Professors of getting up at eight, shaving close at a quarter past, breakfasting at nine, going to the City at ten, coming home at half-past five, and dining at seven. Music: a respectable performance (without variations) on stringed and wind instruments, sedately expressive of getting up at eight, shaving close at a quarter past, breakfasting at nine, going to the City at ten, coming home at half-past five, and dining at seven. Nothing else to be permitted to those same vagrants the Arts, on pain of excommunication. Nothing else To Be—anywhere!

As a so-eminently respectable man, Mr. Podsnap was sensible of its being required of him to take Providence under his protection. Consequently, he always knew exactly what Providence meant. Inferior and less respectable men might fall short of that mark, but Mr. Podsnap was always up to it. And it was very remarkable (and must have been very comfortable) that what Providence meant was invariably what Mr. Podsnap meant.

These may be said to have been the articles of a faith and school which the present chapter takes the liberty of calling, after its representative man, Podsnappery. They were confined within close bounds, as Mr. Podsnap's own head was confined by his shirt collar; and they were enunciated with a sounding pomp that smacked of the creaking of Mr. Podsnap's own boots.

There was a Miss Podsnap. And this young rocking-horse was being trained in her mother's art of prancing in a stately manner without ever getting on. But the high parental action was not yet imparted to her, and in truth she was but an undersized damsel, with high shoulders, low spirits, chilled elbows, and a rasped surface of nose, who seemed to take occasional frosty peeps out of childhood into womanhood, and to shrink back again, overcome by her mother's headdress and her father from head to foot—crushed by the mere dead weight of Podsnappery.

A certain institution in Mr. Podsnap's mind, which he called "the young person," may be considered to have been embodied in Miss Podsnap, his daughter. It was an inconvenient and exacting institution, as requiring everything in the universe to be filed down and fitted to it. The question about everything was, Would it bring a blush into the cheek of the young person? And the inconvenience of the young person was that, according to Mr. Podsnap, she seemed always liable to burst into blushes when there was no need at all. There appeared to be no line of demarcation between the young person's excessive innocence, and another person's guiltiest knowledge. Take Mr. Podsnap's word for it, and the soberest tints of drab, white, lilac, and grey were all flaming red to this troublesome Bull of a young person.

The Podsnaps lived in a shady angle adjoining Portman Square. They were a kind of people certain to dwell in the shade, wherever they dwelt. Miss Podsnap's life had been, from her first appearance on this planet, altogether of a shady order; for Mr. Podsnap's young person was likely to get little good out of association with other young persons, and had, therefore, been restricted to companionship with not very congenial older persons, and with massive furniture. Miss Podsnap's early views of life being principally derived from the reflections of it in her father's boots, and in the walnut and rosewood tables of the dim drawing-rooms, and in their swarthy giants of looking-glasses, were of a sombre cast; and it was not wonderful that now, when she was on most days solemnly tooled through the Park by the side of her mother in a great, tall, custard-coloured phaeton, she showed above the apron of that vehicle like a dejected young person sitting up in bed to take a startled look at things in general, and very strongly desiring to get her head under the counterpane again.

Said Mr. Podsnap to Mrs. Podsnap, "Georgiana is almost eighteen."

Said Mrs. Podsnap to Mr. Podsnap, assenting, "Almost eighteen."

Said Mr. Podsnap then to Mrs. Podsnap, "Really I think we should have some people on Georgiana's birthday."

Said Mrs. Podsnap then to Mr. Podsnap, "Which will enable us to clear off all those people who are due."

So it came to pass that Mr. and Mrs. Podsnap requested the honour of the company of seventeen friends of their souls at dinner; and that they substituted other friends of their souls for such of the original seventeen friends of their souls as deeply regretted that a prior engagement prevented their having the honour of dining with Mr. and Mrs. Podsnap, in pursuance of their kind invitation; and that Mrs. Podsnap said of all these inconsolable personages, as she checked them off with a pencil in her list, "Asked, at any rate, and got rid of"; and that they successfully disposed of a good many friends of their souls in this way, and felt their consciences much lightened.

There were still other friends of their souls who were not entitled to be asked to dinner, but had a claim to be invited to come and take a haunch-of-mutton vapour bath at half-past nine. For the clearing off of these worthies, Mrs. Podsnap added a small and early evening to the dinner, and looked in at the music shop to bespeak a well-conducted automaton to come and play quadrilles for a carpet dance.

Mr. and Mrs. Veneering, and Mr. and Mrs. Veneering's brand-new bride and bridegroom, were of the dinner company; but the Podsnap establishment had nothing else in common with the Veneerings. Mr. Podsnap could tolerate taste in a mushroom man who stood in need of that sort of thing, but was far above it himself. Hideous solidity was the characteristic of the Podsnap plate. Everything was made to look as heavy as it could, and to take up as much room as possible. Everything said boastfully, "Here you have as much of me in my ugliness as if I were only lead; but I am so many ounces of precious metal, worth so much an ounce;—wouldn't you like to melt me down?" A corpulent straddling epergne, blotched all over as if it had broken out in an eruption rather than been ornamented, delivered this address from an unsightly silver platform in the centre of the table. Four silver wine coolers, each furnished with four staring heads, each head obtrusively carrying a big silver ring in each of its ears, conveyed the sentiment up and down the table, and handed it on to the pot-bellied silver salt-cellars. All the big silver spoons and forks widened the mouths of the company expressly for the purpose of thrusting the sentiment down their throats with every morsel they ate.

The majority of the guests were like the plate, and included several heavy articles weighing ever so much. But there was a foreign gentleman among them: whom Mr. Podsnap had invited after much debate with himself—believing the whole European continent to be in mortal alliance against the young person—and there was a droll disposition, not only on the part of Mr. Podsnap, but of everybody else, to treat him as if he were a child who was hard of hearing.

As a delicate concession to this unfortunately born foreigner, Mr. Podsnap, in receiving him, had presented his wife as "Madame Podsnap"; also his daughter as "Mademoiselle Podsnap," with some inclination to add *"ma fille,"* in which bold venture, however, he checked himself. The Veneerings being at that time the only other arrivals, he had added (in a condescendingly explanatory manner), "Monsieur Vey-nair-reeng," and had then subsided into English.

"How Do You Like London?" Mr. Podsnap now inquired from his station of host, as if he were administering something in the nature of a powder or potion to the deaf child; "London, Londres, London?"

The foreign gentleman admired it.

"You find it Very Large?" said Mr. Podsnap spaciously.

The foreign gentleman found it very large.

"And Very Rich?"

The foreign gentleman found it, without doubt, *énormément riche.*

"Enormously Rich, We say," returned Mr. Podsnap in a condescending manner. "Our English adverbs do not terminate in Mong, and We Pronounce the 'ch' as if there were a 't' before it. We Say Ritch."

"Reetch," remarked the foreign gentleman.

"And Do You Find, Sir," pursued Mr. Podsnap with dignity, "Many Evidences that Strike You of our British Constitution in the Streets Of The World's Metropolis, London, Londres, London?"

The foreign gentleman begged to be pardoned, but did not altogether understand.

"The Constitution Britannique," Mr. Podsnap explained, as if he were teaching in an infant school. "We Say British, But You Say Britannique, You Know" (forgivingly, as if that were not his fault). "The Constitution, Sir."

The foreign gentleman said, "Mais, yees; I know eem."

A youngish, sallowish gentleman in spectacles, with a lumpy forehead, seated in a supplementary chair at a corner of the table, here caused a profound sensation by saying, in a raised voice, "ESKER," and then stopping dead.

"Mais oui," said the foreign gentleman, turning towards him. "Est-ce que? Quoi donc?"

But the gentleman with the lumpy forehead, having for the time delivered himself of all that he found behind his lumps, spake for the time no more.

"I Was Inquiring," said Mr. Podsnap, resuming the thread of his discourse, "Whether You Have Observed in our Streets as We should say, Upon our Pavvy as You would say, any Tokens—"

The foreign gentleman with patient courtesy entreated pardon: "But what was tokenz?"

"Marks," said Mr. Podsnap; "Signs, you know, Appearances—Traces."

"Ah! of a 'Orse?" inquired the foreign gentleman.

"We call it Horse," said Mr. Podsnap, with forbearance. "In England, Angleterre, England, We Aspirate the 'H,' and We Say 'Horse.' Only our Lower Classes Say ' 'Orse!' "

"Pardon," said the foreign gentleman; "I am alwiz wrong!"

"Our Language," said Mr. Podsnap, with a gracious consciousness of being always right, "is Difficult. Ours is a Copious Language, and Trying to Strangers. I will not Pursue my Question."

But the lumpy gentleman, unwilling to give it up, again madly said, "ESKER," and again spake no more.

"It merely referred," Mr. Podsnap explained, with a sense of meritorious proprietorship, "to Our Constitution, Sir. We Englishmen are Very Proud of our Constitution, Sir. It Was Bestowed Upon Us By Providence. No Other Country is so Favoured as This Country."

"And ozer countries—" the foreign gentleman was beginning, when Mr. Podsnap put him right again.

"We do not say Ozer; we say Other: the letters are 'T' and 'H'; you say Tay and Aish, You Know; (still with clemency). The sound is 'th'—'th!' "

"And other countries," said the foreign gentleman. "They do how?"

"They do, Sir," returned Mr. Podsnap, gravely shaking his head; "they do—I am sorry to be obliged to say it—as they do."

"It was a little particular of Providence," said the foreign gentleman, laughing; "for the frontier is not large."

"Undoubtedly," assented Mr. Podsnap; "But So it is. It was the Charter of the Land. This Island was Blessed, Sir, to the Direct Exclusion of such Other Countries as—as there may happen to be. And if we were all Englishmen present, I would say," added Mr. Podsnap, looking round upon his compatriots, and sounding solemnly his theme, "that there is in the Englishman a combination of qualities, a modesty, an independence, a responsibility, a repose, combined with an absence of everything calculated to call a blush into the cheek of a young person, which one would seek in vain among the Nations of the Earth."

Having delivered this little summary, Mr. Podsnap's face flushed as he thought of the remote possibility of its being at all qualified by any prejudiced citizen of any other country; and, with his favourite right-arm flourish, he put the rest of Europe, and the whole of Asia, Africa, and America, nowhere.

[From *Our Mutual Friend*]

Edward Lear

The humor of nonsense is probably nearly as old as language; witness its popularity among small children. However, most of it persists only orally. It isn't the kind of thing a Babylonian would have bothered to engrave on a brick. There are, indeed, certain literary persistences. The French coq-à-l'âne, *which flourished in the early sixteenth century, was a pure nonsense* genre. *W. H. Auden, in his* Oxford Book of Light Verse, *quotes a Nonsense Carol of about 1550. And so on.*

Edward Lear was the great Master of Nonsense. But this "old Derrydown Derry, who loved to make little folks merry" was not merry in secret. He was a chronic epileptic, whose life was lived in fear.

INCIDENTS IN THE LIFE OF MY UNCLE ARLY

Oh! my aged Uncle Arly,
Sitting on a heap of barley
   Through the silent hours of night,
Close beside a leafy thicket;
On his nose there was a cricket,
In his hat a Railway Ticket,
   (But his shoes were far too tight).

Long ago, in youth, he squander'd
All his goods away, and wander'd
   To the Timskoop Hills afar.
There on golden sunsets glazing,
Every evening found him gazing,
Singing, "Orb! you're quite amazing!
   How I wonder what you are!"

Like the ancient Medes and Persians,
Always by his own exertions
   He subsisted on those hills;

171

Whiles, by teaching children spelling,
Or at times by merely yelling,
Or at intervals by selling
"Propter's Nicodemus Pills."

Later, in his morning rambles,
He perceived the moving brambles
  Something square and white disclose:—
'Twas a First-class Railway Ticket;
But on stooping down to pick it
Off the ground, a pea-green cricket
  Settled on my uncle's nose.

Never, nevermore, oh! never
Did that cricket leave him ever,—
  Dawn or evening, day or night;
Clinging as a constant treasure,
Chirping with a cheerious measure,
Wholly to my uncle's pleasure,
  (Though his shoes were far too tight).

So for three and forty winters,
Till his shoes were worn to splinters,
  All those hills he wander'd o'er,—
Sometimes silent, sometimes yelling;
Till he came to Borley-Melling,
Near his old ancestral dwelling,
  (But his shoes were far too tight).

On a little heap of barley
Died my aged Uncle Arly,
  And they buried him one night
Close beside the leafy thicket;
There, his hat and Railway Ticket;
There, his ever faithful cricket;
  (But his shoes were far too tight).

A LETTER FROM EDWARD LEAR TO EVELYN BARING, LORD CROMER

THRIPPY PILLIWINX,—
                     Inkly tinky pobblebockle
able-squabs? Flosky! Beebul trimble flosky! Okul scratch
abibblebongibo, viddle squibble tog-a-tog, ferry moyassity
amsky flamsky damsky crocklefether squiggs.
                     Flinky wisty pomm,
                                               SLUSHYPIPP

HOW PLEASANT TO KNOW MR. LEAR

"How pleasant to know Mr. Lear!"
  Who has written such volumes of stuff!
Some think him ill-tempered and queer,
  But a few think him pleasant enough.

His mind is concrete and fastidious,
  His nose is remarkably big;
His visage is more or less hideous,
  His beard it resembles a wig.

He has ears, and two eyes, and ten fingers,
  Leastways if you reckon two thumbs;
Long ago he was one of the singers,
  But now he is one of the dumbs.

He sits in a beautiful parlour,
  With hundreds of books on the wall;
He drinks a great deal of Marsala,
  But never gets tipsy at all.

He has many friends, laymen and clerical,
  Old Foss is the name of his cat:
His body is perfectly spherical,
  He weareth a runcible hat.

When he walks in a waterproof white,
The children run after him so!
Calling out, "He's come out in his night-
gown, that crazy old Englishman, oh!"

He weeps by the side of the ocean,
He weeps on the top of the hill;
He purchases pancakes and lotion,
And chocolate shrimps from the mill.

He reads but he cannot speak Spanish,
He cannot abide ginger-beer:
Ere the days of his pilgrimage vanish,
How pleasant to know Mr. Lear!

Frederick Locker-Lampson

A TERRIBLE INFANT

I recollect a nurse call'd Ann,
    Who carried me about the grass,
And one fine day a fine young man
    Came up, and kiss'd the pretty lass.
She did not make the least objection!
        Thinks I, "Aha!
    When I can talk I'll tell Mamma!"
—And that's my earliest recollection.

Robert B. Brough

Robert B. Brough (1828-60) is a remarkable phenomenon. At a time when most humorists made their butts of the ill-bred, the lowly born, the badly dressed, he dared to mock the aristocracy. My two examples are taken from his rare Songs of the Governing Classes. *If he had lived, Brough might have become a major satirist.*

By the way, Trollope belongs in here. Unfortunately, his great bravura passages, such as Mrs. Proudie's reception, proved merely bewildering when tried on subjects who did not know the particular novel as a whole.

MY LORD TOMNODDY

My Lord Tomnoddy's the son of an Earl,
His hair is straight, but his whiskers curl;
His Lordship's forehead is far from wide,
But there's plenty of room for the brains inside.
He writes his name with indifferent ease,
He's rather uncertain about the "d's,"—
But what does it matter, if three or one,
To the Earl of Fitzdotterel's eldest son?

My Lord Tomnoddy to college went,
Much time he lost, much money he spent;
Rules, and windows, and heads, he broke—
Authorities wink'd—young men will joke!
He never peep'd inside of a book—
In two years' time a degree he took;
And the newspapers vaunted the honours won
By the Earl of Fitzdotterel's eldest son.

My Lord Tomnoddy came out in the world,
Waists were tighten'd, and ringlets curl'd.
Virgins languish'd, and matrons smil'd—
'Tis true, his Lordship is rather wild;

In very queer places he spends his life;
There's talk of some children, by nobody's wife—
But we mustn't look close into what is done
By the Earl of Fitzdotterel's eldest son.

My Lord Tomnoddy must settle down—
There's a vacant seat in the family town!
('Tis time he should sow his eccentric oats)—
He hasn't the wit to apply for votes:
He cannot e'en learn his election speech,
Three phrases he speaks—a mistake in each!
And then breaks down—but the borough is won
For the Earl of Fitzdotterel's eldest son.

My Lord Tomnoddy prefers the Guards,
(The House is a bore!) so it's on the cards!
My Lord's a Lieutenant at twenty-three,
A Captain at twenty-six is he—
He never drew sword, except on drill;
The tricks of parade he has learnt but ill—
A full-blown Colonel at thirty-one
Is the Earl of Fitzdotterel's eldest son!

My Lord Tomnoddy is thirty-four;
The Earl can last but a few years more.
My Lord in the Peers will take his place:
Her Majesty's councils his words will grace.
Office he'll hold, and patronage sway;
Fortunes and lives he will vote away—
And what are his qualifications?—ONE!
He's the Earl of Fitzdotterel's eldest son!

SIR GYPES TOLLODDLE, J. P.

'Tis said the age is sinking into indolence and "coddle,"
And that, of ev'ry manly English type, we've lost the model.
A lay to prove the contrary but now has struck my noddle,
Descriptive of the virtues of my friend Sir Gypes Tolloddle,
      Who's a fine Old English Gentleman,
        Worthy the olden time.

Half Snobshire's his—of Flunkeyshire, he owns at least a fourth,
Besides in Wales at Llandevowrdd, a spacious foot of earth,
In Ireland too, Kilbeggarman—Clapmammon, in the North;
Sir Gypes thinks highly of himself, yet knows not half he's worth—
      As a fine Old English Gentleman,
        Worthy the olden time.

He's sixty-five; his age, at most, at fifty-four you'd fix;
He's six feet high,—you'd take your oath Sir Gypes was six feet six,
So like a lion's is his tread, you fear a lion's tricks,
And when he's pass'd, feel thankful you've escaped from blows or
    kicks,
      From this fine Old English Gentleman,
        Worthy the olden time.

He dresses like a farming man, in russet grey or brown,
He carries bundles, cracks his jest with common folk "down town,"
"No pride, you see! like one of us!" but, freedom to keep down,
Lurks more than bowstring terror in the true Al Raschid frown,
      Of this fine Old English Gentleman,
        Worthy the olden time.

At Quarter Sessions sits Sir Gypes, a judge as Minos grim,
A poacher upon his estates, he'd sunder limb from limb;
Sir Gypes is not a cruel man, but has a notion dim,
Long taught him, that the greatest crime's a liberty with *him*.
      Like a fine Old English Gentleman,
        Worthy the olden time.

He's not a sage; but ears, to catch his sayings, so incline,
The dullest phrase, he speaks as from an oracle divine,
You somehow feel quite grateful when he says "the day is fine,"
For placing it past question that the sun *does really* shine,
   Like a fine Old English Gentleman,
    Worthy the olden time.

A hat two seconds on a head, he scarcely ever saw;
The earliest word he learnt to speak was register'd as law;
Were you and I to laugh at him, he'd look on us with awe
As lunatics escap'd from dungeon, whipping-post, and straw,
   Would this fine Old English Gentleman,
    Worthy the olden time.

His butler is a gentleman with thousands in the bank,
His housekeeper, a lady, ne'er to mix with tradesfolk sank.
Sir Gypes, of some ten thousand souls, enjoys the foremost rank
As Number One—the others making up the ciphers blank,
   To this fine Old English Gentleman,
    Worthy the olden time.

"But is it not," I hear you ask, "a goodly sight to view?
And would you to the earth a tree, such fruit that gives us, hew?
Is he not hospitable, brave—above the grov'lling crew
In stainless honour as in rank—?" I frankly answer—True!
   He's a fine Old English Gentleman,
    Worthy the olden time.

He's loyal, generous—his word's his bond, to king or clown.
I grant him type of all those gifts—have won our land renown;
And yet 'tis hard!—six parishes, twelve hamlets, and a town,
This splendid sample to produce, should be, as 'twere, boil'd down,
   Of a fine Old English Gentleman,
    Worthy the olden time.

Charles Stuart Calverley

Charles Stuart Calverley (1831-1884) is the great master of vers de société. Most modern light versifiers are, consciously or unconsciously, his imitators. His verse is nearly perfect in form; it delights the sensitive palate like a mouthful of Keats. His delicate incongruities evoke an aesthetic pleasure which contains a shuddering dose of aesthetic torture.

PEACE

He stood, a worn-out City clerk—
    Who'd toil'd, and seen no holiday
For forty years from dawn to dark—
    Alone beside Caermarthen Bay.

He felt the salt spray on his lips;
    Heard children's voices on the sands;
Up the sun's path he saw the ships
    Sail on and on to other lands;

And laugh'd aloud. Each sight and sound
    To him was joy too deep for tears;
He sat him on the beach, and bound
    A blue bandanna round his ears,

And thought how, posted near his door,
    His own green door on Camden Hill,
Two bands at least, most likely more,
    Were mingling at their own sweet will

Verdi with Vance. And at the thought
    He laugh'd again, and softly drew
That Morning Herald that he'd brought
    Forth from his breast, and read it through.

LOVERS, AND A REFLECTION

In moss-prankt dells which the sunbeams flatter
  (And heaven it knoweth what that may mean;
Meaning, however, is no great matter)
  Where woods are a-tremble, with rifts atween;

Through God's own heather we wonned together,
  I and my Willie (O love, my love):
I need hardly remark it was glorious weather,
  And flitterbats wavered alow, above:

Boats were curtseying, smiling, bowing,
  (Boats in that climate are so polite),
And sands were a ribbon of green endowing
  And oh, the sundazzle on bark and bight!

Through the rare red heather we danced together,
  (O love, my Willie!) and smelt for flowers:
I must mention again it was glorious weather,
  Rhymes are so scarce in this world of ours:—

By rises that flushed with their purple favours,
  Through becks that brattled o'er grasses sheen,
We walked and waded, we two young shavers,
  Thanking our stars we were both so green.

We journeyed in parallels, I and Willie,
  In fortunate parallels! Butterflies,
Hid in weltering shadows of daffodilly
  Or marjoram, kept making peacock eyes:

Songbirds darted about, some inky
  As coal, some snowy, (I ween) as curds;
Or rosy as pinks, or as roses pinky—
  They reck of no eerie To-come, those birds!

But they skim over bents which the mill stream washes,
　Or hang in the lift 'neath a white cloud's hem;
They need no parasols, no goloshes;
　And good Mrs. Trimmer she feedeth them.

Then we thrid God's cowslips (as erst his heather)
　That endowed the wan grass with their golden blooms
And snapped—(It was perfectly charming weather)
　Our fingers at fate and her goddess-glooms:

And Willie 'gan sing (Oh, his notes were fluty;
　Wafts fluttered them out to the white-winged sea)—
Something made up of rhymes that have done much duty,
　Rhymes (better to put it) of "ancientry":

Bowers of flowers encountered showers
　In William's carol—(O love, my Willie!)
Then he bade sorrow borrow from blithe tomorrow
　I quite forget what—say a daffodilly:

A nest in a hollow, "with buds to follow,"
　I think occurred next in his nimble strain;
And clay that was "kneaden" of course in Eden—
　A rhyme most novel, I do maintain:

Mists, bones, the singer himself, love-stories,
　And all least furlable things got "furled";
Not with any designs to conceal their glories,
　But simply and solely to rhyme with "world."

Oh, if billows and pillows and hours and flowers
　And all the brave rhymes of an elder day
Could be furled together, this genial weather,
　And carted or carried on "wafts" away,
Nor ever again trotted out—ah me!
How much fewer volumes of verse there'd be!

FIRST LOVE

O my earliest love, who, ere I number'd
  Ten sweet summers, made my bosom thrill!
Will a swallow—or a swift, or some bird—
  Fly to her and say, I love her still?

Say my life's a desert drear and arid,
  To its one green spot I aye recur:
Never, never—although three times married—
  Have I cared a jot for aught but her.

No, mine own! though early forced to leave you,
  Still my heart was there where first we met;
In those "Lodgings with an ample sea-view,"
  Which were, forty years ago, "To Let."

There I saw her first, our landlord's oldest
  Little daughter. On a thing so fair
Thou, O Sun—who (so they say) beholdest
  Everything,—hast gazed, I tell thee, ne'er.

There she sat—so near me, yet remoter
  Than a star—a blue-eyed bashful imp:
On her lap she held a happy bloater,
  'Twixt her lips a yet more happy shrimp.

And I loved her, and our troth we plighted
  On the morrow by the shingly shore:
In a fortnight to be disunited
  By a bitter fate forevermore.

O my own, my beautiful, my blue-eyed!
  To be young once more, and bite my thumb
At the world and all its cares with you, I'd
  Give no inconsiderable sum.

Hand in hand we tramp'd the golden seaweed,
  Soon as o'er the grey cliff peep'd the dawn:
Side by side, when came the hour for tea, we'd
  Crunch the mottled shrimp and hairy prawn:—

Has she wedded some gigantic shrimper,
  That sweet mite with whom I loved to play?
Is she girt with babes that whine and whimper,
  That bright being who was always gay?

Yes—she has at least a dozen wee things!
  Yes—I see her darning corduroys,
Scouring floors, and setting out the tea-things,
  For a howling herd of hungry boys,

In a home that reeks of tar and sperm-oil!
  But at intervals she thinks, I know,
Of those days which we, afar from turmoil,
  Spent together forty years ago.

O my earliest love, still unforgotten,
  With your downcast eyes of dreamy blue!
Never, somehow, could I seem to cotton
  To another as I did to you!

Lewis Carroll

It is strange that Lewis Carroll, after writing the inspired Alice in Wonderland, Through the Looking-Glass, *and* The Hunting of the Snark, *should have descended to the murky dullness of* Sylvie and Bruno *and the other works of his long decline. For great nonsense is surrealist art in its highest form; but most nonsense is just nonsense. It seems silly to reprint here selections from the masterworks, which most fine-grained people can quote almost by heart, so I choose a passage from* The Three Voices, *which preceded* Alice. *This would be creditable enough for most writers, though obviously it is not one of the greatest creations of the Wagner of Nonsense. It is evidently a burlesque, though not a parody, of Elizabeth Barrett Browning's* A Vision of Poets.

THE THREE VOICES
(Selection)

THE FIRST VOICE

He trilled a carol fresh and free,
He laughed aloud for very glee:
There came a breeze from off the sea:

It passed athwart the glooming flat—
It fanned his forehead as he sat—
It lightly bore away his hat,

All to the feet of one who stood
Like maid enchanted in a wood,
Frowning as darkly as she could.

With huge umbrella, lank and brown,
Unerringly she pinned it down,
Right through the centre of the crown.

Then, with an aspect cold and grim,
Regardless of its battered rim,
She took it up and gave it him.

A while like one in dreams he stood,
Then faltered forth his gratitude
In words just short of being rude:

For it had lost its shape and shine,
And it had cost him four-and-nine,
And he was going out to dine.

"To dine!" she sneered in acid tone,
"To bend thy being to a bone
Clothed in a radiance not its own!"

The tear-drop trickled to his chin:
There was a meaning in her grin
That made him feel on fire within.

"Term it not 'radiance,'" said he:
"'Tis solid nutriment to me.
Dinner is Dinner: Tea is Tea."

And she, "Yea so? Yet wherefore cease?
Let thy scant knowledge find increase.
Say 'Men are Men, and Geese are Geese.'"

He moaned: he knew not what to say.
The thought "That I could get away!"
Strove with the thought "But I must stay."

"To dine!" she shrieked in dragon-wrath.
"To swallow wines all foam and froth!
To simper at a table-cloth!

"Say, can thy noble spirit stoop
To join the gormandising troop
Who find a solace in the soup?

"Canst thou desire or pie or puff?
Thy well-bred manners were enough,
Without such gross material stuff."

"Yet well-bred men," he faintly said,
"Are not unwilling to be fed:
Nor are they well without the bread."

Her visage scorched him ere she spoke:
"There are," she said, "a kind of folk
Who have no horror of a joke.

"Such wretches live: they take their share
Of common earth and common air:
We come across them here and there:

"We grant them—there is no escape—
A sort of semi-human shape
Suggestive of the man-like Ape."

"In all such theories," said he,
"One fixed exception there must be.
That is, the Present Company."

Baffled, she gave a wolfish bark:
He, aiming blindly in the dark,
With random shaft had pierced the mark.

She felt that her defeat was plain,
Yet madly strove with might and main
To get the upper hand again.

Fixing her eyes upon the beach,
As though unconscious of his speech,
She said "Each gives to more than each."

He could not answer yea or nay:
He faltered "Gifts may pass away."
Yet knew not what he meant to say.

"If that be so," she straight replied,
"Each heart with each doth coincide.
What boots it? For the world is wide."

"The world is but a Thought," said he:
"The vast unfathomable sea
Is but a Notion—unto me."

And darkly fell her answer dread
Upon his unresisting head,
Like half a hundredweight of lead.

"The Good and Great must ever shun
That reckless and abandoned one
Who stoops to perpetrate a pun.

"The man that smokes—that reads *The Times*—
That goes to Christmas Pantomimes—
Is capable of *any* crimes!"

. . . .

So passed they on with even pace:
Yet gradually one might trace
A shadow growing on his face.

THE SECOND VOICE

They walked beside the wave-worn beach;
Her tongue was very apt to teach,
And now and then he did beseech

She would abate her dulcet tone,
Because the talk was all her own,
And he was dull as any drone.

She urged "No cheese is made of chalk";
And ceaseless flowed her dreary talk,
Tuned to the footfall of a walk.

Her voice was very full and rich,
And when at length she asked him "Which?"
It mounted to its highest pitch.

.   .   .   .   .

"Shall Man be Man? And shall he miss
Of other thoughts no thought but this,
Harmonious dews of sober bliss?

"What boots it? Shall his fevered eye
Through towering nothingness descry
The grisly phantom hurry by?

"And hear dumb shrieks that fill the air;
See mouths that gape, and eyes that stare
And redden in the dusky glare?

"The meadows breathing amber light,
The darkness toppling from the height,
The feathery train of granite Night?

"Shall he, grown gray among his peers,
Through the thick curtain of his tears
Catch glimpses of his earlier years,

"And hear the sounds he knew of yore,
Old shufflings on the sanded floor,
Old knuckles tapping at the door?

"Yet still before him as he flies
One pallid form shall ever rise,
And bodying forth in glassy eyes

"The vision of a vanished good,
Low peering through the tangled wood,
Shall freeze the current of his blood."

Still from each fact, with skill uncouth
And savage rapture, like a tooth
She wrenched some slow reluctant truth.

Till, like a silent water-mill,
When summer suns have dried the rill,
She reached a full stop, and was still.

Dead calm succeeded to the fuss,
As when the loaded omnibus
Has reached the railway terminus:

When, for the tumult of the street,
Is heard the engine's stifled beat,
The velvet tread of porters' feet.

With glance that ever sought the ground,
She moved her lips without a sound,
And every now and then she frowned.

He gazed upon the sleeping sea,
And joyed in its tranquillity,
And in that silence dead, but she

To muse a little space did seem,
Then, like the echo of a dream,
Harked back upon her threadbare theme.

Still an attentive ear he lent
But could not fathom what she meant:
She was not deep, nor eloquent.

He marked the ripple on the sand:
The even swaying of her hand
Was all that he could understand.

He saw in dreams a drawing-room,
Where thirteen wretches sat in gloom,
Waiting—he thought he knew for whom:

He saw them drooping here and there,
Each feebly huddled on a chair,
In attitudes of blank despair:

Oysters were not more mute than they,
For all their brains were pumped away,
And they had nothing more to say—

Save one, who groaned "Three hours are gone!"
Who shrieked "We'll wait no longer, John!
Tell them to set the dinner on!"

Richard Garnett

Richard Garnett, progenitor of a literary family, was keeper of printed books in the British Museum, a man of enormous and varied learning, and a prodigious writer on all sorts of scholarly subjects. The Twilight of the Gods, from which this story is taken, is rich in intellectual humor, in the Voltaire tradition. I hope that radiant and witty book will not be utterly forgotten.

ABDALLAH THE ADITE

An aged hermit named Sergius dwelt in the wilds of Arabia, addicting himself to the pursuit of religion and alchemy. Of his creed it could only be said that it was so much better than that of his neighbours as to cause him to be commonly esteemed a Yezidi, or devil worshipper. But the better informed deemed him a Nestorian monk, who had retired into the wilderness on account of differences with his brethren, who sought to poison him.

The imputation of Yezidism against Sergius was the cause that a certain inquisitive young man resorted to him, trusting to obtain light concerning the nature of demons. But he found that Sergius could give him no information on that subject, but, on the contrary, discoursed so wisely and beautifully on holy things, that his pupil's intellect was enlightened, and his enthusiasm was inflamed, and he longed to go forth and instruct the ignorant people around him; the Saracens, and the Sabaeans, and the Zoroastrians, and the Carmathians, and the Baphometites, and the Paulicians, who are a remnant of the ancient Manichees.

"Nay, good youth," said Sergius, "I have renounced the sending forth of missionaries, having made ample trial with my spiritual son, the Prophet Abdallah."

"What!" exclaimed the youth, "was Abdallah the Adite thy disciple?"

"Even so," said Sergius. "Hearken to his history.

"Never have I instructed so promising a pupil as Abdallah, nor

191

when he was first my disciple do I deem that he was other than the most simple-minded and well-intentioned of youths. I always called him son, a title I have never bestowed on another. Like thee, he had compassion on the darkness around him, and craved my leave to go forth and dispel it.

"'My son,' said I, 'I will not restrain thee: thou art no longer a child. Thou hast heard me discourse on the subject of persecution, and knowest that poison was administered to me personally on account of my inability to perceive the supernatural light emanating from the navel of Brother Gregory. Thou art aware that thou wilt be beaten with rods and pricked with goads, chained and starved in a dungeon, very probably blinded, very possibly burned with fire?'

"'All these things I am prepared to undergo,' said Abdallah; and he embraced me and bade me farewell.

"After certain moons he returned covered with weals and scars, and his bones protruded through his skin.

"'Whence are these weals and scars?' asked I, 'and what signifies this protrusion of thy bones?'

"'The weals and the scars,' answered he, 'proceed from the floggings inflicted upon me by command of the Caliph; and my bones protrude by reason of the omission of his officers to furnish me with either food or drink in the dungeon wherein I was imprisoned by his orders.'

"'O my son,' exclaimed I, 'in the eyes of faith and right reason these scars are lovelier than the moles of beauty, and the sight of thy bones is like the beholding of hidden treasure!'

"And Abdallah strove to look as though he believed me; nor did he entirely fail therein. And I took him, and fed him, and healed him, and sent him forth a second time into the world.

"And after a space he returned, covered as before with wounds and bruises, but comely and somewhat fat.

"'Whence this sleekness of body, my son?' I asked.

"'Through the charity of the Caliph's wives,' he answered, 'who have fed me secretly, I have assured them that in remembrance of this good work each of them in the world to come would have seven husbands.'

"'How knewest thou this, my son?' I inquired.

"'In truth, father,' he said, 'I did not know it; but I thought it probable.'

"'O my son! my son!' exclaimed I, 'thou art on a dangerous road. To win over weak ignorant people by promises of what they shall receive in a future life, whereof thou knowest no more than they do! Knowest thou not that the inestimable blessings of religion are of an inward and spiritual nature? Did I ever promise any disciple any recompense for his enlightenment and good deeds, save flogging, starvation, and burning?'

"'Never, father,' said he, 'and therefore thou hast had no follower of thy law save one, and he hath broken it.'

"He left me after a shorter stay than before, and again went forth to preach. After a long time he returned in good condition of body, yet manifestly having something upon his mind.

"'Father,' he said, 'thy son hath preached with faithfulness and acceptance, and turned thousands unto righteousness. But a sorcerer hath arisen, saying, "Why follow ye Abdallah, seeing that he breathes not fire out of his mouth and nostrils?" And the people give ear unto the words that come from this man's lips, when they behold the flame that cometh from his nose. And unless thou teachest me to do as he doth I shall assuredly perish.'

"And I told Abdallah that it was better to perish for the truth's sake than to prolong life by lies and deceit. But he wept and lamented exceeding sore, and in the end he prevailed with me; and I taught him to breathe flame and smoke out of a hollow nut filled with combustible powder. And I took a certain substance called soap, but little known in this country, and anointed his feet therewith. And when he and the sorcerer met, both breathing flame, the people knew not which to follow; but when Abdallah walked over nine hot ploughshares, and the sorcerer could not touch one of them, they beat his brains out, and became Abdallah's disciples.

"A long time afterward Abdallah came to me again, this time with a joyful, and yet with somewhat of a troubled look, carrying a camel-hair blanket, which he undid, and lo! it was full of bones.

"'O father,' he said, 'I bring thee happy tidings. We have found the bones of the camel of the prophet Ad, upon which his revelation was engraved by him.'

"'If this be so,' said I, 'thou art acquainted with the precepts of the prophet, and hast no need of mine.'

"'Nay, but father,' said he, 'although the revelation was without question originally engraved by the prophet on these very bones, it hath come to pass by the injury of time that not one letter of his writing can be distinguished. I have therefore come to ask thee to write it over again.'

"'What!' I exclaimed, 'I forge a revelation in the name of the prophet Ad! Get thee behind me!'

"'Thou knowest, father,' he rejoined, 'that if we had the original words of the prophet Ad here they would profit us nought, as by reason of their antiquity none would understand them. Seeing therefore that I myself cannot write, it is meet that thou shouldst set down in his name those things which he would have desired to deliver had he been now among us; but if thou wilt not, I shall ask Brother Gregory.'

"And when I heard him speak of having recourse to that cheat and impostor my spirit was grieved within me, and I wrote the Book of Ad myself. And I was heedful to put in none but wholesome and profitable precepts, and more especially did I forbid polygamy, having perceived a certain inclination thereunto in my disciple.

"After many days he came again, and this time he was in violent terror and agitation, and hair was wanting to the lower part of his countenance.

"'O Abdallah,' I inquired, 'where is thy beard?'

"'In the hands of my ninth wife,' said he.

"'Apostate!' I exclaimed, 'hast thou dared to espouse more wives than one? Rememberest thou not what is written in the Book of the Prophet Ad?'

"'O father,' he said, 'the revelation of Ad being, as thou knowest, so exceedingly ancient, doth of necessity require a commentary. This hath been supplied by one of my disciples, a young Syrian and natural son of Gregory, as I opine. This young man can not only write, but write to my dictation, an accomplishment in which thou hast been found lacking, O Sergius. In this gloss it is set forth how, since woman hath the ninth part of the soul of man, the prophet, in enjoining us Adites (as we now call ourselves) to take but one wife, doth instruct us to take nine; to espouse a tenth would, I grant, be damnable. It ensues, therefore, that having become enamoured of a most charming young virgin, I am constrained to repudiate one of the wives whom I have taken already. To this, each thinking that it may be her turn speedily, if not now, they will in no wise consent, and have maltreated me as thou seest, and the dens of wild beasts are at this moment abodes of peace, compared to my seraglio. What is even worse, they threaten to disclose to the people the fact, of which they have unhappily become aware, that the revelation of the blessed Ad is not written upon the bones of a camel at all, but of a cow, and will therefore be accounted spurious, inasmuch as the prophet is not recorded to have ridden upon this quadruped. And seeing that thou didst inscribe the characters, O father, I cannot but fear that the fury of the people will extend unto thee, and that thou wilt be even in danger of thy life from them.'

"This argument of Abdallah's had much weight with me, and I the more readily consented to his request as he did not on this occasion require any imposture at my hands, but merely the restitution of his domestic peace. And I went with him to his wives, and discoursed with them, and they agreed to abide by my sentence. And, willing to please him, I directed that he should marry the beautiful virgin, and put away one of his wives who was old and ugly, and endowed with the disposition of Sheitan.

"'O father,' said Abdallah, 'thou hast brought me from death unto life! And thou, Zarah,' he continued, 'wilt lose nought, but gain exceedingly, in becoming the spouse of the wise and virtuous Sergius.'

"'I marry Zarah!' I exclaimed, 'I! a monk!'

"'Surely,' said he, 'thou would'st not take away her husband without giving her another in his stead?'

"'If he does I will throttle him,' cried Zarah.

"And I wept sore, and made great intercession. And it was agreed that there should be a delay of forty days, in which space if any one else would marry Zarah, I should be free of her. And I promised all my substance to any one who would do this, and no one was found. And she was offered to thirteen criminals doomed to suffer death, and they all chose death. And at the last I was constrained to marry her. And truly I have now the comfort of thinking that if I have offended by encouraging Abdallah's deceits, or otherwise, the debt is paid, and Eternal Justice hath now nothing against me; for verily I was an inmate of Gehenna until it came to pass that she was herself translated thither. And respecting the manner of her translation, inquire not thou too curiously. It was doubtless a token of the displeasure of Heaven at her enormities that the water of the well of Kefayat, which had been known as the Diamond of the Desert, became about this time undrinkable, and pernicious to man and beast.

"As I sat in my dwelling administering to the estate of my deceased wife, which consisted principally of wines and strong liquors, Abdallah again appeared before me.

" 'Hast thou come,' said I, 'to solicit me to abet thee in any new imposture? Know, once for all, that I will not.'

" 'On the contrary,' said he, 'I am come to set thee at ease by proving to thee that I shall not again require thy assistance. Follow me.'

"And I followed him to a great plain, where was a host of armed horsemen and footmen, more than I could number. And they bore banners on which the name of Abdallah was embroidered in letters of gold. And in the midst was an ark of gold, with the bones of Ad's camel, or cow. And by this was a great pile of the heads of men, and warriors were continually casting more and more upon the heap.

" 'How many?' asked Abdallah.

" 'Twelve thousand, O Apostle of God,' answered they, 'but there are more to come.'

" 'Thou monster!' said I to Abdallah.

" 'Nay, father,' said he, 'there will not be more than sixteen thousand in all, and these men were unbelievers. Moreover we have spared such of their women as were young and handsome, and have taken them for our concubines, as is ordained in the eleventh supplement to the Book of Ad, just promulgated by my authority. But come, I have other things to manifest unto thee.'

"And he led me where a stake was driven into the earth, and a man was chained unto it, and fuel was heaped all around him, and many stood by with lighted torches in their hands.

" 'O Abdallah,' I exclaimed, 'wherefore this atrocity?'

" 'This man,' he replied, 'is a blasphemer, who hath said that the Book of Ad is written on the bones of a cow.'

" 'But it *is* written on the bones of a cow!' I cried.

" 'Even so,' said he, 'and therefore is his heresy the more damnable, and his punishment the more exemplary. Had it been indeed written on the bones of a camel, he might have affirmed what pleased him.'

"And I shook off the dust from my feet, and hastened to my dwelling. The rest of Abdallah's acts thou knowest, and how he fell warring with the Carmathians. And now I ask thee, art thou yet minded to go forth as a missionary of the truth?' "

"O Sergius," said the young man, "I perceive that the temptations are greater, and the difficulties far surpassing what I had thought. Yet will I go, and I trust by Heaven's grace not to fail utterly."

"Then go," said Sergius, "and Heaven's blessing go with thee! Come back in ten years, should I be living, and if thou canst declare that thou hast forged no scriptures, and worked no miracles, and persecuted no unbelievers, and flattered no potentate, and bribed no one with the promise of aught in heaven or earth, I will give thee the philosopher's stone."

Samuel Butler

Samuel Butler is a fine example of the author who always wrote exactly how and what he pleased, with the result that none of his books had the smallest success during his lifetime. But now you can buy The Way of All Flesh *at the nearest cigar store for a quarter. Heigh-ho!*

A PSALM OF MONTREAL

The City of Montreal is one of the most rising, and, in many respects, most agreeable on the American continent, but its inhabitants are as yet too busy with commerce to care greatly about the masterpieces of old Greek Art. In the Montreal Museum of Natural History I came upon two plaster casts, one of the Antinous and the other of the Discobolus—not the good one, but in my poem, of course, I intend the good one—banished from public view to a room where were all manner of skins, plants, snakes, insects, etc., and, in the middle of these, an old man stuffing an owl.

"Ah," said I, "so you have some antiques here; why don't you put them where people can see them?"

"Well, sir," answered the custodian, "you see they are rather vulgar."

He then talked a great deal and said his brother did all Mr. Spurgeon's printing.

The dialogue—perhaps true, perhaps imaginary, perhaps a little of the one and a little of the other—between the writer and this old man gave rise to the lines that follow:

Stowed away in a Montreal lumber room
The Discobolus standeth and turneth his face to the wall;
Dusty, cobweb-covered, maimed and set at naught,
Beauty crieth in an attic and no man regardeth:
    O God! O Montreal!

Beautiful by night and day, beautiful in summer and winter,
Whole or maimed, always and alike beautiful—
He preacheth gospel of grace to the skin of owls
And to one who seasoneth the skins of Canadian owls:
O God! O Montreal!

When I saw him I was wroth and I said, "O Discobolus!
Beautiful Discobolus, a Prince both among gods and men!
What doest thou here, how camest thou hither, Discobolus,
Preaching gospel in vain to the skins of owls?"
O God! O Montreal!

And I turned to the man of skins and said unto him, "O thou man of
     skins,
Wherefore hast thou done thus to shame the beauty of the Discobolus?"
But the Lord had hardened the heart of the man of skins
And he answered, "My brother-in-law is haberdasher to Mr. Spurgeon."
O God! O Montreal!

"The Discobolus is put here because he is vulgar—
He has neither vest nor pants with which to cover his limbs;
I, Sir, am a person of most respectable connections—
My brother-in-law is haberdasher to Mr. Spurgeon."
O God! O Montreal!

Then I said, "O brother-in-law to Mr. Spurgeon's haberdasher,
Who seasonest also the skins of Canadian owls,
Thou callest trousers 'pants,' whereas I call them 'trousers,'
Therefore thou art in hell-fire and may the Lord pity thee!"
O God! O Montreal!

"Preferrest thou the gospel of Montreal to the gospel of Hellas,
The gospel of thy connection with Mr. Spurgeon's haberdashery to the
     gospel of the Discobolus?"
Yet none the less blasphemed he beauty saying, "The Discobolus hath
     no gospel,
But my brother-in-law is haberdasher to Mr. Spurgeon."
O God! O Montreal!

William Schwenk Gilbert

I have been horrified to discover that More Bab Ballads *is out of print. Can this mean that people no longer read these monumental works?*

The illustrations are W. S. Gilbert's own, and are reproduced because they are essential to a complete understanding of the text.

THE RIVAL CURATES

List while the poet trolls
    Of Mr. CLAYTON HOOPER,
Who had a cure of souls
    At Spiffton-extra-Sooper.

He lived on curds and whey,
    And daily sang their praises,
And then he'd go and play
    With buttercups and daisies.

Wild croquet HOOPER banned,
    And all the sports of Mammon,
He warred with cribbage, and
    He exorcised backgammon.

His helmet was a glance
 That spoke of holy gladness;
A saintly smile his lance,
 His shield a tear of sadness.

His Vicar smiled to see
 This armour on him buckled;
With pardonable glee
 He blessed himself and chuckled:

"In mildness to abound
 My curate's sole design is,
In all the country round
 There's none so mild as mine is!"

And HOOPER, disinclined
 His trumpet to be blowing,
Yet didn't think you'd find
 A milder curate going.

A friend arrived one day
 At Spiffton-extra-Sooper,
And in this shameful way
 He spoke to MR. HOOPER:

"You think your famous name
 For mildness can't be shaken,
That none can blot your fame—
 But, HOOPER, you're mistaken!

"Your mind is not as blank
 As that of HOPLEY PORTER,
Who holds a curate's rank
 At Assesmilk-cum-Worter.

"*He* plays the airy flute,
 And looks depressed and blighted,
Doves round about him 'toot,'
 And lambkins dance delighted.

"*He* labours more than you
  At worsted work, and frames it;
In old maids' albums, too,
  Sticks seaweed—yes, and names it!"

The tempter said his say,
  Which pierced him like a needle—
He summoned straight away
  His sexton and his beadle.

These men were men who could
  Hold liberal opinions:
On Sundays they were good—
  On week-days they were minions.

"To HOPLEY PORTER go,
  Your fare I will afford you—
Deal him a deadly blow,
  And blessings shall reward you.

"But stay—I do not like
  Undue assassination,
And so, before you strike,
  Make this communication:

"I'll give him this one chance—
    If he'll more gaily bear him,
Play croquet, smoke and dance,
    I willingly will spare him."

They went, those minions true,
    To Assesmilk-cum-Worter,
And told their errand to
    The REVEREND HOPLEY PORTER.

"What?" said that reverend gent,
    "Dance through my hours of leisure?
Smoke?—bathe myself with scent?—
    Play croquet? Oh, with pleasure!

"Wear all my hair in curl?
    Stand at my door, and wink—so—
At every passing girl?
    My brothers, I should think so!

"For years I've longed for some
    Excuse for this revulsion:
Now that excuse has come—
    I do it on compulsion!!!"

He smoked and winked away—
This REVEREND HOPLEY PORTER—
The deuce there was to pay
At Assesmilk-cum-Worter.

And HOOPER holds his ground,
In mildness daily growing—
They think him, all around,
The mildest curate going.

ETIQUETTE

The *Ballyshannon* foundered off the coast of Cariboo,
And down in fathoms many went the captain and the crew;
Down went the owners—greedy men whom hope of gain allured:
Oh, dry the starting tear, for they were heavily insured.

Besides the captain and the mate, the owners and the crew,
The passengers were also drowned excepting only two:
Young PETER GRAY, who tasted teas for BAKER, CROOP, AND CO.,
And SOMERS, who from Eastern shores imported indigo.

These passengers, by reason of their clinging to a mast,
Upon a desert island were eventually cast.
They hunted for their meals, as ALEXANDER SELKIRK used,
But they couldn't chat together—they had not been introduced.

For PETER GRAY, and SOMERS too, though certainly in trade,
Were properly particular about the friends they made;
And somehow thus they settled it without a word of mouth—
That GRAY should take the northern half, while SOMERS took the
    south.

On PETER's portion oysters grew—a delicacy rare,
But oysters were a delicacy PETER couldn't bear.
On SOMERS' side was turtle, on the shingle lying thick,
Which SOMERS couldn't eat, because it always made him sick.

GRAY gnashed his teeth with envy as he saw a mighty store
Of turtle unmolested on his fellow-creature's shore:
The oysters at his feet aside impatiently he shoved,
For turtle and his mother were the only things he loved.

And SOMERS sighed in sorrow as he settled in the south,
For the thought of PETER's oysters brought the water to his mouth.
He longed to lay him down upon the shelly bed, and stuff:
He had often eaten oysters, but had never had enough.

How they wished an introduction to each other they had had
When on board the *Ballyshannon!* And it drove them nearly mad
To think how very friendly with each other they might get,
If it wasn't for the arbitrary rule of etiquette!

One day, when out a-hunting for the *mus ridiculus,*
Gray overheard his fellow-man soliloquising thus:
"I wonder how the playmates of my youth are getting on,
M'CONNELL, S. B. WALTERS, PADDY BYLES, and ROBINSON?"

These simple words made PETER as delighted as could be,
Old chummies at the Charterhouse were ROBINSON and he!
He walked straight up to SOMERS, then he turned extremely red,
Hesitated, hummed and hawed a bit, then cleared his throat, and
    said:

"I beg your pardon—pray forgive me if I seem too bold,
But you have breathed a name I knew familiarly of old.
You spoke aloud of ROBINSON—I happened to be by—
You know him?" "Yes, extremely well." "Allow me—so do I!"

It was enough: they felt they could more sociably get on,
For (ah, the magic of the fact!) they each knew ROBINSON!
And MR. SOMERS' turtle was at PETER's service quite,
And MR. SOMERS punished PETER's oyster-beds all night.

They soon became like brothers from community of wrongs;
They wrote each other little odes and sang each other songs;
They told each other anecdotes disparaging their wives;
On several occasions, too, they saved each other's lives.

They felt quite melancholy when they parted for the night,
And got up in the morning soon as ever it was light;
Each other's pleasant company they reckoned so upon,
And all because it happened that they both knew ROBINSON!

They lived for many years on that inhospitable shore,
And day by day they learned to love each other more and more.
At last, to their astonishment, on getting up one day,
They saw a vessel anchored in the offing of the bay!

To PETER an idea occurred. "Suppose we cross the main?
So good an opportunity may not occur again."
And SOMERS thought a minute, then ejaculated, "Done!
I wonder how my business in the City's getting on?"

"But stay," said MR. PETER: "when in England, as you know,
I earned a living tasting teas for BAKER, CROOP, AND Co.,
I may be superseded—my employers think me dead!"
"Then come with me," said SOMERS, "and taste indigo instead."

But all their plans were scattered in a moment when they found
The vessel was a convict ship from Portland, outward bound!
When a boat came off to fetch them, though they felt it very kind,
To go on board they firmly but respectfully declined.

As both the happy settlers roared with laughter at the joke,
They recognised an unattractive fellow pulling stroke:
'Twas ROBINSON—a convict, in an unbecoming frock!
Condemned to seven years for misappropriating stock!!!

They laughed no more, for SOMERS thought he had been rather rash
In knowing one whose friend had misappropriated cash;
And PETER thought a foolish tack he must have gone upon
In making the acquaintance of a friend of ROBINSON.

At first they didn't quarrel very openly, I've heard;
They nodded when they met, and now and then exchanged a word:
The word grew rare, and rarer still the nodding of the head,
And when they meet each other now, they cut each other dead.

To allocate the island they agreed by word of mouth,
And PETER takes the north again, and SOMERS takes the south;
And PETER has the oysters, which he loathes with horror grim,
And SOMERS has the turtle—turtle disagrees with him.

William De Morgan

De Morgan began to write at the age of sixty-five. He then suddenly write nine novels, all of them long and most of them very good. This does not prove that we can all write a novel, but it proves that we can all expect to.

JOSEPH VANCE
(Selection)

My Father and Mother never could come to a clear understanding about what had disagreed with my Father the day he lost his situation at Fothergill's.

My Father thought it was the sausage and mashed potatoes he had for lunch at the Rose and Crown, at fourpence, and as much mustard and pepper as you liked. My Mother thought it was the beer.

There was something to be said for my Mother's view, on the score of quantity.

"Everything," she said, "I bring to figures, and my Aunt Elizabeth Hannah taught me to it." And sure enough figures did show that my Father, who had a shilling and threepence in his pocket when he left home at six-thirty in the morning, must have spent eightpence on beer, or lost some of it.—Because, if we allow a penny for the 'bus, and twopence for a 'arf an ounce of barker which he bought (I do not like to give his exact words) at a tobacconist's with a hæmorrhage on his way home, there's the price of two quarts of four ale left, put it how you may.—"And your Father always had a weak head," said my Mother in after years, in the many times over she told me the story.

Anyhow, something must have disagreed with him, or he wouldn't have called Mr. Wotherspoon, the head clerk at Fothergill's, an old herring-gut when he told him to put his trolley somewhere else, and not leave it stood in the orfice door.

"Of course it wasn't a civil remark, in the manner of speaking," said my Mother, "but your Father, my dear, was that simple and honourable himself he never had a suspicion of guile.—And well did Mr.

Wotherspoon deserve the epithet if my belief is true (and I shall hold it to my dying day) that the old man only similated deafness all those years to one day catch your Father out. For I need 'ardly say to you, my dear, that the remark was a outside remark, as the sayin' is, and not intended to reach its audience."

If my recollection of my Father's conversation isn't coloured by subsequent experience of hoarse men in taprooms, resembling his personal friends at this date in their accent and the bias of their philosophy, Mr. Wotherspoon must have taken a good deal of unnecessary trouble to procure a conviction. Indeed, I remember my Mother saying once that the strength of language was proverbial, and that Vance was no exception to the rule, and not to be expected. My Mother's way of putting things may have been inconsequent, but then, one never had the slightest doubt of what she meant.

Anyhow, my Father's outside remarks frequently reached their audience, and laid him open to martyrdom in the cause of free speech many times before the incident recorded—my Mother's version of which was probably authentic; although she must have had some of it on hearsay.

"I decline to repeat his language," said Mr. Wotherspoon to Mr. Fothergill, "but it was not respectful, and I should say he deserved the sack."

"Give him his screw and put on another warehouseman," said Mr. Fothergill. So my Father had to accept the sack on the Saturday following.

I was a small boy of seven at this time, but I must have been observant, from the vividness of my recollection of the events of that Saturday afternoon. My young mind, catching its impressions from my Mother's way of looking at the situation, and supported by the cheerfulness (which may have been partly artificial) with which my Father accepted the sack, drew the inference that my Father had dismissed Fothergill's, and was now open to all kinds of preferment which his late employers' malice had hitherto prevented reaching him. This coloured our conversation as we walked along the main road towards London after the family dinner. I accompanied him on the pretext that I was competent and willing to prevent his taking more than a pint at the Roebuck.

"Could you lick three men?" I said, breaking silence disconnectedly.

"Could I lick free me?" repeated my Father after me. "In course I could! Who's to prevent me, young 'un, hay?"

I was silent and counted sixteen paving stones before I returned to the charge. I couldn't count seventeen as it was a sudden introduction of a new metre, so to speak, into the counting. So I resumed my enquiries.

"Could you lick three men if two of 'em was policemen?"

"That's accordin' to who the other might be," said my Father after reflection, which convinced my simplicity that he was replying in good faith.

"Could you lick three men if one of them was Mr. Fothergill and two of 'em was p'licemen?" This was a home-thrust, and my Father's prompt counterstroke showed that he appreciated the connection with the recent conversation at dinner.

"If one of 'em was Mr. Fothergill I could lick six, and if two of 'em was Mr. Fothergill and Mr. Wotherspoon I could lick twelve."

I accepted this as meaning that the intense insignificance of the two would act as a drawback on the effectiveness of the police force; and I believe now that my Father intended this, and did not refer to any stimulus to his prowess which the sight of his recent employers might occasion. But I felt explanation was necessary, and sought for it in my Father's remarks at dinner.

"Is that because you expected a beggar to be an angel?" was my next question. For my Father had stopped my Mother in some too lenient view of Mr. Wotherspoon's conduct with, "An old herring-gut like that has no call to expect a poor beggar to be an angel," and this had been a little beyond my comprehension.

"What's the young nipper a-driving at?" said my parent. "I tell you what, young man, if young beginners are going to ask questions as if they was blooming grandmothers, we shall never get to this here public house."

"This one ain't the Roebuck," said I, as my Father pushed me through a swing door into a sound of bad men and a smell of worse beer.

"No, it ain't, and I ain't a-going to it. If I goes to the Roebuck I ain't at liberty, accordin' to my ideas of honour, to take more than a pint. I want p'r'aps a pint and a 'arf, and I comes in 'ere.—Quart o' four ale, Miss!"

The equivocation did not seem wrong to my infant mind; in fact, it impressed me as doing my Father credit, and made me resolve to be equally honourable. But the ordering of the quart brought a doubt to my face, to which my Father yielded an explanation.

" 'Arf a pint for the young nipper, and three 'arf-pints for daddy—that's the 'rithmetic! What the nipper don't drink of his 'arf-pint, I drinks for his sake—so he mayn't get drunk, which at seven is vice."

The nipper didn't drink much of the half-pint, fortunately for him, and his Father performed the act of altruism imposed on him. Having done so, his attention appeared to be attracted by something inside the pewter.

"Strike me blind," he said, "if there ain't a bloody little hinseck at the bottom of the pot!"

There was, apparently, and he fell out with a heeltap of beer on the metal counter, out of my sight.

"Pick me up, Daddy," said I. "For to see the hinseck," I added by way of explanation. I can remember now exactly how my Father's hand felt as he grasped me by the trousers and lifted me up, and the sound of his question. "What do young sucking bantams want with insects?"

"He'll be for crockin' him," said a Sweep with inflamed eyelids. "Crock him, yoong 'un, with your fingernail."

But my Father, who was getting toward the quarrelsome stage of beer, interposed upon the suggestion, not from any humanitarian motives, but in order to contradict the Sweep.

"This here hinseck," he said, "come out of my beer, wot I paid for, square. Consequent this here hinseck I account as *my* hinseck—and this here son of mine has been too well educated, though young, to presoom to crock this here hinseck unless I give leave.—Hay, young 'un? Or for that matter," added my parent with a sudden aggressive enlargement of his claim—"anyone else."

"Anyone else, wot?" said the Sweep.

My Father, instead of answering, addressed himself over the bar to the young lady thereof, as an umpire secure from intimidation behind a fortress of brass and pewter.

"I ask you, Miss," said he, "have I said or have I not said clear and plain, that I regard this here hinseck as belonging? And have I said or have I not said, equally clear and plain, that if any man (or for that matter any other) was to presoom to crock this hinseck on this here counter, I would fetch him a smack over the mouth?"

The young woman was filling one pot alternately at two taps and had taken too little from tap number one. So she had to exercise great discretion in stopping tap number two at the right moment. When she had done this, she referred again to number one, and it being an easy task to merely fill up to the brim, she took the opportunity to reply to my Father.

"Can't say I heard any such expression. Fourpence," the last word referring to the transaction in hand.

"Anyhow you put it," said the Sweep, "I'd crock him myself for a farden."

And without waiting for any security of payment, he did it straightway, over my shoulder.

I glanced around to see the effect of the smack. It had followed the provocation so quickly that the Sweep's hand was not back in time to stop it.

"All outside. Nothing in here. Nor yet in the street." Thus far the lady of the beer-handles—I was close to her; so I heard her voice above the tumult of awakened partisanship which filled the bar the moment after the smack. I heard that, and I noted with some disappointment that the smack had *not* been over the Sweep's mouth. It was the first time I had ever had a doubt of my Father's infallibility.

"Right you are, Miss."—"Git 'em outside."—"Git 'em round the Rents and down the lane."—"Git 'em round the bark o' Chepstow's, and across."—"Git 'em along the Gas-gardens—land to let on building-lease—that'll do, shove along—land to let on building lease. If a copper don't spot you, you'll 'ave it quiet enough for 'arf an hour. Git your man out; we'll git ours."

"Don't let the child go after them," said the bar lady.—But the child had slipped down off the bar, and the only person left to stop him was too drunk to take instructions—had he not been so, he would have been sober enough to follow the rabble. The child was outside the swing door just in time to see the tail of the crowd turn a corner and disappear. But he could have followed even guided only by the scattered pursuing units that came from far behind him, endowed with a mysterious knowledge (acquired Heaven knows how) that there was a fight, and that it would be found (if not too late) acrost the Gas-gardens on some land with a board up—and that you were on no account to turn round by the eel shop, but follow on. This came hoarsely from one swift of foot as he passed a man with a wooden leg, who said sadly, "T'other side Chepstow's. It'll be done afore I ever gets there." He added that

he was by nature unfortunate, and was always a-missing of everything.

"So I just gives in, I does," said he. "What's the young beggar roaring
about? 'It's moy Father!—It's moy Father!' *What's* your Father?"

"It's his Father what's a-goin' to fight," struck in another runner,
speaking rapidly. "He's a-goin' for to fight Mr. Gunn, the buttin'
Sweep, down the Rents and beyont the Piannerforty works, and you
better look sharp if you want for to see anythink."

How on earth these particulars had been acquired I cannot imagine,
but they revived the failing energies of the wooden leg in a miraculous
way. The owner forgot my howls in his intensified interest, and
resolving to "try it on anyhow," stumped away.

I followed on as fast as my small legs would carry me, but concealing
my despair—for a laundress had shown a disposition towards com-
miseration and I didn't want to be stopped by benevolence or any
other motive. The stragglers got fewer and farther between till they
were revived by the new event of a police-constable, to whom particulars appeared to be needless, as he merely said, "Shut up, all on yer!" in
reply to volunteered information. This last group vanished round a
corner, and I panted after it. But I was getting frightened of what I
might see when I arrived. I believe that had my Father really "landed"
on the Sweep's mouth I should have gone on confident. But my faith
had been shaken, and I went slower, wiping my eyes and recovering
my breath.

I saw nothing of the fight. I was only in time to see, across the canal
as I stood near the wooden foot-bridge, a returning crowd and a group
it left behind. The crowd was returning as a cortège of certain Policemen, who had come mysteriously from the four quarters of heaven,
and were conducting a black object, which I could see from the raised
platform of the bridge was the Sweep who had crocked the insect. I
looked for my Father in vain. Then my eyes went across to the group
across the water, and in the middle of it distinguished a motionless
figure on the ground, and I knew it was my Father.

I had before me a plain issue of Duty, to be done or left undone;
and I should be glad to think that in after life I had always shown
the resolution that I, a midget between seven and eight, showed on
this occasion. I never hesitated a moment. The Sweep had killed my
Father, and I could hear his bellowings of triumph as he came along,
the centre of an admiring audience conducted by two Policemen. 1

cannot repeat them in full, but they recorded his conviction that the method he had employed (I heard what it was later) was the correct way to do the dags of such a one as his late opponent. The terms he applied to him could only be reported if it were certain that their meaning to my readers would be as obscure as they then were to me. They did not seem to me to make the fact that he had killed my Father (as I thought) any the worse. All that was left was to look for a missile. I saw one with a fragment of "Bass's Bitter" label left on it, lying against a dead cat by the pathway, a horrible jagged piece of glass. And in the middle of my recollection of that unwholesome dream, I see that jagged piece of glass and that cat's head, and the string tight round his throat that had strangled it, as clear as I saw it then. There was a round side to it to hold it by, so I was able to close my hand well on it. On came the Sweep and the Policemen's hats (they wore hats in those days), and the admiring throng. On they came to the bridge, and the tramp on the mud changed resonantly to tramp on the planks.

"I could larn you two bloody orficers a lesson sim'lar to that other ...if I chose to, but—"

But no one ever knew the reason of Mr. Gunn's forbearance; for his last word merged in a hideous yell as the jagged bottle-end pierced his eye. It was by the merest chance that I hit him. Of course I had aimed, but what is the aim of a child of seven? Anyhow, it went to the right place—and the howls and curses of its human target bore witness to its arrival.

I had been concealed behind a scrap of fence at the bridge end when I made my shot. But so had two other boys—barefooted street Arabs of the sort the Board-Schools have cleared away. And these boys, seeing instantly that my crime would be ascribed to *them* as universal culprits, scapegoats of humanity, exclaimed to each other in the same breath, "Make yer 'ooks, Matey!"—and bolted one to the left and one to the right, but keeping within whistling and yelling distance. An amiable young Policeman followed at a walk, on a line of pursuit bisecting the angle of the two lines of flight. He caught neither of the fugitives, of course, but he rejoined the procession at the nearest doctor's shop, having slipped round by another road to avoid humiliation; and Mr. Gunn was taken in for provisional treatment at the expense of the authorities.

I was convinced my Father was killed, and too terrified to wait and see the second procession that I knew must cross the bridge later on;

besides, there was Mother! So I left the crowd gazing blankly at two bottles of "show colour," and one leech, in the shop window; and set out for home, too heartbroken and scared even to feel the satisfaction of revenge.

Halfway I met two Policemen bearing a stretcher. I knew what was coming back on that stretcher. I had no need of the information volunteered by another boy rather older than I.

"Don't you know what that is, you little hass?" said he, seeing my gaze fixed upon it. "That there's the stretcher fur to put the beggar on what's dead. Straight out flat! Then he'll have a funeral, he will— corpses, 'earses, plooms, mutes!"—And he began a sort of pantomime of solemn obsequies; but as perhaps he felt the cast was insufficient, gave it up and danced.

The whole thing was getting more and more of a nightmare, and I was consciously becoming incapable of finding my way home. I began calling aloud for my Father to come and help me, even while I knew what had happened, and that he could not. Then I heard a stumping on the pavement behind me, and recognised it as the wooden leg of an hour ago. I felt that its owner was almost an old friend, especially when he too recognised me.

"Who's this here little chap a-hollering for his Father? He's number two, this is.—No—he ain't,—by gum! It's the very same over again," and then his voice changed as he added: "Look here, old man, I'll give you a lift. Wipe your eyes. Where do you want to go to?"

"Stallwood's Cottages, No. 13. It's the only house, please, that hasn't no name on the door, and it's next door to the laundry."

"There ain't no such place," struck in the boy who had called me a little ass, and who I really believe was a fiend in human form. "Don't you believe him. He's a-kidding of yer."

But the wooden-legged man seemed to be endowed with insight into character; for, merely remarking that he would half murder the speaker if he ever laid hands on him, he swung me on his shoulder and stumped on. The fiend, however, having acquired a sort of footing in the affair, didn't mean to be left behind, and pursued us as close as he dared.

"'Arf murder me if yer like—I give leave! You may 'ole murder me too if yer like, if yer ever find such a s'elp-me-Goard place—"

And more to the same effect. But even the attempt to throw the statement into the form of an affidavit did not influence the wooden leg, which went steadily on, growing less and less perceptible to my failing senses, until at last it became a mere rhythmic accompaniment to a dream that I forgot as I woke to find myself deposited on the pavement, and the voice of my bearer saying: "Right you are, old chap! No name on the door, and next door to the laundry. You git along in sharp and go to bed."

And then in answer to my unspoken question (for the words wouldn't come), he added: "Never you fret your kidneys about your Father! *He* ain't dead! Trust *him!*—he'll live to be concerned in many quarts yet. Good-bye!"

And he whistled "Lucy Neal" and stumped off.

I did not share his confidence about my Father, but he had cheered me up. Had he been altogether fallible, he would have fallen a victim to the misstatements of the funeral boy. And him he had simply flouted! So I collected my courage, and jumped up to the bell-handle,—which was a pull-down one, or I couldn't have rung it,—I heard voices inside, and my Mother came to the door.

"Bless my soul, it's Joe without his Father again! Joseph, you let your Father go to the Roebuck! Where is he now?"

I was far more afraid of telling the awful truth to my Mother than I had been of anything else on that dreadful afternoon, so I resolved to give details later on. I had just enough voice in me for my Mother, stooping down to my level, to hear me exonerate the Roebuck, which I could do truthfully.

"Then if your Father didn't go to the Roebuck what for are you crying? Where did you leave him?"

I affirmed, truthfully, that I saw him last a-going away with several men towards the canal. I added, untruthfully, that I had losted my way, and the boys told me wrong. I thought my Mother was going to slap me. It would have made my mind happier if she had. But she only said, "Dearie me, whoever would be a woman! You come along and get to bed and go to sleep at once, and no nonsense." I was very soon wiping my eyes on a small dirty nightshirt, and contributing an occasional sob to the conversation that went on in the next room. I had declined supper, not so much because I did not want it, as to get out of sight and cry in the dark. I should now wonder at myself for this, if I had not behaved in the same way fifty times since; indeed, the sorrow's crown of sorrows has always been to me not what the poet sings, but the communication of bad news to happy unsuspicion. I always feel as I then felt; as if it was my fault and *I* was responsible.

"What's the matter with the child?"—Thus the conversation ran on between my Mother and her neighbor, Mrs. Packles, from Packleses' laundry next door, who had come in to tea and gossip.

"It's to be hoped nothing's the matter ser'ous, Mrs. Vance."

"Law, Mrs. Packles, Ma'am," said my Mother, "if I was to worrit every time Vance comes home late, there'd never be an end. Your petticoat is a-scorching."

"It ain't my best. If you was to spare me the toasting-fork, now your piece is browned, I wouldn't spoil the knife-end in the fire over mine. Being likewise the butter-knife."

"I was looking for it."—And my Mother began to butter her piece (as I could hear by the scraping), but she stopped uneasily and came into the bedroom and looked at me. I pretended to be asleep. She kissed me, making matters ten times worse; and I suffered pangs of conscience, but kept my counsel. She returned to the toast, and resumed the conversation.

"It's your *dress* scorching now, Mrs. Packles—do 'ee double it back like I do mine."

I heard Mrs. P. accept the suggestion.

"Vance is that particular about bloaters that I was thinking we might wait till he comes? Tea-time,—he said. One bloater kept back to be done later, has a feeling of discomfort when you come in and other folks has finished. Don't you think so, Ma'am?"

There was the slightest shade of asperity in the question and I read in it that Mrs. Packles had looked unsympathetic. She also said something, but I failed to catch it, owing to Mrs. P. having a defect in her speech. Like Timour, she had only one tooth above and one below; but then they didn't extend all along the gum, like his. However, she had the reputation of being a Tartar, and Mr. Packles used to confirm this report in public—perhaps I should say in publics. What Mrs. Packles had said evidently reflected on my Father.

"No, Ma'am," said my Mother. "On the contrary, Vance is by nature a sober man—not like neighbors of his I could name whose habits are proverbial, as the sayin' is. In some cases, as you know, Ma'am, the smell of beer is transparent, and in such, credit is given undeserved. In others, secrecy throws a veil, even I am told in high places, and none suspect. But Vance was ever that open nature! However, we will put the bloaters on the trivet if you say the word."

Mrs. Packles couldn't say the word for the reason I have mentioned, nor any word distinctly. But I understood that she waived defence of Packles against my Mother's insinuation, in consideration of the bloaters. Also that, to avoid the quicksands the conversation had so narrowly escaped, she passed in review the condiments or accompaniments to bloaters sanctioned by judges. I heard my Mother's answer:

"Accordin' to me, Mrs. Packles, and I am not sing'lar, gin on no account! Coffee also, though no objection can be raised, if popular in quarters, is, to my thinking, contrary to bloaters. Now to 'ot tea and buttered toast, there can be no exception."

I felt that I was an exception. And how I repented my rash renunciation of supper while under excitement! I was getting very hungry, and there was no prospect of relief till breakfast, unless I cut into the conversation and risked further catechism about my afternoon. So I lay still and sucked my nightgown, of which I can distinctly recollect the flavour to this day. I only wish *it* had been an accompaniment of bloaters and hot tea and toast. Taken alone, nightgown juice is not nutritious.

Mrs. Packles murmured assent, and was about to enlarge on the gratifying topic when she was interrupted by a footstep outside.

"It's at your house," said my Mother; "somebody is ringing the laundry bell."—And Mrs. P. went out to investigate. A distant colloquy followed, between a man's voice and Mrs. Packles's substitute for one; but nothing audible to me, until my Mother's sudden—"Well, now!"— following on something she heard and I did not. The teacup she put down suddenly spilled and clicked on the saucer; but she disregarded it and went straight out after Mrs. Packles. Before the door had time to slam, I caught the words—"Are you Mrs. Vance?"—and recognised the step of a Policeman on the garden path. Then followed narrative of an unexcited sort from the Policeman, sobs and exclamations from my Mother, and sympathy from Mrs. Packles, who I felt sure was endeavouring to claim a fulfilment of prophecy recently and clearly by herself.

"Oh, Joey, Joey, Joey!" cried my Mother, "go to bed again this minute. Your Father's in the Hospital, and I must go to him."

I had got out of bed and was standing in the doorway of the bedroom. As I find that I have in memory a picture of a small boy crying, with a very rough head, as well as of a large Policeman dripping (for it was raining hard) and my Mother pulling a hurried shawl on, and Mrs. Packles exhibiting sympathy, with the slightest flavour of triumph, I am inclined to think that the fifty-odd years that have passed since then have made me mix what I actually do recollect with what my Mother told me many times later. Otherwise how do I seem to myself to see, from the front room, that small boy standing in the doorway rubbing his grubby little face with his nightgown?

Perhaps I went back to bed; perhaps I didn't! Anyhow, my next clear memory is of sitting by the fire with Mrs. Packles, and of great satisfaction from fresh hot toast, which Mrs. Packles (who remained behind by request) intentionally made the vehicle of much less butter than she took herself.

I don't think she suspected me of having any story to tell beyond what she had already heard—or she would certainly have pumped me for it, instead of making the conversation turn on the moral improvement of little boys. I was much too frightened to tell anything, even if I had not been too sleepy and greedy at the same moment. I wasn't hypocrite enough at that early age to pretend I wanted to know what the Policeman had said. Or possibly I mistrusted my powers of playing out the part, if I embarked on enquiry from Mrs. Packles. Besides—it didn't matter! *I* knew what the Policeman had said a great deal better than I knew what Mrs. Packles was saying about (1) the necessity for the young to curb their inherent vices, or there was no knowing, (2) the accumulation of misfortunes all but herself were free from, but that she had to put up with, (3) her patience and fortitude under disaster, and (4) her power of anticipating events and no attention paid, not if she talked herself 'oarse!

Perhaps if I could have kept awake I should have known what it was to hear Mrs. Packles under a further drawback from hoarseness. But sleep overcame me, and I remember no more.

Thomas Hardy

ANDREY SATCHEL AND THE PARSON
AND CLERK

[This is one of a series of stories told by a very gossipy group of passengers in the carrier's van, on its way to Longpuddle.]

It all arose, you must know, from Andrey being fond of a drop of drink at that time—though he's a sober enough man now by all account, so much the better for him. Jane, his bride, you see, was somewhat older than Andrey; how much older I don't pretend to say; she was not one of our parish, and the register alone may be able to tell that. But, at any rate, her being a little ahead of her young man in mortal years, coupled with other bodily circumstances owing to that young man—

("Ah, poor thing!" sighed the women.)

—made her very anxious to get the thing done before he changed his mind; and 'twas with a joyful countenance (they say) that she, with Andrey and his brother and sister-in-law, marched off to church one November morning as soon as 'twas day a'most, to be made one with Andrey for the rest of her life. He had left our place long before it was light, and the folks that were up all waved their lanterns at him, and flung up their hats as he went.

The church of her parish was a mile and more from where she lived, and, as it was a wonderful fine day for the time of year, the plan was that as soon as they were married they would make out a holiday by driving straight off to Port Bredy, to see the ships and the sea and the sojers, instead of coming back to a meal at the house of the distant relation she lived wi', and moping about there all the afternoon.

Well, some folk noticed that Andrey walked with rather wambling steps to church that morning; the truth o't was that his nearest neighbour's child had been christened the day before, and Andrey, having stood godfather, had stayed all night keeping up the christening, for he had said to himself, "not if I live to be a thousand shall I again be made a godfather one day, and a husband the next, and perhaps a father the next, and therefore I'll make the most of the blessing." So that when he started from home in the morning he had not been in bed at all. The result was, as I say, that when he and his bride-to-be walked up the church to get married, the pa'son (who was a very strict man inside the church, whatever he was outside) looked hard at Andrey, and said, very sharp:

"How's this, my man? You are in liquor. And so early, too. I'm ashamed of you!"

"Well, that's true, sir," says Andrey. "But I can walk straight enough for practical purposes. I can walk a chalk line," he says (meaning no offence), "as well as some other folk: and—' (getting hotter)—I reckon that if you, Pa'son Billy Toogood, had kept up a christening all night so thoroughly as I have done, you wouldn't be able to stand at all; d—— me if you would!"

This answer made Pa'son Billy—as they used to call him—rather spitish, not to say hot, for he was a warm-tempered man if provoked, and he said, very decidedly: "Well, I cannot marry you in this state; and I will not! Go home and get sober!" And he slapped the book together like a rat-trap.

Then the bride burst out crying as if her heart would break, for very fear that she would lose Andrey after all her hard work to get him, and begged and implored the pa'son to go on with the ceremony. But no.

"I won't be a party to your solemnizing matrimony with a tipsy man," says Mr. Toogood. "It is not right and decent. I am sorry for you, my young woman, seeing the condition you are in, but you'd better go home again. I wonder how you could think of bringing him here drunk like this!"

"But if—if he don't come drunk he won't come at all, sir!" she says, through her sobs.

"I can't help that," says the pa'son; and plead as she might, it did not move him. Then she tried him another way.

"Well, then, if you'll go home, sir, and leave us here, and come back to the church in an hour or two, I'll undertake to say that he shall be as sober as a judge," she cries. "We'll bide here, with your permission; for if he once goes out of this here church unmarried, all Van Amburgh's horses won't drag him back again!"

"Very well," says the parson. "I'll give you two hours, and then I'll return."

"And please, sir, lock the door, so that we can't escape!" says she.

"Yes," says the parson.

"And let nobody know that we are here."

The pa'son then took off his clane white surplice, and went away; and the others consulted upon the best means for keeping the matter a secret, which it was not a very hard thing to do, the place being so lonely, and the hour so early. The witnesses, Andrey's brother and brother's wife, neither one o' which cared about Andrey's marrying Jane, and had come rather against their will, said they couldn't wait two hours, in that hole of a place, wishing to get home to Longpuddle before dinner-time. They were altogether so crusty that the clerk said there was no difficulty in their doing as they wished. They could go home as if their brother's wedding had actually taken place and the married couple had gone onward for their day's pleasure jaunt to Port Bredy as intended. He, the clerk, and any casual passer-by would act as witnesses when the pa'son came back.

This was agreed to, and away Andrey's relations went, nothing loath, and the clerk shut the church door and prepared to lock in the couple. The bride went up and whispered to him, with her eyes a-streaming still.

"My dear good clerk," she says, "if we bide here in the church, folk may see us through the windows, and find out what has happened; and 'twould cause such a talk and scandal that I never should get over it: and perhaps, too, dear Andrey might try and get out and leave me! Will ye lock us up in the tower, my dear good clerk?" she says. "I'll tole him in there if you will."

The clerk had no objection to do this to oblige the poor young woman, and they toled Andrey into the tower, and the clerk locked 'em both up straightway, and then went home, to return at the end of the two hours.

Pa'son Toogood had not been long in his house after leaving the church when he saw a gentleman in pink and top-boots ride past his windows, and with a sudden flash of heat he called to mind that the hounds met that day just on the edge of his parish. The pa'son was one who dearly loved sport, and much he longed to be there.

In short, except o' Sundays and at tide-times in the week, Pa'son Billy was the life o' the Hunt. 'Tis true that he was poor, and that he rode all of a heap, and that his black mare was rat-tailed and old, and his tops older, and all over of one colour, whitey-brown, and full o' cracks. But he'd been in at the death of three thousand foxes. And— being a bachelor man—every time he went to bed in summer he used to open the bed at bottom and crawl up head foremost, to mind en of the coming winter and the good sport he'd have, and the foxes going to earth. And whenever there was a christening at the Squire's, and he had dinner there afterwards, as he always did, he never failed to christen the chiel over again in a bottle of port wine.

Now the clerk was the parson's groom and gardener and general manager, and had just got back to his work in the garden when he, too, saw the hunting man pass, and presently saw lots more of 'em, noblemen and gentry, and then he saw the hounds, the huntsman, Jim Treadhedge, the whipper-in, and I don't know who besides. The clerk loved going to cover as frantical as the pa'son, so much so that when- ever he saw or heard the pack he could no more rule his feelings than if they were the winds of heaven. He might be bedding, or he might be sowing—all was forgot. So he throws down his spade and rushes in to the pa'son, who was by this time as frantical to go as he.

"That there mare of yours, sir, do want exercise bad, very bad, this morning!" the clerk says, all of a tremble. "Don't ye think I'd better trot her round the downs for an hour, sir?"

"To be sure, she does want exercise badly. I'll trot her round myself," says the parson.

"Oh,—you'll trot her yerself? Well, there's the cob, sir. Really, that cob is getting oncontrollable through biding in a stable so long! If you wouldn't mind my putting on the saddle—"

"Very well. Take him out, certainly," says the pa'son, never caring what the clerk did so long as he himself could get off immediately. So, scrambling into his riding-boots and breeches as quick as he could, he rode off towards the meet, intending to be back in an hour. No sooner was he gone than the clerk mounted the cob, and was off after him. When the pa'son got to the meet he found a lot of friends, and was as jolly as he could be: the hounds found a'most as soon as they threw off, and there was great excitement. So, forgetting that he had meant to go back at once, away rides the pa'son with the rest o' the hunt, all across the fallow ground that lies between Lippet Wood and Green's Copse; and as he galloped he looked behind for a moment, and there was the clerk close to his heels.

"Ha, ha, clerk—you here?" he says.

"Yes, sir, here be I," says t'other.

"Fine exercise for the horses!"

"Ay, sir—hee, hee!" says the clerk.

So they went on and on, into Green's Copse, then across to Higher Jirton; then on across this very turnpike-road to Waterston Ridge, then away towards Yalbury Wood: up hill and down dale, like the very wind, the clerk close to the pa'son, and the pa'son not far from the hounds. Never was there a finer run knowed with that pack than they had that day; and neither pa'son nor clerk thought one word about the unmarried couple locked up in the church tower waiting to get j'ined.

"These hosses of yours, sir, will be much improved by this!" says the clerk as he rode along, just a neck behind the pa'son. " 'Twas a happy thought of your reverent mind to bring 'em out today. Why, it may be frosty and slippery in a day or two, and then the poor things mid not be able to leave the stable for weeks."

"They may not, they may not, it is true. A merciful man is merciful to his beast," says the pa'son.

"Hee, hee!" says the clerk glancing sly into the pa'son's eye.

"Ha, ha!" says the pa'son, a-glancing back into the clerk's. "Halloo!" he shouts, as he sees the fox break cover at that moment.

"Halloo!" cries the clerk. "There he goes! Why, dammy, there's two foxes—"

"Huh, clerk, hush! Don't let me hear that word again! Remember our calling."

"True, sir, true. But really, good sport do carry away a man so, that he's apt to forget his high persuasion!" And the next minute the corner of the clerk's eye shot again into the corner of the pa'son's, and the pa'son's back again to the clerk's. "Hee, hee!" said the clerk.

"Ha, ha!" said Pa'son Toogood.

"Ah, sir," says the clerk again, "this is better than crying Amen to your Ever-and-ever on a winter's morning!"

"Yes, indeed, clerk! To everything there's a season," says Pa'son Toogood, quite pat, for he was a learned Christian man when he liked, and had chapter and ve'se at his tongue's end, as a pa'son should.

At last, late in the day, the hunting came to an end by the fox running into a' old woman's cottage, under her table, and up the clockcase.

The pa'son and clerk were among the first in at the death, their faces a-staring in at the old woman's winder, and the clock striking as he'd never been heard to strike before. Then came the question of finding their way home.

Neither the pa'son nor the clerk knowed how they were going to do this, for their beasts were well-nigh tired down to the ground. But they started back-along as well as they could, though they were so done up that they could only drag along at a' amble, and not much of that at a time.

"We shall never, never get there!" groaned Mr. Toogood, quite bowed down.

"Never!" groans the clerk. " 'Tis a judgment upon us for our iniquities!"

"I fear it is," murmurs the pa'son.

Well, 'twas quite dark afore they entered the pa'sonage gate, having crept into the parish as quiet as if they'd stole a hammer, little wishing their congregation to know what they'd been up to all day long. And as they were so dog-tired, and so anxious about the horses, never once did they think of the unmarried couple. As soon as ever the horses had been stabled and fed, and the pa'son and clerk had had a bit and a sup theirselves, they went to bed.

Next morning when Pa'son Toogood was at breakfast, thinking of the glorious sport he'd had the day before, the clerk came in a hurry to the door and asked to see him.

"It has just come into my mind, sir, that we've forgot all about the couple that we was to have married yesterday!"

The half-chawed victuals dropped from the pa'son's mouth as if he'd been shot. "Bless my soul," says he, "so we have! How very awkward!"

"It is, sir; very. Perhaps we've ruined the 'ooman!"

"Ah—to be sure—I remember! She ought to have been married before."

"If anything has happened to her up in that there tower, and no doctor or nuss—"

(—"Ah—poor thing!" sighed the women.)

"—'twill be a quarter-sessions matter for us, not to speak of the disgrace to the Church!"

"Good God, clerk, don't drive me wild!" says the pa'son. "Why the hell didn't I marry 'em, drunk or sober!" (Pa'sons used to cuss in them days like plain honest men.) "Have you been to the church to see what happened to them, or inquired in the village?"

"Not I, sir! It only came into my head a moment ago, and I always like to be second to you in church matters. You could have knocked me down with a sparrow's feather when I thought o't, sir; I assure 'ee you could!"

Well, the pa'son jumped up from his breakfast, and together they went off to the church.

"It is not at all likely that they are there now," says Mr. Toogood, as they went; "and indeed I hope they are not. They be pretty sure to have escaped and gone home."

However, they opened the church-hatch, entered the churchyard, and looking up at the tower there they seed a little small white face at the belfry-winder, and a little small hand waving. 'Twas the bride.

"God my life, clerk," says Mr. Toogood, "I don't know how to face 'em!" And he sank down upon a tombstone. "How I wish I hadn't been so cussed particular!"

"Yes—'twas a pity we didn't finish it when we'd begun," the clerk said. "Still, since the feelings of your holy priestcraft wouldn't let ye, the couple must put up with it."

"True, clerk, true! Does she look as if anything premature had took place?"

"I can't see her no lower down than her arm-pits, sir."

"Well—how do her face look?"

"It do look mighty white!"

"Well, we must know the worst! Dear me, how the small of my back do ache from that ride yesterday! ... But to more godly business!"

They went on into the church, and unlocked the tower stairs, and immediately poor Jane and Andrey busted out like starved mice from a cupboard, Andrey limp and sober enough now, and his bride pale and cold, but otherwise as usual.

"What," says the pa'son, with a great breath of relief, "you haven't been here ever since?"

"Yes, we have, sir!" says the bride sinking down upon a seat in her weakness. "Not a morsel, wet or dry, have we had since! It was impossible to get out without help, and here we've stayed!"

"But why didn't you shout, good souls?" said the pa'son.

"She wouldn't let me," says Andrey.

"Because we were so ashamed at what had led to it," sobs Jane. "We felt that if it were noised abroad it would cling to us all our lives! Once or twice Andrey had a good mind to toll the bell, but then he said: 'No; I'll starve first. I won't bring disgrace on my name and yours, my dear.' And so we waited and waited, and walked round and round; but never did you come till now!"

"To my regret!" says the parson. "Now, then, we will soon get it over."

"I—I should like some victuals," said Andrey; "'twould gie me courage to do it, if it is only a crust o' bread and a' onion; for I am that leery that I can feel my stomach rubbing against my backbone."

"I think we had better get it done," said the bride, a bit anxious in manner; "since we are all here convenient, too!"

Andrey gave way about the victuals, and the clerk called in a second witness who wouldn't be likely to gossip about it, and soon the knot was tied, and the bride looked smiling and calm forthwith, and Andrey limper than ever.

"Now," said Pa'son Toogood, "you two must come to my house, and have a good lining put to your insides before you go a step further."

They were very glad of the offer, and went out of the churchyard by one path while the pa'son and clerk went out by the other, and so did not attract notice, it being still early. They entered the rectory as if they'd just come back from their trip to Port Bredy; and then they knocked in the victuals and drink till they could hold no more.

It was a long while before the story of what they had gone through was known, but it was talked of in time, and they themselves laugh over it now; though what Jane got for her pains was no great bargain after all. 'Tis true she saved her name.

[From *A Few Crusted Characters*]

THE RUINED MAID

"O 'Melia, my dear, this does everything crown!
Who could have supposed I should meet you in town?
And whence such fair garments, such prosperi-ty?"—
"O didn't you know I'd been ruined?" said she.

—"You left us in tatters, without shoes or socks,
Tired of digging potatoes, and spudding up docks;
And now you've gay bracelets and bright feathers three."—
"Yes: that's how we dress when we're ruined," said she.

—"At home in the barton you said 'thee' and 'thou,'
And 'thik oon,' and 'theäs oon,' and 't'other'; but now
Your talking quite fits 'ee for high company!"—
"Some polish is gained with one's ruin," said she.

—"Your hands were like paws then, your face blue
    and bleak,
But now I'm bewitched by your delicate cheek,
And your little gloves fit as on any la-dy!"—
"We never do work when we're ruined," said she.

—"You used to call home-life a hag-ridden dream,
And you'd sigh, and you'd sock; but at present you
    seem
To know not of megrims or melancho-ly!"—
"True. There's an advantage in ruin," said she.

—"I wish I had feathers, a fine sweeping gown,
And a delicate face, and could strut about Town!"—
"My dear—a raw country girl, such as you be,
Isn't equal to that. You ain't ruined," said she.

EPITAPH ON A PESSIMIST

I'm Smith of Stoke, aged sixty-odd,
    I've lived without a dame
From youth-time on; and would to God
    My dad had done the same.

George T. Lanigan

Lanigan was a Canadian, a brilliant journalist whose career lay in part in the United States. His Ahkoond of Swat *is in most of the anthologies. And his* Amateur Orlando *contains these exquisitely chiseled lines:*

> *"A·squeak's heard in the orchestra*
> *As the leader draws across*
> *Th' intestines of the agile cat*
> *The tail of the noble hoss."*

He wrote his Fables *in 1877, for the New York* World.

THE SOCRATIC CHIMPANZEE AND THE SHALLOW BABOON

A Chimpanzee who had long viewed with Envy the Popularity of a Shallow but Pretentious Baboon, asked him to account for the presence of the Milk in the Cocoa-nut. The Baboon replied that his Questioner believed in the Darwinian Theory that Monkeys degenerated into Man; an answer which so delighted the Spectators that they tore the Chimpanzee into Pieces, while the Baboon's work on the Conflict of Science and Orthodoxy attained a Hundredth Edition.

Moral.—A Hard Question turneth away Argument.

THE CENTIPEDE AND THE BARBARIC YAK

While a Centipede was painfully toiling over the Libyan Desert he was encountered by a barbaric Yak, who scornfully asked him how were his poor Feet. The humble Creature made no reply at the time, but some days later found the barbaric Yak taken in the nets of the Hunter and almost devoured by Insects, which fled at the approach of the Centipede. "Help, help, my good friend!" exclaimed the unfortunate Beast. "I cannot move a muscle in these cruel Toils, and the ravenous Insects have devoured my delicate Flesh." "Say you so?" responded the Centipede. "Can you really not defend yourself?" "Alas, how can I?" replied the Yak. "See you not how straitly I am bound?" "And is your Flesh then so delicate?" "It is, though I say it who should not." "Then," said the Centipede, "I guess I'll take a bite myself."

Moral.—The other man's Extremity is often our Opportunity.

THE GRASSHOPPER AND THE ANT

A frivolous Grasshopper, having spent the Summer in Mirth and Revelry, went on the Approach of the inclement Winter to the Ant, and implored it of its charity to stake him. "You had better go to your Uncle," replied the prudent Ant; "had you imitated my Forethought and deposited your Funds in a Savings Bank you would not now be compelled to regard your Duster in the light of an Ulster." Thus saying, the virtuous Ant retired, and read in the Papers next morning that the Savings Bank where he had deposited his Funds had suspended.

Moral.—Dum Vivimus, Vivamus.

William H. Mallock

This number, like Garnett's Abdallah the Adite, *is a conte philoso-phique, and betrays a considerable debt to* Candide. *It is a satire on posi-tivism, which flourished in the mid-nineteenth century. Positivism as an organized faith has disappeared, but Mallock's mockery seems to me as lively as ever. The smile remains when the Cheshire cat has vanished.* The New Paul and Virginia *is very hard to come by now; if anyone has a copy for sale let me know.*

THE NEW PAUL AND VIRGINIA
(Selection)

CHAPTER I

The magnificent ocean-steamer the *Australasian* was bound for Eng-land, on her homeward voyage from Melbourne, carrying Her Majesty's mails and ninety-eight first-class passengers. Never did ves-sel start under happier auspices. The skies were cloudless; the sea was smooth as glass. There was not a sound of sickness to be heard any-where; and when dinner-time came there was not a single absentee nor an appetite wanting.

But the passengers soon discovered they were lucky in more than weather. Dinner was hardly half over before two of the company had begun to attract general attention; and everyone all round the table was wondering, in whispers, who they could possibly be.

One of the objects of this delightful curiosity was a large-boned, middle-aged man, with gleaming spectacles, and lank, untidy hair; whose coat fitted him so ill, and who held his head so high, that one saw at a glance he was some great celebrity. The other was a beautiful lady of about thirty years of age, the like of whom nobody present had ever seen before. She had the fairest hair and the darkest eyebrows, the largest eyes and the smallest waist conceivable; art and nature had been plainly struggling as to which should do the most for her; whilst her bearing was so haughty and distinguished, her glance so tender, and her dress so expensive and so fascinating, that she seemed at the same time to defy and to court attention.

Evening fell on the ship with a soft warm witchery. The air grew purple, and the waves began to glitter in the moonlight. The passengers gathered in knots upon the deck, and the distinguished strangers were still the subject of conjecture. At last the secret was discovered by the wife of an old colonial judge; and the names spread like wildfire. In a few minutes all knew that there were on board the *Australasian* no less personages than Professor Paul Darnley and the superb Virginia St. John.

CHAPTER II

Miss St. John had, for at least six years, been the most renowned woman in Europe. In Paris and St. Petersburg, no less than in London, her name was equally familiar both to princes and to pot-boys; indeed, the gaze of all the world was fixed on her. Yet, in spite of this exposed situation, scandal had proved powerless to wrong her; she defied detraction. Her enemies could but echo her friends' praise of her beauty; her friends could but confirm her enemies' description of her character. Though of birth that might almost be called humble, she had been connected with the heads of many distinguished families; and so general was the affection she inspired, and so winning the ways in which she contrived to retain it, that she found herself, at the age of thirty, mistress of nothing except a large fortune. She was now converted with surprising rapidity by a Ritualistic priest, and she became in a few months a model of piety and devotion. She made lace trimmings for the curate's vestments; she bowed at church as often and profoundly as possible; she enjoyed nothing so much as going to confession; she learnt to despise the world. Indeed, such utter dross did her riches now seem to her, that, despite all the arguments of her ghostly counsellor, she remained convinced that they were far too worthless to offer to the Church, and she saw nothing but to still keep them for herself. The mingled humility and discretion of this resolve so won the heart of a gifted colonial bishop, then on a visit to England, that, having first assured himself that Miss St. John was sincere in making it, he besought her to share with him his humble mitre, and make him the happiest prelate in the whole Catholic Church. Miss St. John consented. The nuptials were celebrated with the most elaborate ritual, and after a short honeymoon the bishop departed for his South Pacific diocese of the Chasauble Islands, to prepare a home for his bride, who was to follow him by the next steamer.

Professor Paul Darnley, in his own walk of life, was even more famous than Virginia had been in hers. He had written three volumes on the origin of life, which he had spent seven years in looking for in infusions of hay and cheese; he had written five volumes on the entozoa of the pig, and two volumes of lectures, as a corollary to these, on the sublimity of human heroism and the whole duty of man. He was renowned all over Europe and America as a complete embodiment of enlightened modern thought. He criticised everything; he took nothing on trust, except the unspeakable sublimity of the human race and its august terrestrial destinies. And, in his double capacity of a seer and a *savant,* he had destroyed all that the world had believed in the past, and revealed to it all that it is going to feel in the future. His mind indeed was like a sea, into which the other great minds of the age discharged themselves, and in which all the slight discrepancies of the philosophy of the present century mingled together and formed one harmonious whole. Nor was he less successful in his own private life. He married, at the age of forty, an excellent evangelical lady, ten years his senior, who wore a green gown, grey corkscrew curls, and who had a fortune of two hundred thousand pounds. Deeply pledged though she was to the most vapid figments of Christianity, Mrs. Darnley was yet proud beyond measure of her husband's world-wide fame, for she did but imperfectly understand the grounds of it. Indeed, the only thing that marred her happiness was the single tenet of his that she had really mastered. This, unluckily, was that he disbelieved in hell. And so, as Mrs. Darnley conceived that that place was designed mainly to hold those who doubted its existence, she daily talked her utmost, and left no text unturned to convince her darling of his very dangerous error. These assiduous arguments soon began to tell. The Professor grew moody and brooding, and he at last suggested to his medical man that a voyage round the world, unaccompanied by his wife, was the prescription most needed by his failing patience. Mrs. Darnley at length consented with a fairly good grace. She made her husband pledge himself that he would not be absent for above a twelvemonth, or else, she said, she should immediately come after him. She bade him the tenderest of adieus, and promised to pray till his return for his recovery of a faith in hell.

The Professor, who had but exceeded his time by six months, was

now on board the *Australasian,* homeward bound to his wife. Virginia
was outward bound to her husband.

CHAPTER III

The sensation created by the presence of these two celebrities was
profound beyond description; and the passengers were never weary
of watching the gleaming spectacles and the square-toed boots of the
one, and the liquid eyes and the ravishing toilettes of the other. Virginia's acquaintance was made almost instantly by three pale-faced
curates, and so well did their friendship prosper, that they soon sang at
nightfall with her a beautiful vesper hymn. Nor did the matter end
here, for the strains sounded so lovely, and Virginia looked so devo-
tional, that most of the passengers the night after joined in a repetition
of this touching evening office.

The Professor, as was natural, held quite aloof, and pondered over
a new species of bug, which he had found very plentiful in his berth.
But it soon occurred to him that he often heard the name of God being
uttered otherwise than in swearing. He listened more attentively to
the sounds which he had at first set down as negro-melodies, and he
soon became convinced that they were something whose very existence
he despised himself for remembering—namely, Christian hymns. He
then thought of the three curates, whose existence he despised himself
for remembering also. And the conviction rapidly dawned on him that,
though the passengers seemed fully alive to his fame as a man of
science, they could yet know very little of all that science had done for
them; and of the death-blow it had given to the foul superstitions of
the past. He therefore resolved that next day he would preach them
a lay-sermon.

At the appointed time the passengers gathered eagerly round him—
all but Virginia, who retired to her cabin when she saw that the
preacher wore no surplice, as she thought it would be a mortal sin to
listen to a sermon without one.

The Professor began amidst a profound silence. He first proclaimed
to his hearers the great primary axiom on which all modern thought
bases itself. He told them that there was but one order of things—it
was so much neater than two; and if we would be certain of anything,
we must never doubt this. Thus, since countless things exist that the
senses *can* take account of, it is evident that nothing exists that the

senses can *not* take account of. The senses can take no account of God; therefore God does not exist. Men of science can only see theology in a ridiculous light, therefore theology has no side that is not ridiculous. He then told them a few of the names that enlightened thinkers had applied to the Christian deity—how Professor Tyndall had called him an "atom-manufacturer," and Professor Huxley a "pedantic drill-sergeant." The passengers at once saw how demonstrably at variance with fact was all religion, and they laughed with a sense of humour that was quite new to them. The Professor's tones then became more solemn, and, having extinguished error, he at once went on to unveil the brilliant light of truth. He showed them how, viewed by modern science, all existence is a chain, with a gas at one end and no one knows what at the other; and how Humanity is a link somewhere; but— holy and awful thought!—we can none of us tell where. "However," he proceeded, "of one thing we can be quite certain: all that is, is matter; the laws of matter are eternal, and we cannot act or think without conforming to them; and if," he said, "we would be solemn and high, and happy, and heroic, and saintly, we have but to strive and struggle to do what we cannot for an instant avoid doing. Yes," he exclaimed, "as the sublime Tyndall tells us, let us struggle to attain to a deeper knowledge of matter, and a more faithful conformity to its laws!"

The Professor would have proceeded, but the weather had been rapidly growing rough, and he here became violently sea-sick.

"Let us," he exclaimed hurriedly, "conform to the laws of matter and go below."

Nor was the advice premature. A storm arose, exceptional in its suddenness and its fury. It raged for two days without ceasing. The *Australasian* sprang a leak; her steering gear was disabled; and it was feared she would go ashore on an island that was seen dimly through the fog to the leeward. The boats were got in readiness. A quantity of provisions and of the passengers' baggage was already stowed in the cutter; when the clouds parted, the sun came out again, and the storm subsided almost as quickly as it arose.

CHAPTER IV

No sooner were the ship's damages in a fair way to be repaired than the Professor resumed his sermon. He climbed into the cutter, which was still full of the passengers' baggage, and sat down on the largest of Virginia's boxes. This so alarmed Virginia that she incontinently followed the Professor into the cutter, to keep an eye on her property; but she did not forget to stop her ears with her fingers, that she might not be guilty of listening to an unsurpliced minister.

The Professor took up the thread of his discourse just where he had broken it off. Every circumstance favoured him. The calm sea was sparkling under the gentlest breeze; all Nature seemed suffused with gladness; and at two miles' distance was an enchanting island, green with every kind of foliage, and glowing with the hues of a thousand flowers. The Professor, having reminded his hearers of what nonsense they now thought all the Christian teachings, went on to show them the blessed results of this. Since the God that we once called all-holy is a fable, that Humanity is all-holy must be a fact. Since we shall never be sublime, and solemn, and unspeakably happy hereafter, it is evident that we can be sublime, and solemn, and unspeakably happy here. "This," said the Professor, "is the new Gospel. It is founded on exact thought. It is the Gospel of the kingdom of man; and had I only here a microscope and a few chemicals, I could demonstrate its eternal truth to you. There is no heaven to seek for; there is no hell to shun. We have nothing to strive and live for except to be unspeakably happy."

This eloquence was received with enthusiasm. The captain in particular, who had a wife in every port he touched at, was overjoyed at hearing that there was no hell; and he sent for all the crew, that they might learn the good news likewise. But soon the general gladness was marred by a sound of weeping. Three-fourths of the passengers, having had time to reflect a little, began exclaiming that as a matter of fact, they were really completely miserable, and that for various reasons they could never be anything else. "My friends," said the Professor, quite undaunted, "that is doubtless completely true. You are not happy now; you probably never will be. But that, I can assure you, is of very little moment. Only conform faithfully to the laws of matter, and your children's children will be happy in the course of a few centuries; and you will like that far, far better than being happy yourselves. Only consider the matter in this light, and you yourselves will in an instant become happy also; and whatever you say, and whatever you do, think only of the effect it will have five hundred years afterwards."

At these solemn words, the anxious faces grew calm. An awful sense of the responsibility of each one of us, and the infinite consequences of every human act, was filling the hearts of all; when by a faithful conformity to the laws of matter, the boiler blew up, and the *Australasian* went down. In an instant the air was rent with yells and cries; and all the Humanity that was on board the vessel was busy, as the Professor expressed it, uniting itself with the infinite azure of the past. Paul and Virginia, however, floated quietly away in the cutter, together with the baggage and provisions.

Virginia was made almost senseless by the suddenness of the catastrophe; and on seeing five sailors sink within three yards of her, she fainted dead away. The Professor begged her not to take it so much to heart, as these were the very men who had got the cutter in readiness; "and they are, therefore," he said, "still really alive in the fact of our happy escape." Virginia, however, being quite insensible, the Professor turned to the last human being still to be seen above the waters, and shouted to him not to be afraid of death, as there was certainly no hell, and that his life, no matter how degraded and miserable, had been a glorious mystery, full of infinite significance. The next moment the struggler was snapped up by a shark. Our friends, meanwhile, borne by a current, had been drifting rapidly towards the island. And the Professor, spreading to the breeze Virginia's beautiful lace parasol, soon brought the cutter to the shore on a beach of the softest sand.

CHAPTER V

The scene that met Paul's eyes was one of extreme loveliness. He found himself in a little fairy bay, full of translucent waters, and fringed with silvery sands. On either side it was protected by fantastic rocks, and in the middle it opened inland to an enchanting valley, where tall tropical trees made a grateful shade, and where the ground was carpeted with the softest moss and turf.

Paul's first care was for his fair companion. He spread a costly cashmere shawl on the beach, and placed her, still fainting, on this. In a few moments she opened her eyes; but was on the point of fainting again, as the horrors of the last half hour came back to her, when she caught sight in the cutter of the largest of her own boxes, and she began to recover herself. Paul begged her to remain quiet whilst he went to reconnoitre.

He had hardly proceeded twenty yards into the valley, when to his infinite astonishment he came on a charming cottage, built under the shadow of a bread-tree, with a broad verandah, plate-glass windows, and red window-blinds. His first thought was that this could be no desert island at all, but some happy European settlement. But, on approaching the cottage, it proved to be quite untenanted, and from the cobwebs woven across the doorway it seemed to have been long abandoned. Inside there was abundance of luxurious furniture; the floors were covered with gorgeous Indian carpets; and there was a pantry well stocked with plate and glass and table-linen. The Professor could not tell what to make of it, till, examining the structure more closely, he found it composed mainly of a ship's timbers. This seemed to tell its own tale, and he at once concluded that he and Virginia were not the first castaways who had been forced to make the island for some time their dwelling-place.

Overjoyed at this discovery, he hastened back to Virginia. She was by this time apparently quite recovered, and was kneeling on the cashmere shawl, with a rosary in her hands designed especially for the use of Anglo-Catholics, alternately lifting up her eyes in gratitude to heaven, and casting them down in anguish at her torn and crumpled dress. The poor Professor was horrified at the sight of a human being in this degrading attitude of superstition. But as Virginia quitted it with alacrity as soon as ever he told his news to her, he hoped he might soon convert her into a sublime and holy Utilitarian.

The first thing she besought him to do was to carry her biggest box to this charming cottage, that she might change her clothes, and appear in something fit to be seen in. The Professor most obligingly at once did as she asked him; and whilst she was busy at her toilette, he got from the cutter what provisions he could, and proceeded to lay the table. When all was ready, he rang a gong which he found suspended in the lobby; Virginia appeared shortly in a beautiful pink dressing-gown, embroidered with silver flowers; and just before sunset the two sat down to an excellent meal. The bread-tree at the door of the cottage contributed some beautiful French rolls; close at hand also they discovered a butter-tree; and the Professor had produced from the cutter a variety of salt and potted meats, *pâté de foie gras,* cakes, preserved fruits, and some bottles of fine champagne. This last helped much to raise their spirits. Virginia found it very dry, and exactly suited to her palate. She had but drunk five glasses of it, when her natural smile returned to her, though she was much disappointed because Paul took no notice of her dressing-gown; and when she had drunk three glasses more she quietly went to sleep on the sofa.

The moon had by this time risen in dazzling splendour, and the Professor went out and lit a cigar. All during dinner there had been a feeling of dull despair in his heart, which even the champagne did not dissipate. But now, as he surveyed in the moonlight the wondrous Paradise in which his strange fate had cast him, his mood changed. The air was full of the scents of a thousand night-smelling flowers; the sea murmured on the beach in soft, voluptuous cadences. The Professor's cigar was excellent. He now saw his situation in a truer light. Here was a bountiful island, where earth unbidden brought forth all her choicest fruits, and most of the luxuries of civilisation had already been wafted thither. Existence here seemed to be purified from all its evils. Was not this the very condition of things which all the sublimest and exactest thinkers of modern times had been dreaming and lecturing and writing books about for a good half-century? Here was a place where Humanity could do justice to itself, and realise those glorious destinies which all exact thinkers take for granted must be in store for it. True, from the mass of Humanity he was completely cut away; but Virginia was his companion. Holiness, and solemnity, and unspeakably significant happiness did not, he argued, depend on the multiplication table. He and Virginia represented Humanity as well as a million couples. They were a complete humanity in themselves and a humanity in perfectible shape; and the very next day they would make preparations for fulfilling their holy destiny, and being as solemnly and unspeakably happy as it was their stern duty to be.

The Professor turned his eyes upward to the starry heavens, and a sense came over him of the eternity and the immensity of Nature, and the demonstrable absence of any intelligence that guided it. These reflections naturally brought home to him with more vividness the stupendous and boundless importance of Man. His bosom swelled violently, and he cried aloud, his eyes still fixed on the firmament, "Oh, important All! oh, important Me!"

When he came back to the cottage he found Virginia just getting off the sofa, and preparing to go to bed. She was too sleepy even to say good night to him, and with evident want of temper was tugging at the buttons on her dressing-gown. "Ah!" she murmured as she left the room, "if God, in His infinite mercy, had only spared my maid!"

Virginia's evident discontent gave profound pain to Paul. "How solemn," he exclaimed, "for half Humanity to be discontented!" But he was still more disturbed at the appeal to a chimerical manufacturer of atoms; and he groaned in tones of yet more sonorous sorrow, "How solemn for half Humanity to be sunk lower than the beasts of superstition!"

However, he hoped that these stupendous evils might, under the present favourable conditions, vanish in the course of a few days' progress; and he went to bed, full of august auguries.

Anonymous

This is taken from W. H. Auden's Oxford Book of Light Verse. *As for its provenience, Auden says only that it comes from a scrapbook of Victorian ballads, songs, and broadsheets.*

UNDER THE DROOPING WILLOW TREE

On a small six-acre farm dwelt John Grist the miller,
Near a pond not far beyond grew a drooping willow,
Underneath its spreading leaves sat Jane, his only daughter,
Meditating suicide in the muddy water,
Element Aqua Pura, Aqua Impura.
She sat by a duck pond of dark water,
Under the drooping willow tree.

She'd been jilted by a youth who had joined the Rifles,
A young man not worth a rap, who never stuck at trifles.
Though he promised to keep true, act like a faithful lover,
When his rifle suit he got, then leg bail he gave her,
Hooked it, stepped it, toddled, mizzled.
She sat by a duck pond of dark water,
Under the drooping willow tree.

"All alone I'm left," says she, "my poor heart is bursting;
Dearly did I love my Joe, though he wore plain fustian.
But my nose is out of joint, and don't it make me nettled.
In this pond I'll drown myself, then I shall be settled,
Bottled, finished, done for, flummoxed."
She sat by a duck pond of dark water,
Under the drooping willow tree.

She'd no wish to spoil her clothes, so undressed that minute;
But the water felt so cold when her toes were in it.
"If it weren't so cold," said she, "I'd jump in like winking."

Then she wiped her nose, and sat upon the edge thinking,
Pondering, puzzling, considering, ruminating.
She sat by a duck pond of dark water,
Under the drooping willow tree.

Like a Venus she sat in her nude state staying;
Presently she was frightened by a donkey braying.
Like a frog she gave a leap, but worse luck she stumbled,
Lost her equilibrium, and in the water tumbled,
Fell in, pitched in, dropped in, popped in.
She fell in the duck pond of dark water,
Under the drooping willow tree.

When she found she'd fallen in, she then took to swooning;
Very long it would not have been, before she took to drowning.
But her Joseph was close by, saw her in the water,
With his crooked walking stick by the wool he caught her,
Nabbed her, grabbed her, seized her, collared her
From out of the duck pond of dark water,
Under the drooping willow tree.

He beheld her coming to with great acclamation,
And the tree bore witness to their reconciliation.
There it stands in all its pride, and will stand, moreover,
Unless the spot should be required by the London, Chatham and Dover
Railway, Company, Limited, Good Dividends.
They'll sit by the duck pond of dark water,
Under the drooping willow tree.

Edward W. Thomson

Edward W. Thomson, born in Canada, was at home on both sides of the border. He fought in our Civil War, and then returned to Canada to be a civil engineer, and a journalist in Toronto. He was an editor of the Youth's Companion *in Boston for eleven years, and finally a journalist in Ottawa. His stories of French-Canadian and Scottish-Canadian life are witty and well observed.*

OLD MAN SAVARIN

Old Ma'ame Paradis had caught seventeen small doré, four suckers, and eleven channel-catfish before she used up all the worms in her tomato-can. Therefore she was in a cheerful and loquacious humour when I came along and offered her some of my bait.

"Merci; non, M'sieu. Dat's 'nuff fishin' for me. I got too old now for fish too much. You like me make you present of six or seven doré? Yes? All right. Then you make me present of one quarter dollar."

When this transaction was completed, the old lady got out her short black clay pipe, and filled it with *tabac blanc*.

"Ver' good smell for scare mosquitoes," said she. "Sit down, M'sieu. For sure I like to be here, me, for see the river when she's like this."

Indeed the scene was more than picturesque. Her fishing-platform extended twenty feet from the rocky shore of the great Rataplan Rapid of the Ottawa, which, beginning to tumble a mile to the westward, poured a roaring torrent half a mile wide into the broader, calm brown reach below. Noble elms towered on the shores. Between their trunks we could see many whitewashed cabins, whose doors of blue or green or red scarcely disclosed their colors in that light.

The sinking sun, which already touched the river, seemed somehow the source of the vast stream that flowed radiantly from its blaze. Through the glamour of the evening mist and the maze of June flies we could see a dozen men scooping for fish from platforms like that of Ma'ame Paradis.

Each scooper lifted a great hoop-net set on a handle some fifteen feet long, threw it easily up stream, and swept it on edge with the current to the full length of his reach. Then it was drawn out and at once thrown upward again, if no capture had been made. In case he had taken fish, he came to the inshore edge of his platform, and upset the net's contents into a pool separated from the main rapid by an improvised wall of stones.

"I'm too old for scoop some now," said Ma'ame Paradis, with a sigh.

"You were never strong enough to scoop, surely," said I.

"No, eh? All right, M'sieu. Then you hain't nev' hear 'bout the time Old Man Savarin was catched up with. No, eh? Well, I'll tol' you 'bout that." And this was her story as she told it to me:

Der was fun dose time. Nobody ain't nev' catch up with dat old rascal ony other time since I'll know him first. Me, I'll be only fifteen den. Dat's long time 'go, eh? Well, for sure, I ain't so old like what I'll look. But Old Man Savarin was old already. He's old, old, old, when he's only thirty; an' *mean*—baptême! If de old Nick ain' got de hottest place for dat old stingy—yes, for sure!

You'll see up dere where Frawce Seguin is scoop? Dat's the Laroque platform by right. Me, I was a Laroque. My fader was use for scoop dere, an' my gran'fader—the Laroques scoop dere all de time since ever dere was some Rapid Rataplan. Den Old Man Savarin he's buyed the land up dere from Felix Ladoucier, an' he's told my fader, "You can't scoop no more wisout you pay me rent."

"Rent!" my fader say. "*Saprie!* Dat's my fader's platform for scoop fish! You ask anybody."

"Oh, I'll know all 'bout dat," Old Man Savarin is say. "Ladoucier let you scoop front of his land, for Ladoucier one big fool. De lan's mine now, an' de fishin' right is mine. You can't scoop dere wisout you pay me rent."

"*Baptême!* I'll show you 'bout dat," my fader say.

Next mawny he is go for scoop same like always. Den Old Man Savarin is fetch my fader up before de magistrate. De magistrate make my fader pay nine shillin'!

"Mebbe dat's learn you one lesson," Old Man Savarin is say.

My fader swear pretty good, but my moder say: "Well, Narcisse, dere hain' no use for take it out in *malediction*. De nine shillin' is paid. You scoop more fish—dat's the way."

So my fader he is go out early, early nex' mawny. He's scoop, he's scoop. He's catch plenty fish before Old Man Savarin come.

"You ain't got 'nuff yet for fishin' on my land, eh? Come out of dat," Old Man Savarin is say.

"*Saprie!* Ain' I pay nine shillin' for fish here?" my fader say.

"*Oui*—you pay nine shillin' for fish here *wisout* my leave. But you ain't pay nothin' for fish here *wis* my leave. You is goin' up before de magistrate some more."

So he is fetch my fader up anoder time. An' de magistrate make my fader pay twelve shillin' more!

"Well, I s'pose I can go fish on my fader's platform now," my fader is say.

Old Man Savarin was laugh. "Your honor, dis man tink he don't have for pay me no rent, because you'll make him pay two fines for trespass on my land."

So de magistrate told my fader he hain't got no more right for go on his own platform than he was at the start. My fader is ver' angry. He's cry, he's tear his shirt; but Old Man Savarin only say, "I guess I learn you one good lesson, Narcisse."

De whole village ain't told de old rascal how much dey was angry 'bout dat, for Old Man Savarin is got dem all in debt at his big store. He is grin, grin, and told everybody how he learn my fader two good lesson. An' he is told my fader: "You see what I'll be goin' for do wis you if ever you go on my land again wisout you pay me rent."

"How much you want?" my fader say.

"Half de fish you catch."

"*Monjee!* Never!"

"Five dollar a year, den."

"*Saprie,* no. Dat's too much."

"All right. Keep off my lan', if you hain't want anoder lesson."

"You's a tief," my fader say.

"Hermidas, make up Narcisse Laroque bill," de old rascal say to his clerk. "If he hain't pay dat bill tomorrow, I sue him."

So my fader is scare mos' to death. Only my moder she's say, "*I'll* pay dat bill, me."

So she's take the money she's saved up long time for make my weddin' when it come. An' she's paid de bill. So den my fader hain't scare no more, an' he is shake his fist good under Old Man Savarin's ugly nose. But dat old rascal only laugh an' say, "Narcisse, you like to be fined some more, eh?"

"*Tort Dieu.* You rob me of my place for fish, but I'll take my platform anyhow," my fader is say.

"Yes, eh? All right—if you can get him wisout go on my land. But you go on my land, and see if I don't learn you anoder lesson," Old Man Savarin is say.

So my fader is rob of his platform, too. Nex' ting we hear, Frawce Seguin has rent dat platform for five dollar a year.

Den de big fun begin. My fader an Frawce is cousin. All de time before den dey was good friend. But my fader he is go to Frawce Seguin's place an' he is told him, "Frawce, I'll goin' lick you so hard you can't nev' scoop on my platform."

Frawce only laugh. Den Old Man Savarin come up de hill.

"Fetch him up to de magistrate an' learn him anoder lesson," he is say to Frawce.

"What for?" Frawce say.

"For try to scare you."

"He hain't hurt me none."

"But he's say he will lick you."

"Dat's only because he's vex," Frawce say.

"*Baptême! Non!*" my fader say. "I'll be goin' for lick you good, Frawce."

"For sure?" Frawce say.

"*Saprie!* Yes; for sure."

"Well, dat's all right den, Narcisse. When you goin' for lick me?"

"First time I'll get drunk. I'll be goin' for get drunk dis same day."

"All right, Narcisse. If you goin' get drunk for lick me, I'll be goin' get drunk for lick you"—*Canadien* hain't nev' fool 'nuff for fight, M'sieu, only if dey is got drunk.

Well, my fader he's go on old Marceau's hotel, an' he's drink all day. Frawce Seguin he's go cross de road on Joe Maufraud's hotel, an' *he's* drink all day. When de night come, dey's bose stand out in front of de two hotel for fight.

Dey's bose yell an' yell for make de oder feller scare bad before dey begin. Hermidas Laronde an' Jawny Leroi dey's hold my fader for fear he's go 'cross de road for keel Frawce Seguin dead. Pierre Seguin an' Magloire Sauve is hold Frawce for fear he's come 'cross de road for keel my fader dead. And dose men fight dat way 'cross de road, till dey hain't hardly able for stand up no more.

My fader he's tear his shirt and he's yell, "Let me at him!" Frawce he's tear his shirt and he's yell, "Let me at him!" But de men hain't goin' for let dem loose, for fear one is strike de oder ver' hard. De whole village is shiver 'bout dat offle fight—yes, seh, shiver bad!

Well, dey's fight like dat for more as four hours, till dey hain't able for yell no more, an dey hain't got no money left for buy wheeskey for de crowd. Den Marceau and Joe Maufraud tol' dem bose it was a shame for two cousins to fight so bad. An' my fader he's say he's ver' sorry dat he lick Frawce so hard, and dey's bose sorry. So dey's kiss one another good—only all their clo'es is tore to pieces.

An' what you think 'bout Old Man Savarin? Old Man Savarin is just stand in front of his store all de time, an' he's say: "I'll tink I'll fetch him *bose* hup to de magistrate, an' I'll learn him *bose* a lesson."

Me, I'll be only fifteen, but I hain't scare 'bout dat fight same like my moder is scare. No more is Alphonsine Seguin scare. She's seventeen, an' she wait for de fight to be all over. Den she take her fader home, same like I'll take my fader home for bed. Dat's after twelve o'clock of night.

Nex' mawny early my fader he's groaned and he's groaned: "Ah— ugh—I'm sick, sick, me. I'll be goin' for die dis time, for sure."

"You get up an' scoop some fish," my moder she's say, angry. "Den you hain't be sick no more."

"Ach—ugh—I'll hain't be able. Oh, I'll be so sick. An' I hain' got no place for scoop fish now no more. Frawce Seguin has rob my platform."

"Take de nex' one lower down," my moder she's say.

"Dat's Jawnny Leroi's."

"All right for dat. Jawnny he's hire for run timber today."

"Ugh—I'll not be able for get up. Send for M'sieu le Curé—I'll be goin' for die for sure."

"*Mis re,* but dat's no *man!* Dat's a drunk pig," my moder she's say, angry. "Sick, eh? Lazy, lazy—dat's so. An' dere hain't no fish for de little chilluns, an' it's Friday mawny." So my moder she's begin for cry.

Well, M'sieu, I'll make de rest short; for de sun is all gone now. What you tink I do dat mawny? I take de big scoop-net an' I'll come up here for see if I'll be able for scoop some fish on Jawnny Leroi's platform. Only dere hain't nev' much fish dere.

Pretty quick I'll look up and I'll see Alphonsine Seguin scoop, scoop on my fader's old platform. Alphonsine's fader is sick, sick, same like my fader, an' all de Seguin boys is too little for scoop, same like my brudders is too little. So dere Alphonsine she's scoop, scoop for breakfas'.

What you tink I'll see some more? I'll see Old Man Savarin. He's watchin' from de corner of de cedar bush, an' I'll know ver' good what he's watch for. He's watch for catch my fader go on his own platform. He's want for learn my fader anoder lesson. *Saprie!* dat's make me ver' angry, M'sieu!

Alphonsine she's scoop, scoop plenty fish. I'll not be scoop none. Dat's make me more angry. I'll look up where Alphonsine is, an' I'll talk to myself:—

"Dat's my fader's platform," I'll be say. "Dat's my fader's fish what you catch, Alphonsine. You hain't nev' be my cousin no more. It is mean, mean for Frawce Seguin to rent my fader's platform for please dat old rascal Savarin." Mebby I'll not be so angry at Alphonsine, M'sieu, if I was able for catch some fish; but I hain't able—I don't catch none.

Well, M'sieu, dat's de way for long time—half-hour mebby. Den I'll hear Alphonsine yell good. I'll look up de river some more. She's try for lift her net. She's try hard, hard, but she hain't able. De net is down in de rapid, an' she's only able for hang on to de hannle. Den I'll know she's got one big sturgeon, an' he's so big she can't pull him up.

Monjee! what I care 'bout dat! I'll laugh me. Den I'll laugh good some more, for I'll want Alphonsine for see how I'll laugh big. And I'll talk to myself:—

"Dat's good for dose Seguins," I'll say. "De big sturgeon will pull away de net. Den Alphonsine she will lose her fader's scoop wis de sturgeon. Dat's good 'nuff for dose Seguins! Take my fader platform, eh?"

For sure, I'll want for go an' help Alphonsine all de same—she's my cousin, an' I'll want for see de sturgeon, me. But I'll only just laugh, laugh. *Non, M'sieu;* dere was not one man out on any of de oder platform dat mawny for to help Alphonsine. Dey was all sleep ver' late, for dey was all out ver' late for see de offle fight I told you 'bout.

Well, pretty quick, what you tink? I'll see Old Man Savarin goin' to my fader's platform. He's take hold for help Alphonsine an' dey's bose pull, and pretty quick de big sturgeon is up on de platform. I'll be more angry as before.

Oh, *tort Dieu!* What you tink come den? Why, dat Old Man Savarin is want for take de sturgeon!

First dey hain't speak so I can hear, for de Rapid is too loud. But pretty quick dey's bose angry, and I hear dem talk.

"Dat's my fish," Old Man Savarin is say. "Didn't I save him? Wasn't you goin' for lose him, for sure?"

Me—I'll laugh good. Dass *such* an old rascal.

"You get off dis platform, quick!" Alphonsine she's say.

"Give me my sturgeon," he's say.

"Dat's a lie—it hain't your sturgeon. It's *my* sturgeon," she's yell.

"I'll learn you one lesson 'bout dat," he's say.

Well, M'sieu, Alphonsine she's pull back de fish just when Old Man Savarin is make one grab. An' when she's pull back, she's step to one side, an' de old rascal he is grab at de fish, an' de heft of de sturgeon is make him fall on his face, so he's tumble in de Rapid when Alphonsine let go de sturgeon. So dere's Old Man Savarin floating in de river—and *me!* I'll don' care eef he's drown one bit!

One time he is on his back, one time he is on his face, one time he is all under de water. For sure he's goin' for be draw into de *culbute* an' get drown' dead, if I'll not be able for scoop him when he's go by my platform. I'll want for laugh, but I'll be too much scare.

Well, M'sieu, I'll pick up my fader's scoop and I'll stand out on de edge of de platform. De water is run so fast, I'm mos' 'fraid de old man is boun' for pull me in when I'll scoop him. But I'll not mind for dat, I'll throw de scoop an' catch him; an' for sure, he's hold on good.

So dere's de old rascal in de scoop, but when I'll get him safe, I hain't able for pull him in one bit. I'll only be able for hold on an' laugh, laugh—he's look *ver'* queer! All I can do is to hold him dere so he can't go down de *culbute*. I'll can't pull him up if I'll want to.

De old man is scare ver' bad. But pretty quick he's got hold of de cross-bar of de hoop, an' he's got his ugly old head up good.

"Pull me in," he say, ver' angry.

"I'll hain't be able," I'll say.

Jus' den Alphonsine she come 'long, an' she's laugh so she can't hardly hold on wis me to de hannle. I was laugh good some more.

When de old villain see us have fun, he's yell: "I'll learn you bose one lesson for this. Pull me ashore!"

"Oh! you's learn us bose one lesson, M'sieu Savarin, eh?" Alphonsine she's say. "Well, den, us bose will learn M'sieu Savarin one lesson first. Pull him up a little," she's say to me.

So we pull him up, an' den Alphonsine she's say to me: "Let out de hannle, quick"—and he's under de water some more. When we stop de net, he's got hees head up pretty quick.

"*Monjee!* I'll be drown' if you don't pull me out," he's mos' cry.

"Ver' well—if you's drown, your family be ver' glad," Alphonsine she's say. "Den they's got all your money for spend quick, quick."

M'sieu, dat scare him offle. He's begin for cry like one baby.

"Save me out," he's say. "I'll give you anything I've got."

"How much?" Alphonsine she's say.

He's tink, and he's say, "Quarter dollar."

Alphonsine an' me is laugh, laugh.

"Save me," he's cry some more. "I hain't fit for die dis mawny."

"You hain't fit for live no mawny," Alphonsine she's say. "One quarter dollar, eh? Where's my sturgeon?"

"He's got away when I fall in," he's say.

"How much you goin' give me for lose my big sturgeon?" she's ask.

"How much you'll want, Alphonsine?"

"Two dollare."

"Dat's too much for one sturgeon," he's say. For all he was not feel fit for die, he was more 'fraid for pay out his money.

"Let him down some more," Alphonsine she's say.

"Oh, *misère, misère!* I'll pay de two dollare," he's say when his head come up some more.

"Ver' well, den," Alphonsine she's say; "I'll be willin' for save you, *me*. But you hain't scooped by *me*. You's in Marie's net. I'll only come for help Marie. You's her sturgeon," an' Alphonsine she's laugh an' laugh.

"I didn't lose no sturgeon for Marie," he's say.

"No, eh?" I'll say mysef. "But you's steal my fader's platform. You's take his fishin' place. You's got him fined two times. You's make my moder pay his bill wis *my* weddin' money. What you goin' pay for all dat? You tink I'll be goin' for mos' kill mysef pullin' you out for noting? When you ever do someting for anybody for noting, eh, M'sieu Savarin?"

"How much you want?" he's say.

"Ten dollare for de platform, dat's all."

"Never—dat's robbery," he's say, an' he's begin to cry like *ver'* li'll baby.

"Pull him hup, Marie, an' give him some more," Alphonsine she's say.

But de old rascal is so scare 'bout dat, dat he's say he's pay right off. So we's pull him up near to de platform, only we hain't big 'nuff fool for let him out of de net till he's take out his purse an' pay de twelve dollare.

Monjee, M'sieu! If ever you see one angry old rascal! He not even stop for say: "T'ank you for save me from be drown' dead in the *culbute!*" He's run for his house an' he's put on dry clo'es, an' he's go up to de magistrate first ting for learn me an' Alphonsine one big lesson.

But de magistrate hain' ver' bad magistrate. He's only laugh an' he's say:—

"M'sieu Savarin, de whole river will be laugh at you for let two young girl take eet out of smart man like you like dat. Hain't you tink your life worth twelve Dollare? Didn't dey save you from de *culbute?* *Monjee!* I'll tink de whole river not laugh so ver' bad if you pay dose young girl one hunder dollare for save you so kind."

"One hunder dollare!" he's mos' cry. "Hain't you goin' to learn dose girl one lesson for take advantage of me dat way?"

"Didn't you pay dose girl yoursef? Didn't you took out your purse yoursef? Yes, eh? Well, den, I'll goin' for learn you one lesson yoursef, M'sieu Savarin," de magistrate is say. "Dose two young girl is ver' wicked, eh? Yes, dat's so. But for why? Hain't dey just do to you what you been doin' ever since you was in beesness? Don' I know? You hain' never yet got advantage of nobody wisout you rob him all you can, an' dose wicked young girl only act just like you give dem a lesson all your life."

An' de best fun was de whole river *did* laugh at M'sieu Savarin. An' my fader and Frawce Seguin is laugh most of all, till he's catch hup wis bose of dem anoder time. You come for see me some more, an' I'll tol' you 'bout dat.

T. Edgar Pemberton

Someone could write an interesting volume on the Decline and Fall of the Practical Joke. A good medieval practical joke ended in the loss of a limb by the victim, or even in a witty decapitation. Jonathan Swift's enormous jokes were designed only to drive the butt insane. With the softening of manners in the nineteenth century, the practical joke became a simple device for causing physical and mental pain. Our current jesters aim at producing a bewildered frenzy in the victim, who sees the most fantastic results proceed from apparently familiar causes. A modern joker seeks to reproduce on the intellectual plane the phenomena of the exploding cigar.

Edward A. Sothern, the celebrated actor, the creator of Lord Dundreary in Our American Cousin, *devoted his apparently ample leisure to the prosecution of practical jokes. I choose a few examples from the many given by his adoring biographer. I will say that they are funny, at least to read about.*

HIGH HUMOURS OF E. A. SOTHERN

These American spiritualistic experiments, and the success which attended them, undoubtedly gave Sothern his insatiable taste for practical joking. He had learnt how easily people could be gulled; he had become an adept in all the little arts and contrivances necessary for such purposes; he had acquired a relish for "selling" (he used this word in his letter, and it was with him a favourite one) all with whom he came in contact, both friends and strangers; and so when, in the days of his popularity and the long runs of his pieces, he had plenty of time on his hands, he mounted and furiously rode his hobby horse.

Before I give instances· of his more elaborate enterprises in this direction, I will speak of the odd freaks that he delighted to play with the post. On one occasion, when he was playing in a country theatre, the local postmaster refused to receive and forward a package because it was just a trifle over the regulation limits. Sothern was annoyed at what he considered official obstructiveness, and, having obtained from the postmaster the precise limits (particularly with regard to weight) of the parcels he would receive, he went to a hatter's shop in the town, and purchased two dozen of empty hat-boxes of the usual cardboard make. These he addressed by aid of the local directory to the principal inhabitants of a notably breezy suburb, and from a dozen different offices had them posted. His delight at seeing the local post-man staggering along in a high wind with the huge pile of hat-boxes on his back was infinite, and in the next town that he visited he repeated the performance, only varying it by addressing the two dozen boxes to one individual. Often and often, as he recalled the incident, have I heard Sothern say how much he would have given to have seen the face of this unknown person when the boxes had been stacked away in his hall.

Playing pranks with the post became from this point his almost daily practice. He had his envelopes printed with all sorts of odd devices, such as, "Refuge for Reformed Atheists," "Mail Boat *Betsy Jane*," "Society for the Propagation of Pure Deism," "Troop Ship *Crocodile*," "Asylum for Confirmed Virgins," "Court of Faculties," "Boodles' Bee Hive," and (these were evidently designed to strike terror into the soul of the nervous letter receiver) "Southwell Smallpox Hospital," "Home for Incurable Itch," and "Curious Specimen of Contagious Bedding." In the last named he would usually enclose a small piece of linen or a fragment cut from a blanket. Then he had a practice of addressing an envelope in pencil to a friend, say, in Brussels, writing to that friend to rub out the address and redirect the letter in pencil to a friend in Glasgow, and so successively sending the letter round a dozen places until the envelope was almost covered with postmarks. Then, having got it back from the last of his correspondents, he would erase the pencilled address, and, putting in ink the name and residence of a gentleman in a London Square, and enclosing an invitation to dinner for a date a month old, he would revel in the confident expectation that the recipient, utterly unable to conceive why a plainly addressed letter to "Mr. Suchaone, Lowndes Square," should have been sent round by Brussels, Glasgow, Dublin, Brighton, Inverness, Chester, Northampton, Cork, Scarborough, etc., would indignantly complain to the Postmaster-General, who would in the usual routine send the letter again on its rounds to the bewilderment of all the postmasters.

One of these extraordinary postmark-bestudded envelopes is before me now, stamped Edinburgh, Bradford, Glasgow, Rio de Janeiro,

Liverpool, Dundee, London, Suez Canal, and, finally, Birmingham. . . .

The bogus telegram was an all-too-favourite instrument of warfare with Sothern himself, and he would think nothing of "wiring" to a friend in a distant part as follows:

"Poor Suchaone" (naming a complete stranger) "died last night at ten o'clock. Please arrange for the reception of his remains in your town tomorrow morning"; and this would be followed by another, saying, "His poor wife and children will start by the 12:30 train. For pity's sake, meet and console them. You will find the wife pretty, and the children most interesting. Your kindness will be appreciated by all parties."

I think that it must have been these postal and telegraphic feats that set Sothern thinking that something odd and whimsical ought to be done with letter-carrying pigeons. Certainly I know that while filling a professional engagement in a provincial town, celebrated for the fanciers of "homing birds," he took extraordinary pains, and spent a good deal of money, to procure some of "the right sort"; but, except a marvellous story that he used with much unction to relate, I do not think that out of this notion anything came. I will relate it in his own words:

"I used to get a lot of fellows together in the billiard-room at home" (Sothern's circle of acquaintance was a large one, and on the occasions when this trick was aired he no doubt secured the attendance—and I was not one of them—of the most credulous among his friends), "and after we had smoked and chatted for a time someone, who would be in my confidence, would lead the conversation up to pigeon-flying and the wonderful exploits of the extraordinary birds in my possession. At this I would express annoyance, and my friends asking 'Why?' I would say, 'Oh, nobody believes what my birds have done, and can do, and since I am very fond of them, and, after all, only keep them for my own amusement, I don't somehow care to hear them slightingly talked of. Let us change the subject.' After this, of course, no one would change the subject, and some extraordinary pigeon yarns were told by my confidant, myself, and other men who did not like to appear ignorant on the matter. Then I would say, with a smile, 'Ah, if only old Jim was at his best I could show these fellows what a pigeon could really do!' 'Old Jim!' my confederate would cry out. 'What! you don't mean to say that *he's* alive still—the bird that came home from the Himalayas, and that has crossed the Atlantic a hundred and fifty times?'

'Oh, come, come, that's rather too much!' someone would now be sure
to say. 'I don't believe that!' 'Then, damme, sir, you *shall* believe it!'
I would answer, ringing the bell in apparent ill-temper, and instructing
the servant to bring in old Jim; and then, when in a wicker cage that
eighteen-penny impostor made his appearance, I would take him out,
and, stroking his feathers, say: 'Yes, there's the bird that has brought
home to my family a report of my receipts from every provincial town
in the three kingdoms, who has secured me one or two splendid American engagements, to whose swift wings, indeed, I owe much of my
success. Poor old Jim! He's had the pip, he's got the roup, and some
day he'll moult for the last time; but his work's done, and if it costs me
a thousand a year he'll now roost in peace until the end of his days.'
'Couldn't you,' my confederate would now say, 'send Jim just a little
distance, just to show how extraordinary his powers are?' And then,
after much refusal and more persuasion, I would say, 'Well, well, he
shall go just as far as Blisworth with a message to Jones. I dare say,
after all, a little night-fly like that will freshen the dear old boy up.'
Then the message to Jones would be written, affixed to Jim's wing, and
through the window the bird would be released. After an hour of
billiards and general talk, relieved with good cigars and anything in
the way of refreshment that anybody cared to take, a fluttering at the
window-panes would be heard, and, rushing out, I would return
with *an* exhausted and bedraggled Jim, faithfully bearing Jones's reply
to my message. Believe it or not as you will, not one of the people who
witnessed this thing ever realised the absurdity of sending a pigeon *to*
a place to bring a message back *from* it. They received Jim's double
as a prodigy, and wended their innocent ways homeward, placidly
murmuring 'Marvellous!' "

It was with Miss Neilson's husband, Mr. Philip Lee, for a victim,
that he perpetrated that which was probably the most extensive (and
expensive) of all his extravagantly conceived and carefully carried out
"sells." Unfortunately for Mr. Lee, he expressed, on the occasion of his
first visit to New York, and in Sothern's presence, doubts as to the existence of the wild and delightful American Bohemian life of which he
had heard. Sothern told him that his letters of introduction were all
to the wrong people, but that if he liked he could introduce him to
the right set, and Mr. Lee having expressed his gratitude, a supper-
party was arranged. Covers were laid for twelve, Sothern presiding, and
Mr. Lee, as the guest of the evening, sitting on his right hand. Pre-

viously, it should be stated, he had been introduced by his host and Mr. W. J. Florence (also an inveterate joker, and of course in the secret) to the other (supposed) notabilities who gathered round the sumptuously spread board. For a time all went well, but while the soup was being served one well-known man was seen to take from under his coat a battle-axe, and another celebrity drew from beneath his collar a dirk-knife with a blade over a foot long, which he gravely unclasped and placed beside his plate. Then another took a "six-shooter" from his pocket, while his neighbour drew a scythe and a policeman's staff from under the table, and laid them in the middle of the board.

"For Heaven's sake," whispered the astonished Mr. Lee into Sothern's ear, "what *does* this mean?"

"Keep quiet," replied Sothern; "it is just what I most feared. These gentlemen have been drinking, and they have quarrelled about a friend of theirs, a Mr. Weymyss Jobson, quite an eminent scholar, and a very estimable gentleman; but I hope, for our sakes, they will not attempt to settle their quarrel here. It is dreadful; but I hope, dear boy, that they will go away quietly and have no row. It is a fashion they have here to settle their disputes at a table, or wherever they meet. All we can do now is to await events."

"But there will be murder here!" exclaimed Mr. Lee. "Can we not give warning to the police?"

"Impossible, my dear fellow," said Sothern, regretfully. "Were you even to be suspected by these men of any desire to leave the room, you would be shot like a dog, and no satisfaction would ever be given your relatives in a court of justice. Such is the country."

"It is an infernal country, then!" muttered the guest.

For a few moments all went well, when suddenly a quarrel broke out at the end of the table, and one of the party, springing to his feet, fiercely exclaimed:

"Whoever says that the *History of the French Revolution,* written by my friend David Weymyss Jobson, is not as good a book in every respect as that written by Tom Carlyle on the same subject, is a liar and a thief; and if there is any fool present who desires to take it up, I am his man!"

All the guests rose suddenly, and every man grasped his weapon; shots were fired, and the room was filled with smoke and uproar; several of the guests closed and struggled with each other, and one of the conspirators, thrusting a long knife into the amazed victim's now trembling hand, said:

"Defend yourself! This is butchery—sheer butchery!"

But Sothern sat quietly by, and gave as his advice:

"Keep cool, and *don't get shot.*"

By this time the whole hotel was roused, and I fancy that the "joke" went further than even Sothern in his wildest mood intended. His guests of the evening were a troupe of knock-about negro minstrels, who had been instructed how to act.

Among many amusing stories that that clever comedian Mr. John T. Raymond had to tell of his English travelling experiences with Sothern was the following: They were journeying together from Glasgow to Birmingham, and, having agreed to appear to be strangers to each other, they entered a first-class non-smoking compartment, in which sat two typical English gentlemen. "Do you object to smoking?" asked Raymond of them. "Certainly not," they politely replied; and the same question was put to Sothern, who angrily answered, "I *do,* sir—I do most assuredly. It is a piece of impertinence on your part to ask such a question." "I beg your pardon," replied Raymond, modestly. "I am only an American, and quite unused to the customs of this country." "That's easy enough to see, sir," said the apparently indignant Sothern. "You are evidently either an American or a fool. We don't conduct ourselves that way in England." As if terrified half out of his life, Raymond sank back into a corner of the carriage, and the two disgusted Englishmen expressed themselves freely and audibly concerning Sothern's apparently offensive and overbearing conduct. Gazing at them calmly, Sothern quietly took from his pocket a cigar, lighted it, and puffed away in the most easy manner, as indifferent to his surroundings as if he had been alone. This was too much for the honest-minded Englishmen. They looked at the small and inoffensive Raymond—they looked at the well-knit, aggressive Sothern, and they "went for him." At first they talked "at" him, then they talked to him; they tried to make him put his cigar out, explain, apologise; they declared they would call the guard, they threatened all kinds of things; but Sothern sat imperturbable and silent as the sphynx, calmly smoking his cigar, and filling the compartment with smoke. In the midst of this scene the train stopped at a station; and then Sothern, throwing a contemptuous look on the Englishmen, and taking

Raymond by the arm, said, "Come, John, we'll change carriages here. We'll leave these ill-mannered fellows to themselves!"

Once, taking a midnight railway journey after a late and exhausting performance, he made efforts to secure a compartment to himself; but at the last moment, just as the train was starting, another traveller, somewhat rudely pushed by the porter in attendance, opened the door, and claimed and asserted his right of admission. Sothern said nothing, but when the train had started he opened his travelling-bag, and, looking malevolently at his fellow-passenger, commenced stropping his razors. After the first stopping-station had been passed he had that compartment to himself.

The following story has been told (with variations) by Mr. Toole, but it is so characteristic of Sothern's peculiar vein of humour that it must needs be repeated here. With Mrs. John Wood he entered an ironmonger's shop, and, advancing to the counter, said, "Have you the second edition of Macaulay's *History of England?*" The shop assistant explained the nature of the business, and suggested the name of a neighbouring bookseller. "Well, it don't matter whether it is bound in calf or not," said Sothern. "But, sir, this is *not* a bookseller's," was the reply. "It doesn't matter how you wrap it up," said Sothern; "a piece of brown paper will do—the sort of thing that you would select for your own mother." "Sir," shouted the man, "we don't keep books; this is an ironmonger's shop." "Yes," said Sothern, "I see the binding differs, but as long the the proper fly-leaf is in, I'm not very particular." "Sir," fairly shrieked the bewildered man, "can't you see you have made a mistake and come into the wrong shop?" "Certainly," said Sothern; "I'm in no hurry, and I'll wait while you reach it down." Believing that his strange customer was either deaf or mad, the man went off to the back part of the premises, and returned with the proprietor of the establishment. "What is it that you require, sir?" asked that individual of Sothern, in a bland yet determined voice. "I want," was the prompt and lucid reply, "a small, ordinary file, about six inches in length." "Certainly, sir," said the ironmonger, producing the article, and casting a look of supreme disgust upon his unfortunate assistant. Mrs. John Wood, who, when they entered the shop, had no idea what her madcap companion was going to do, very nearly spoiled the joke by her ill-restrained but not inexcusable laughter.

His pranks with tradespeople were, indeed, innumerable. Amongst other experiences in this connection, I have been with him when he walked into a post-office, and bewildered the person behind the counter by asking for "some nice *fresh* stamps, suitable for an invalid." And then, after he had inspected sheets of all the different values, declaring that this was a case in which expense need not be considered, rejecting them all because he "really feared they were not quite *fresh* enough." . . .

Mr. Stephen Fiske has also related some curious experiences that befell him when in the company of this incorrigible practical joker. He was walking with Sothern down Regent Street one day, when he said, "You go ahead a little, Fiske, and I'll go back, but we will both take the Atlas omnibus." "I" (says Mr. Fiske) "followed his instructions, and, entering the omnibus, found Sothern sitting in the diagonally opposite corner. I naturally looked at him with some curiosity to know why he had asked me to go on ahead. Perceiving this, he assumed a very fierce and belligerent expression, and exclaimed, 'Are you staring at me, sir?' The omnibus was filled with several elderly ladies, two quiet gentlemen who looked like clergymen, and a farmer from the country. I took the cue at once, and replied, 'No; if I wanted to stare at anybody, I would stare at a better-looking man than yourself.' At this Sothern's indignation apparently became uncontrollable, and it required all the force of the clergymen, seconded by the farmer, to keep him in his seat, and prevent him from throwing himself upon me. Finally, he insisted upon stopping the 'bus,' and invited me to step outside, and either apologise then and there for the insult or fight him on the spot. I pretended to prefer to do the latter, but said I would remain in the omnibus; whereupon Sothern took off his overcoat, and handed it to the nearest old lady to hold for him while he chastised me for my inpertinence. In the course of the desultory remarks in which we then indulged, he said that he would allow nobody except his friend John Robinson, of Philadelphia, to speak to him in that way and live; whereupon I immediately informed him that my name was Robinson, Christian name John, and that I had just arrived from America, but that I hadn't the pleasure of his acquaintance, nor did I particularly desire it. In an instant Sothern's manner completely changed, and, climbing over the old ladies, the clergymen, and the farmer, to my corner of the omnibus, he endeavoured to embrace me like a long lost friend. He declared that he had never been more delighted in his life, stopped the omnibus, and proposed that we should get out together, which we thereupon proceeded to do. The comedy we had enacted, and the astonishment depicted on the faces of the inmates of the vehicle, exceeded anything I ever saw on the stage, and afforded food for laughter for many days." ...

Sothern also told the following story: "One morning at breakfast in the public-room of the Continental Hotel, Philadelphia, I observed an old gentleman who was obviously very much annoyed at the delay of the waiter in bringing his breakfast. He was continually looking at his watch and apparently muttering oaths of abdominal origin. For some time I paid little attention to him, but at last, becoming either interested or annoyed with him, I asked the head-waiter who he was. He told me he was General So-and-so, an irascible old bachelor, and one of the regular boarders of the house. While waiting for my own breakfast, I had emptied my pockets of the letters which I had to acknowledge that morning, and among them found what we call a 'property letter,' that had accidentally found its way among my old papers. A property letter, you know, means a letter used on the stage, and this one read as follows:

Young man, I know thy secret—thou lovest above thy station; if thou hast wit, courage, and discretion, I can secure to thee the realisation of thy most sanguine hopes, etc., etc.

"It is the letter which *Claude Melnotte* reads in *The Lady of Lyons*. It struck me on the instant that I would enclose it in an envelope, send it to the old gentleman, and watch the effect; so, calling one of the waiters—a coloured man—I told him to go outside in the hall, remain there for five minutes, and then return and deliver the letter, saying that the writer would call for a reply during the day. I also instructed the waiter, after giving this reply, to retire quickly, and not be seen again in the hotel until the next day, and that I would make it all right with his employer.

"Agreeably to my orders, in a few minutes the servant walked up to the General, and put the letter in his hands. The old gentleman adjusted his spectacles, tore open the envelope, and in an amazed tone commenced to read half aloud, 'Young man, I know thy secret,' and so on. He read it over two or three times, and I never saw anybody more bewildered. At last he called for the head-waiter and demanded to see the servant who had delivered the letter; of course he was not to be found. The longer he pondered, the more he seemed inclined to fly into a passion, and when his breakfast came the storm burst. 'D—n the breakfast!' he exclaimed, almost kicking over the table. 'I want to see the lunatic who calls me a "young man," and says he knows my secret, and can secure the realisation of my fondest hopes. I haven't got any secret, and my fondest hope is to kick the idiot who sent me this insane note!'

"During this time two or three ladies had joined me at the breakfast table, and, noticing the extraordinary excitement of the General, asked me if I knew who he was. I told them to keep very quiet, and not to attract his attention; that he was a fratricide, and an escaped lunatic, whose keepers were outside behind the doors waiting for him, and that the letter was only a decoy to enable them to secure him without any unnecessary violence. This thoroughly alarmed them, and they hurriedly left the table, retreating through the door at the other end of the room.

"At this moment the second head-waiter, who had noticed the agitation of the ladies, walked up to me, and asked if they were not satisfied with the breakfast.

"'Oh, yes,' I replied, 'I presume so; but the youngest lady is a dangerous maniac at times, and the instant she saw her father, General So-and-so, disturbed in his mind by the letter she had written, I whispered to her friend to take her out of the room.'

"In a few moments, having finished my breakfast, I took my own departure. On reaching the office of the hotel, I inquired of one of the principal clerks whether his head-waiter was quite sound in his mind. He asked me my reason for making the inquiry. I said that I didn't want to get my name mixed up in the matter, but it struck me that the one weak point of his intellect was his apparently intense dislike to the General, and I observed, 'If I were you I should just test it by going up to him suddenly, and saying: "Don't you think you will get yourself into trouble about that letter of the General's?"'"

"Taking my advice, the clerk walked up to the head-waiter and abruptly put this question to him. Of course the waiter got very much confused and stammered in endeavouring to make an explanation; whereupon I, who was behind him, intimated by signs to the clerk that he had better get out of the way, as the fellow had a knife about him and might become very violent.

"In the meantime I saw the General approach the office to make inquiries, and in a minute or two there was a tremendous hum of conversation. Half a dozen men were talking loudly and excitedly together, among whom were the clerk and the two head-waiters. I hastily paid my bill, seized my travelling bag, jumped into a conveyance at the door, and was driven away. I never learned what was the result, because I never dared to inquire." ...

During one of his American engagements (it was in 1878) he inveigled someone into writing to the *Inter-Ocean* as follows:

Is Mr. Sothern a medium? This is the question that fifteen puzzled investigators are asking themselves this morning, after witnessing a number of astounding manifestations at a private *séance* given by Mr. Sothern last night.

It lacked a few minutes of twelve when a number of Mr. Sothern's friends, who had been given to understand that something remarkable was to be performed, assembled in the former's rooms at the Sherman House, and took seats in a circle around a marble-top table which was placed in the centre of the apartment. On the table were a number of glasses, two very large bottles, and five lemons. A sprightly young gentleman attempted to crack a joke about spirits being confined in the bottles, but the company frowned him down, and for once Mr. Sothern had a sober audience to begin with.

There was a good deal of curiosity regarding the object of the gathering, but no one was able to explain. Each gentleman testified to the fact that Mr. Sothern's agent had waited upon him, and solicited his presence at a little exhibition to be given by the actor, *not* of a comical nature.

Mr. Sothern himself soon after appeared; and, after shaking hands with the party, thus addressed them:

"Gentlemen, I have invited you here this evening to witness a few manifestations, demonstrations, tests, or whatever you choose to call them, which I have accidentally discovered that I am able to perform.

"I am a fire-eater, as it were. [Applause] I used to *dread* the fire, having been scorched once when an innocent child. [A laugh] I hope there will be no levity here, and I wish to say now that demonstrations of any kind are liable to upset me, while demonstrations of particular kinds may upset the audience."

Silence and decorum being restored, Mr. Sothern then continued:

"Thirteen weeks ago, while walking up Greenwich Street in New York, I stepped into a store to buy a cigar. To show you there was no trick about it, here are cigars out of the same box from which I selected the one that I that day lighted."

Here Mr. Sothern passed round a box of tolerable cigars.

"Well! I stepped to the little hanging gas-jet to light it, and, having done so, stood contemplatively holding the cigar and the gas-jet in either hand, thinking what a saving it would be to smoke a pipe, when, in my absentmindedness, I dropped the cigar and put the gas-jet into my mouth. Strange as it may appear, I felt no pain, and stood there holding the thing in my mouth and puffing, until the man in charge yelled out to me that I was swallowing his gas. Then I looked up, and sure enough there I was, pulling away at the slender flame that came from the glass tube.

"I dropped it instantly and felt my mouth, but noticed no inconvenience or unpleasant sensation whatever.

" 'What do you mean by it?' asked the proprietor.

"As I didn't know what I meant by it I couldn't answer, so I picked up my cigar and went home. Once there, I tried the experiment again, and in doing so I found that not only my mouth, but my hands and face, indeed, all my body, was proof against fire. I called on a physician, and he examined me and reported nothing wrong with my flesh, which appeared to be in its normal condition. I said nothing about it publicly, but the fact greatly surprised me, and I have invited you here tonight to witness a few experiments."

Saying this, Mr. Sothern, who had lit a cigar while pausing in his speech, turned the fire-end into his mouth, and sat down smoking unconcernedly.

"I suppose you wish to give us the fire-test?" remarked one of the company.

There was probably a company never more dumfounded than that present in the room. A few questions were asked, and then five gentlemen were appointed to examine Mr. Sothern's hands, etc., before he began his experiments. Having thoroughly washed the parts that he proposed to subject to the flames, Mr. Sothern began by baring his arm, and passing it through the gas-jet very slowly, twice stopping the motion, and holding it still in the flames. He then picked up a poker with a sort of hook on the end, and proceeded to fish a small coil of wire from the grate. The wire came out fairly white with heat. Mr. Sothern took the coil in his hands and coolly proceeded to wrap it round his left leg to the knee. Having done so, he stood on the table in the centre of the circle, and requested the committee to examine the wrappings and the leg, and report if both were there. The committee did so, and reported in the affirmative.

While this was going on there was a smile, almost seraphic in its beauty, on Sothern's face.

After this, an enormous iron, in the shape of a horseshoe, was brought in, and after being heated red-hot, was placed over his neck and shoulders like a horse-collar, where it cooled, and was taken off without leaving a sign of a burn.

As a final test a tailor's goose was put on the coals, and, after being thoroughly heated, was placed on Mr. Sothern's chair. The latter lighted a fresh cigar, and then coolly took his seat on the goose without the least seeming inconvenience. During the last experiment, Mr. Sothern sang in excellent taste and voice, "I'm sitting on the stile, Mary."

The question now is, were the fifteen auditors of Mr. Sothern fooled and deceived, or was this a genuine manifestation of extraordinary power? Sothern is such an inveterate joker that he may have put the thing upon the boys for his own amusement, but if so it was one of the nicest tricks ever witnessed by,

Yours truly,

ONE OF THE COMMITTEE

P.S.—What is equally marvellous to me is that the fire didn't burn his clothes where it touched them, any more than his flesh.

Although he inserted this remarkable communication, the editor of the *Inter-Ocean* seems to "have had his doubts," for he adds in a footnote:

[There is nothing new in this. Mr. Sothern has long been known as one of the most expert jugglers in the profession. Some years ago he gained the sobriquet of "the Fire King." He frequently amuses his friends by eating fire, although he long since ceased to give public exhibitions. Probably the success of the experiments last night was largely owing to the presence of the lemons. There is a good deal of trickery in those same lemons.]

I will conclude a chapter which, if I related all the jokes in which Sothern acted as principal or took part, might be spun out into a goodly sized volume, with an account of one (I am afraid it has often been told before) eminently characteristic of him. At a dinner party in his own house, at which ten gentlemen were present, his friend and sometime agent, Mr. English, was apparently unexpectedly announced. Sothern immediately appealed to his guests to conceal themselves under the dinner-table, declaring that they would "sell" English in a manner beyond all precedent. His compliant friends at once fell in with his request, and Mr. English, coming into the room, sat down by Sothern, and, without taking any notice of the vacant chairs or the disordered table, began leisurely to discuss the business that had brought him to the house. Sothern on his part said nothing about his guests, until one by one, tired with their position under the table, and quite unable to see where the humour of the situation came in, they crawled out, took their seats, and the interrupted dinner went on. Neither Sothern nor his agent (of course he was on this occasion also his accomplice) took the slightest notice of them, and to the end of their days they will fail to see how it was that "English was sold."

[From *Lord Dundreary*]

William Henry Drummond

Drummond was born in Ireland, but was brought up among the French-Canadians. His charming habitant poems are animated by a deep affection for those winning and simple people. They have not resented his kindly comedy. Louis Fréchette, the great French-Canadian poet, testifies that nowhere in Drummond's work can the most subtle critic discover the malign exaggeration of caricature.

M'SIEU SMIT'; THE ADVENTURES OF AN ENGLISHMAN IN THE CANADIAN WOODS

Wan morning de walkin' boss say "Damase,
  I t'ink you're good man on canoe d'écorce,
So I'll ax you go wit' your frien' Philéas
  An' meet M'sieu Smit' on Chenail W'ite Horse.

"He'll have I am sure de grosse baggage—
  Mebbe some valise—mebbe six or t'ree—
But if she's too moche for de longue portage
  'Poleon he will tak' 'em wit' mail buggee."

W'en we reach Chenail, plaintee peep be dere,
  An' wan frien' of me, call Placide Chretien,
'Splain all dat w'en he say man from Angleterre
  Was spik heem de crowd on de "Parisien."

Fonny way dat Englishman he'll be dress,
  Leetle pant my dear frien' jus' come on knee,
Wit' coat dat's no coat at all—only ves'
  An' hat—de more stranger I never see!

Wall! dere he sit on de en' some log
  An' swear heem in English purty loud
Den talk Français, w'ile hees chien boule dog
  Go smellim an' smellim aroun' de crowd.

I spik im "Bonjour, M'sieu Smit', Bonjour,
 I hope dat yourse'f and famille she's well?"
M'sieu Smit's he is also say "Bonjour,"
 An' call off hees dog dat's commence for smell.

I tell heem my name dat's Damase Labrie;
 I am come wit' Philéas for mak' de trip,
An' he say I'm de firs' man he never see
 Spik English encore since he lef' de ship.

De groun' she is pile wit' baggage—Sapré!
 An' I see purty quick we got plaintee troub—
Two tronk, t'ree valise, four-five fusil,
 An' w'at M'sieu Smit' he is call "bat' tubbe."

M'sieu Smit' he's tole me w'at for's dat t'ing,
 An' it seem Englishman he don't feel correc'
Until he's go plonge on some bat' morning
 An' sponge it hees possibill high hees neck.

Of course dat's not'ing of my beez-nesse,
 He can plonge on de water mos' ev'ry day,
But I t'ink for mese'f it mak' foolishness
 An' don't do no good w'en your bonne santé.

W'en I tell 'Poleon he mus' mak' dat job,
 Dere's leetle too moche for canoe d'écorce,
He's mad right away an' say "Sapré diable!
 You t'ink I go work lak wan niggerhorse?

"I'm not manufacture dat way, bâ non,
 Dat rich stranger man he have lot monee,
I go see my frien' Onésime Gourdon,
 An' tole heem bring horse wit' some more buggee."

Wall! affer some w'ile dey'll arrange all dat,
 'Poleon an' hees frien' Onésime Gourdon,
But w'en 'Poleon is tak' hole of bat',
 He receive it beeg scare immediatement!

Dat chien boule dog, I was tole you 'bout
I am not understan' w'at good she's for,
Eat 'Poleon's leg w'it hees teet' and mout,
'Poleon he is feel very mad—by Gor!

Of course I am poule heem his tail toute suite
But I don't know some reason mak' all dis troub',
W'en I hear me dat Englishman, M'sieu Smit'
Say 'Poleon, w'at for you took my tubbe?

"Leff 'im dere—for I don't 'low nobodee
Walk heem off on any such way lak dat;
You may tak' all de res', an' I don't care me—
But de man he'll be keel whô is tak' my bat'.

"I will carry heem wit' me," say M'sieu Smit'—
"W'erever dat tubbe she mus' go, I go—
No matter de many place we visite,
An' my sponge I will tak' mese'f also."

At las' we are start on voyage, sure nuff,
M'sieu Smit' carry tubbe on de top hees head,
Good job, I t'ink so, de lac isn't rough,
Or probably dis tam, we're all come dead.

De dog go wit' Onésime Gourdon,
An' Onésime afferwar' say to me,
"Dat chien boule dog is eat 'Poleon
Was de more quiet dog I never see."

But fun she's commence on very nex' day
W'en we go camp out on de Castor Noir.
Dat Englishman he'll come along an' say
"I hope some wil' Injun she don't be dere.

"I have heard many tam, dat de wood be foule
Of Injun w'at tak' off de hair your head
But so surely my name she's Johnnie Boule
If I see use dem feller I shoot it dead."

Philéas den pray harder, more quick he can
    Mebbe he's t'ink dat's hees las' portage
De moder hees fader, she's Injun man
    Derefore an' also, he is wan Sauvage.

I say "Don' mak' it some excitement;
    Season she is 'close' on de spring an' fall,
An' dem peep dat work on de Gouvernement
    Don' lak you shoot Injun dis mont' at all."

Nex' day M'sieu Smit' is perform hees plonge;
    We see heem go done it—Philéas an' me,
An' w'en he's hang up bat' tubbe an' sponge
    We go on de wood for mak' Chasse perdrix.

An' mebbe you will not believe to me,
    But w'en we come back on de camp encore
De sponge of dat Englishman don't be see,
    An' we fin' beeg bear she's go dead on shore.

Very fonny t'ing how he's loss hees life,
    But Philéas he'll know hese'f purty quick,
He cut M'sieu Bear wit' hees hunter knife,
    An' sponge she's fall out on de bear stummick.

. . . .

Nex' day—dat's Dimanche—he is spik to me,
    "Damase, you mus' feel leetle fatigue,
You may sle'p wit' Philéas w'ile I go an' see
    I can't get some nice quiet tam today."

So for keep 'way skeeter, an' fly also
    Bouteille from de shelf M'sieu Smit' he tak',
Den he start wit' his chien boule dog an' go
    For nice quiet walk on shore of lac.

We don't sle'p half hour we'n dere's beeg, beeg yell,
    Lak somet'ing I'm sure don't hear long tam,
An' we see wan feller we cannot tell,
    Till he spik it, "Damase! Philéas! dam dam!!!"

Den we know it at once, mon cher ami,
    But she's swell up hees face—hees neck an' han'!
It seem all de skeeter on w'ole contree
    Is jump on de head of dat Englishman.

Some water on poor M'sieu Smit' we'll trow,
    An w'en he's tranquille fin' out ev'ryt'ing;
Bouteille he's rub on, got some nice sirop
    I was mak' mese'f on de wood las' spring.

T'ree day affer dat, we start out on lac
    For ketch on de water wan Cariboo,
But win' she blow strong, an' we can't get back
    Till we t'row ourse'f out on dat canoe.

We t'ink M'sieu Smit' he is sure be drown,
    Leetle w'ile we can't see heem again no more,
An' den he's come up from de place go down
    An' jomp on hees bat' tubbe an' try go shore.

W'en he's pass on de bat', he say "Hooraw!"
    An' commence right away for mak' some sing;
I'm sure you can hear heem ten-twelve arpent
    'Bout "Brittanie, she alway' mus' boss somet'ing."

Dat's all I will tole you jus' now, my frien';
    I s'pose you don't know de more fonny case,
But if Englishman go on wood again
    I'll have more storee w'en you pass my place.

Oscar Wilde

Oscar Wilde's epigrams are about as good as they come. But as for the epigram in general, I am reminded of a leader in the London Daily Telegraph, *in August, 1906. This was noted, preserved, remembered, and restored to the world by the incomparable Harry P. Taber.*

"A writer in a monthly magazine complains, as other writers have complained before him, that we are not the funny dogs we once were. According to him there was a time when mirth-provoking sallies flashed about the drawing-room, and gilded salons rocked to the laughter inspired by the almost incessant ejaculation of good things. The epigram, he says, has had its day.

"This is good hearing. Nothing dams the flow of conversation more than a pun. But next to the pun comes the epigram. Just as one is talking one's best in a smooth, turgid way infinitely soothing to the nerves of one's audience, some dastardly person fires off an epigram. There is an awkward silence, a nervous laugh, and the thread of one's ideas is cut. By the time we are ready to get going again, somebody else has the ear of the room. Is the art of conversation really dead? There is plenty of quantity, but very little quality. We have said some uncommonly good things ourselves from time to time, but the general standard is not high. We are inclined to think that the best dialogue that can be heard nowadays is that provided by the courts of justice. There is a charming inconsequence about it. Counsel asks witness if he is a married man. Witness replies that he had a brother who was. This sort of thing is better than any number of artificial epigrams."

EPIGRAMS, APHORISMS, AND APOPHTHEGMS

One should never make one's debut with a scandal, one should reserve that to give interest to one's old age.

The only way a woman can ever reform a man is by boring him so completely that he loses all possible interest in life.

The value of an idea has nothing whatever to do with the sincerity of the man who expresses it.

There is no such thing as good influence. All influence is immoral—immoral from the scientific point of view.

Being natural is simply a pose.

I can stand brute force, but brute reason is quite unbearable. There is something unfair about its use. It is hitting below the intellect.

The only thing to do with good advice is to pass it on. It is never of any use to oneself.

To love oneself is the beginning of a lifelong romance.

I can resist everything except temptation.

Nowadays to be intelligible is to be found out.

The world is packed with good women. To know them is a middle-class education.

The youth of today are quite monstrous. They have absolutely no respect for dyed hair.

The amount of women who flirt with their own husbands is scandalous. It is simply washing one's clean linen in public.

Twenty years of romance make a woman look like a ruin, but twenty years of marriage make her something like a public building.

When good Americans die they go to Paris, when bad Americans die they go to America.

Nothing that actually occurs is of the smallest importance.

If one tells the truth, one is sure, sooner or later, to be found out.

Ambition is the last refuge of the failure.

Nowadays most people die of a sort of creeping common sense, and discover, when it is too late, that the only thing one never regrets are one's mistakes.

Being adored is a nuisance. Women treat us just as Humanity treats its gods. They worship us, and are always bothering us to do something for them.

Art reveals Nature's lack of design, her curious crudities, her absolutely unfinished condition. Nature has good intentions, but she cannot carry them out. Art is our gallant attempt to teach Nature her proper place.

Life imitates Art far more than Art imitates Life.

All bad poetry springs from genuine feeling. To be natural is to be obvious, and to be obvious is to be inartistic.

Though of all poses a moral pose is the most offensive, still to have a pose at all is something. It is a form of recognition of the importance of treating life from a definite and reasoned standpoint.

A. D. Godley

THE MOTOR BUS

What is this that roareth thus?
Can it be a Motor Bus?
Yes, the smell and hideous hum
Indicat Motorem Bum!
Implet in the Corn and High
Terror me Motoris Bi:
Bo Motori clamitabo
Ne Motore caedar a Bo—
Dative be or Ablative
So thou only let us live:—
Whither shall thy victims flee?
Spare us, spare us, Motor Be!
Thus I sang; and still anigh
Came in hordes Motores Bi,
Et complebat omne forum
Copia Motorum Borum.
How shall wretches live like us
Cincti Bis Motoribus?
Domine, defende nos
Contra hos Motores Bos!

"F. Anstey"

F. Anstey (whose real name was Thomas Anstey Guthrie) is still happily remembered for his Vice-Versa, and other novels. His favorite device was to accept some fantastic absurdity, such as a djinn in a bottle, and then to develop the consequences with perfect sobriety.

BURGLAR BILL
A Recitation

The compiler would not be acting fairly if, in recommending the following poem as a subject for earnest study, he did not caution him— or her—not to be betrayed by the apparent simplicity of this exercise into the grave error of under-estimating its real difficulty.

It is true that it is an illustration of Pathos of an elementary order (we shall reach the advanced kind at a later stage), but, for all that, this piece bristles with as many points as a porcupine, and consequently requires the most cautious and careful handling.

Upon the whole, it is perhaps better suited to students of the softer sex.

Announce the title with a suggestion of shy innocence—in this way way:—Burglar (now open both eyes very wide) Bill.

(Then go on in a hushed voice, and with an air of wonder at the world's iniquity.)

I

Through a window in the attic
  Brawny Burglar Bill has crept;
Seeking stealthily a chamber
  Where the jewellery is kept.
(Pronounce either "jewellery" or "joolery," according to taste.)

II

He is furnished with a "jemmy,"
Centre-bit and carpet-bag,
For the latter "comes in handy,"
So he says, "to stow the swag."
*("Jemmy," "centre-bit," "carpet-bag," are important words—put
good colouring into them.)*

III

Here, upon the second landing,
He, secure, may work his will:
Down below's a dinner party,
Up above—the house is still.
*(Here start and extend first finger, remembering to make it
waggle slightly, as from fear.)*

IV

Suddenly—in spell-bound horror,
All his satisfaction ends—
For a little white-robed figure
By the bannister descends!
*(This last line requires care in delivery, or it may be imagined
that the little figure is sliding* down *the bannisters, which
would simply ruin the effect. Note the bold but classic use of
the singular in "bannister," which is more pleasing to a nice
ear than the plural.)*

V

Bill has reached for his revolver
(Business here with your fan.)
Yet he hesitates to fire...
Child is it? *(in a dread whisper)* or—apparition,
That provokes him to perspire?

VI

Can it be his guardian angel,
    Sent to stay his hand from crime?
(*In a tone of awe.*)
    He could wish he had selected,
        Some more seasonable time!
(*Touch of peevish discontent here.*)

VII

"Go away!" he whispers hoarsely,
    "Burglars hev their bread to earn.
I don't need no Gordian angel
    Givin' of me sech a turn!"
(*Shudder here, and retreat, shielding eyes with hand. Now
change your manner to a naïve surprise; this, in spite of anything we may have said previously, is in this particular instance, not best indicated by a shrill falsetto.*)

VIII

But the blue eyes open wider,
    Ruby lips reveal their pearl;
(*This must not be taken to refer to the Burglar.*)
    "I is not a Garden angel,
        Only—dust a yickle dirl!
(*Be particularly artless here and through next stanza.*)

IX

"On the thtairs to thit I'm doin'
    Till the tarts and dellies tum;
Partingthon (our butler) alwayth
    Thaves for Baby Bella thome!

X

"Poor man, 'oo ith yookin' 'ungry—
Leave 'oo burgling fings up dere;
Tum wiz me and share the sweeties,
Thitting on the bottom thtair!"
(*In rendering the above the young reciter shall strive to be
idiomatic without ever becoming idiotic—which is not so
easy as might be imagined.*)

XI

"Reely, Miss, you must excoose me!"
Says the Burglar with a jerk:
(*Indicate embarrassment here by smoothing down the folds of
your gown, and swaying awkwardly.*)
"Dooty calls, and time is pressing;
I must set about my work!"
(*This with gruff conscientiousness.*)

XII

(*Now assume your wide-eyed innocence again.*)
"Is 'oo work to bweak in houses?
Nana told me so, I'm sure!
Will 'oo twy if 'oo can manage
To bweak in my *dolls' house* door?

XIII

"I tan never det it undone,
So my dollies tan't det out;
They don't *yike* the fwont to open
Evewy time they'd walk about!

XIV

"Twy—and—if 'oo does it nithely—
When I'm thent upthtairs to thleep,
(*Don't overdo the lisp.*)
I will bring 'oo up thome goodies,
'Oo shall have them all—to keep!"

XV

(*Pause here, then with intense feeling and sympathy*)—
Off the little "angel" flutters;
(*Delicate stress on "angel."*)
But the Burglar wipes his brow.
He is wholly unaccustomed
To a kindly greeting now!
(*Tremble in voice here.*)

XVI

Never with a smile of welcome
Has he seen his entrance met!
Nobody—except the policeman—(*bitterly*)
Ever wanted *him* as yet!

XVII

Many a stately home he's entered,
But with unobtrusive tact,
He has ne'er in paying visits,
Called attention to the fact.

XVIII

Gain he counts it, on departing,
Should he have avoided strife.
(*In tone of passionate lament.*)
Ah, my Brothers, but the Burglar's
Is a sad, a lonely life.

XIX

All forgotten now the jewels,
  Once the purpose of his "job":
Down he sinks upon the doormat,
  With a deep and choking sob.

XX

There the infant's plea recalling,
  Seeks the nursery above;
Looking for the Lilliputian
  Crib he is to crack—for *Love!*
(*It is more usually done for* MONEY.)

XXI

In the corner stands the Dolls' house,
  Gaily painted green and red;
(*Colouring again here.*)
  And its door declines to open,
  Even as the child has said!

XXII

Forth come centre-bit and jemmy (*briskly*)
  All his implements are plied; (*enthusiastically*)
Never has he burgled better!
  As he feels, with honest pride.

XXIII

Deftly is the task accomplished,
  For the door will open well;
When—a childish voice behind him
  Breaks the silence—like a bell.

XXIV

"Sank 'oo, Misser Burglar, sank 'oo!
     And, betause 'oo's been so nice,
See what I have dot—a cheese-cake!
     Gweat big gweedies ate the ice."
(*Resentful accent on "ate."*)

XXV

"Papa says he wants to see 'oo,
     Partingthon is tummin too—
Tan't 'oo wait?"
(*This with guileless surprise—then change to husky emotion.*)
     "Well, *not* this evenin',
So, my little dear (*brusquely*), a doo!"

XXVI

(*You are now to produce your greatest effect; the audience
     should be made actually to* SEE *the poor hunted victim of so-
     cial prejudice escaping, consoled in the very act of flight by
     memories of this last adventure—the one bright and cheery
     episode, possibly, in his entire professional career.*)
     Fast he speeds across the housetops!
(*Rapid delivery for this.*)
     (*Very gently.*) But his bosom throbs with bliss,
     For upon his rough lips linger
          Traces of a baby's kiss.
(*Most delicate treatment will be necessary in the last couplet—
     or the audience may understand it in a painfully literal
     sense.*)

          .   .   .

(*You have nothing before you now but the finale. Make the con-
     trast as marked as possible.*)

XXVII

Dreamily on downy pillow
(*Soft musical intonation for this.*)
　　Baby Bella murmurs sweet:
(*Smile here with dreamy tenderness.*)
　　"Burglar, tum again and thee me ...
　　I will dive 'oo cakes to eat!"
(*That is one side of the medal—now for the other.*)

XXVIII

(*Harsh but emotional.*)
　　In a garret, worn, and weary,
　　　Burglar Bill has sunk to rest,
　　Clasping tenderly a crumpled
　　　Cheese-cake to his lonely breast.
(*Dwell lovingly on the word "cheese-cake"—which you should
press home on every one of your hearers, remembering to
fold your hands lightly over your breast as you conclude. If
you do not find that several susceptible and eligible bachelors
have been knocked completely out of time by this little
recitation, you will have made less progress in your Art than
may be confidently anticipated.*)

George Bernard Shaw

Shaw now objects to figuring as a humorist, although he has proved himself a master of every department of comedy. When he was a dramatic critic, he would spray bad plays with his own deadly playbane, of which this is an example.

BOILED HEROINE

True Blue: a new and original drama of the ROYAL NAVY, in five acts, by Leonard Outram and Stuart Gordon, Lieut. R.N., Olympic Theatre, 19 March, 1896.

I am often told by people who never go to the theatre that they like melodramas, because they are so funny. Those who do go know better than that. A melodrama must either succeed as a melodrama or else fail with the uttermost ignominies of tedium. But I am fain to admit that "True Blue" is an exception to this rule. It is funnier by a good deal than "H.M.S. Pinafore" in the absurd parts, and not bad, as melodramas go, in the presentable parts. The authorship has evidently been divided among many hands. In some of the epithets which Mrs. Raleigh, as the lady matador, hurls at the villain, it is impossible not to recognize the vivid style of Mr. Raleigh. One of the unnamed authors—I do not know which—is clearly an idiot; for it is not conceivable that the unspeakable fatuities of the plot can have proceeded from the same brain as the part of Strachan, or the dialogue, a good deal of which is animated and businesslike. Probably the idiot was the original begetter of the drama. As I conjecture, he submitted his play to Mr. Leonard Outram, who, as an experienced actor, at once fell under the spell which unredeemed literary and dramatic idiocy never fails to throw over his profession. He called in Lieutenant Stuart Gordon to look after the naval realism, and supply technically correct equivalents for the Avast Heavings, and Abaft the Binnacles, and Splicing the Main Braces which we may presume the original manuscript to have contained. The Lieutenant, not being an experienced actor, no doubt suggested that if his naval realism could be supplemented by a gleam or two of common sense, it would be all the better; and I can imagine Sir Augustus Harris, on being approached on the subject of finance, not only supporting the naval officer's view with some vehemence, but taking the dialogue in hand to a certain extent himself, with his popular collaborator, Mr. Raleigh, to lend a hand when time ran short. If this hypothesis be correct, we get four authors besides the nameless idiot; and it is no small degree remarkable that the play has succeeded because the collaborators, in a sort of inspired desperation, played up to the idiot instead of trying to reclaim him. Take for example the main situation of the piece. A British cruiser is anchored at Gibraltar. Its deck is used as a sort of dramatic exchange where villains and villainesses, heroes and heroines, stroll in, like bolts out of the blue, to hatch plots and make love. First there is the lady matador who loves the captain and hates the heroine, whom the captain loves. Then there is the heroine, who also loves the captain. And there is the heroine's maid, who loves the comic sailor, who loves the bottle. Suddenly the cruiser is ordered to up anchor and sweep England's enemies from the seas. The women resolve not to desert the men they love in the hour of danger. The matadoress, a comparatively experienced and sensible woman, slips quietly into the pantry adjoining the captain's cabin. The maid gets into one of those settee music boxes which are, it appears, common objects on the decks of cruisers, and is presently carried into the captain's cabin. The heroine, taught by love to divine a surer hiding-place, gets into one of the ship's boilers. Here the hand of the idiot is apparent, striking out a situation which would never have occurred to Shakespeare. Once fairly at sea, the matadoress gives way to an inveterate habit of smoking, and is smelt out by the captain. She throws her arms boldly about him, and declares that he is hers for ever. Enter, inopportunely, the navigating officer. He is scandalized, but retires. When he thinks it safe to return, it is only to find the maid emerging from the settee to dispute possession of the captain, on behalf of the heroine, with the matadoress. Hereupon he describes the ship as the captain's harem, and is placed under arrest. Then comes the great dramatic opportunity of the matadoress. Becoming acquainted, Heaven knows how, with the hiding-place of the heroine, she takes the stage alone, and draws a thrilling picture of her rival's impending doom. She describes her in the clammy darkness and dank cold of that boiler, listening to the wild beats of her own heart. Then the sensation of wet feet, the water rising to her ankles, her knees, her waist, her neck, until only by standing on tiptoe, with frantic upturned face, can she breathe. One mercy alone seems vouchsafed to her: the water has lost its deadly chill. Nay, it is getting distinctly warm, even hot—hotter—*scalding!* Immortal Powers, it is BOILING; and what a moment ago was a beautiful English girl, in the first exquisite budding of her beautiful womanhood, is now but a boilerful of soup, and in another moment will be a condenserful of low-pressure steam. I must congratulate Mrs. Raleigh on the courage with which she hurled this terrible word-picture at a house half white with its purgation by pity and terror, and half red with a voiceless, apoplectic laughter. Need I describe the following scene in the stokehold ("stokehole," it appears, is a solecism)—how the order comes to fill the boiler; how the comic sailor, in shutting the manhole thereof, catches sight of the white finger of the captain's young lady; how the matadoress in disguise comes in, and has all but turned on the boiling water when the comic sailor disables the tap by a mighty blow from a sledgehammer; how he rushes away to tell the captain of his discovery; how in his absence the fires are lighted and the cold water turned on; and how at the last moment the captain dashes in, shouting, "Draw the fires from No. 7" (the heroine is in No. 7), rushes up the ladder to the manhole, and drags out the heroine safe and sound, without a smudge on her face or a crumple in her pretty white frock, amid the delirious cheers of an audience which contemplates the descending curtain as men who have eaten of the insane root that takes the reason prisoner. Many more terrors does that melodrama contain, including the public drowning of the matadoress like a rat in a trap, but nothing quite so novel as the boiling scene. The last act degenerates into mere ordinary blood and thunder, only relieved by the touching acting of Mr. Rignold on becoming suddenly penetrated, for no mortal reason that anybody can discover, with a sense of his own unworthiness and the nobility of his donkey of a captain, who, though a sufficiently handsome and pleasant fellow, displays just ability enough to justify a steamboat company in trusting him, under the guidance of an intelligent boy, with the sale of tickets for a Thames steamer. Mr. Rignold, however, is not the man to allow himself to be bereaved of a bit of acting by the absence of any motive for it. He has the only real part in the play: and he makes the most of it to the end.

Nearly thirty actors and actresses, most of them capable and vigorous people with more or less distinct stage talents, are provided with salaries by this melodrama. They have for the most part about as much to do as the hundreds of painted spectators in the first scene (which I forgot to mention, as it is only a bullfight). Mr. Bucklaw, as the gallant, but brainless, captain, showed that he only needs to smarten himself a little—mostly in the way of enunciating his consonants—to become popular in such parts. Miss Laura Graves was irresistible as the parboiled heroine, being powerfully aided by the fact that the authors of the dialogue have thoroughly mastered the great Shakespearean secret of always making the woman woo the man. In actual life there is no point upon which individuals vary more widely than in the effect of publicity on the demonstrativeness of their affections. Some people would rather die than offer or receive the slightest endearment with anyone looking on. Others are stimulated to exceptional ardour by the presence of an audience; and it is a tragic fact that these diverse temperaments are rather apt to attract one another. The shy, conscious man whose impulsive and warmhearted wife *will* caress him before a roomful of people, and the fastidious reticent woman whose husband's attitude is openly and blubberingly amorous, are familiar figures in our civilisation. But I cannot recall on the stage any *ingénue* quite so reckless under the sway of the tenderer emotions as the one played by Miss Laura Graves. On all public occasions she positively showers kisses on the objects of her attachment. One wonders what a French audience would think of her. It is only when she is alone with the captain in his cabin that she subsides into something like the customary reserve of the bright and beautiful English girls of whom she is offered as an authentic type. The maid is hardly behind her mistress in respect of her indifference to publicity; but she does not take the initiative—is, in fact, more kissed against than kissing—the effect being so much worse that nobody less clever than Miss Kate Phillips could make the part popular. As it is, I congratulate the part on Miss Phillips, without in any way congratulating Miss Phillips on the part.

One of the humours of the piece is that the three stowaway ladies never enter twice in the same costume. They change as freely as if Worth had a branch establishment on board. The fact that this gross impossibility does not interfere in the least with the illusion (such as it is) of the drama is an illustration of the fact that melodramatic stage illusion is not an illusion of real life, but an illusion of the embodiment of our romantic imaginings. If melodramatists would only grasp this fact, they would save themselves a good deal of trouble and their audiences a good deal of boredom. Half the explanations and contrivances with which they burden their pieces are superfluous attempts to persuade the audience to accept, as reasonably brought about, situations which it is perfectly ready to accept without any bringing about whatever. The second-rate dramatist always begins at the beginning of his play; the first-rate one begins in the middle; and the genius—Ibsen, for instance—begins at the end. Nothing is odder about "True Blue" than the way in which the same authors who heroically disregard the commonest physical possibilities in the matter of boilers and millinery, timidly and superstitiously waste half the first and second acts in useless explanations of the villain's designs. The thousands of fiery Spaniards waiting for the bull to appear in the ring are repeatedly supposed to sit in respectful silence for five minutes at a stretch whilst the first and second villains stroll into the arena to discuss at great length the political situation which has led to the presence of a British cruiser at Gibraltar (as if that were the most improbable place for it in the world), and which renders it desirable, from their own point of view, that the cruiser should be sunk. Even if these explanations were intelligible or plausible, they would only waste time: as it is, they are stupid.

In looking over one or two criticisms of "True Blue" I have been astonished to find the writers complaining that there is too much realism and too little melodrama in it. When a man who has just been regaled on boiled heroine asks for more, it is only good manners to congratulate him on his appetite; but it is also well to point out that he has not the public on his side. The really entertaining part of "True Blue" is Lieutenant Stuart Gordon's part. The cooking of Alice Marjoribanks is only funny as a bogus monstrosity at a fair is funny; but the weighing of the anchor is both interesting and exciting. It is true that the interest is not strictly dramatic: it is the sort of interest that makes people visit a man-of-war at Portsmouth; but then this is the very sort of interest to which "True Blue" is addressed. The fact that I did not catch half the expository dialogue in the first act did not disappoint me in the least—quite the contrary; but I deeply resented the gruff unintelligibility of the orders by which the anchor-weighing process was directed, as I really wanted to know about that. What "True Blue" wants is more of the fresh naval routine, and less of the stale melodramatic routine. Why not allow the captain to descry the Venezuelan fleet on the horizon, and give us the process of preparing for action? Why not display in the third act a more interesting section of the ship, showing us both above and between decks? Why allow the catastrophe to be brought about by an impossible valet lamely rubbing out the pencil-marks on the captain's chart with a piece of india-rubber, instead of by a torpedo, or a hundred-ton projectile from the enemy, or—if the maximum of probability is preferable—a collision with some other British cruiser? I am convinced, with all respect to the contrary opinion of some of my colleagues, that in this play Lieutenant Gordon worked on the right lines, and his melodramatist collaborators on the wrong ones. The play is emphatically not the thing at the Olympic; and that is precisely why "True Blue" is better worth seeing than most exhibitions of its class.

Jerome K. Jerome

Mr. Romeyn Berry, the Aristotle of Swamp College School District, writes me: "Don't overlook Three Men in a Boat. Many aging Americans now ascribe their bladder trouble to laughing over passages in that one." It has not been overlooked.

HARRIS SINGS A COMIC SONG

You have never heard Harris sing a comic song, or you would understand the service I had rendered to mankind. It is one of Harris's fixed ideas that he *can* sing a comic song; the fixed idea, on the contrary, among those of Harris's friends who have heard him try, is that he *can't,* and never will be able to, and that he ought not to be allowed to try.

When Harris is at a party, and is asked to sing, he replies: "Well, I can only sing a *comic* song, you know"; and he says it in a tone that implies that his singing of *that,* however, is a thing that you ought to hear once, and then die.

"Oh, that *is* nice," says the hostess. "Do sing one, Mr. Harris"; and Harris gets up and makes for the piano, with the beaming cheeriness of a generous-minded man who is just about to give somebody something.

"Now, silence, please, everybody," says the hostess, turning round: "Mr. Harris is going to sing a comic song!"

"Oh, how jolly!" they murmur; and they hurry in from the conservatory, and come up from the stairs, and go and fetch each other from all over the house, and crowd into the drawing-room, and sit round, all smirking in anticipation.

Then Harris begins.

Well, you don't look for much of a voice in a comic song. You don't expect correct phrasing or vocalisation. You don't mind if a man does find out, when in the middle of a note, that he is too high, and comes down with a jerk. You don't bother about time. You don't mind a man being two bars in front of the accompaniment, and easing up in

289

the middle of a line to argue it out with the pianist, and then starting the verse afresh. But you do expect the words.

You don't expect a man to never remember more than the first three lines of the first verse, and to keep on repeating these until it is time to begin the chorus. You don't expect a man to break off in the middle of a line, and snigger, and say, it's very funny, but he's blest if he can think of the rest of it, and then try and make it up for himself, and, afterward, suddenly recollect it, when he has got to an entirely different part of the song, and break off, without a word of warning, to go back and let you have it then and there. You don't—well, I will just give you an idea of Harris's comic singing, and then you can judge of it for yourself.

HARRIS (*standing up in front of piano and addressing the expectant mob*): I'm afraid it's a very old thing, you know. I expect you all know it, you know. But it's the only thing I know. It's the Judge's song out of *Pinafore*—no, I don't mean *Pinafore*—I mean—you know what I mean—the other thing, you know. You must all join in the chorus, you know.

(*Murmurs of delight and anxiety to join in the chorus. Brilliant performance of prelude to the Judge's song in* Trial by Jury *by* NERVOUS PIANIST. *Moment arrives for* HARRIS *to join in.* HARRIS *takes no notice of it.* NERVOUS PIANIST *commences prelude over again, and* HARRIS, *commencing singing at the same time, dashes off the first two lines of the First Lord's song out of* Pinafore. NERVOUS PIANIST *tries to push on with prelude, gives it up, and tries to follow* HARRIS *with accompaniment to Judge's song out of* Trial by Jury, *finds that doesn't answer, and tries to recollect what he is doing, and where he is, feels his mind giving way, and stops short.*)

HARRIS (*with kindly encouragement*): It's all right. You're doing it very well, indeed—go on.

NERVOUS PIANIST: I'm afraid there's a mistake somewhere. What are you singing?

HARRIS (*promptly*): Why, the Judge's song out of *Trial by Jury*. Don't you know it?

SOME FRIEND OF HARRIS'S (*from the back of the room*): No, you're not, you chucklehead, you're singing the Admiral's song from *Pinafore*.

(*Long argument between* HARRIS *and* HARRIS's FRIEND *as to what* HARRIS *is really singing.* FRIEND *finally suggests that it doesn't matter what* HARRIS *is singing so long as* HARRIS *gets on and sings it, and* HARRIS, *with an evident sense of injustice rankling inside him, requests* PIANIST *to begin again.* PIANIST, *thereupon, starts prelude to the Admiral's song, and* HARRIS, *seizing what he considers to be a favorable opening in the music, begins.*)

HARRIS: "When I was young and called to the Bar."

(*General roar of laughter, taken by* HARRIS *as a compliment.* PIANIST, *thinking of his wife and family, gives up the unequal contest and retires; his place being taken by a stronger-nerved man.*)

THE NEW PIANIST (*cheerily*): Now then, old man, you start off, and I'll follow. We won't bother about any prelude.

HARRIS (*upon whom the explanation of matters has slowly dawned— laughing*): By Jove! I beg your pardon. Of course—I've been mixing up the two songs. It was Jenkins confused me, you know. Now then.

(*Singing; his voice appearing to come from the cellar, and suggesting the first low warnings of an approaching earthquake.*)

"When I was young I served a term
As office-boy to an attorney's firm."

(*Aside to pianist*): It is too low, old man; we'll have that over again, if you don't mind.

(*Sings first two lines over again, in a high falsetto this time. Great surprise on the part of the audience. Nervous old lady near the fire begins to cry, and has to be led out.*)

HARRIS (*continuing*):

"I swept the windows and I swept the door,
And I—"

No—no, I cleaned the windows of the big front door. And I polished up the floor—no, dash it—I beg your pardon—funny thing, I can't think of that line. And I—and I—oh, well, we'll get on to the chorus, and chance it (*sings*):

"And I diddle-diddle-diddle-diddle-diddle-diddle-de,
Till now I am the ruler of the Queen's navee."

Now then chorus—it's the last two lines repeated, you know.

GENERAL CHORUS:

"And he diddle-diddle-diddle-diddle-diddle-diddle-dee'd,
Till now he is the ruler of the Queen's navee."

And Harris never sees what an ass he is making of himself, and how he is annoying a lot of people who never did him any harm. He honestly imagines that he has given them a treat, and says he will sing another comic song after supper.

[From *Three Men in a Boat*]

OVERHAULING A BICYCLE

I have had experience on this "overhauling." There was a man at Folkestone; I used to meet him on the Lees. He proposed one evening we should go for a long bicycle-ride together on the following day, and I agreed. I got up early, for me; I made an effort, and was pleased with myself. He came half an hour late: I was waiting for him in the garden. It was a lovely day. He said:

"That's a good-looking machine of yours. How does it run?"

"Oh, like most of them!" I answered; "easily enough in the morning; goes a little stiffly after lunch."

He caught hold of it by the front wheel and the fork, and shook it violently.

I said: "Don't do that; you'll hurt it."

I did not see why he should shake it; it had not done anything to him. Besides, if it wanted shaking, I was the proper person to shake it. I felt much as I should had he started whacking my dog.

He said: "This front wheel wobbles."

I said: "It doesn't if you don't wobble it." It didn't wobble, as a matter of fact—nothing worth calling a wobble.

He said: "This is dangerous; have you got a screw-hammer?"

I ought to have been firm, but I thought that perhaps he really did know something about the business. I went to the tool-shed to see what I could find. When I came back he was sitting on the ground with the front wheel between his legs. He was playing with it, twiddling it round between his fingers; the remnant of the machine was lying on the gravel path beside him.

He said: "Something has happened to this front wheel of yours."

"It looks like it, doesn't it?" I answered. But he was the sort of man that never understands satire.

He said: "It looks to me as if the bearings were all wrong."

I said: "Don't you trouble about it any more; you will make yourself tired. Let us put it back and get off."

He said: "We may as well see what is the matter with it, now it is out." He talked as though it had dropped out by accident.

Before I could stop him he had unscrewed something somewhere, and out rolled all over the path some dozen or so little balls.

"Catch 'em!" he shouted; "catch 'em! We mustn't lose any of them." He was quite excited about them.

We grovelled round for half an hour, and found sixteen. He said he hoped we had got them all, because, if not, it would make a serious difference to the machine. He said there was nothing you should be more careful about in taking a bicycle to pieces than seeing you did not lose any of the balls. He explained that you ought to count them as you took them out and see that exactly the same number went back in each place. I promised, if ever I took a bicycle to pieces I would remember his advice.

I put the balls for safety in my hat, and I put my hat upon the doorstep. It was not a sensible thing to do, I admit. As a matter of fact, it was a silly thing to do. I am not as a rule addle-headed; his influence must have affected me.

He then said that while he was about it he would see to the chain for me, and at once began taking off the gear-case. I did try to persuade him from that. I told him what an experienced friend of mine once said to me solemnly:

"If anything goes wrong with your gear-case, sell the machine and buy a new one; it comes cheaper."

He said: "People talk like that who understand nothing about machines. Nothing is easier than taking off a gear-case."

I had to confess he was right. In less than five minutes he had the gear-case in two pieces, lying on the path, and was grovelling for screws. He said it was always a mystery to him the way screws disappeared.

We were still looking for the screws when Ethelbertha came out. She seemed surprised to find us there; she said she thought we had started hours ago.

He said: "We shan't be long now. I'm just helping your husband to overhaul this machine of his. It's a good machine; but they all want going over occasionally."

Ethelbertha said: "If you want to wash yourselves when you have done you might go into the back kitchen, if you don't mind; the girls have just finished the bedrooms."

She told me that if she met Kate they would probably go for a sail; but that in any case she would be back to lunch. I would have given a sovereign to be going with her. I was getting heartily sick of standing about watching this fool breaking up my bicycle.

Common sense continued to whisper to me: "Stop him, before he does any more mischief. You have a right to protect your own property from the ravages of a lunatic. Take him by the scruff of the neck, and kick him out of the gate!"

But I am weak when it comes to hurting other people's feelings, and I let him muddle on.

He gave up looking for the rest of the screws. He said screws had a knack of turning up when you least expected them; and that now he would see to the chain. He tightened it till it would not move; next he loosened it until it was twice as loose as it was before. Then he said we had better think about getting the front wheel back into its place again.

I held the fork open, and he worried with the wheel. At the end of ten minutes I suggested he should hold the forks, and that I should handle the wheel; and we changed places. At the end of his first minute, he dropped the machine, and took a short walk round the croquet lawn, with his hands pressed together between his thighs. He explained as he walked that the thing to be careful about was to avoid getting your fingers pinched between the forks and the spokes of the wheel. I replied I was convinced, from my own experience, that there was much truth in what he said. He wrapped himself up in a couple of dusters, and we commenced again. At length we did get the thing into position; and the moment it was in position he burst out laughing.

I said: "What's the joke?"

He said: "Well, I am an ass!"

It was the first thing he had said that made me respect him. I asked him what had led him to the discovery.

He said: "We've forgotten the balls!"

I looked for my hat; it was lying topsy-turvy in the middle of the path, and Ethelbertha's favourite hound was swallowing the balls as fast as he could pick them up.

"He will kill himself," said Ebbson—I have never met him since that day, thank the Lord; but I think his name was Ebbson—"they are solid steel."

I said: "I am not troubling about the dog. He has had a bootlace and a packet of needles already this week. Nature's the best guide; puppies seem to require this kind of stimulant. What I am thinking about is my bicycle."

He was of a cheerful disposition. He said: "Well, we must put back all we can find, and trust to Providence."

We found eleven. We fixed six on one side and five on the other, and half an hour later the wheel was in its place again. It need hardly be added that it really did wobble now; a child might have noticed it. Ebbson said it would do for the present. He appeared to be getting a bit tired himself. If I had let him, he would, I believe, at this point have gone home. I was determined now, however, that he should stop and finish; I had abandoned all thoughts of a ride. My pride in the machine he had killed. My only interest lay now in seeing him scratch and bump and pinch himself. I revived his drooping spirits with a glass of beer and some judicious praise. I said:

"Watching you do this is of real use to me. It is not only your skill and dexterity that fascinates me, it is your cheery confidence in yourself, your inexplicable hopefulness, that does me good."

Thus encouraged, he set to work to refix the gear-case. He stood the bicycle against the house, and worked from the off side. Then he stood it against a tree, and worked from the near side. Then I held it for him, while he lay on the ground with his head between the wheels, and worked at it from below, and dropped oil upon himself. Then he took it away from me, and doubled himself across it like a pack-saddle, till he lost his balance and slid over onto his head. Three times he said:

"Thank Heaven, that's right at last!"

And twice he said:

"No, I'm damned if it is after all!"

What he said the third time I try to forget.

Then he lost his temper and tried bullying the thing. The bicycle, I was glad to see, showed spirit; and the subsequent proceedings degenerated into little else than a rough-and-tumble fight between him and the machine. One moment the bicycle would be on the gravel-path, and he on top of it; the next, the position would be reversed—he on the gravel-path, the bicycle on him. Now he would be standing flushed with victory, the bicycle firmly fixed between his legs. But his triumph would be short-lived. By a sudden, quick movement it would free itself, and, turning upon him, hit him sharply over the head with one of its handles.

At a quarter to one, dirty and dishevelled, cut and bleeding, he said: "I think that will do," and rose and wiped his brow.

The bicycle looked as if it also had had enough of it. Which had received most punishment it would have been difficult to say. 1 took him into the back kitchen, where, so far as was possible without soda and proper tools, he cleaned himself, and sent him home.

The bicycle I put into a cab and took round to the nearest repairing-shop. The foreman of the works came up and looked at it.

"What do you want me to do with that?" said he.

"I want you," I said, "so far as is possible, to restore it."

"It's a bit far gone," said he; "but I'll do my best."

He did his best, which came to two pounds ten.

[From *Three Men on the Bummel*]

Kenneth Grahame

The Wind in the Willows *is surely immortal, as the perfect book for parents to read aloud. It is animated by a sweet and delicate fancy, of the sort that the British do better than any other people. Mr. Toad, a fanatic for motoring, as it was practiced in 1908, has been imprisoned for impulsively stealing a car, and has escaped in the disguise of a washerwoman. The rest will probably be clear enough.*

THE FURTHER ADVENTURES OF TOAD

He had travelled some miles, his horse and he, and he was feeling drowsy in the hot sunshine, when the horse stopped, lowered his head, and began to nibble the grass; and Toad, waking up, just saved himself from falling off by an effort. He looked about him and found he was on a wide common, dotted with patches of gorse and bramble as far as he could see. Near him stood a dingy gipsy caravan, and beside it a man was sitting on a bucket turned upside down, very busy smoking and staring into the wide world. A fire of sticks was burning near by, and over the fire hung an iron pot, and out of that pot came forth bubblings and gurglings, and a vague suggestive steaminess. Also smells—warm, rich, and varied smells—that twined and twisted and wreathed themselves at last into one complete, voluptuous, perfect smell that seemed like the very soul of Nature taking form and appearing to her children, a true Goddess, a mother of solace and comfort. Toad now knew well that he had not been really hungry before. What he had felt earlier in the day had been a mere trifling qualm. This was the real thing at last, and no mistake; and it would have to be dealt with speedily, too, or there would be trouble for somebody or something. He looked the gipsy over carefully, wondering vaguely whether it would be easier to fight him or cajole him. So there he sat, and sniffed and sniffed, and looked at the gipsy; and the gipsy sat and smoked, and looked at him.

Presently the gipsy took his pipe out of his mouth and remarked in a careless way, "Want to sell that there horse of yours?"

Toad was completely taken aback. He did not know that gipsies were very fond of horsedealing, and never missed an opportunity, and he had not reflected that caravans were always on the move and took a deal of drawing. It had not occurred to him to turn the horse into cash, but the gipsy's suggestion seemed to smooth the way towards the two things he wanted so badly—ready money and a solid breakfast.

"What?" he said, "me sell this beautiful young horse of mine? Oh, no; it's out of the question. Who's going to take the washing home to my customers every week? Besides, I'm too fond of him, and he simply dotes on me."

"Try and love a donkey," suggested the gipsy. "Some people do."

"You don't seem to see," continued Toad, "that this fine horse of mine is a cut above you altogether. He's a blood horse, he is, partly; not the part you see, of course—another part. And he's been a Prize Hackney, too, in his time—that was the time before you knew him, but you can still tell it on him at a glance, if you understand anything about horses. No, it's not to be thought of for a moment. All the same, how much might you be disposed to offer me for this beautiful young horse of mine?"

The gipsy looked the horse over, and then he looked Toad over with equal care, and looked at the horse again. "Shillin' a leg," he said briefly, and turned away, continuing to smoke and try to stare the wide world out of countenance.

"A shilling a leg?" cried Toad. "If you please, I must take a little time to work that out, and see just what it comes to."

He climbed down off his horse, and left it to graze, and sat down by the gipsy, and did sums on his fingers, and at last he said, "A shilling a leg? Why, that comes to exactly four shillings, and no more. Oh, no; I could not think of accepting four shillings for this beautiful young horse of mine."

"Well," said the gipsy, "I'll tell you what I will do. I'll make it five shillings, and that's three-and-sixpence more than the animal's worth. And that's my last word."

Then Toad sat and pondered long and deeply. For he was hungry and quite penniless, and still some way—he knew not how far—from home, and enemies might still be looking for him. To one in such a situation, five shillings may very well appear a large sum of money. On the other hand, it did not seem very much to get for a horse. But then, again, the horse hadn't cost him anything; so whatever he got was all clear profit. At last he said firmly, "Look here, gipsy! I tell you what we will do; and this is *my* last word. You shall hand me over six shillings and sixpence, cash down; and further, in addition thereto, you shall give me as much breakfast as I can possibly eat, at one sitting of course, out of that iron pot of yours that keeps sending forth such delicious and exciting smells. In return, I will make over to you my spirited young horse, with all the beautiful harness and trappings that are on him freely thrown in. If that's not good enough for you, say so, and I'll be getting on. I know a man near here who's wanted this horse of mine for years."

The gipsy grumbled frightfully, and declared if he did a few more deals of that sort he'd be ruined. But in the end he lugged a dirty canvas bag out of the depths of his trouser pocket, and counted out six shillings and sixpence into Toad's paw. Then he disappeared into the caravan for an instant, and returned with a large iron plate and a knife, fork, and spoon. He tilted up the pot, and a glorious stream of hot rich stew gurgled into the plate. It was, indeed, the most beautiful stew in the world, being made of partridges, and pheasants, and chickens, and hares, and rabbits, and peahens, and guinea-fowls, and one or two other things. Toad took the plate on his lap, almost crying, and stuffed, and stuffed, and stuffed, and kept asking for more, and the gipsy never grudged it him. He thought that he had never eaten so good a breakfast in all his life.

When Toad had taken as much stew on board as he thought he could possibly hold, he got up and said good-bye to the gipsy, and took an affectionate farewell of the horse; and the gipsy, who knew the riverside well, gave him directions which way to go, and he set forth on his travels again in the best possible spirits. He was, indeed, a very different Toad from the animal of an hour ago. The sun was shining brightly, his wet clothes were quite dry again, he had money in his pocket once more, he was nearing home and friends and safety, and, most and best of all, he had had a substantial meal, hot and nourishing, and felt big, and strong, and careless, and self-confident.

As he tramped along gaily, he thought of his adventures and escapes, and how when things seemed at their worst he had always managed to find a way out; and his pride and conceit began to swell within him. "Ho, ho!" he said to himself as he marched along with his chin in the air, "what a clever Toad I am! There is surely no animal equal to me for cleverness in the whole world! My enemies shut me up in prison, encircled by sentries, watched night and day by warders; I walk out through them all, by sheer ability coupled with courage. They pursue me with engines, and policemen, and revolvers; I snap my fingers at them, and vanish, laughing, into space. I am, unfortunately, thrown into a canal by a woman fat of body and very evil-minded. What of it? I swim ashore, I seize her horse, I ride off in triumph, and I sell the horse for a whole pocketful of money and an excellent breakfast! Ho, ho! I am the Toad, the handsome, the popular, the successful Toad!" He got so puffed up with conceit that he made up a song as he walked in praise of himself, and sang it at the top of his voice, though there was no one to hear it but him. It was perhaps the most conceited song that any animal ever composed.

> "The world has held great Heroes,
> As history-books have showed;
> But never a name to go down to fame
> Compared with that of Toad!

> "The clever men at Oxford
> Know all that there is to be knowed.
> But they none of them know one half as much
> As intelligent Mr. Toad!

> "The animals sat in the Ark and cried,
> Their tears in torrents flowed.
> Who was it said, 'There's land ahead'?
> Encouraging Mr. Toad!

> "The Army all saluted
> As they marched along the road.
> Was it the King? Or Kitchener?
> No. It was Mr. Toad!

"The Queen and her Ladies-in-waiting
Sat at the window and sewed.
She cried, 'Look! who's that *handsome* man?'
They answered, 'Mr. Toad.' "

There was a great deal more of the same sort, but too dreadfully conceited to be written down. These are some of the milder verses.

He sang as he walked, and he walked as he sang, and got more inflated every minute. But his pride was shortly to have a severe fall.

After some miles of country lanes he reached the high road, and as he turned into it and glanced along its white length, he saw approaching him a speck that turned into a dot and then into a blob, and then into something very familiar; and a double note of warning, only too well known, fell on his delighted ear.

"This is something like!" said the excited Toad. "This is real life again, this is once more the great world from which I have been missed so long! I will hail them, my brothers of the wheel, and pitch them a yarn, of the sort that has been so successful hitherto; and they will give me a lift, of course, and then I will talk to them some more; and, perhaps, with luck, it may even end in my driving up to Toad Hall in a motor-car! That will be one in the eye for Badger!"

He stepped confidently out into the road to hail the motor-car, which came along at an easy pace, slowing down as it neared the lane; when suddenly he became very pale, his heart turned to water, his knees shook and yielded under him, and he doubled up and collapsed with a sickening pain in his interior. And well he might, the unhappy animal; for the approaching car was the very one he had stolen out of the yard of the Red Lion Hotel on that fatal day when all his troubles began! And the people in it were the very same people he had sat and watched at luncheon in the coffee-room!

He sank down in a shabby, miserable heap in the road, murmuring to himself in his despair, "It's all up! It's all over now! Chains and policemen again! Prison again! Dry bread and water again! Oh, what a fool I have been! What did I want to go strutting about the country for, singing conceited songs, and hailing people in broad day on the high road, instead of hiding till nightfall and slipping home quietly by back ways! O hapless Toad! O ill-fated animal!"

The terrible motor-car drew slowly nearer and nearer, till at last he heard it stop just short of him. Two gentlemen got out and walked round the trembling heap of crumpled misery lying in the road, and one of them said, "Oh, dear! this is very sad! Here is a poor old thing —a washerwoman apparently—who has fainted in the road! Perhaps she is overcome by the heat, poor creature; or possibly she has not had any food today. Let us lift her into the car and take her to the nearest village, where doubtless she has friends."

They tenderly lifted Toad into the motor-car and propped him up with soft cushions, and proceeded on their way.

When Toad heard them talk in so kind and sympathetic a manner, and knew that he was not recognised, his courage began to revive, and he cautiously opened first one eye and then the other.

"Look!" said one of the gentlemen, "she is better already. The fresh air is doing her good. How do you feel now, ma'am?"

"Thank you kindly, sir," said Toad in a feeble voice, "I'm feeling a great deal better!"

"That's right," said the gentleman. "Now keep quite still, and, above all, don't try to talk."

"I won't," said Toad. "I was only thinking, if I might sit on the front seat there, beside the driver where I could get the fresh air full in my face, I should soon be all right again."

"What a very sensible woman!" said the gentleman. "Of course you shall." So they carefully helped Toad into the front seat beside the driver, and on they went once more.

Toad was almost himself again by now. He sat up, looked about him, and tried to beat down the tremors, the yearnings, the old cravings that rose up and beset him and took possession of him entirely.

"It is fate!" he said to himself. "Why strive? why struggle?" and he turned to the driver at his side.

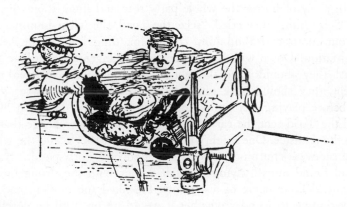

"Please, sir," he said, "I wish you would kindly let me try and drive the car for a little. I've been watching you carefully, and it looks so easy and so interesting, and I should like to be able to tell my friends that once I had driven a motor-car!"

The driver laughed at the proposal, so heartily that the gentleman inquired what the matter was. When he heard, he said, to Toad's delight, "Bravo, ma'am! I like your spirit. Let her have a try, and look after her. She won't do any harm." Toad eagerly scrambled into the seat vacated by the driver, took the steering-wheel in his hands, listened with affected humility to the instructions given him, and set the car in motion, but very slowly and carefully at first, for he was determined to be prudent.

The gentlemen behind clapped their hands and applauded, and Toad heard them saying, "How well she does it! Fancy a washerwoman driving a car as well as that, the first time!"

Toad went a little faster; then faster still, and faster.

He heard the gentlemen call out warningly, "Be careful, washerwoman!" And this annoyed him, and he began to lose his head.

The driver tried to interfere, but he pinned him down in his seat with one elbow, and put on full speed. The rush of air in his face, the hum of the engine, and the light jump of the car beneath him intoxicated his weak brain. "Washerwoman, indeed!" he shouted recklessly. "Ho! Ho! I am the Toad, the motor-car snatcher, the prisonbreaker, the Toad who always escapes! Sit still, and you shall know what driving really is, for you are in the hands of the famous, the skillful, the entirely fearless Toad!"

With a cry of horror the whole party rose and flung themselves on him. "Seize him!" they cried, "seize the Toad, the wicked animal who stole our motor-car! Bind him, chain him, drag him to the nearest police-station! Down with the desperate and dangerous Toad!"

Alas! they should have thought, they ought to have been more prudent, they should have remembered to stop the motor-car somehow before playing any pranks of that sort. With a half-turn of the wheel the Toad sent the car crashing through the low hedge that ran along the roadside. One mighty bound, a violent shock, and the wheels of the car were churning up the thick mud of a horse-pond.

Toad found himself flying through the air with the strong upward rush and delicate curve of a swallow. He liked the motion, and was just beginning to wonder whether it would go on until he developed wings and turned into a Toad-bird, when he landed on his back with a thump, in the soft rich grass of a meadow. Sitting up, he could just see the motor-car in the pond, nearly submerged; the gentlemen and the driver, encumbered by their long coats, were floundering helplessly in the water.

He picked himself up rapidly, and set off running across country as hard as he could, scrambling through hedges, jumping ditches, pounding across fields, till he was breathless and weary, and had to settle down into an easy walk. When he had recovered his breath somewhat, and was able to think calmly, he began to giggle, and from giggling he took to laughing, and he laughed till he had to sit down under a hedge. "Ho, ho!" he cried, in ecstasies of self-admiration, "Toad again! Toad, as usual, comes out on top! Who was it got them to give him a lift? Who managed to get on the front seat for the sake of fresh air? Who persuaded them into letting him see if he could drive? Who landed them all in a horse-pond? Who escaped, flying gaily and unscathed through the air, leaving the narrow-minded, grudging, timid excursionists in the mud where they should rightly be? Why, Toad, of course; clever Toad, great Toad, *good* Toad!"

Then he burst into song again, and chanted with uplifted voice—

"The motor-car went Poop-poop-poop,
    As it raced along the road.
Who was it steered it into a pond?
    Ingenious Mr. Toad!"

"Oh, how clever I am! How clever, how clever, how very clev—"

A slight noise at a distance behind him made him turn his head and look. O horror! O misery! O despair!

About two fields off, a chauffeur in his leather gaiters and two large rural policemen were visible, running towards him as hard as they could go!

Poor Toad sprang to his feet and pelted away again, his heart in his mouth. "Oh, my!" he gasped, as he panted along, "what an *ass* I am! What a *conceited* and heedless ass! Swaggering again! Shouting and singing songs again! Sitting still and gassing again! Oh, my! Oh, my! Oh, my!"

He glanced back, and saw to his dismay that they were gaining on him. On he ran desperately, but kept looking back, and saw that they still gained steadily. He did his best, but he was a fat animal, and his legs were short, and still they gained. He could hear them close behind him now. Ceasing to heed where he was going, he struggled on blindly and wildly, looking back over his shoulder at the now triumphant enemy, when suddenly the earth failed under his feet, he grasped at the air, and, splash! he found himself head over ears in deep water, rapid water, water that bore him along with a force he could not contend with; and he knew that in his blind panic he had run straight into the river!

He rose to the surface and tried to grasp the reeds and the rushes that grew along the water's edge close under the bank, but the stream was so strong that it tore them out of his hands. "Oh, my!" gasped poor Toad, "if ever I steal a motor-car again! If ever I sing another conceited song"—then down he went, and came up breathless and spluttering. Presently he saw that he was approaching a big dark hole in the bank, just above his head, and as the stream bore him past he reached up with a paw and caught hold of the edge and held on. Then slowly and with difficulty he drew himself up out of the water, till at last he was able to rest his elbows on the edge of the hole. There he remained for some minutes, puffing and panting, for he was quite exhausted.

As he sighed and blew and stared before him into the dark hole, some bright small things shone and twinkled in its depths, moving towards him. As it approached, a face grew up gradually around it, and it was a familiar face!

Brown and small, with whiskers.

Grave and round, with neat ears and silky hair.

It was the Water Rat!

[From *The Wind in the Willows*]

A. E. Housman

Observe the action of mustard on Mamma, and observe also the beautiful rise and fall of the lines, the perfect disposition of vowels and consonants. Housman could have been one of our greatest light versifiers if he had not been distracted by poetry.

AMELIA MIXED THE MUSTARD...

Amelia mixed the mustard,
  She mixed it good and thick;
She put it in the custard
  And made her Mother sick,
And showing satisfaction
  By many a loud huzza,
"Observe," she said, "the action
  Of mustard on Mamma."

WHEN ADAM DAY BY DAY...

When Adam day by day
  Woke up in Paradise,
He always used to say
  "Oh, this is very nice."

But Eve from scenes of bliss
  Transported him for life.
The more I think of this
  The more I beat my wife.

James M. Barrie

It is the fashion today to condemn the whimsy out of hand. It seems to me more just to say that there are good whimsies and bad whimsies. While I hold no brief for Peter Pan, *I will hold a brief case full of them for* My Lady Nicotine. *This book turned numberless young Britons into pipe-smokers and made the fortune of two rival brands of Arcadia Mixture. The monumental whimsy at the basis of the book is the fact that Barrie did not smoke.*

MY TOBACCO-POUCH

I once knew a lady who said of her husband that he looked nice when sitting with a rug over him. My female relatives seemed to have the same opinion of my tobacco-pouch; for they never saw it, even in my own room, without putting a book or a pamphlet over it. They called it "that thing," and made tongs of their knitting-needles to lift it; and when I indignantly returned it to my pocket they raised their hands to signify that I would not listen to reason. It seemed to come natural to other persons as well as to them to present me with new tobacco-pouches, until I had nearly a score lying neglected in drawers. But I am not the man to desert an old friend that has been with me everywhere and thoroughly knows my ways. Once, indeed, I came near to being unfaithful to my tobacco-pouch, and I mean to tell how; partly as a punishment to myself.

The incident took place several years ago. Gilray and I had set out on a walking tour of the Shakspeare country; but we separated at Stratford, which was to be our starting-point, because he would not wait for me. I am more of a Shakspearian student than Gilray, and Stratford affected me so much that I passed day after day smoking reverently at the hotel door; while he, being of the pure tourist type (not that I would say a word against Gilray), wanted to rush from one place of interest to another. He did not understand what thoughts came to me as I strolled down the Stratford streets; and in the hotel when I lay down on the sofa he said I was sleeping, though I was really picturing to myself Shakspeare's boyhood. Gilray even went the length of arguing that it would not be a walking tour at all if we never made a start; so, upon the whole, I was glad when he departed alone. The next day was a memorable one to me. In the morning I wrote to my London tobacconist for more Arcadia. I had quarrelled with both of the Stratford tobacconists. The one of them, as soon as he saw my tobacco-pouch, almost compelled me to buy a new one. The second was even more annoying. I paid with a half-sovereign for the tobacco I had got from him; but after gazing at the pouch he became suspicious of the coin, and asked if I could not pay him in silver. An insult to my pouch I considered an insult to myself; so I returned to those shops no more. The evening of the day on which I wrote to London for tobacco brought me a letter from home saying that my sister was seriously ill. I had left her in good health, so that the news was the more distressing. Of course I returned home by the first train. Sitting alone in a dull railway compartment, my heart was filled with tenderness, and I recalled the occasions on which I had carelessly given her pain. Suddenly I remembered that more than once she had besought me with tears in her eyes to fling away my old tobacco-pouch. She had always said that it was not respectable. In the bitterness of self-reproach I pulled the pouch from my pocket, asking myself whether, after all, the love of a good woman was not a far more precious possession. Without giving myself time to hesitate, I stood up and firmly cast my old pouch out at the window. I saw it fall at the foot of a fence. The train shot on.

By the time I reached home my sister had been pronounced out of danger. Of course I was much relieved to hear it, but at the same time this was a lesson to me not to act rashly. The retention of my tobacco-pouch would not have retarded her recovery, and I could not help picturing my pouch, my oldest friend in the world, lying at the foot of that fence. I saw that I had done a wrong in casting it from me. I had not even the consolation of feeling that if anyone found it he would cherish it, for it was so much damaged that I knew it could never appeal to a new owner as it appealed to me. I had intended telling my sister of the sacrifice made for her sake; but after seeing her so much better, I left the room without doing so. There was Arcadia Mixture in the house, but I had not the heart to smoke. I went early to bed, and fell into a troubled sleep, from which I awoke with a shiver. The rain was driving against my window; tapping noisily on it as if calling on me to awake and go back for my tobacco-pouch. It rained far on into the morning, and I lay miserably, seeing nothing before me but a wet fence and a tobacco-pouch among the grass at the foot of it.

On the following afternoon I was again at Stratford. So far as I could remember I had flung away the pouch within a few miles of the station, but I did not look for it until dusk. I felt that the porters had their eyes on me. By crouching along hedges I at last reached the railway a mile or two from the station, and began my search. It may be thought that the chances were against my finding the pouch; but I recovered it without much difficulty. The scene as I flung my old friend out at the window had burned itself into my brain, and I could go to the spot today as readily as I went on that occasion. There it was, lying among grass, but not quite in the place where it had fallen. Apparently some navvy had found it, looked at it, and then dropped it. It was half-full of water, and here and there it was sticking together; but I took it up tenderly, and several times on the way back to the station I felt in my pocket to make sure that it was really there.

I have not described the appearance of my pouch, feeling that to be unnecessary. It never, I fear, quite recovered from its night in the rain, and as my female relatives refused to touch it I had to sew it together now and then myself. Gilray used to boast of a way of mending a hole in a tobacco-pouch that was better than sewing. You put the two pieces of gutta-percha close together, and then cut them sharply with scissors. This makes them run together, he says, and I believed him until he experimented upon my pouch. However, I did not object to a hole here and there. Wherever I laid that pouch it left a small deposit of tobacco, and thus I could generally get together a pipeful at times when other persons would be destitute. I never told my sister that my pouch was once all but lost, but ever after that, when she complained that I had never even tried to do without it, I smiled tenderly.

MY SMOKING-TABLE

Had it not been for a bootblack at Charing Cross I should probably never have bought the smoking-table. I had to pass that boy every morning. In vain did I scowl at him, or pass with my head to the side. He always pointed derisively (as I thought) at my boots. Probably my boots were speckless, but that made no difference: he jeered and sneered. I have never hated anyone as I loathed that boy, and to escape him I took to going round by the Lowther Arcade. It was here that my eye fell on the smoking-table. In the Lowther Arcade if the attendants catch you looking at any article for a fraction of a second it is done up in brown paper, you have paid your money, and they have taken down your address before you realize that you don't want anything. In this way I became the owner of my smoking-table, and when I saw it in a brown-paper parcel on my return to my chambers I could not think what it was until I cut the strings. Such a little gem of a table no smoker should be without; and I am not ashamed to say that I was in love with mine as soon as I had fixed the pieces together. It was of walnut, and consisted mainly of a stalk and two round slabs not much bigger than dinner-plates. There were holes in the centre of these slabs, for the stalk to go through, and the one slab stood two feet from the floor, the other a foot higher. The lower slab was fitted with a walnut tobacco-jar and a pipe-rack, while on the upper slab were exquisite little recesses for cigars, cigarettes, matches, and ashes. These held respectively three cigars, two cigarettes, and four wax vestas. The smoking-table was an ornament to any room; and the first night I had it I raised my eyes from my book to look at it every few minutes. I got all my pipes together and put them in the rack; I filled the jar with tobacco, the recesses with three cigars, two cigarettes, and four matches; and then I thought I would have a smoke. I swept my hand confidently along the mantel-piece, but it did not stop at a pipe. I rose and looked for a pipe. I had half a dozen, but not one was to be seen, none on the mantelpiece, none on the window-sill, none on the hearthrug, none being used as book-markers. I tugged at the bell till William John came in quaking, and then I asked him fiercely what he had done with my pipes. I was so obviously not to be trifled with that William John (as we called him, because some thought his name was William, while others thought it was John) very soon handed me my favourite pipe, which he found in the rack on the smoking-table. This incident illustrates one of the very few drawbacks of smoking-tables. Not being used to them, you forget about them. William John, however, took the greatest pride in the table, and whenever he saw a pipe lying on the rug he pounced upon it and placed it, like a prisoner, in the rack. He was also most particular about the three cigars, the two cigarettes, and the four wax vestas, keeping them carefully in their proper compartments, where, unfortunaely, I seldom thought of looking for them.

The fatal defect of the smoking-table, however, was that it was generally rolling about the floor: the stalk in one corner, the slabs here and there, the cigars on the rug to be trampled on, the lid of the tobacco-jar beneath a chair. Every morning William John had to put the table together. Sometimes I had knocked it over accidentally. I would fling a crumpled piece of paper into the waste-paper basket. It missed the basket but hit the smoking-table, which went down like a wooden soldier. When my fire went out, just because I had taken my eyes off it for a moment, I called it names and flung the tongs at it. There was a crash—the smoking-table again. In time I might have remedied this; but there is one weakness which I could not stand in any smoking-table. A smoking-table ought to be so constructed that from where you are sitting you can stretch out your feet, twist them round the stalk, and so lift the table to the spot where it will be handiest. This my smoking-table would never do. The moment I had it in the air it wanted to stand on its head.

Though I still admired smoking-tables as much as ever, I began to want very much to give this one away. The difficulty was not so much to know whom to give it to as how to tie it up. My brother was the very person, for I owed him a letter, and this, I thought, would do instead. For a month I meant to pack the table up and send it to him; but I always put off doing it, and at last I thought the best plan would be to give it to Scrymgeour, who liked elegant furniture. As a smoker Scrymgeour seemed the very man to appreciate a pretty, useful little table. Besides, all I had to do was to send William John down with it. Scrymgeour was out at the time; but we left it at the side of his fireplace as a pleasant surprise. Next morning, to my indignation, it was back at the side of my fireplace, and in the evening Scrymgeour came and upbraided me for trying, as he most unworthily expressed it, "to palm the thing off on him." He was no sooner gone than I took the table to pieces to send to my brother. I tied the stalk up in brown paper, meaning to get a box for the other parts. William John sent off the stalk, and for some days the other pieces littered the floor. My brother wrote me saying he had received something from me, for which his best thanks; but would I tell him what it was, as it puzzled everybody? This was his impatient way; but I made an effort, and sent off the other pieces to him in a hat-box.

That was a year ago, and since then I have only heard the history of the smoking-table in fragments. My brother liked it immensely; but he thought it was too luxurious for a married man, so he sent it to Reynolds, in Edinburgh. Not knowing Reynolds, I cannot say what his opinion was; but soon afterwards I heard of its being in the possession of Grayson, who was charmed with it, but gave it to Peele because it was hardly in its place in a bachelor's establishment. Later a town man sent it to a country gentleman as just the thing for the country; and it was afterwards in Liverpool as the very thing for a town.

There I thought it was lost, so far as I was concerned. One day, however, Boyd, a friend of mine who lives in Glasgow, came to me for a week, and about six hours afterwards he said that he had a present for me. He brought it into my sitting-room—a bulky parcel—and while he was undoing the cords he told me it was something quite novel: he had bought it in Glasgow the day before. When I saw a walnut leg I started; in another two minutes I was trying to thank Boyd for my own smoking-table. I recognized it by the dents. I was too much the gentleman to insist on an explanation from Boyd; but, though it seems a harsh thing to say, my opinion is that these different persons gave the table away because they wanted to get rid of it. William John has it now.

WHEN MY WIFE IS ASLEEP AND ALL THE HOUSE IS STILL

Perhaps the heading of this chapter will deceive some readers into thinking that I smoke nowadays in camera. It is, I know, a common jest among smokers that such a promise as mine is seldom kept, and I allow that the Arcadians tempt me still. But never shall it be said of me with truth that I have broken my word. I smoke no more, and, indeed, though the scenes of my bachelorhood frequently rise before me in dreams, painted as Scrymgeour could not paint them, I am glad, when I wake up, that they are only dreams. Those selfish days are done, and I see that though they were happy days, the happiness was a mistake. As for the struggle that is supposed to take place between a man and tobacco after he sees smoking in its true colours, I never experienced it. I have not even any craving for the Arcadia now, though it is a tobacco that should only be smoked by our greatest men. Were we to present a tin of it to our national heroes, instead of the freedom of the city, they would probably thank us more. Jimmy and the others are quite unworthy to smoke it; indeed, if I had my way they would give up smoking altogether. Nothing, perhaps, shows more completely how I have severed my bonds than this: that my wife is willing to let our friends smoke in the study, but I will not hear of it. There shall be no smoking in my house; and I have determined to speak to Jimmy about smoking out at our spare bedroom window. It is a mere contemptible pretence to say that none of the smoke comes back into the room. The curtains positively reek of it, and we must have them washed at once. I shall speak plainly to Jimmy because I want him to tell the others. They must understand clearly on what terms they are received in this house, and if they prefer making chimneys of themselves to listening to music, by all means let them stay at home.

But when my wife is asleep and all the house is still, I listen to the man through the wall. At such times I have my briar in my mouth, but there is no harm in that, for it is empty. I did not like to give away my briar, knowing no one who understood it, and I always carry it about with me now to remind me of my dark past. When the man through the wall lights up I put my cold pipe in my mouth and we have a quiet hour together.

I have never to my knowledge seen the man through the wall, for his door is round the corner, and, besides, I have no interest in him until half-past eleven P.M. We begin then. I know him chiefly by his pipes, and them I know by his taps on the wall as he knocks the ashes out of them. He does not smoke the Arcadia, for his temper is hasty, and he breaks the coals with his foot. Though I am compelled to say that I do not consider his character very lovable he has his good points, and I like his attachment to his briar. He scrapes it, on the whole, a little roughly, but that is because he is so anxious to light up again, and I discovered long ago that he has signed an agreement with his wife to go to bed at half-past twelve. For some time I could not understand why he had a silver rim put on the bowl. I noticed the change in the tap at once, and the natural conclusion would have been that the bowl had cracked. But it never had the tap of a cracked bowl. I was reluctant to believe that the man through the wall was merely some vulgar fellow, and I felt that he could not be so or else he would have smoked his meerschaum more. At last I understood. The bowl had worn away on one side, and the silver rim had been needed to keep the tobacco in. Undoubtedly this was the explanation, for even before the rim came I was a little puzzled by the taps of the briar. He never seemed to hit the wall with the whole mouth of the bowl, but of course the reason was that he could not. At the same time I do not exonerate him from blame. He is a clumsy smoker to burn his bowl at one side, and I am afraid he lets the stem slip round in his teeth. Of course I see that the mouthpiece is loose, but a piece of blotting-paper would remedy that.

His meerschaum is not such a good one as Jimmy's. Though Jimmy's boastfulness about his meerschaum was hard to bear, none of us ever denied the pipe's worth. The man through the wall has not a cherry-wood stem to his meerschaum, and consequently it is too light. A ring has been worn into the palm of his left hand, owing to his tapping the meerschaum there, and it is as marked as Jimmy's ring, for, though Jimmy tapped more strongly, the man through the wall has to tap oftener.

What I chiefly dislike about the man through the wall is his treatment of his clay. A clay, I need scarcely say, has an entirely different tap from a meerschaum, but the man through the wall does not treat these two pipes as if they were on an equality. He ought to tap his clay on the palm of his hand, but he seldom does so, and I am strongly of opinion that when he does, it is only because he has forgotten that this is not the meerschaum. Were he to tap the clay on the wall or on the ribs of the fire he would smash it, so he taps it on a coal. About this there is something contemptible. I am not complaining because he has little affection for his clay. In face of all that has been said in honour of clays, and knowing that this statement will occasion an outcry against me, I admit that I never cared for clays myself. A rank tobacco is less rank through a churchwarden, but to smoke the Arcadia through a clay is to incur my contempt, and even my resentment. But to disbelieve in clays is one thing and to treat them badly is another. If the man through the wall has decided after reflection and experiment that his clay is a mistake, I say let him smoke it no more; but so long as he does smoke it I would have it receive consideration from him. I very much question whether, if he read his heart, he could learn from it that he loves his meerschaum more than his clay, yet because the meerschaum cost more he taps it on his palm. This is a serious charge to bring against any man, but I do not make it lightly.

The man through the wall smokes each of these three pipes nightly, beginning with the briar. Thus he does not like a hot pipe. Some will hold that he ought to finish with the briar, as it is his favourite, but I am not of that opinion. Undoubtedly, I think, the first pipe is the sweetest; indeed, I feel bound to make a statement here. I have an uneasy feeling that I never did justice to meerschaums, and for this reason: I only smoked them after my briar was hot, so that I never gave them a fair chance. If I had begun the day with a meerschaum, might it not have shown itself in a new light? That is a point I shall never be able to decide now, but I often think of it, and I leave the verdict to others.

Even though I did not know that the man through the wall must retire at half-past twelve, his taps at that hour would announce it. He then gives each of his pipes a final tap, not briskly as before, but slowly, as if he was thinking between each tap. I have sometimes decided to send him a tin of the only tobacco to smoke, but on the whole I could not undertake the responsibility of giving a man, whom I have only studied for a few months, such a testimonial. Therefore when his last tap says good-night to me I take my cold briar out of my mouth, tap it on the mantelpiece, smile sadly and so to bed.

Walter Raleigh

Walter Raleigh was Professor of English Literature at Oxford. I give these selections from his letters as examples of scholarly-epistolary· wit. He amuses his correspondent by irreverent treatment of the language that both, in fact, reverence, and by deft literary allusiveness. More fundamentally, he amuses because he reveals, as if unaware, the duality of his mind. He is a scholar who has emerged from scholarship, who has passed through literature to life.

LETTERS

TO MRS. F. GOTCH

Liverpool, July 2, 1898

Wee Klere oute of hear
tomoro.

Doe you lyke my newe phancy in the matere of Spelynge? I have growen wery of Spelynge wordes allwaies in one waye and now affecte diversite. The cheif vertew of my reform is that it makes the spelynge express the moode of the wryter. Frinsns, if yew fealin frenly, ye kin spel frenly-like. Butte if yew wyshe to indicate that thogh nott of hyghe bloode, yew are compleately atte one wyth the aristokrasy you canne double alle youre consonnantts, prollonge mosstte of yourre vowelles, and addde a fynalle "e" wherevverre itte iss requuquirred.

Thysse gyvves a sensse of leissuure, ande quiette dygnittie.

Temore Ime goin to get mi golf Klubbs bak from Hoylik. I have swyped around that linx ownly wanss thyss yere. It took me 131 strokes and 46 of them were for the last eight holes. Wodger thinco that? Wun hoal wos a Atene, ohing to reining bloz on a balle in a buncre, my long sufring tempre having broken down. Sum of the skelpes was in the heir, counting ech as won scelp but doing kno werk. Queery: if a man hoo duzz no werk is unworthie of the nayme

317

of man, whi shuld a skelp that does no werk be entitled to the ful stile emoluments & privyledges of a skelp?

Thys is not soe at billiards whyche is therefer the nobbler game— throo neglecting of the eydel.

To say that a man who stands swishing a stikke in the ere haz taykne 230 stroax to go around the lynx seemes to mi pore honestie a mere subterfuge.

It is by suche petty foging insinuashns that my averidge aperes as 162.

_____

TO MRS. DOWDALL

March 9, 1902

... We met Marie Corelli. I put her on to writing a book in defence of Shakespeare.

I thought of three things to say to her and they all suited very well:

(1) "O Miss Corelli, how *do* you think of all those lovely things?"

(2) "O Miss Corelli, since I read *Barabbas,* I think that Christianity is just too sweet!"

(3) "O Miss Corelli, isn't it wonderful to know that there are thousands and thousands of people in the world who have no ideas but what you put into their heads?"

_____

TO MRS. GOTCH, ON A POST CARD

Stanford, 7 June, 1902

So there is no maw gaw to shed in the Baw Waw. The paw praw-Baws will feel saw! The praw-Baws are an awful baw! They gained no eclaw by taking the flaw! I set no staw by them. They are rotten at the caw. So no maw from

Yaws,

W. A. R.

_____

TO JOHN SAMPSON

New Year's Eve, Oxford, 1904

.... Bradley's book on Shakespeare is good. Of course it is not nearly
gutsy enough, but he gets there all the same. Even with it I can't help
feeling that critical admiration for what another man has written is an
emotion for spinsters. Shakes. didn't want it. Jerome K. Jerome is in
some ways a far decenter writer than Brunetière or Saintsbury or any
of the professed critics. He goes and begets a brat for himself, and
doesn't pule about other people's amours. If I write an autobiography
it shall be called "Confessions of a Pimp."

Goodbye, old man. Tell Mackay to stop founding Universities.
There's no sense in them. Bottled men, gone putrid, that's all. And
they spread like mould on cheese. If a University or two would bust
up, or resolve itself into an Agapemone, my spirits would go up. Damn
the Education of the young, anyhow. They're too good to be fouled this
way.

––––––

TO MRS. WALTER CRUM

12 Northmoor Road, Oxford, 30-iv-05

I was back at Oxford at seven o'clock that same day. I am drawing
up a liturgy [*sic*] for use after a visit.

For all the pleasures of my visit I beg you to accept my thanks.

For the shelter of Dalnotter, for the room in the Permanent Residents' Wing, for the fire of an evening and the tea of a morning,
I beg you to accept my thanks.

For all the viands of the Table, for the Five Meals and Fifty Dishes,
for the fishes and birds and beasts but especially * (for the Crab)

* (Here shall be inserted the name of any dish which it is desired to com-
memorate.)

I beg you to accept my thanks.

For the beautiful days at Erskine, for the games of golf, for the good
strokes of my partners and for the bad strokes of my enemies, I
beg you to accept my thanks.

For the noble company of my fellow guests, for the Edinburgh Professor and the Brown Immortelle, for the Lawyer and the Publisher, for the wise man with the two-eared bag and for the man in the mutton coloured suit, for my supplanter and his helpmete, for the discreet Rose and spirited Carolina and for the man Robert, I beg you to accept my thanks.

For all drinks and potions, for the tea and the coffee, the claret and the sherry, for the fifty-one port and the eighty-one port, for the whisky and the very old brandy, I beg you to accept my thanks.

(Here shall be inserted the Collect for use after Bridge.)

For all my quarrels at Bridge, for my failures to make myself socially useful, for putting J. M. in a swither, for reprehending R. L., and for all ridiculous and offensive behaviour, I humbly beg your pardon.

(Here shall be inserted the prayer to be said by those who desire to be asked again.)

TO CYNTHIA CHARTERIS

Ferry Hinksey, 10. ii. 10

...I am a Man of Letters, so I have to write letters to be the ones that I am a man of. I do want to say that Americans are quite incredible. We went to a Thanksgiving Day where they were all together and spoke to each other. It was the queerest feeling. They don't seem to have any private life. Yesterday

I blinked on my perch like a vulture,
When they crept up the hill unawares,
To talk of the progress of culture
And deposit their bodies in chairs.

I wish I loved them better, which I can't do while they stay so husky. They are so bright and snappy—the click without the spark. And oh, how they do explain! Lucie says that when you travel from Scotland everyone explains things till you get south of Birmingham, and then it all stops and you rest. I suppose the English are the only race who don't explain.

TO JOHN SAMPSON

Ferry Hinksey, 16 Sept. 1910

I took most of your suggestions you'll see—and jolly thankful. My wife says that if an ordinary well educated woman were left alone with the book [Raleigh's *Six Essays on Johnson*] in a railway carriage, it wouldn't take her half a minute to find out that she couldn't possibly read it, and even if the journey lasted eight hours she wouldn't try twice. This was a facer, so I asked why. The reasons are—

(i) There are too many prig words.

(ii) When you get to the end of a sentence you've mostly forgotten what the beginning was about.

I believe this is correct. What am I to do to be popular, now that the bottom's out of transcribing Boswell?

My own belief is that there's only one popular English. It's not spoken by anyone. But it's the English that women think men ought to write love-letters in. You see it in feuilletons. It's bloody difficult to ram old Johnson into it, but I think perhaps I ought to try, and that's what makes me not so bright as usual. I feel distinctly aggravated at being reluctantly driven to have recourse to this expedient. There—I shall fetch it presently.

———

TO WALTER PECK

Ferry Hinksey, 13 Oct., 1920

...Mind you don't write any professional English, the garbage of words that conceals lack of thought. "The development of the poet's individuality constitutes a subject of profound interest" and that sort of thing. Write for Oxford cabmen—in that way you will say more in less space. In most American university books I can't see the fish for the weeds.

Don't say "mentality." Except where it is used to mean nothing, there's no need for it.

———

THE WISHES OF AN ELDERLY MAN

(At a Garden Party, June 1914)

I wish I loved the Human Race;
I wish I loved its silly face;
I wish I liked the way it walks;
I wish I liked the way it talks;
And when I'm introduced to one
I wish I thought *What Jolly Fun!*

E. Œ. Somerville and Martin Ross

It was very hard to choose among the tales of those incomparable Irishwomen who write as the team of Somerville and Ross. The hunting stories are the most famous, but Americans miss a good deal of them, by not knowing the sacred ritual of the fox-hunt. E. V. Lucas considered The House of Fahy *the funniest story ever written. But I have a particular fondness for this account of a nightmare train-journey across Ireland.*

POISSON D'AVRIL

The atmosphere of the waiting-room set at naught at a single glance the theory that there can be no smoke without fire. The station-master, when remonstrated with, stated, as an incontrovertible fact, that any chimney in the world would smoke in a south-easterly wind, and further, said there wasn't a poker, and that if you poked the fire the grate would fall out. He was, however, sympathetic, and went on his knees before the smouldering mound of slack, endeavouring to charm it to a smile by subtle proddings with the handle of the ticket-punch. Finally, he took me to his own kitchen fire and talked politics and salmon-fishing, the former with judicious attention to my presumed point of view, and careful suppression of his own, the latter with no less tactful regard for my admission that for three days I had not caught a fish, while the steam rose from my wet boots, in witness of the ten miles of rain through which an outside car had carried me.

Before the train was signalled I realised for the hundredth time the magnificent superiority of the Irish mind to the trammels of official-dom, and the inveterate supremacy in Ireland of the Personal Element.

"You might get a foot-warmer at Carrig Junction," said a species of lay porter in a knitted jersey, ramming my suit-case upside down under the seat. "Sometimes they're in it, and more times they're not."

The train dragged itself rheumatically from the station, and a cold spring· rain—the time was the middle of a most inclement April—smote it in flank as it came into the open. I pulled up both windows

323

and began to smoke; there is, at least, a semblance of warmth in a thoroughly vitiated atmosphere.

It is my wife's habit to assert that I do not read her letters, and being now on my way to join her and my family in Gloucestershire, it seemed a sound thing to study again her latest letter of instructions.

"I am starting today, as Alice wrote to say we must be there two days before the wedding, so as to have a rehearsal for the pages. Their dresses have come, and they look too delicious in them—"

(I here omit profuse particulars not pertinent to this tale)—

"It is sickening for you to have had such bad sport. If the worst comes to the worst, couldn't you buy one?—"

I smote my hand upon my knee. I had forgotten the infernal salmon! What a score for Philippa! If these contretemps would only teach her that I was not to be relied upon, they would have their uses, but experience is wasted upon her; I have no objection to being called an idiot, but, that being so, I ought to be allowed the privileges and exemptions proper to idiots. Philippa had, no doubt, written to Alice Hervey, and assured her that Sinclair would be only too delighted to bring her a salmon, and Alice Hervey, who was rich enough to find much enjoyment in saving money, would reckon upon it, to its final fin in mayonnaise.

Plunged in morose meditations, I progressed through a country parcelled out by shaky and crooked walls into a patchwork of hazel scrub and rocky fields, veiled in rain. About every six miles there was a station, wet and windswept; at one the sole occurrence was the presentation of a newspaper to the guard by the station-master; at the next the guard read aloud some choice excerpts from the same to the porter. The Personal Element was potent on this branch of the Munster and Connaught Railway. Routine, abhorrent to all artistic minds, was sheathed in conversation; even the engine-driver, a functionary ordinarily as aloof as the Mikado, alleviated his enforced isolation by sociable shrieks to every level crossing, while the long row of public-houses that formed, as far as I could judge, the town of Carrig, received a special and, as it seemed, humorous salutation.

The Time-table decreed that we were to spend ten minutes at Carrig Junction; it was fifteen before the crowd of market people on the platform had been assimilated; finally, the window of a neighboring carriage was flung open, and a wrathful English voice asked how much longer the train was going to wait. The station-master, who was at the moment engrossed in conversation with the guard and a man who was carrying a long parcel wrapped in newspaper, looked around, and said gravely—

"Well now, that's a mystery!"

The man with the parcel turned away, and convulsively studied a poster. The guard put his hand over his mouth.

The voice, still more wrathfully, demanded the earliest hour at which its owner could get to Belfast.

"Ye'll be asking me next when I take me breakfast," replied the station-master, without haste or palpable annoyance.

The window went up again with a bang, the man with the parcel dug the guard in the ribs with his elbow, and the parcel slipped from under his arm and fell on the platform.

"Oh my! oh my! Me fish!" exclaimed the man, solicitously picking up a remarkably good-looking salmon that had slipped from its wrapping of newspaper.

Inspiration came to me, and I, in my turn, opened my window and summoned the station-master.

Would his friend sell me the salmon? The station-master entered upon the mission with ardour, but without success.

No; the gentleman was only just after running down to the town for it in the delay, but why wouldn't I run down and get one for myself? There was half-a-dozen more of them below at Coffey's selling cheap; there would be time enough, the mail wasn't signalled yet.

I jumped from the carriage and doubled out of the station at top speed, followed by an assurance from the guard that he would not forget me.

Congratulating myself on the ascendancy of the Personal Element, I sped through the soapy limestone and towards the public-houses. En route I met a heated man carrying yet another salmon, who, without preamble, informed me that there were three or four more good fish in it, and that he was after running down from the train himself.

"Ye have whips o' time!" he called after me. "It's the first house that's not a public-house. Ye'll see boots in the window—she'll give them for tenpence a pound if ye're stiff with her!"

I ran past the public-houses.

"Tenpence a pound!" I exclaimed inwardly, "at this time of year! That's good enough."

Here I perceived the house with boots in the window, and dived into its dark doorway.

A cobbler was at work behind a low counter. He mumbled something about Herself, through lengths of waxed thread that hung across his mouth, a fat woman appeared at an inner door, and at that moment I heard, appallingly near, the whistle of the incoming mail. The fat woman grasped the situation in an instant, and with what appeared but one movement, snatched a large fish from the floor of the room behind her and flung a newspaper round it.

"Eight pound weight!" she said swiftly. "Ten shillings!"

A convulsive effort of mental arithmetic assured me that this was more than tenpence a pound, but it was not the moment for stiffness. I shoved a half-sovereign into her fishy hand, clasped my salmon in my arms, and ran.

Needless to say it was uphill, and at the steepest gradient another whistle stabbed me like a spur; above the station roof successive and advancing puffs of steam warned me that the worst had probably happened, but still I ran. When I gained the platform my train was already clear of it, but the Personal Element held good. Every soul in the station, or so it seemed to me, lifted up his voice and yelled. The station-master put his fingers in his mouth and sent after the departing train an unearthly whistle, with a high trajectory and a serrated edge. It took effect; the train slackened, I plunged from the platform and followed it up the rails, and every window in both trains blossomed with the heads of deeply interested spectators. The guard met me on the line, very apologetic and primed with an explanation that the gentleman going for the boat-train wouldn't let him wait any longer, while from our rear came an exultant cry from the station-master.

"Ye *told* him ye wouldn't forget him!"

"There's a few countrywomen in your carriage, sir," said the guard, ignoring the taunt, as he shoved me and my salmon up the side of the train, "but they'll be getting out in a couple of stations. There wasn't another seat in the train for them!"

My sensational return to my carriage was viewed with the utmost sympathy by no less than seven shawled and cloaked countrywomen. In order to make room for me, one of them seated herself on the floor with her basket in her lap, another, on the seat opposite to me, squeezed herself under the central elbow flap that had been turned up to make more room. The aromas of wet cloaks, turf smoke, and salt fish formed a potent blend. I was excessively hot, and the eyes of the seven women were fastened upon me with intense and unwearying interest.

"Move west a small piece, Mary Jack, if you please," said a voluminous matron in the corner, "I declare we're as throng as three in a bed this minute!"

"Why then, Julia Casey, there's little throubling yourself," grumbled the woman under the flap. "Look at the way meself is! I wonder is it to be putting humps on themselves the gentry has them things down on top o' them! I'd sooner be carrying a basket of turnips on me back than to be scrooged this way!"

The woman on the floor at my feet rolled up at me a glance of compassionate amusement at this rustic ignorance, and tactfully changed the conversation by supposing that it was at Coffey's I got the salmon.

I said it was.

There was a silence, during which it was obvious that one question burnt in every heart.

"I'll go bail she axed him tinpence!" said the woman under the flap, as one who touches the limits of absurdity.

"It's a beautiful fish!" I said defiantly. "Eight pounds weight. I gave her ten shillings for it."

What is described in newspapers as "sensation in court" greeted this confession.

"Look!" said the woman under the flap, darting her head out of the hood of her cloak, like a tortoise, " 'tis what it is, ye haven't as much roguery in your heart as'd make ye a match for her!"

"Divil blow the ha'penny Eliza Coffey paid for that fish!" burst out the fat woman in the corner. "Thim lads o' her's had a creel full o' thim snatched this morning before it was making day!"

"How would the gentleman be a match for her!" shouted the woman on the floor through a long-drawn whistle that told of a coming station. "Sure a Turk itself wouldn't be a match for her! That one has a tongue that'd clip a hedge!"

At the station they clambered out laboriously, and with groaning. I handed down to them their monster baskets, laden, apparently, with ingots of lead; they told me in return that I was a fine *grauver* man, and it was a pity there weren't more like me; they wished, finally, that my journey might well thrive with me, and passed from my ken, bequeathing to me, after the agreeable manner of their kind, a certain comfortable mental sleekness that reason cannot immediately dispel. They also left me in possession of the fact that I was about to present the irreproachable Alice Hervey with a contraband salmon.

The journey passed cheerlessly into evening, and my journey did not conspicuously thrive with me. Somewhere in the dripping twilight I changed trains, and again later on, and at each change the salmon moulted some more of its damp raiment of newspaper, and I debated seriously the idea of interring it, regardless of consequences, in my portmanteau. A lamp was banged into the roof of my carriage, half an inch of orange flame, poised in a large glass globe, like a gold-fish, and of about as much use as an illuminant. Here also was handed in the dinner basket that I had wired for, and its contents, arid though they were, enabled me to achieve at least some measure of mechanical distension, followed by a dreary lethargy that was not far from drowsiness.

At the next station we paused long; nothing whatever occurred, and the rain drummed patiently upon the roof. Two nuns and some school-girls were in the carriage next door, and their voices came plaintively and in snatches through the partition; after a long period of apparent collapse, during which I closed my eyes to evade the cold gaze of the salmon through the netting, a voice in the next carriage said resourcefully:

"Oh, girls, I'll tell you what we'll do! We'll say the Rosary!"

"Oh, that will be lovely!" said another voice; "well, who'll give it out? Theresa Condon, you'll give it out."

Theresa Condon gave it out, in a not unmelodious monotone, interspersed with the responses, always in a lower cadence; the words were indistinguishable, but the rise and fall of the western voices was lulling as the hum of bees. I fell asleep.

I awoke in total darkness; the train was motionless, and complete and profound silence reigned. We were at a station, that much I discerned by the light of the dim lamp at the far end of a platform glistening with wet. I struck a match and ascertained that it was eleven o'clock, precisely the hour at which I was to board the mail train. I jumped out and ran down the platform; there was no one in the train; there was no one even on the engine, which was forlornly hissing to itself in the silence. There was not a human being anywhere. Every door was closed, and all was dark. The nameboard of the station was faintly visible; with a lighted match I went along it letter by letter. It seemed as if the whole alphabet were in it, and by the time I had got to the end I had forgotten the beginning. One fact I had, however, mastered, that it was not the junction at which I was to catch the mail.

I was undoubtedly awake, but for a moment I was inclined to entertain the idea that there had been an accident, and that I had entered upon existence in another world. Once more I assailed the station house and the appurtenances thereof, the ticket-office, the waiting room, finally, and at some distance, the goods store, outside which the single lamp of the station commented feebly on the drizzle and the darkness. As I approached it a crack of light under the door became perceptible, and a voice was suddenly uplifted within.

"Your best now agin that! Throw down your Jack!"

I opened the door with pardonable violence, and found the guard, the station-master, the driver, and the stoker, seated on barrels round a packing case, on which they were playing a game of cards.

To have too egregiously the best of a situation is not, to a generous mind, a source of strength. In the perfection of their overthrow I permitted the driver and stoker to wither from their places, and to fade away into the outer darkness without any suitable send-off; with the guard and the station-master, I dealt more faithfully, but the pleasure of throwing water on drowned rats is not a lasting one. I accepted the statements that they thought there wasn't a Christian in the train, that a few minutes here or there wouldn't signify, that they would have me at the junction in twenty minutes, and it was often the mail was late.

Fired by this hope I hurried back to my carriage, preceded at an emulous gallop by the officials. The guard thrust in with me the lantern from the card table, and fled to his van.

"Mind the goods train, Tim!" shouted the station-master, as he slammed my door, "she might be coming anytime now!"

The answer travelled magnificently back from the engine.

"Let her come! She'll meet her match!" A war-whoop upon the steam whistle fittingly closed the speech, and the train sprang into action.

We had about fifteen miles to go, and we banged and bucketed over it in what was, I should imagine, record time. The carriage felt as if it were galloping on four wooden legs, my teeth chattered in my head, and the salmon slowly churned its way forth from its newspaper, and moved along the netting with dreadful stealth.

All was of no avail.

"Well," said the guard, as I stepped forth on to the deserted platform of Loughranny, "that owld Limited Mail's th' unpunctualest thrain in Ireland! If you're a minute late she's gone from you, and may be if you were early you might be half-an-hour waiting for her!"

On the whole the guard was a gentleman. He said he would show me the best hotel in the town, though he feared I would be hard set to get a bed anywhere because of the *"Feis"* (a Feis, I should explain, is a Festival, devoted to competitions in Irish songs and dances). He shouldered my portmanteau, he even grappled successfully with the salmon, and, as we traversed the empty streets, he explained to me how easily I could catch the morning boat from Rosslare, and how it was, as a matter of fact, quite the act of Providence that my original scheme had been frustrated.

All was dark at the uninviting portals of the hotel favoured by the guard. For a full five minutes we waited at them, ringing hard: I suggested that we should try elsewhere.

"He'll come," said the guard, with the confidence of the Pied Piper of Hamelin, retaining an implacable thumb upon the button of the electric bell. "He'll come. Sure it rings in his room!"

The victim came, half awake, half dressed, and with an inch of dripping candle in his fingers. There was not a bed there, he said, nor in the town neither.

I said I would sit in the dining-room till the time for the early train.

"Sure there's five beds in the dining-room," replied the boots, "and there's mostly two in every bed."

His voice was firm, but there was a wavering look in his eye.

"What about the billiard-room, Mike?" said the guard, in wooing tones.

"Ah, God bless you! we have a mattress on the table this minute!" answered the boots, wearily, "and the fellow that got the First Prize for Reels asleep on top of it!"

"Well, and can't ye put the palliasse on the floor under it, ye omadhawn?" said the guard, dumping my luggage and the salmon in the hall, "sure there's no snugger place in the house! I must run away home now, before Herself thinks I'm dead altogether!"

His retreating footsteps went lightly away down the empty street.

"Annything don't throuble *him!*" said the boots bitterly.

As for me, nothing save the Personal Element stood between me and destitution.

It was in the dark of the early morning that I woke again to life and its troubles. A voice, dropping, as it were, over the edge of some smothering over-world, had awakened me. It was the voice of the First Prize for Reels, descending through a pocket of the billiard-table.

"I beg your pardon, sir, are ye going on the 5 to Cork?"

I grunted a negative.

"Well, if ye were, ye'd be late," said the voice.

I received this useful information in indignant silence, and endeavoured to wrap myself again in the vanishing skirts of a dream.

"I'm going on the 6:30 meself," proceeded the voice, "and it's unknown to me how I'll put on me boots. Me feet is swelled the size o' three-pound loaves with the dint of the little dancing-shoes I had on me in the competition last night. Me feet's delicate that way, and I'm a great epicure about me boots."

I snored aggressively, but the dream was gone. So, for all practical purposes, was the night.

The First Prize for Reels arose, presenting an astonishing spectacle of grass-green breeches, a white shirt, and pearl-grey stockings, and accomplished a toilet that consisted of removing these and putting on ordinary garments, completed by the apparently excruciating act of getting into his boots. At any other hour of the day I might have been sorry for him. He then removed himself and his belongings to the hall, and there entered upon a resounding conversation with the boots, while I crawled forth from my lair to renew the strife with circumstances and to endeavour to compose a telegram to Alice Hervey of explanation and apology that should cost less than seven and sixpence. There was also the salmon to be dealt with.

Here the boots intervened, opportunely, with a cup of tea, and the intelligence that he had already done up the salmon in straw bottle-covers and brown paper, and that I could travel Europe with it if I liked. He further informed me that he would run up to the station with the luggage now, and that maybe I wouldn't mind carrying the fish myself; it was on the table in the hall.

My train went at 6:15. The boots had secured for me one of many empty carriages, and lingered conversationally till the train started; he regretted politely my bad night at the hotel, and assured me that only for Jimmy Durkan having a little drink taken—Jimmy Durkan was the First Prize for Reels—he would have turned him off the billiard table for my benefit. He finally confided to me that Mr. Durkan was engaged to his sister, and was a rising baker in the town of Limerick, "indeed," he said, "any girl might be glad to get him. He dances like whalebone, and he makes grand bread!"

Here the train started.

It was late that night, when, stiff, dirty, with tired eyes blinking in the dazzle of electric light, I was conducted by the Herveys' beautiful footman into the Herveys' baronial hall, and was told by the Herveys' imperial butler that dinner was over, and the gentlemen had just gone into the drawing-room. I was in the act of hastily declining to join them there, when a voice cried—

"Here he is!"

And Philippa, rustling and radiant, came forth into the hall, followed in shimmers of satin, and flutterings of lace, by Alice Hervey, by the bride elect, and by the usual festival rout of exhilarated relatives, male and female, whose mission it is to keep things lively before a wedding.

"Is this a wedding present for me, Uncle Sinclair?" cried the bride elect, through a deluge of questions and commiserations, and snatched from under my arm the brown paper parcel that had remained there from force of direful habit.

"I advise you not to open it!" I exclaimed; "it's a salmon!"

The bride elect, with a shriek of disgust, and without an instant of hesitation, hurled it at her nearest neighbour, the head bridesmaid. The head bridesmaid, with an answering shriek, sprang to one side, and the parcel that I had cherished with a mother's care across two countries and a stormy channel, fell, with a crash, on the flagged floor.

Why did it crash?

"A salmon!" screamed Philippa, gazing at the parcel, round which a pool was already forming, "why, that's whisky! Can't you smell it?"

The footman here respectfully interposed, and kneeling down, cautiously extracted from folds of brown paper a straw bottle cover full of broken glass and dripping with whisky.

"I'm afraid the other things are rather spoiled, sir," he said seriously, and drew forth, successively, a very large pair of high-low shoes, two long grey worsted stockings, and a pair of grass-green breeches.

They brought the house down, in a manner doubtless familiar to them when they shared the triumphs of Mr. Jimmy Durkan, but they left Alice Hervey distinctly cold.

"You know, darling," she said to Philippa afterwards, "I don't think it was very clever of dear Sinclair to take the wrong parcel. I *had* counted on that salmon."

W. W. Jacobs

Many scholars would prefer one of the night-watchman stories: Bill's
Lapse, *possibly, or* The Money-Box. *With such a reasonable judgment I
cannot quarrel. But Bob Pretty seems to me as great a creation as
Ginger Dick, Peter Russet, and Old Sam Small. He is the reincarna-
tion of Prometheus, culture-hero, as the anthropologists say. If W. W.
Jacobs were Aeschylus, he would have written great tragedies,* Bob
Pretty Bound, *and* Bob Pretty Unbound.

THE PERSECUTION OF BOB PRETTY

The old man sat on his accustomed bench outside the Cauliflower.
A generous measure of beer stood in a blue and white jug by his
elbow, and little wisps of smoke curled slowly upwards from the
bowl of his churchwarden pipe. The knapsacks of two young men lay
where they were flung on the table, and the owners, taking a noon-
tide rest, turned a polite, if bored, ear to the reminiscences of grateful
old age.

Poaching [said the old man, who had tried topics ranging from
early turnips to horseshoeing]—poaching ain't wot it used to be in
these 'ere parts. Nothing is like it used to be, poaching nor anything
else; but that there man you might ha' noticed as went out about ten
minutes ago and called me "Old Truthfulness" as 'e passed is the
worst one I know. Bob Pretty 'is name is, and of all the sly, artful,
deceiving men that ever lived in Claybury 'e is the worst—never did
a honest day's work in 'is life, and never wanted the price of a glass
of ale.

Bob Pretty's worst time was just after old Squire Brown died. The
old squire couldn't afford to preserve much, but by-and-by a gentleman with plenty of money, from London, named Rockett, took 'is place
and things began to look up. Pheasants was 'is favourites, and 'e spent
no end o' money rearing of 'em, but anything that could be shot at
suited 'im, too.

He started by sneering at the little game that Squire Brown 'ad

334

left, but all 'e could do didn't seem to make much difference; things disappeared in a most eggstrordinary way, and the keepers went pretty near crazy, while the things the squire said about Claybury and Claybury men was disgraceful.

Everybody knew as it was Bob Pretty and one or two of 'is mates from other places, but they couldn't prove it. They couldn't catch 'im nohow, and at last the squire 'ad two keepers set off to watch 'im by night and by day.

Bob Pretty wouldn't believe it; he said 'e couldn't. And even when it was pointed out to 'im that Keeper Lewis was follering of 'im he said that it just 'appened he was going the same way, that was all. And sometimes he'd get up in the middle of the night and go for a fifteen-mile walk 'cos 'e'd got the toothache, and Mr. Lewis, who 'adn't got it, had to tag along arter 'im till he was fit to drop. O' course, it was one keeper the less to look arter the game, and by-and-by the squire see that and took 'im off.

All the same they kept a pretty close watch on Bob, and at last one arternoon they sprang out on 'im as he was walking past Gray's farm, and asked him wot it was he 'ad got in his pockets.

"That's my bisness, Mr. Lewis," ses Bob Pretty.

Mr. Smith, the other keeper, passed 'is hands over Bob's coat and felt something soft and bulgy.

"You take your 'ands off of me," ses Bob. "You don't know 'ow partikler I am."

He jerked 'imself away, but they caught 'old of 'im agin, and Mr. Lewis put 'is hand in his inside pocket and pulled out two brace o' partridges.

"You'll come along of us," he ses, catching 'im by the arm.

"We've been looking for you a long time," ses Keeper Smith, "and it's a pleasure for us to 'ave your company."

Bob Pretty said 'e wouldn't go, but they forced 'im along and took 'im all the way to Cudford, four miles off, so that Policeman White could lock 'im up for the night. Mr. White was a'most as pleased as the keepers, and 'e warned Bob solemn not to speak becos all 'e said would be used agin 'im.

"Never mind about that," ses Bob Pretty. "I've got a clear conscience, and talking can't 'urt me. I'm very glad to see you, Mr. White; if these two clever, experienced keepers hadn't brought me I

should 'ave looked you up myself. They've been and stole my partridges."

Them as was standing round laughed, and even Policeman White
couldn't 'elp giving a little smile.

"There's nothing to laugh at," ses Bob, 'olding his 'ead up. "It's a
fine thing when a working man—a 'ard working man—can't take
home a little game for 'is family without being stopped and robbed."

"I s'pose they flew into your pocket?" ses Policeman White.

"No, they didn't," ses Bob. "I'm not going to tell any lies about
it; I put 'em there. The partridges in my inside coat-pocket and the
bill in my waistcoat-pocket."

"The *bill?*" ses Keeper Lewis, staring at 'im.

"Yes, the bill," ses Bob Pretty, staring back; "the bill from Mr.
Keen, the poulterer, at Wickham."

He fetched it out of 'is pocket and showed it to Mr. White, and
the keepers was like madmen a'most 'cos it was plain to see that Bob
Pretty 'ad been and bought them partridges just for to play a game
on 'em.

"I was curious to know wot they tasted like," he ses to the policeman. "Worst of it is, I don't s'pose my pore wife'll know 'ow to cook
'em."

"You get off 'ome," ses Policeman White, staring at 'im.

"But ain't I goin' to be locked up?" ses Bob. "'Ave I been brought
all this way just to 'ave a little chat with a policeman I don't like?"

"You go 'ome," ses Policeman White, handing the partridges back
to 'im.

"All right," ses Bob, "and I may 'ave to call you to witness that these
'ere two men laid hold o' me and tried to steal my partridges. I shall
go up and see my loryer about it."

He walked off 'ome with his 'ead up as high as 'e could hold it,
and the airs 'e used to give 'imself arter this was terrible for to
behold. He got 'is eldest boy to write a long letter to the squire about
it, saying that 'e'd overlook it this time, but 'e couldn't promise for
the future. Wot with Bob Pretty on one side and Squire Rockett on
the other, them two keepers' lives was 'ardly worth living.

Then the squire got a head-keeper named Cutts, a man as was said
to know more about the ways of poachers than they did themselves.
He was said to 'ave cleared out all the poachers for miles round the

place 'e came from, and pheasants could walk into people's cottages and not be touched.

He was a sharp-looking man, tall and thin, with screwed-up eyes and a little red beard. The second day 'e came 'e was up here at this 'ere Cauliflower, having a pint o' beer and looking round at the chaps as he talked to the landlord. The odd thing was that men who'd never taken a hare or a pheasant in their lives could 'ardly meet 'is eye, while Bob Pretty stared at 'im as if 'e was a wax-works.

"I 'ear you 'ad a little poaching in these parts afore I came," ses Mr. Cutts to the landlord.

"I think I 'ave 'eard something o' the kind," ses the landlord, staring over his 'ead with a far-away look in 'is eyes.

"You won't hear of much more," ses the keeper. "I've invented a new way of catching the dirty rascals; afore I came 'ere I caught all the poachers on three estates. I clear 'em out just like a ferret clears out rats."

"Sort o' man-trap?" ses the landlord.

"Ah, that's tellings," ses Mr. Cutts.

"Well, I 'ope you'll catch 'em here," ses Bob Pretty; "there's far too many of 'em about for my liking. Far too many."

"I shall 'ave 'em afore long," ses Mr. Cutts, nodding his 'ead.

"Your good 'ealth," ses Bob Pretty, holding up 'is mug. "We've been wanting a man like you for a long time."

"I don't want any of your impidence, my man," ses the keeper. "I've 'eard about you, and nothing good either. You be careful."

"I am careful," ses Bob, winking at the others. "I 'ope you'll catch all them low poaching chaps; they give the place a bad name, and I'm a'most afraid to go out arter dark for fear o' meeting 'em."

Peter Gubbins and Sam Jones began to laugh, but Bob Pretty got angry with 'em, and said he didn't see there was anything to laugh at. He said that poaching was a disgrace to their native place, and instead o' laughing they ought to be thankful to Mr. Cutts for coming to do away with it all.

"Any help I can give you shall be given cheerful," ses he to the keeper.

"When I want your help I'll ask you for it," ses Mr. Cutts.

"Thankee," ses Bob Pretty. "I on'y 'ope I sha'n't get my face knocked about like yours 'as been, that's all; cos my wife's so partikler."

"Wot d'ye mean?" ses Mr. Cutts, turning on him. "My face ain't been knocked about."

"Oh, I beg your pardin," ses Bob; "I didn't know it was natural."

Mr. Cutts went black in the face a'most and stared at Bob Pretty as if 'e was going to eat 'im, and Bob stared back, looking fust at the keeper's nose and then at 'is eyes and mouth, and then at 'is nose agin.

"You'll know me agin, I s'pose?" ses Mr. Cutts, at last.

"Yes," ses Bob, smiling; "I should know you a mile off—on the darkest night."

"We shall see," ses Mr. Cutts, taking up 'is beer and turning 'is back on him. "Those of us as live the longest 'll see the most."

"I'm glad I've lived long enough to see 'im," ses Bob to Bill Chambers. "I feel more satisfied with *myself* now."

Bill Chambers coughed, and Mr. Cutts, arter finishing 'is beer, took another look at Bob Pretty, and went off boiling a'most.

The trouble he took to catch Bob Pretty arter that you wouldn't believe, and all the time the game seemed to be simply melting away, and Squire Rockett was finding fault with 'im all day long. He was worn to a shadder a'most with watching, and Bob Pretty seemed to be more prosperous than ever.

Sometimes Mr. Cutts watched in the plantations, and sometimes 'e hid 'imself near Bob's house, and at last one night, when 'e was crouching behind the fence of Frederick Scott's front garden, 'e saw Bob Pretty come out of 'is house and, arter a careful look round, walk up the road. He held 'is breath as Bob passed 'im, and was just getting up to foller 'im when Bob stopped and walked slowly back agin, sniffing.

"Wot a delicious smell o' roses!" he ses out loud.

He stood in the middle o' the road nearly opposite where the keeper was hiding, and sniffed so that you could ha' heard him the other end o' the village.

"It can't be roses," he ses, in a puzzled voice, "becos there ain't no roses hereabouts, and besides, it's too late for 'em. It must be Mr. Cutts, the clever new keeper."

He put 'is head over the fence and bid 'im good evening, and said wot a fine night for a stroll it was, and asked 'im whether 'e was waiting for Frederick Scott's aunt. Mr. Cutts didn't answer 'im a word; 'e was pretty near bursting with passion. He got up and shook 'is fist in Bob Pretty's face, and then 'e went off stamping down the road as if 'e was going mad.

And for a long time Bob Pretty seemed to 'ave all the luck on 'is side. Keeper Lewis got rheumatic fever, which 'e put down to sitting about night arter night in damp places watching for Bob, and, while 'e was in the thick of it, with the doctor going every day, Mr. Cutts fell in getting over a fence and broke 'is leg. Then all the work fell on Keeper Smith, and to 'ear 'im talk you'd think that rheumatic fever and broken legs was better than anything else in the world. He asked the squire for 'elp, but the squire wouldn't give it to 'im, and he kept telling 'im wot a feather in 'is cap it would be if 'e did wot the other two couldn't do, and caught Bob Pretty. It was all very well, but, as Smith said, wot 'e wanted was feathers in 'is piller, instead of 'aving to snatch a bit o' sleep in 'is chair or sitting down with his 'ead agin a tree. When I tell you that 'e fell asleep in this public-'ouse one night while the landlord was drawing a pint o' beer he 'ad ordered, you'll know wot 'e suffered.

O' course, all this suited Bob Pretty as well as could be, and he was that good-tempered 'e'd got a nice word for everybody, and when Bill Chambers told 'im 'e was foolhardy 'e only laughed and said 'e knew wot 'e was about.

But the very next night 'e had reason to remember Bill Chambers's words. He was walking along Farmer Hall's field—the one next to the squire's plantation—and, so far from being nervous, 'e was actually a-whistling. He'd got a sack over 'is shoulder, loaded as full as it could be, and 'e 'ad just stopped to light 'is pipe when three men burst out o' the plantation and ran towards 'im as 'ard as they could run.

Bob Pretty just gave one look and then 'e dropped 'is pipe and set off like a hare. It was no good dropping the sack, because Smith, the keeper, 'ad recognised him and called 'im by name, so 'e just put 'is teeth together and did the best he could, and there's no doubt that if it 'adn't ha' been for the sack 'e could 'ave got clear away.

As it was, 'e ran for pretty near a mile, and they could 'ear 'im breathing like a pair o' bellows; but at last 'e saw that the game was up. He just managed to struggle as far as Farmer Pinnock's pond, and then, waving the sack round his 'ead, 'e flung it into the middle of it, and fell down gasping for breath.

"Got—you—this time—Bob Pretty," ses one o' the men, as they came up.

"Wot—*Mr. Cutts?*" ses Bob, with a start.

"That's me, my man," ses the keeper.

"Why—I thought—you was—. Is that *Mr. Lewis?* It can't be."

"That's me," ses Keeper Lewis. "We both got well sudden-like, Bob Pretty, when we 'eard you was out. You ain't so sharp as you thought you was."

Bob Pretty sat still, getting 'is breath back and doing a bit o' thinking at the same time.

"You give me a start," he ses, at last. "I thought you was both in bed, and, knowing 'ow hard-worked Mr. Smith 'as been, I just came round to 'elp 'im keep watch like. I promised to 'elp you, Mr. Cutts, if you remember."

"Wot was that you threw in the pond just now?" ses Mr. Cutts.

"A sack," ses Bob Pretty; "a sack I found in Farmer Hall's field. It felt to me as though it might 'ave birds in it, so I picked it up, and I was just on my way to your 'ouse with it, Mr. Cutts, when you started arter me."

"Ah!" ses the keeper, "and wot did you run for?"

Bob Pretty tried to laugh. "Becos I thought it was the poachers arter me," he ses. "It seems ridiklous, don't it?"

"Yes, it does," ses Lewis.

"I thought you'd know me a mile off," ses Mr. Cutts. "I should ha' thought the smell o' roses would ha' told you I was near."

Bob Pretty scratched 'is 'ead and looked at 'im out of the corner of 'is eye, but he 'adn't got any answer. Then 'e sat biting his finger-nails and thinking, while the keepers stood argyfying as to who should take 'is clothes off and go into the pond arter the pheasants. It was a very cold night and the pond was pretty deep in places, and none of 'em seemed anxious.

"Make 'im go in for it," ses Lewis, looking at Bob; " 'e chucked it in."

"On'y becos I thought you was poachers," ses Bob. "I'm sorry to have caused so much trouble."

"Well, you go in and get it out," ses Lewis, who pretty well guessed who'd have to do it if Bob didn't. "It'll look better for you, too."

"I've got my defence all right," ses Bob Pretty. "I ain't set a foot on the squire's preserves, and I found this sack a 'undered yards away from it."

"Don't waste more time," ses Mr. Cutts to Lewis. "Off with your clothes and in with you. Anybody'd think you was afraid of a little cold water."

"Whereabouts did 'e pitch it in?" ses Lewis.

Bob Pretty pointed with 'is finger exactly where 'e thought it was, but they wouldn't listen to 'im, and then Lewis, arter twice saying wot a bad cold he'd got, took 'is coat off very slow and careful.

"I wouldn't mind going in to oblige you," ses Bob Pretty, "but the pond is so full o' them cold, slimy efts; I don't fancy them crawling up agin me, and, besides that, there's such a lot o' deep holes in it. And wotever you do don't put your 'ead under; you know 'ow foul that water is."

Keeper Lewis pretended not to listen to 'im. He took off 'is clothes very slowly and then 'e put one foot in and stood shivering, although Smith, who felt the water with his 'and, said it was quite warm. Then Lewis put the other foot in and began to walk about careful, arfway up to 'is knees.

"I can't find it," he ses, with 'is teeth chattering.

"You 'aven't looked," ses Mr. Cutts; "walk about more; you can't expect to find it all at once. Try the middle."

Lewis tried the middle, and 'e stood there up to 'is neck, feeling about with his foot and saying things out loud about Bob Pretty, and other things under 'is breath about Mr. Cutts.

"Well, I'm off 'ome," ses Bob Pretty, getting up. "I'm too tender-'earted to stop and see a man drownded."

"You stay 'ere," ses Mr. Cutts, catching 'old of him.

"Wot for?" ses Bob; "you've got no right to keep me 'ere."

"Catch 'old of 'im, Joe," ses Mr. Cutts, quick-like.

Smith caught 'old of his other arm, and Lewis left off trying to find the sack to watch the struggle. Bob Pretty fought 'ard, and once or twice 'e nearly tumbled Mr. Cutts into the pond, but at last he gave in and lay down panting and talking about 'is loryer. Smith 'eld him down on the ground while Mr. Cutts kept pointing out places with 'is finger for Lewis to walk to. The last place 'e pointed to wanted a much taller man, but it wasn't found out till too late, and the fuss Keeper Lewis made when 'e could speak agin was terrible.

"You'd better come out," ses Mr. Cutts; "you ain't doing no good. We know where they are and we'll watch the pond till daylight— that is, unless Smith'd like to 'ave a try."

"It's pretty near daylight now, I think," ses Smith.

Lewis came out and ran up and down to dry 'imself, and finished off on his pocket-'andkerchief, and then with 'is teeth chattering 'e began to dress 'imself. He got 'is shirt on, and then stood turning over 'is clothes as if 'e was looking for something.

"Never mind about your stud now," ses Mr. Cutts; "hurry up and dress."

"*Stud?*" ses Lewis, very snappish. "I'm looking for my trowsis."

"Your trowsis?" ses Smith, 'elping 'im look.

"I put all my clothes together," ses Lewis, a'most shouting. "Where are they? I'm 'arf perished with cold. Where are they?"

"He 'ad 'em on this evening," ses Bob Pretty, " 'cos I remember noticing 'em."

"They must be somewhere about," ses Mr. Cutts; "why don't you use your eyes?"

He walked up and down, peering about, and as for Lewis he was 'opping round 'arf crazy.

"I wonder," ses Bob Pretty, in a thoughtful voice, to Smith—"I wonder whether you or Mr. Cutts kicked 'em in the pond while you was struggling with me. Come to think of it, I seem to remember 'earing a splash."

"He's done it, Mr. Cutts," ses Smith; "never mind, it'll go all the 'arder with 'im."

"But I do mind," ses Lewis, shouting. "I'll be even with you for this, Bob Pretty. I'll make you feel it. You wait till I've done with you. You'll get a month extra for this, you see if you don't."

"Don't you mind about me," ses Bob; "you run off 'ome and cover up them legs of yours. I found that sack, so my conscience is clear."

Lewis put on 'is coat and waistcoat and set off, and Mr. Cutts and Smith, arter feeling about for a dry place, set theirselves down and began to smoke.

"Look 'ere," ses Bob Pretty, "I'm not going to sit 'ere all night to please you; I'm going off 'ome. If you want me you'll know where to find me."

"You stay where you are," ses Mr. Cutts. "We ain't going to let you out of our sight."

"Very well, then, you take me 'ome," ses Bob. "I'm not going to catch my death o' cold sitting 'ere. I'm not used to being out of a night like you are. I was brought up respectable."

"I daresay," ses Mr. Cutts. "Take you 'ome, and then 'ave one o' your mates come and get the sack while we're away."

Then Bob Pretty lost 'is temper, and the things 'e said about Mr. Cutts wasn't fit for Smith to hear. He threw 'imself down at last full length on the ground and sulked till the day broke.

Keeper Lewis was there a'most as soon as it was light, with some long hay-rakes he borrowed, and I should think that pretty near 'arf the folks in Claybury 'ad turned up to see the fun. Mrs. Pretty was crying and wringing 'er 'ands; but most folk seemed to be rather pleased that Bob 'ad been caught at last.

In next to no time 'arf-a-dozen rakes was at work and the things they brought out o' that pond you wouldn't believe. The edge of it was all littered with rusty tin pails and sauce-pans and such-like, and by-and-by Lewis found the things he'd 'ad to go 'ome without a few hours afore, but they didn't seem to find that sack, and Bob Pretty, wot was talking to 'is wife, began to look hopeful.

But just then the squire came riding up with two friends as was staying with 'im, and he offered a reward of five shillings to the man wot found it. Three or four of 'em waded in up to their middle then and raked their 'ardest, and at last Henery Walker give a cheer and brought it to the side, all heavy with water.

"That's the sack I found, sir," ses Bob, starting up. "It wasn't on your land at all, but on the field next to it. I'm an honest, 'ardworking man, and I've never been in trouble afore. Ask anybody 'ere and they'll tell you the same."

Squire Rockett took no notice of 'im. "Is that the sack?" he asks, turning to Mr. Cutts.

"That's the one, sir," ses Mr. Cutts. "I'd swear to it anywhere."

"You'd swear a man's life away," ses Bob. " 'Ow can you swear to it when it was dark?"

Mr. Cutts didn't answer 'im. He went down on 'is knees and cut the string that tied up the mouth o' the sack, and then 'e started back as if 'e'd been shot, and 'is eyes a'most started out of 'is 'ead.

"What's the matter?" ses the squire.

Mr. Cutts couldn't speak; he could only stutter and point at the sack with 'is finger, and Henery Walker, as was getting curious, lifted up the other end of it and out rolled about a score of as fine cabbages as you could wish to see.

I never see people so astonished afore in all my born days, and as for Bob Pretty 'e stood staring at them cabbages as if 'e couldn't believe his eyesight.

"And that's wot I've been kept 'ere all night for," he ses at last, shaking his 'ead. "That's wot comes o' trying to do a kindness to keepers, and 'elping of 'em in their difficult work. P'r'aps that ain't the sack arter all, Mr. Cutts. I could ha' sworn they was pheasants in the one I found, but I may be mistook, never 'aving 'ad one in my 'ands afore. Or p'r'aps somebody was trying to 'ave a game with you, Mr. Cutts, and deceived me instead."

The keepers on'y stared at him.

"You ought to be more careful," ses Bob. "Very likely while you was taking all that trouble over me, and Keeper Lewis was catching 'is death o' cold, the poachers was up at the plantation taking all they wanted. And, besides, it ain't right for Squire Rockett to 'ave to pay Henery Walker five shillings for finding a lot of old cabbages. I shouldn't like it myself."

He looked out of the corner of 'is eye at the squire, as was pretending not to notice Henery Walker touching 'is cap to him, and then 'e turns to 'is wife and he ses:

"Come along, old gal," 'e ses. "I want my breakfast bad, and arter that I shall 'ave to lose a honest day's work in bed."

William J. Locke

*I thought that I was the only person who remembered Aristide Pujol,
until I discovered that Messrs. Cerf and Moriarty had chosen* The
Adventure of the Kind Mr. Smith *for their* Bedside Book of Famous
British Short Stories. *Well, it's worth reading twice.*

THE ADVENTURE OF THE KIND MR. SMITH

Aristide Pujol started life on his own account as a *chasseur* in a Nice
café—one of those luckless children tightly encased in bottle-green cloth
by means of brass buttons, who earn a sketchy livelihood by enduring
with cherubic smiles the continuous maledictions of the establishment.
There he soothed his hours of servitude by dreams of vast ambitions.
He would become the manager of a great hotel—not a contemptible
hostelry where commercial travellers and seedy Germans were indiffer-
ently bedded, but one of those white palaces where milords (English)
and millionaires (American) paid a thousand francs a night for a bedroom and five louis for a glass of beer. Now, in order to derive such
profit from the Anglo-Saxon, a knowledge of English was indispensable.
He resolved to learn the language. How he did so, except by sheer
effrontery, taking linguistic toll of frequenters of the *café,* would be a
mystery to anyone unacquainted with Aristide. But to his friends his
mastery of the English tongue in such circumstances is comprehensible.
To Aristide the impossible was ever the one thing easy of attainment;
the possible the one thing he never could achieve. That was the para-
doxical nature of the man. Before his days of hunted-little-devildom
were over he had acquired sufficient knowledge of English to carry him,
a few years later, through various vicissitudes in England, until, fired by
new social ambitions and self-educated in a haphazard way, he found
himself appointed Professor of French in an academy for young ladies.
    One of these days, when I can pin my dragonfly friend down to a
plain, unvarnished autobiography, I may be able to trace some chron-
ological sequence in the kaleidoscopic changes in his career. But
hitherto, in his talks with me, he flits about from any one date to any

345

other during a couple of decades, in a manner so confusing that for the present I abandon such an attempt. All I know of the date of the episode I am about to chronicle is that it occurred immediately after the termination of his engagement at the academy just mentioned. Somehow, Aristide's history is a category of terminations.

If the head mistress of the academy had herself played dragon at his classes, all would have gone well. He would have made his pupils conjugate irregular verbs, rendered them adepts in the mysteries of the past participle and the subjunctive mood, and turned them out quite innocent of the idiomatic quaintnesses of the French tongue. But *dis aliter visum.* The gods always saw wrong-headedly otherwise in the case of Aristide. A weak-minded governess—and in a governess a sense of humour and of novelty is always a sign of a weak mind—played dragon during Aristide's lessons. She appreciated his method, which was colloquial. The colloquial Aristide was jocular. His lessons therefore were a giggling joy from beginning to end. He imparted to his pupils delicious knowledge. *En avez-vous des-z-homards? Oh, les sales bêtes, elles ont du poil aux pattes,* which, being translated, is: "Have you any lobsters? Oh, the dirty animals, they have hair on their feet"—a catch phrase which, some years ago, added greatly to the gaiety of Paris, but in which I must confess to seeing no gleam of wit—became the historic property of the school. He recited to them, until they were word-perfect, a music-hall ditty of the early eighties, *Sur le bi, sur le banc, sur le bi du bout du banc,* and delighted them with dissertations on Mme Yvette Guilbert's earlier repertoire. But for him they would have gone to their lives' end without knowing that *pognon* meant money; *rouspétance,* assaulting the police; *thune,* a five-franc piece; and *bouffer,* to take nourishment. He made (according to his own statement) French a living language. There was never a school in Great Britain, the Colonies, or America on which the Parisian accent was so electrically impressed. The retort, *Eh! ta soeur,* was the purest Montmartre; also *Fich'-moi la paix, mon petit,* and *Tu as un toupet, toi;* and the delectable locution, *Allons étrangler un perroquet* (let us strangle a parrot), employed by Apaches when inviting each other to drink a glass of absinthe, soon became current French in the school for invitations to surreptitious cocoa-parties.

The progress that academy made in a real grip of the French language was miraculous; but the knowledge it gained in French grammar and syntax was deplorable. A certain mid-term examination—the paper being set by a neighbouring vicar—produced awful results. The phrase, "How do you do, dear?" which ought, by all the rules of Stratford-atte-Bowe, to be translated by *Comment vous portez-vous, ma chère?* was rendered by most of the senior scholars *Eh, ma vieille, ça boulotte?* One innocent and anachronistic damsel, writing on the execution of Charles I, declared that he *cracha dans le panier* in 1649, thereby mystifying the good vicar, who was unaware that "to spit into the basket" is to be guillotined. This wealth of vocabulary was discounted by abject poverty in other branches of the language. No one could give a list of the words in *al* that took *s* in the plural, no one knew anything at all about the defective verb *échoir,* and the orthography of the school would have disgraced a kindergarten. The head mistress suspected a lack of method in the teaching of M. Pujol, and one day paid his class a surprise visit.

The sight that met her eyes petrified her. The class, including the governess, bubbled and gurgled and shrieked with laughter. M. Pujol, his bright eyes agleam with merriment and his arms moving in frantic gestures, danced about the platform. He was telling them a story—and when Aristide told a story, he told it with the eloquence of his entire frame. He bent himself double and threw out his hands.

"Il était saoûl comme un porc," he shouted.

And then came the hush of death. The rest of the artless tale about the man as drunk as a pig was never told. The head mistress, indignant majesty, strode up the room.

"M. Pujol, you have a strange way of giving French lessons."

"I believe, madame," said he, with a polite bow, "in interesting my pupils in their studies."

"Pupils have to be taught, not interested," said the head mistress. "Will you kindly put the class through some irregular verbs?"

So for the remainder of the lesson Aristide, under the freezing eyes of the head mistress, put his sorrowful class through irregular verbs, of which his own knowledge was singularly inexact, and at the end received his dismissal. In vain he argued. Outraged Minerva was implacable. Go he must.

We find him, then, one miserable December evening, standing on the arrival platform of Euston Station (the academy was near Manchester), an unwonted statue of dubiety. At his feet lay his meagre valise; in his hand was an enormous bouquet, a useful tribute of esteem from his disconsolate pupils; around him luggage-laden porters and passengers hurried; in front were drawn up the long line of cabs, their drivers' waterproofs glistening with wet; and in his pocket rattled the few paltry coins that, for Heaven knew how long, were to keep him from starvation. Should he commit the extravagance of taking a cab or should he go forth, valise in hand, into the pouring rain? He hesitated.

"*Sacré mille cochons! Quel chien de climat!*" he muttered.

A smart footman standing by turned quickly and touched his hat.

"Beg pardon, sir; I'm from Mr. Smith."

"I'm glad to hear it, my friend," said Aristide.

"You're the French gentleman from Manchester?"

"Decidedly," said Aristide.

"Then, sir, Mr. Smith has sent the carriage for you."

"That's very kind of him," said Aristide.

The footman picked up the valise and darted down the platform. Aristide followed. The footman held invitingly open the door of a cosy brougham. Aristide paused for the fraction of a second. Who was this hospitable Mr. Smith?

"Bah!" said he to himself, "the best way of finding out is to go and see."

He entered the carriage, sank back luxuriously on the soft cushions, and inhaled the warm smell of leather. They started, and soon the pelting rain beat harmlessly against the windows. Aristide looked out at the streaming streets, and, hugging himself comfortably, thanked Providence and Mr. Smith. But who was Mr. Smith? *Tiens,* thought he, there were two little Miss Smiths at the academy; he had pitied them because they had chilblains, freckles, and perpetual colds in their heads; possibly this was their kind papa. But, after all, what did it matter whose papa he was? He was expecting him. He had sent the carriage for him. Evidently a well-bred and attentive person. And *tiens!* there was even a hot-water can on the floor of the brougham. "He thinks of everything, that man," said Aristide. "I feel I am going to like him."

The carriage stopped at a house in Hampstead, standing, as far as he could see in the darkness, in its own grounds. The footman opened the door for him to alight and escorted him up the front steps. A neat parlourmaid received him in a comfortably furnished hall and took his hat and great-coat and magnificent bouquet.

"Mr. Smith hasn't come back yet from the City, sir; but Miss Christabel is in the drawing-room."

"Ah!" said Aristide. "Please give me back my bouquet."

The maid showed him into the drawing-room. A pretty girl of three-and-twenty rose from a fender-stool and advanced smilingly to meet him.

"Good afternoon, M. le Baron. I was wondering whether Thomas would spot you. I'm so glad he did. You see, neither Father nor I could give him any description, for we had never seen you."

This fitted in with his theory. But why Baron? After all, why not? The English loved titles.

"He seems to be an intelligent fellow, mademoiselle."

There was a span of silence. The girl looked at the bouquet, then at Aristide, who looked at the girl, then at the bouquet, then at the girl again.

"Mademoiselle," said he, "will you deign to accept these flowers as a token of my respectful homage?"

Miss Christabel took the flowers and blushed prettily. She had dark hair and eyes and a fascinating, upturned little nose, and the kindest little mouth in the world.

"An Englishman would not have thought of that," she said.

Aristide smiled in his roguish way and raised a deprecating hand.

"Oh, yes, he would. But he would not have had—what you call the cheek to do it."

Miss Christabel laughed merrily, invited him to a seat by the fire, and comforted him with tea and hot muffins. The frank charm of his girl-hostess captivated Aristide and drove from his mind the riddle of his adventure. Besides, think of the Arabian Nights' enchantment of the change from his lonely and shabby bed-sitting-room in the Rusholme Road to this fragrant palace with princess and all to keep him company! He watched the firelight dancing through her hair, the dainty play of laughter over her face, and decided that the brougham had transported him to Bagdad instead of Hampstead.

"You have the air of a veritable princess," said he.

"I once met a princess—at a charity bazaar—and she was a most matter-of-fact businesslike person."

"Bah!" said Aristide. "A princess of a charity bazaar! I was talking of the princess in a fairy-tale. They are the only real ones."

"Do you know," said Miss Christabel, "that when men pay such compliments to English girls they are apt to get laughed at?"

"Englishmen, yes," replied Aristide, "because they think over a compliment for a week, so that by the time they pay it, it is addled, like a bad egg. But we of Provence pay tribute to beauty straight out of our hearts. It is true. It is sincere. And what comes out of the heart is not ridiculous."

Again the girl coloured and laughed. "I've always heard that a Frenchman makes love to every woman he meets."

"Naturally," said Aristide. "If they are pretty. What else are pretty women for? Otherwise they might as well be hideous."

"Oh!" said the girl, to whom this Provençal point of view had not occurred.

"So, if I make love to you, it is but your due."

"I wonder what my fiancé would say if he heard you?"

"Your—?"

"My fiancé! There's his photograph on the table beside you. He is six foot one, and so jealous!" she laughed again.

"The Turk!" cried Aristide, his swiftly conceived romance crumbling into dust. Then he brightened up. "But when this six feet of muscle and egotism is absent, surely other poor mortals can glean a smile?"

"You will observe that I'm not frowning," said Miss Christabel. "But you must not call my fiancé a Turk, for he's a very charming fellow whom I hope you'll like very much."

Aristide sighed. "And the name of this thrice-blessed mortal?"

Miss Christabel told his name—one Harry Ralston—and not only his name, but, such was the peculiar, childlike charm of Aristide Pujol, also many other things about him. He was the Honourable Harry Ralston, the heir to a great brewery peerage, and very wealthy. He was a member of Parliament, and but for Parliamentary duties would have dined there that evening; but he was to come in later, as soon as he could leave the House. He also had a house in Hampshire, full of the most beautiful works of art. It was through their common hobby that her father and Harry had first made acquaintance.

"We're supposed to have a very fine collection here," she said, with a motion of her hand.

Aristide looked round the walls and saw them hung with pictures in gold frames. In those days he had not acquired an extensive culture. Besides, who having before him the firelight gleaming through Miss Christabel's hair could waste his time over painted canvas? She noted his cursory glance.

"I thought you were a connoisseur?"

"I am," said Aristide, his bright eyes fixed on her in frank admiration.

She blushed again; but this time she rose.

"I must go and dress for dinner. Perhaps you would like to be shown your room?"

He hung his head on one side.

"Have I been too bold, Mademoiselle?"

"I don't know," she said. "You see, I've never met a Frenchman before."

"Then a world of undreamed-of homage is at your feet," said he.

A servant ushered him up broad, carpeted staircases into a bedroom such as he had never seen in his life before. It was all curtains and hangings and rugs and soft couches and satin quilts and dainty writing-tables and subdued lights, and a great fire glowed red and cheerful, and before it hung a clean shirt. His poor little toilet apparatus was laid on the dressing-table, and (with a tact which he did not appreciate, for he had, sad to tell, no dress-suit) the servant had spread his precious frock-coat and spare pair of trousers on the bed. On the pillow lay his night-shirt, neatly folded.

"Evidently," said Aristide, impressed by these preparations, "it is expected that I wash myself now and change my clothes, and that I sleep here for the night. And for all that the ravishing Miss Christabel is engaged to her Honourable Harry, this is none the less a corner of Paradise."

So Aristide attired himself in his best, which included a white tie and a pair of nearly new brown boots—a long task, as he found that his valise had been spirited away and its contents, including the white tie of ceremony (he had but one), hidden in unexpected drawers and wardrobes—and eventually went downstairs into the drawing-room. There he found Miss Christabel and, warming himself on the hearthrug, a bald-headed, beefy-faced Briton, with little pig's eyes and a hearty manner, attired in a dinner-suit.

"My dear fellow," said this personage, with outstretched hand. "I'm delighted to have you here. I've heard so much about you; and my little girl has been singing your praises."

"Mademoiselle is too kind," said Aristide.

"You must take us as you find us," said Mr. Smith. "We're just ordinary folk, but I can give you a good bottle of wine and a good cigar—it's only in England, you know, that you can get champagne fit to drink and cigars fit to smoke—and I can give you a glimpse of a modest English home. I believe you haven't a word for it in French."

"*Ma foi,* no," said Aristide, who had once or twice before heard this lunatic charge brought against his country. "In France the men all live in *cafés,* the children are all put out to nurse, and the women, saving the respect of mademoiselle—well, the less said about them the better."

"England is the only place, isn't it?" Mr. Smith declared, heartily. "I don't say that Paris hasn't its points. But after all—the Moulin Rouge and the Folies Bergère and that sort of thing soon pall, you know— soon pall."

"Yet Paris has its serious side," argued Aristide. "There is always the tomb of Napoleon."

"Papa will never take me to Paris," sighed the girl.

"You shall go there on your honeymoon," said Mr. Smith.

Dinner was announced. Aristide gave his arm to Miss Christabel, and proud not only of his partner, but also of his frock-coat, white tie, and shiny brown boots, strutted into the dining-room. The host sat at the end of the beautifully set table, his daughter on his right, Aristide on his left. The meal began gaily. The kind Mr. Smith was in the best of humours.

"And how is our dear old friend, Jules Dancourt?" he asked.

"*Tiens!*" said Aristide, to himself, "we have a dear friend Jules Dancourt. Wonderfully well," he replied at a venture, "but he suffers terribly at times from the gout."

"So do I, confound it!" said Mr. Smith, drinking sherry.

"You and the good Jules were always sympathetic," said Aristide. "Ah! he has spoken to me so often about you, the tears in his eyes."

"Men cry, my dear, in France," Mr. Smith explained. "They also kiss each other."

"*Ah, mais c'est un beau pays, mademoiselle!*" cried Aristide, and he began to talk of France and to draw pictures of his country which set the girl's eyes dancing. After that he told some of the funny little stories which had brought him disaster at the academy. Mr. Smith, with jovial magnanimity, declared that he was the first Frenchman he had ever met with a sense of humour.

"But I thought, Baron," said he, "that you lived all your life shut up in that old château of yours?"

"*Tiens!*" thought Aristide. "I am still a Baron, and I have an old château."

"Tell us about the château. Has it a fosse and a drawbridge and a Gothic chapel?" asked Miss Christabel.

"Which one do you mean?" inquired Aristide, airily. "For I have two."

When relating to me this Arabian Nights' adventure, he drew my special attention to his astuteness.

His host's eye quivered in a wink. "The one in Languedoc," said he.

Languedoc! Almost Pujol's own country! With entire lack of morality, but with picturesque imagination, Aristide plunged into a description of that non-existent baronial hall. Fosse, drawbridge, Gothic chapel were but insignificant features. It had tourelles, emblazoned gateways, bastions, donjons, barbicans; it had innumerable rooms; in the salle des chevaliers two hundred men-at-arms had his ancestors fed at a sitting. There was the room in which François Premier had slept, and one in which Joan of Arc had almost been assassinated. What the name of himself or his ancestors was supposed to be Aristide had no ghost of an idea. But as he proceeded with the erection of his airy palace he gradually began to believe in it. He invested the place with a living atmosphere; conjured up a staff of family retainers, notably one Marie-Joseph Loufoque, the wizened old major-domo, with his long white whiskers and blue and silver livery. There were also Madeline Mioulles the cook, and Bernadet the groom, and Le Petite Fripette the goose girl. Ah, they should see La Petite Fripette! And he kept dogs and horses and cows and ducks and hens—and there was a great pond whence frogs were drawn to be fed for the consumption of the household.

Miss Christabel shivered. "I should not like to eat frogs."

"They also eat snails," said her father.

"I have a snail farm," said Aristide. "You never saw such interesting little animals. They are so intelligent. If you're kind to them they come and eat out of your hand."

"You've forgotten the pictures," said Mr. Smith.

"Ah! the pictures," cried Aristide, with a wide sweep of his arms. "Galleries full of them. Raphael, Michelangelo, Wiertz, Reynolds—"

He paused, not in order to produce the effect of a dramatic aposiopesis, but because he could not for the moment remember other names of painters.

"It is a truly historical château," said he.

"I should love to see it," said the girl.

Aristide threw out his arms across the table. "It is yours, mademoiselle, for your honeymoon," said he.

Dinner came to an end. Miss Christabel left the gentlemen to their wine, an excellent port whose English qualities were vaunted by the host. Aristide, full of food and drink and the mellow glories of the castle in Languedoc, and smoking an enormous cigar, felt at ease with all the world. He knew he should like the kind Mr. Smith, hospitable though somewhat insular man. He could stay with him for a week— or a month—why not a year?

After coffee and liqueurs had been served Mr. Smith rose and switched on a powerful electric light at the end of the large room, showing a picture on an easel covered by a curtain. He beckoned to Aristide to join him and, drawing the curtain, disclosed the picture.

"There!" said he. "Isn't it a stunner?"

It was a picture all grey skies and grey water and grey feathery trees, and a little man in the foreground wore a red cap.

"It is beautiful, but indeed it is magnificent!" cried Aristide, always impressionable to things of beauty.

"Genuine Corot, isn't it?"

"Without doubt," said Aristide.

His host poked him in the ribs. "I thought I'd astonish you. You wouldn't believe Gottschalk could have done it. There it is—as large as life and twice as natural. If you or any one else can tell it from a genuine Corot I'll eat my hat. And all for eight pounds."

Aristide looked at the beefy face and caught a look of cunning in the little pig's eyes.

"Now are you satisfied?" asked Mr. Smith.

"More than satisfied," said Aristide, though what he was to be satisfied about passed, for the moment, his comprehension.

"If it was a copy of an existing picture, you know—one might have understood it—that, of course, would be dangerous—but for a man to go and get bits out of various Corots and stick them together like this is miraculous. If it hadn't been for a matter of business principle I'd have given the fellow eight guineas instead of pounds—hanged if I wouldn't! He deserves it."

"He does indeed," said Aristide Pujol.

"And now that you've seen it with your own eyes, what do you think you might ask me for it? I suggested something between two and three thousand—shall we say three? You're the owner, you know." Again the process of rib-digging. "Came out of that historic château of yours.

My eye! You're a holy terror when you begin to talk. You almost persuaded me it was real."

"*Tiens!*" said Aristide to himself. "I don't seem to have a château after all."

"Certainly three thousand," said he, with a grave face.

"That young man thinks he knows a lot, but he doesn't," said Mr. Smith.

"Ah!" said Aristide, with singular laconicism.

"Not a blooming thing," continued his host. "But he'll pay three thousand, which is the principal, isn't it? He's partner in the show, you know, Ralston, Wiggins, and Wix's Brewery"—Aristide pricked up his ears—"and when his doddering old father dies he'll be Lord Ranelagh and come into a million of money."

"Has he seen the picture?" asked Aristide.

"Oh, yes. Regards it as a masterpiece. Didn't Brauneberger tell you of the Lancret we planted on the American?" Mr. Smith rubbed hearty hands at the memory of the iniquity. "Same old game. Always easy. I have nothing to do with the bargaining or the sale. Just an old friend of the ruined French nobleman with the historic château and family treasures. He comes along and fixes the price. I told our friend Harry—"

"Good," thought Aristide. "This is the same Honourable Harry, M.P., who is engaged to the ravishing Miss Christabel."

"I told him," said Mr. Smith, "that it might come to three or four thousand. He jibbed a bit—so when I wrote to you I said two or three. But you might try him with three to begin with."

Aristide went back to the table and poured himself out a fresh glass of his kind host's 1865 brandy and drank it off.

"Exquisite, my dear fellow," said he. "I've none finer in my historic château."

"Don't suppose you have," grinned the host, joining him. He slapped him on the back. "Well," said he, with a shifty look in his little pig's eyes, "let us talk business. What do you think would be your fair commission? You see all the trouble and invention have been mine. What do you say to four hundred pounds?"

"Five," said Aristide, promptly.

A sudden gleam came into the little pig's eyes.

"Done!" said Mr. Smith, who had imagined that the other would demand a thousand and was prepared to pay eight hundred. "Done!" said he again.

They shook hands to seal the bargain and drank another glass of old brandy. At that moment, a servant, entering, took the host aside.

"Please excuse me a moment," said he, and went with the servant out of the room.

Aristide, left alone, lighted another of his kind host's fat cigars and threw himself in a great leathern armchair by the fire, and surrendered himself deliciously to the soothing charm of the moment. Now and then he laughed, finding a certain comicality in his position. And what a charming father-in-law, this kind Mr. Smith!

His cheerful reflections were soon disturbed by the sudden irruption of his host and a grizzled, elderly, foxy-faced gentleman with a white moustache, wearing the ribbon of the Legion of Honour in the button-hole of his overcoat.

"Here, you!" cried the kind Mr. Smith, striding up to Aristide, with a very red face. "Will you have the kindness to tell me who the devil you are?"

Aristide rose, and, putting his hands behind the tails of his frock-coat, stood smiling radiantly on the hearthrug. A wit much less alert than my irresponsible friend's would have instantly appreciated the fact that the real Simon Pure had arrived on the scene.

"I, my dear friend," said he, "am the Baron de Je ne Sais Plus."

"You're a confounded impostor," spluttered Mr. Smith.

"And this gentleman here to whom I have not had the pleasure of being introduced?" asked Aristide, blandly.

"I am M. Poiron, monsieur, the agent of Messrs. Brauneberger and Compagnie, art dealers, of the Rue Notre-Dame des Petits Champs of Paris," said the newcomer, with an air of defiance.

"Ah, I thought you were the Baron," said Aristide.

"There's no blooming Baron at all about it!" screamed Mr. Smith. "Are you Poiron, or is he?"

"I would not have a name like Poiron for anything in the world," said Aristide, "My name is Aristide Pujol, soldier of fortune, at your service."

"How the blazes did you get here?"

"Your servant asked me if I was a French gentleman from Manchester. I was. He said that Mr. Smith had sent his carriage for me. I thought it hospitable of the kind Mr. Smith. I entered the carriage— *et voilà!*"

"Then clear out of here this very minute," said Mr. Smith, reaching forward his hand to the bell-push.

Aristide checked his impulsive action.

"Pardon me, dear host," said he. "It is raining dogs and cats outside, I am very comfortable in your luxurious home. I am here, and here I stay."

"I'm shot if you do," said the kind Mr. Smith, his face growing redder and uglier. "Now, will you go, or will you be thrown out?"

Aristide, who had no desire whatever to be ejected from this snug nest into the welter of the wet and friendless world, puffed at his cigar, and looked at his host with the irresistible drollery of his eyes.

"You forget, *mon cher ami*," said he, "that neither the beautiful Miss Christabel nor her affianced, the Honourable Harry, M.P., would care to know that the talented Gottschalk got only eight pounds, not even guineas, for painting that three-thousand-pound picture."

"So it's blackmail, eh?"

"Precisely," said Aristide, "and I don't blush at it."

"You infernal little blackguard!"

"I seem to be in congenial company," said Aristide. "I don't think our friend M. Poiron has more scruples than he has right to the ribbon of the Legion of Honour which he is wearing."

"How much will you take to go out? I have a cheque-book handy."

Mr. Smith moved a few steps from the hearthrug. Aristide sat down in the armchair. An engaging, fantastic impudence was one of the charms of Aristide Pujol.

"I'll take five hundred pounds," said he, "to stay in."

"Stay in?" Mr. Smith grew apoplectic.

"Yes," said Aristide. "You can't do without me. Your daughter and your servants know me as M. le Baron—by the way, what is my name? And where is my historic château in Languedoc?"

"Mireilles," said M. Poiron, who was sitting grim and taciturn on one of the dining-room chairs. "And the place is the same, near Montpellier."

"I like to meet an intelligent man," said Aristide.

"I should like to wring your infernal neck," said the kind Mr. Smith. "But, by George, if we do let you in you'll have to sign me a receipt implicating yourself up to the hilt. I'm not going to be put into the cart by you, you can bet your life."

"Anything you like," said Aristide, "so long as we all swing together."

Now, when Aristide Pujol arrived at this point in his narrative, I, his chronicler, who am nothing if not an eminently respectable, law-abiding Briton, took him warmly to task for his sheer absence of moral sense. His eyes, as they sometimes did, assumed a luminous pathos.

"My dear friend," said he, "have you ever faced the world in a foreign country in December with no character and fifteen pounds five and threepence in your pocket? Five hundred pounds was a fortune. It is one now. And to be gained just by lending oneself to a good farce, which didn't hurt anybody. You and your British morals! Bah!" said he, with a fine flourish.

Aristide, after much parleying, was finally admitted into the nefarious brotherhood. He was to retain his rank as the Baron de Mireilles, and play the part of the pecuniarily inconvenienced nobleman forced to sell some of his rare collection. Mr. Smith had heard of the Corot through their dear old common friend, Jules Dancourt of Rheims, had mentioned it alluringly to the Honourable Harry, had arranged for the Baron, who was visiting England, to bring it over and despatch it to Mr. Smith's house, and on his return from Manchester to pay a visit to Mr. Smith, so that he could meet the Honourable Harry in person. In whatever transaction ensued Mr. Smith, so far as his prospective son-in-law was concerned, was to be the purely disinterested friend. It was Aristide's wit which invented a part for the supplanted M. Poiron. He should be the eminent Parisian expert who, chancing to be in London, had been telephoned for by the kind Mr. Smith.

"It would not be wise for M. Poiron," said Aristide, chuckling inwardly with puckish glee, "to say here for the night—or for two or three days— or a week—like myself. He must go back to his hotel when the business is concluded."

"Mais, pardon!" cried M. Poiron, who had been formally invited, and had arrived late solely because he had missed his train at Manchester, and come on by the next one. "I cannot go out into the wet, and I have no hotel to go to."

Aristide appealed to his host. "But he is unreasonable, cher ami. He must play his rôle. M. Poiron has been telephoned for. He can't possibly stay here. Surely five hundred pounds is worth one little night of discomfort? And there are a legion of hotels in London."

"Five hundred pounds!" exclaimed M. Poiron. "Qu'est-ce que vous chantez là? I want more than five hundred pounds."

"Then you're jolly well not going to get it," cried Mr. Smith, in a rage. "And as for you"—he turned on Aristide—"I'll wring your infernal neck yet."

"Calm yourself, calm yourself!" smiled Aristide, who was enjoying himself hugely.

At this moment the door opened and Miss Christabel appeared. On seeing the decorated stranger she started with a little "Oh!" of surprise. "I beg your pardon."

Mr. Smith's angry face wreathed itself in smiles.

"This, my darling, is M. Poiron, the eminent Paris expert, who has been good enough to come and give us his opinion on the picture."

M. Poiron bowed. Aristide advanced.

"Mademoiselle, your appearance is like a mirage in a desert."

She smiled indulgently and turned to her father. "I've been wondering what had become of you. Harry has been here for the last half-hour."

"Bring him in, dear child, bring him in!" said Mr. Smith, with all the heartiness of the fine old English gentleman. "Our good friends are dying to meet him."

The girl flickered out of the room like a sunbeam (the phrase is Aristide's), and the three precious rascals put their heads together in a hurried and earnest colloquy. Presently Miss Christabel returned, and with her came the Honourable Harry Ralston, a tall, soldierly fellow, with close-cropped fair curly hair and a fair moustache, and frank blue eyes that, even in Parliament, had seen no harm in his fellow-creatures. Aristide's magical vision caught him wincing ever so little at Mr. Smith's effusive greeting and overdone introductions. He shook Aristide warmly by the hand.

"You have a beauty there, Baron, a perfect beauty," said he, with the insane ingenuousness of youth. "I wonder how you can manage to part with it."

"Ma foi," said Aristide, with his back against the end of the dining-table and gazing at the masterpiece. "I have so many at the Château de Mireilles. When one begins to collect, you know—and when one's grandfather and father have had also the divine mania—"

"You were saying, M. le Baron," said M. Poiron of Paris, "that your respected grandfather bought this direct from Corot himself."

"A commission," said Aristide. "My grandfather was a patron of Corot."

"Do you like it, dear?" asked the Honourable Harry.

"Oh, yes!" replied the girl, fervently. "It is beautiful. I feel like Harry about it." She turned to Aristide. "How can you part with it? Were you really in earnest when you said you would like me to come and see your collection?"

"For me," said Aristide, "it would be a visit of enchantment."

"You must take me, then," she whispered to Harry. "The Baron has been telling us about his lovely old château."

"Will you come, monsieur?" asked Aristide.

"Since I'm going to rob you of your picture," said the young man, with smiling courtesy, "the least I can do is to pay you a visit of apology. Lovely!" said he, going up to the Corot.

Aristide took Miss Christabel, now more bewitching than ever with the glow of young love in her eyes and a flush on her cheek, a step or two aside and whispered:

"But he is charming, your fiancé! He almost deserves his good fortune."

"Why almost?" she laughed, shyly.

"It is not a man, but a demi-god, that would deserve you, mademoiselle."

M. Poiron's harsh voice broke out.

"You see, it is painted in the beginning of Corot's later manner—it is 1864. There is the mystery which, when he was quite an old man, became a trick. If you were to put it up to auction at Christie's it would fetch, I am sure, five thousand pounds."

"That's more than I can afford to give," said the young man, with a laugh. "Mr. Smith mentioned something between three and four thousand pounds. I don't think I can go above three."

"I have nothing to do with it, my dear boy, nothing whatever," said Mr. Smith, rubbing his hands. "You wanted a Corot. I said I thought I could put you on to one. It's for the Baron here to mention his price. I retire now and for ever."

"Well, Baron?" said the young man, cheerfully. "What's your idea?"

Aristide came forward and resumed his place at the end of the table. The picture was in front of him beneath the strong electric light; on his left stood Mr. Smith and Poiron, on his right Miss Christabel and the Honourable Harry.

"I'll not take three thousand pounds for it," said Aristide. "A picture like that! Never!"

"I assure you it would be a fair price," said Poiron.

"You mentioned that figure yourself only just now," said Mr. Smith, with an ugly glitter in his little pig's eyes.

"I presume, gentlemen," said Aristide, "that this picture is my own property." He turned engagingly to his host. "Is it not, *cher ami?*"

"Of course it is. Who said it wasn't?"

"And you, M. Poiron, acknowledge formally that it is mine?" he asked in French.

"Sans aucun doute."

"Eh bien," said Aristide, throwing open his arms and gazing round sweetly. "I have changed my mind. I do not sell the picture at all."

"Not sell it? What the—what do you mean?" asked Mr. Smith, striving to mellow the gathering thunder on his brow.

"I do not sell," said Aristide. "Listen, my dear friends!" He was in the seventh heaven of happiness—the principal man, the star, taking the centre of the stage. "I have an announcement to make to you. I have fallen desperately in love with mademoiselle."

There was a general gasp. Mr. Smith looked at him, red-faced and open-mouthed. Miss Christabel blushed furiously and emitted a sound half between a laugh and a scream. Harry Ralston's eyes flashed.

"My dear sir—" he began.

"Pardon," said Aristide, disarming him with the merry splendour of his glance. "I do not wish to take mademoiselle from you. My love is hopeless! I know it. But it will feed me to my dying day. In return for the joy of this hopeless passion I will not sell you the picture—I give it to you as a wedding present."

He stood, with the air of a hero, both arms extended towards the amazed pair of lovers.

"I give it to you," said he. "It is mine. I have no wish but for your happiness. In my Château de Mireilles there are a hundred others."

"This is madness!" said Mr. Smith, bursting with suppressed indignation, so that his bald head grew scarlet.

"My dear fellow!" said Mr. Harry Ralston. "It is unheard-of generosity on your part. But we can't accept it."

"Then," said Aristide, advancing dramatically to the picture, "I take it under my arm, I put it in a hansom cab, and I go with it back to Languedoc."

Mr. Smith caught him by the wrist and dragged him out of the room.

"You little brute! Do you want your neck broken?"

"Do you want the marriage of your daughter with the rich and Honourable Harry broken?" asked Aristide.

"Oh, damn! Oh, damn! Oh, damn!" cried Mr. Smith, stamping about helplessly and half weeping.

Aristide entered the dining-room and beamed on the company.

"The kind Mr. Smith has consented. Mr. Honourable Harry and Miss Christabel, there is your Corot. And now, may I be permitted?" He rang the bell. A servant appeared.

"Some champagne to drink to the health of the fiancés," he cried. "Lots of champagne."

Mr. Smith looked at him almost admiringly.

"By Jove!" he muttered. "You *have* got a nerve."

"Voilà!" said Aristide, when he had finished the story.

"And did they accept the Corot?" I asked.

"Of course. It is hanging now in the big house in Hampshire. I stayed with the kind Mr. Smith for six weeks," he added, doubling himself up in his chair and hugging himself with mirth, "and we became very good friends. And I was at the wedding."

"And what about their honeymoon visit to Languedoc?"

"Alas!" said Aristide. "The morning before the wedding I had a telegram—it was from my old father at Aigues-Mortes—to tell me that the historic Château de Mireilles, with my priceless collection of pictures, had been burned to the ground."

Barry Pain

MRS. MURPHY ON HONESTY

If you goes out to work at houses, same as I does, and you happens to have a basket, you burn it. Leastwise, leave it at home. For if you takes it to the place where you're working you're making trouble for yourself. A charwoman what carries a basket ain't popular, and only attracts attention.

I remember what happened when I were a deal younger nor what I am now. I was but fifty-four then, and sent for sudden to a job at the "Sycamores," where I'd never been afore. I takes my basket and off I goes. I does my work, and were just starting back when up sails her ladyship with her chin stuck out. She were titled, though not born to it, nor looking it neither.

"I wish to see what you've got in your basket," says she.

So I took and showed her what I'd got. It were my apron, and the key of my door, and my teeth, what I only wears for meals, waste not being a fault of mine.

"Which of these is yours?" says I.

"Don't address me in that way," says her majesty. "I merely wished to know. I have had things taken out of my house before by dishonest charwomen."

"And I hope you may again," I says. "Good-bye, ducky. Take care of yourself."

And with that I leaves her.

No, I hadn't got nothing of hers in my basket. And all I'd got in the pocket under my skirt was a bit of bacon as were too cornerwise for the dining-room rashers, a few potatoes, half a bar of soap, and a box of matches. And most of that had been give me by the cook.

I never took no basket with me after that, not when I were going out to work. It puts ideas into the lady's head, and leads to unpleasantness. I've had to take the rough with the smooth all my life; but suspiciousness is just one of them things as I can't stick. Never could. No honest woman could. Besides, if the pocket under your skirt's large enough, you don't need no basket.

Yes, I'm honest according to my views. And if the lady ain't got the same views, then that's her misfortune. Just look into it for yourself.

Suppose I was to find a diamond tarara when I were doing out the scullery—I ain't never found none yet, but you never knows your luck—what should I do? I should up and take that tarara to her ladyship at once. Shouldn't even stop to wipe my hands and adjust my toilette. There you are. Property worth hundreds, and give back instantaneous by a poor woman out for two-and-a-kick and her dinner.

I've thought that out, and it's right every way. It puts your character right for all time, and the meanest lady as ever stepped couldn't shed less than a sovereign for a tarara come back. And what else are you to do? A nice old sight I should look, round at my uncle's, and asking for fifty on a diamond tarara. Six months with the usual bonus is about what I should get. Not for me, thank you. I comes of a family what has kept theirselves respectable.

But when the cook gives you a trifle, that's a different thing altogether. It's my duty to do what the cook says, and act respectful. If she says: "Hand me this here, Mrs. Murphy," then I hands it. If she says: "Reach me that there," then I reaches. And if she trims a chop off of the end of the loin afore she puts it in, and says I can fry that for my supper, then I borrows a bit of last week's paper to wrap it in.

And I'm right again, and I knows it. It's the lady herself as has given me that chop, acting through the cook, which is her agent. She mayn't know it, and maybe she wouldn't like it if she did, but there it is just the same. That's the law of this land, and I ain't making no mistake about it, for I got it from a solicitor's clerk what lodged with us in brighter days. And a fine upstanding gentleman he was—doing time now, poor chap.

There's a motto as should be chalked up in letters of gold over the bed of every charwoman. And the words of it is, "Keep in with the cook." If she speaks of her rich relatives with the motor-car, keep your temper and listen for all the world as if you believed it. When she tells you what they said about her looks when she were a girl, tell her they might say the same today, and not be so far out. When she starts on the men what she might have married, but wouldn't, don't let yourself go. And if she shows you her new hat, break out into a cold sweat over the marvel of it at the price. Kind words is a good investment, as the hymn says. And so you'll think next morning when you warms up them cold sausages for your breakfast.

I'm not saying as it was the cook as give me that bit of soap and the box of matches. There's many a woman as will leave soap in the water to waste. That's a thing I never did in my life. And what I saves I has a right to half a bar of now and again. As for the matches, matches is cheap enough. It would be a measly sort of lady as would make a song over a box of matches. I acts on principle, and I has what matches I requires, and I ain't bought a box for the last eighteen years, and I ain't going to begin now.

If no lady never comes across no worse sort nor what I am, then she's lucky.

But I do remember one time when I were suspected wrongful, and never spoke back, nor nothing. And why? Because I'm one as can make allowances where reasonable. For one thing, the party in question were a young couple, hardly old enough to blow their own noses, and had just started housekeeping. And then, again, I'd been recommended to them by the parson's wife, and we all knows what that is.

Mostly, the parson's wife recommends them as has been brought to see the error of it, and is wishful to make a fresh start. All right as far as it goes. She's got to back her husband up in his business, same as any other woman. Still, anybody taking anybody on what I calls a rectory character, so to speak, naturally counts the spoons and tries the cupboard where the decanters is kept to see if it's really locked. You've got to look after yourself in this world. And though nothing of the kind in my case, how was that young couple to know?

The first time they sent for me was when the housemaid were upset internal, which was put down to the new paint. That is a thing as may happen, a niece of my own being one as the smell of new paint is death to, as she's proved more than once. However, cook asked me to take a cup of tea up to that suffering housemaid, so I see the girl myself, and what was the matter with her were not paint. Oh, no! And it didn't take me two minutes to find out what her trouble really was. I were right, too. A week later she was sent out on the quick jump, with her box to follow per C.P., and they found the actual whisky bottles.

But that were nothing to do with me at the time. I were there to do her work, and start in on the breakfast-room, which I did. Soon as I come to the mantelshelf I see a silver shilling lying there. Now them as is used to doing out rooms knows when a thing has been put there, and when it's been left there accidental. Ask me the difference, and there I confess you has me, for I couldn't put it in words. All the same, I won't never make a mistake about it. That shilling had been put deliberate, as I'd have swore to before a magistrate. So I ups with it and turns it over, and it were no surprise to me to find a small cross scratched left-hand of the lion.

To think of it—them two poor young Canterbury lambs trying to lay the marked-money trap for me as would be sixty-seven next quarter day! Simply look at it. Their cook ordered what she liked from the tradesmen, and no weights was never checked. Their housemaid was making life one long beano. Smoking fags in the shed were the gardener's principal work. They was done all round, them turtle-doves was. They could never have caught nobody at nothing. And there they was playing at being the C.I.D. along of me.

Well, you couldn't be angry with them—it were too heart-breaking. Made me smile, I can tell you. So to carry the fun on, I put that shilling under a bronze figure of Venus, or Gladstone, or some such person. Then I finishes off there, and hops down to the kitchen for my elevenses. I don't want to drink better beer nor what they kept in that house.

Presently orders was brought me to go up to the breakfast-room, which was what I had expected. There they both was, a nice-looking couple, though nervous. She were pretending to read the paper, and not looking a bit like it. He'd been put up to do the talking, and were standing back to the fire and heartily ashamed of himself, which was to his credit. So I opens the ball by dropping my curtsy, which is old-fashioned but earns money.

"I say, Mrs. Murphy," says he. "I left a shilling on the mantelpiece here this morning, and it seems to have gone. Do you know anything about it?"

"Yes, sir," I says. "It's still there. I slipped it under that little small bronze statute by your elbow, sir, out of sight, sir, and was meaning to have mentioned it. For it didn't hardly look safe with the painter's men coming and going. Of course, they may all be as respectable as the day, but sudden temptation is what finds out the sore point in the armour. And I'm sure I hope I haven't done wrong, sir."

Then she up and spoke, and very pleased with me she were. She said I were a most honest, intelligent, and careful woman. He said he only wished everybody who worked for him had got my common sense. Then they gave me the shilling, and said I deserved it.

Later in the day she brings out a pair of very handsome, showy vases. They'd been given them as a wedding present, but seemingly was not to their taste, and she asked me if I could do with them. So I thanked her warmly, and said they'd make my little home look very bright and gay. And so I dare say they would, if I hadn't sold them that night for half-a-crown and a pie-dish, and believe now I ought to have got more.

And that were not all. Just as I were leaving they were turning out a nice bit of linoleum, as they'd bought, and then not fancied, and I could have it if I liked. So I did. What with them things, and a few trifles as cook had said I could take, I could hardly carry the stuff home.

I still works for that couple, but it ain't the little gold mine here below what it used to be. It's cocoa at eleven now, and all the extra I've had this last twice has been a pair of his old pyjamas. It's a wonderful thing how much a girl picks up in a few months after she's become a married woman.

Now don't what I've told you go to show that the old proverb is right which says as honesty is the best policy? Use it with discretion, same as I have done, and don't make too much of a hobby of it, and you won't go far wrong.

Leonard Merrick

THE BISHOP'S COMEDY

The Bishop of Westborough had seldom found himself in a more delicate position. Since Sweetbay objected so strenuously to its rector being a dramatist, Sweetbay was clearly no place for the rector; and it devolved upon his lordship to intimate the fact. But secretly his lordship was also guilty of dramatic authorship, and instalments of his comedy were even now in the hands of that accomplished actress, Miss Kitty Clarges. For this reason, and another, the Bishop had wakeful nights.

However, he did what was required. With all his customary blandness, and perhaps a shade more, he pointed out to the Rev. Baker Barling that the parish of Sweetbay was unsuitable for him, and offered him instead a living which commended itself to the Barlings not at all. Indeed, Mrs. Baker Barling was so highly incensed by the removal, that the rector had on several occasions to say, "My dear!" to her reprovingly.

The Bishop was young for a bishop. His classical features, and the dignity of his carriage, would have compelled attention even if he had been a mere man. He never said anything noteworthy, but he voiced the sentiments of the unthinking in stately language. This made him generally admired. It is not to be inferred that he was insincere—he had been granted a popular mind; he shared with the majority a strong aversion from disagreeable truths. His widest reflections were bounded by the word "unpleasant," and every truth that was unpleasant was to the Bishop of Westborough "one of those things that are better left undiscussed." He had a warm affection for this phrase, which occurred in all his articles for the cultured reviews. It was a phrase that suggested much earnestness of thought, while it spared him the exertion of thinking at all.

Domestically he had been no less fortunate than in his mental limitations. He possessed a little wife, who listened to him with the utmost patience, and he had seen both his girls make brilliant matches in their first season. The history of the bridegroom had, in each case, been "one of those things that are better left undiscussed." Accordingly, the Bishop boasted a grateful heart; in fact when he reflected how abundantly Providence had blessed him, he was more than normally horrified to think of the impious murmurings of the poor.

That a personage of his environment and disposition had been tempted towards so unepiscopal a course as writing a comedy, proves how true it is that nothing happens but the unforeseen. It was one of the speediest conquests of Miss Clarges' career—a career in which peers had been plentiful, but prelates had hitherto been lacking. He had made her acquaintance at a reception—she was clever off the stage as well as on it and had always tempered her indiscretions with tact; duchesses called her "dear." He thought her the most fascinating woman he had ever met, and talked to her about the conditions of the English stage with considerable satisfaction to himself.

"What a dramatist your lordship would have made if you had not been a bishop!" she murmured, with rapt eyes.

"Oh—er—you are jesting," said the Bishop, asking for more.

"No, indeed—I mean it," returned the lady reverently. "You have what we call the 'sense of the theatre.' And it is so rare! You startled me just now—you know by intuition things that the professional dramatist needs years of experience to find out. I can't tell you how extraordinary it is!" She regarded him as if she were being confronted by a miracle.

Partly because he was very vain, and partly because Miss Clarges was very good-looking, the lie that she forgot almost as soon as it was spoken had lingered caressingly with the Bishop. Sitting in the Palace one afternoon with nothing to do, he found himself scribbling "Act I.— A Drawing Room." He had no definite intention of continuing, still less had he a definite plot; but like everyone who is deficient in self-criticism, he wrote with prodigious facility, and his first act was finished in a few days.

Miss Clarges had been a good deal surprised to receive a semi-humorous note from the Bishop of Westborough, reminding her of their conversation and hinting that he would be glad to have her opinion of "a dramatic bantling." Tea and a tête-à-tête followed in the lady's boudoir. She found Act I all that she had dreaded, and told him it was most original. Beaming with importance, he perpetrated Act II, and read her that. She was contemplating a season of management, and in sanguine moments reflected that a practised hand might knock the Bishop's comedy into something like shape, and that the Bishop's name on the bills would be well worth having. So she offered various suggestions about the leading part, and was at home as often as he chose to call—and for some weeks he had chosen to call very often indeed.

Remember that he was only fifty. He had married when he was twenty-five, married a girl who was taken by his handsome face, and who had brought him a very respectable dower. Though the dower had fascinated him more than the girl, the courtship had comprised his sentimental experiences. As has been said, he had had no reason to complain of the choice—he had been remarkably successful in all his relationships—he felt that his wife worshipped him, and her worship, and his worldly progress, had contented him fully. But now, for the first time in his career, he was thrown into intimate association with a woman who had captivated those who were seeing life, and those who had seen it—and the Bishop of Westborough fell in love with her as violently as many wiser men had done before him.

As for her, it was the first time in the woman's career that she had been openly admired by a bishop. At the beginning she was attracted by his reputation—much as her youngest adorers had been attracted by her own—but presently she was attracted by his homage. He appealed to her one weakness, her vanity. Though she thought it a pity that he wanted to write a comedy, she considered him a great man; his profound belief in himself, supported by a nation's esteem, imposed on her. To have made a conquest of a pillar of the Church flattered her inordinately; the novelty of the situation had its effect on the actress, too— and, to her unspeakable amazement, Kitty Clarges fell in love with the Bishop.

It was at this juncture that circumstances had forced him to mortify the rector of Sweetbay.

"The affair makes me doubt whether I ought to proceed with my own play," he admitted to her one afternoon.

"My dear friend!" She meant, "What rot!" but she no longer said, "What rot!" even to other actresses; and she wore dove-coloured gowns, and had been to hear him preach. The higher life was a little trying, but she liked to feel worthier of him.

"My action in the matter may be misconstrued. Of course, I've simply deferred to the local prejudice, but it may be thought that I disapprove of the man's tendencies. If I figured as a dramatist myself a little later, I might be placed in an ambiguous position. . . . Perhaps we might overcome the difficulty by a pseudonym?"

She looked blank. "Your lordship's name will be a draw; I'm afraid a pseudonym would mean waiving a great deal."

"Financially? The pecuniary result is not important to me."

But it was important to her. "If the secret were really kept, you'd be waiving all the kudos too," she added.

"Well, we must consider," said the Bishop, clinking the ice in his glass; "you shall advise me—though I fear I'm exceeding an author's privileges. By the way, does the manageress always offer the author a whisky-and-soda?"

"She offered you an alternative," said Miss Clarges, laughing; "the whisky-and-soda was your choice. But you don't really mean to throw the comedy up, do you? Think of poor me!"

The Bishop's eyes were eloquent. "Thinking of you," he said, after a lingering gaze, "I have this to say: you will be put to considerable expense in bringing out my work, and, novice as I am, I'm aware that a theatre is a heavy speculation; if I withhold the advantage of my name from the piece, I shall claim to share your risk."

"You are very generous, dear friend; I don't think I could say 'yes' to that."

"It is no more than fair."

"I'd rather not. I—I shouldn't care for you to find money for me!" said Kitty Clarges—and was conscious that she had soared into the higher life indeed.

"You are scarcely treating me as the dear friend you allow me to believe myself," urged the Bishop, missing the greatest compliment of his life.

"Oh!" she said under her breath.

"I should be serving my own ends. And besides—"

"Besides—what?"

"It would make me very happy to think that I served you."

Her eyelids fell. "You have served me."

"I rejoice to hear it. May I ask how?"

"You've served me by your friendship. You've given me different thoughts, taken me out of myself, done me good—in some ways." She sighed deeply. "I've learnt that there are so much realer things than the shams that satisfied me before we met. I've been a very . . . worldly woman; you know, don't you?"

"Few human beings are stronger than temptations, child," he said melodiously; "and yours must have been many."

"I used to want you to think me better than I am. Now I—I do and I don't. Oh, I can't explain!"

"You are showing me your heart—you need not spell it."

"I suppose what I mean really is that I want you to know me as I am, and yet to like me just as much. I wonder if you would?"

He laid a gentle hand upon her shoulder. "Why not put me to the test?"

"I daren't," she said.

"Am I so hard?"

She shook her head, silently.

"What then?"

"I'm so bad," she whispered. She drooped a little nearer to him.

"Why do you say such things?" cried the Bishop; "you hurt me!"

"Haven't you met other sinners?"

"I would have had *your* past free from sin."

"Oh, my past?" she sobbed, and bowed herself in his arms. "My past is past—I'm sinning now!"

Much may be done by earnest endeavour, and he persuaded himself that his embrace was episcopal.

"My child," he murmured at last, soothing her tenderly, "I will not affect to misunderstand what you have said—it would be a false kindness to you. Nor will I be guilty of concealing the transgressions of my own heart. Were I a younger man, I might doubt the righteousness of owning that the attachment is mutual; but the years bring wisdom and at my age we see deeply. My duty is to help you, and I realise that I can help you only by a perfect candour. I acknowledge, therefore, that you are indeed most dear to me."

"Oh, you are great!" she exclaimed. "I shall see you still? Promise you'll come here—don't let me lose you! Say it! Say again you love me!"

"You are indeed most dear to me," repeated the Bishop, who thought this way of putting it sounded more innocent. He got up and paced the room with agitation. "You ask me if I will still come here. I do not disguise from myself that many might think that I should answer 'no'; many might hold it my duty to desert you in the conflict that must be waged, to leave you to bear the brunt of it alone. I am not one of them. Flight is at best the refuge of a coward. Doughtier than to flee temptation is to confront and conquer it." He swept the hair from his brow with a noble gesture. "I recognise that my highest duty is to share your struggles—to solace and sustain you. Yes, I will come! We have a mighty battle before us, you and I—and we will fight side by side, my comrade, till we win!"

In other words, he ventured to go to tea there all the same, and had whisky-and-soda when it wasn't tea-time.

How much of what the Stage Door Club said about them was fact and how much of it was fiction, is a thing that could be decided only by the Bishop or Miss Clarges—neither of whom is to be consulted on the subject. But the Rev. Baker Barling, who frequently dropped into the Club for the house dinner, or a game of poker, heard the gossip; and Baker Barling confided it to Mrs. Baker Barling; and Mrs. Baker Barling, whose wrath against the Bishop had in no way abated, manœuvred for the joy of condoling with the Bishop's wife.

Miss Clarges was paralysed one morning by a note in which "Mrs. Lullieton Meadows," mentioning that her husband was the Bishop of Westborough, requested the actress to receive her upon a matter of the utmost importance the same afternoon. The actress's first impulse was to be "out" when the lady called; her second, to telegraph to the Bishop for advice. The fear of driving Mrs. Meadows to extremities, and the thought that a telegram might fall into the wrong hands, prevented her adopting either course. She could only pray for the ability to persuade the visitor that her suspicions were unfounded, and she felt sick with misgiving as the day wore on.

How extraordinary of the woman! Whether she meant to be offensive, or pathetic, what a folly of her to come! On the stage, of course, such scenes were usual, and Kitty Clarges knew exactly how she would have to behave there—that she would be first mocking, then attentive, and finally moved to repentance. But the theatre was one thing, and life was another. In real life it was preposterous of a person to seek an interview and plead for the return of a husband's heart, even if one wished to do it. And in this case, the wish was lacking; Miss Clarges was so infatuated by the Bishop that she had even been jealous to remember that another woman had a legal claim to him.

At the tingle of the bell, she caught her breath. She had never seen "the other woman," and mixed with her apprehension was a strong curiosity to know what his wife was like. "Mrs. Meadows," announced the maid. The actress turned to the doorway, trembling, and saw that the lady was a dowdy little woman with a dreary face; she looked as if she lived at Tunbridge Wells.

"Mrs. Meadows—how good of you to call!"

Mrs. Meadows advanced awkwardly; it was evident that she was painfully embarrassed. "Miss Clarges? I hope I haven't put you to any inconvenience?" she murmured.

"It is an immense pleasure to me to meet you. Won't you sit down?"

For an instant the Bishop's wife hesitated. Then she sat at the extreme edge of a chair, and moistened her lips.

"My visit must appear very strange to you?"

"Most kind!" said Kitty Clarges. "How is his lordship getting on with his play? It'll soon be finished now, I suppose?"

"I daresay—I really don't know; I didn't come to talk about the play," Mrs. Meadows faltered; "I came because you might do more for me than anybody else alive! Miss Clarges, my husband is in love with you."

The start, the bewilderment in the eyes, was admirable. "My . . . dear Mrs. Meadows?"

"You need not trouble to deny it," said the lady quietly, "because he has acknowledged it to me. But that isn't all—you are in love with my husband."

"Are you here to insult me?" cried Miss Clarges, rising. "I have the honour to be one of his lordship's friends, he has been pleased to discuss his comedy with me. Not unnatural, I think? Especially as I hope to produce the piece. As for . . . what you say, there has never been a word, a syllable—our conversation might have been phonographed for all London to hear." The indignation of her voice quivered into pain. "I wouldn't have had this happen for the world—I can't understand it!" She struggled with a sob, and suppressed it proudly. "It's cruel!"

"I don't wonder that he admires you," said his wife thoughtfully; "you have great talent. But I have seen one of your letters to him. Here it is!"

Miss Clarges gasped, and looked at it. She sat down again very slowly. "All right," she said. "I am fond of your husband! Well?"

"It was finding your letter that made me write to you. I heard weeks ago that he was mad about you, but the letter showed me that you cared for him. Oh, I know that I oughtn't to have written! I considered a long time before I made up my mind. But there was so much at stake, I thought you might help me. If you will listen—"

"What for?" exclaimed Miss Clarges. "What's the use of my listening? Even if I promised you not see him again—I wouldn't promise it, but if I did—would it make him any fonder of *you?* Do you think, if *I* lost a man, I should beg the other woman to give him back to me? I should know she couldn't do it; I should know I might as well beg her to give me back—my innocence. And I shouldn't reproach her, either! I'd reproach myself! I should call myself a fool for not holding my own. Women like me *don't* lose the man they want—we know how easy it is for him to leave us, and we take the trouble to keep him. It's you good women who are always being left; after you've caught the man, you think you've nothing more to do. Marriage is the end of your little story, so you take it for granted it *must* be the end of his. The more you love him, the sooner you bore him. You go bankrupt in the honeymoon—you're a back number to him before you've been married a month—he knows all your life, and all your mind, and all your moods. You haven't a surprise in reserve for him—and then you wonder he yawns. Great heavens! To hold a man's interest, show him your heart as you pull out a tape measure—an inch at a time. I adore your husband; I venerate him! My guilty love has made me a purer woman. You can't realise that—I don't expect you to realise it; but surely you must know that—if you wept and went down on your knees to me—I couldn't say, 'Because the right's all on your side, he shall never think about me any more'?"

"You misunderstand the object of my visit," said Mrs. Meadows meekly. "I didn't come to weep to you. I didn't come to beg you to say that he should never think about you any more. I came to beg you to tell me what you find in him to love."

"Eh?" ejaculated Miss Clarges.

"I came to beg you to tell me what you find in him to love," repeated the elder woman in plaintive tones. "You see, to you he is only an episode; but unless I choose to make a scandal—and I have daughters to consider—*I* must expect to spend many more years with him. If you will help me to discover some attraction in him, it will make life far easier for me."

Kitty Clarges sat staring at her dumbly. "You f-find no attraction in him?" she stammered at last.

"It is unconventional of me to admit it to you; but, as I say, there is so much at stake—I feel justified in asking your assistance. To me he is tedious beyond words to tell. If you would explain why you adore him, if you would show me some merit, some spark of talent, or wit, or humour, something to make his pretentions less intolerable—you don't know how thankful to you I should be."

"Your husband is a great man." She spoke with a touch of uncertainty.

"Oh, no! And I should be foolish to ask so much—a moderately intelligent man is all that a woman like me has the right to expect. The Bishop is unfortunately very, very dull. Believe me, I have tried most conscientiously to be deceived by him. I used to read his Press notices and say, 'Look what the newspapers say about him—it *must* be true!' But I knew it wasn't. I used to listen to his sermons—there aren't many of them; they've been the same sermons for twenty years—and say, 'What lovely language, what noble thoughts! How proud his little Mildred should be!' But, though I was a young girl then I knew that the lovely language was all sound and no sense, and that the noble thoughts came out of the *Dictonary of Quotations*. O Miss Clarges! you are a brilliant woman, far, far cleverer than I—he must have some stray virtue that my earnest search hasn't brought to light or you couldn't gush so romantically about him. Help me to see it! Think how he wearies me—tell me where the virtue is!"

The actress was breathing heavily, her nostrils fluttered; on her bloodless cheeks the delicacy of "Maidenbloom" stood out in unbecoming blotches. To hear that she idolised a man whom this little provincial in last year's fashions disdained as a bore, robbed her of speech. She had not believed there could be such depths of humiliation in the world.

Some seconds passed, while the suppliant watched her wistfully.

"If you don't care for your husband, I'm afraid I couldn't teach you to love him."

"No, no; I only thought you might help me to put up with him; I'm not unreasonable—I'd be grateful for small mercies. If you'd mention a ray of interest in him, I'd keep my eyes on that, and make the most of it. . . . You're not vexed with me for coming?"

"Oh, not at all; I—I suppose you've been very . . . amiable, our interview has been rather quaint; I'm sorry I can't oblige you."

"Well," sighed Mrs. Meadows, "it can't be helped. But I must say I'm disappointed! When I found out there was a woman in love with him, it simply amazed me! I felt it only right to consult you—it seemed such an opportunity to improve matters at home. Still, there it is, if you can't tell me, you can't!" She was very downcast. "Then I'll say 'Good-afternoon.' "

"May I offer you some—tea?" quavered Kitty, clinging to the mantelpiece.

"Thank you so much, but I'm afraid I must be going now; I promised to see our Secretary at the office of the Mission Fund at four o'clock. Good-bye, Miss Clarges. You needn't tell the Bishop that I called. It has been quite useless."

She sighed herself out.

Now, though Kitty Clarges endeavoured to persuade herself by turns that Mrs. Meadows was a fool incapable of appreciating her husband, and that Mrs. Meadows was a diplomat scheming to disenchant her with him, both endeavours were unsuccessful. She could not think the woman an utter idiot, and still less was it possible to think her a genius. Kitty Clarges was less entranced by the Bishop in their next meeting. Between them lurked a dowdy little figure, regarding her with astonished eyes. The astonishment shamed her as no homily could have ever done. The figure was present at all their meetings, and often she lost sight of the Bishop's classical features and could see nothing but his wife's eyes wondering at her. His eloquence was no longer thrilling—she was obsessed by the knowledge that it wasn't good enough for the woman in the *modes* of Tunbridge Wells.

Before long the sight of her own dove-coloured gowns began to get on her nerves, and gradually she discarded them. Once, when the Bishop proposed to visit her, she told him that she would be lunching out. A few days later she wrote that unforeseen circumstances denied her the hope of producing his comedy. His urgent letter of inquiry remained unanswered. When he called for an explanation she was "not at home."

Rudyard Kipling

Kipling's funny stories, which Father could not read aloud without being beaten on the back several times by the whole family, have suffered the usual fate of humor. They have been left open too long; they have ceased to bubble. One of Kipling's favorite comic devices was to describe a vast, laborious hoax, involving a whole village or half the British Navy. But group-hoaxes are extremely rare in ordinary human life, and the hoaxer is usually a bore. Again, Kipling's characters are always roaring with inextinguishable mirth at their own high jinks. He should have known that a description of laughter does not provoke laughter.

Perhaps I am mistaken; I am always being mistaken. Before complaining, however, read over The Taking of Lung-tung-Pen *or* Brugglesmith. *If I am wrong, I will send you a valuable souvenir of the* World of Tomorrow Exposition.

Anyway, here are a couple of Kipling's poems which I do think are funny.

MY RIVAL

I go to concert, party, ball—
    What profit is in these?
I sit alone against the wall
    And strive to look at ease.
The incense that is mine by right
    They burn before her shrine;
And that's because I'm seventeen
    And she is forty-nine.

I cannot check my girlish blush,
    My colour comes and goes.
I redden to my finger-tips,
    And sometimes to my nose.

But She is white where white should be,
    And red where red should shine.
The blush that flies at seventeen
    Is fixed at forty-nine.

I wish *I* had her constant cheek:
    I wish that I could sing
All sorts of funny little songs,
    Not quite the proper thing.
I'm very *gauche* and very shy,
    Her jokes aren't in my line;
And worst of all, I'm seventeen
    While She is forty-nine.

The young men come, the young men go,
    Each pink and white and neat,
She's older than their mothers, but
    They grovel at Her feet.
They walk beside Her *'rickshaw*-wheels—
    None ever walk by mine;
And that's because I'm seventeen
    And She is forty-nine.

She rides with half a dozen men
    (She calls them "boys" and "mashes"),
I trot along the Mall alone;
    My prettiest frocks and sashes
Don't help to fill my programme-card,
    And vainly I repine
From ten to two A. M. Ah me!
    Would I were forty-nine!

She calls me "darling," "pet," and "dear,"
    And "sweet retiring maid."
I'm always at the back, I know—
    She puts me in the shade.
She introduces me to men—
    "Cast" lovers, I opine;
For sixty takes to seventeen,
    Nineteen to forty-nine.

But even She must older grow
   And end Her dancing days,
She can't go on for ever so
   At concerts, balls, and plays.
One ray of priceless hope I see
   Before my footsteps shine;
Just think, that She'll be eighty-one
   When I am forty-nine!

NATURAL THEOLOGY

PRIMITIVE

I ate my fill of a whale that died
   And stranded after a month at sea. . . .
There is a pain in my inside.
   Why have the Gods afflicted me?
Ow! I am purged till I am a wraith!
   Wow! I am sick till I cannot see!
What is the sense of Religion and Faith?
   Look how the Gods have afflicted me!

PAGAN

How can the skin of rat or mouse hold
   Anything more than a harmless flea? . . .
The burning plague has taken my household.
   Why have my Gods afflicted me?
All my kith and kin are deceased,
   Though they were as good as good could be.
I will out and batter the family priest,
   Because my Gods have afflicted me!

MEDIÆVAL

My privy and well drain into each other
   After the custom of Christendie. . . .
Fevers and fluxes are wasting my mother.
   Why has the Lord afflicted me?

The Saints are helpless for all I offer—
  So are the clergy I used to fee.
Henceforward I keep my cash in my coffer,
  Because the Lord has afflicted me.

MATERIAL

I run eight hundred hens to the acre,
  They die by dozens mysteriously. . . .
I am more than doubtful concerning my Maker.
  Why has the Lord afflicted me?
What a return for all my endeavour—
  Not to mention the L. S. D.!
I am an atheist now and for ever,
  Because this God has afflicted me!

PROGRESSIVE

Money spent on an Army or Fleet
  Is homicidal lunacy. . . .
My son has been killed in the Mons retreat.
  Why has the Lord afflicted me?
Why are murder, pillage and arson
  And rape allowed by the Deity?
I will write to the *Times,* deriding our parson,
  Because my God has afflicted me.

CHORUS

We had a kettle: we let it leak:
  Our not repairing it made it worse.
We haven't had any tea for a week. . . .
  The bottom is out of the Universe!

CONCLUSION

This was none of the good Lord's pleasure,
  For the Spirit He breathed in Man is free;
But what comes after is measure for measure
  And not a God that afflicteth thee.
As was the sowing so the reaping
  Is now and evermore shall be.
Thou art delivered to thine own keeping.
  Only Thyself hath afflicted thee!

George A. Birmingham

George A. Birmingham, whose right name is James Owen Hannay, is one of the long line of witty clerics, from Robert Herrick to Ronald A. Knox, who have ornamented the spiritual life of Great Britain. The soil of the old world seems more favorable than our own to the production of these benign blossoms. We need, I fear, a little more time, a little more spiritual fertilizer.

"GOD SAVE THE KING"

"The band will play all afternoon, of course," said Dr. Whitty.

He was speaking about the sports—the "Grand Athletic, Bicycle and Boat Racing Regatta," as the advertisement called the event—which were to be held in Ballintra on the first Saturday in August.

"I don't know will it be able," said Father Henaghan, "and if it is, it'll likely be the last time ever it does play."

He was President—in Connacht everything has a President—of the town band. He was also its Honorary Treasurer.

"And why do you say that?" said Dr. Whitty.

"You know well enough," said the priest, "that we had to give the bandmaster notice for want of funds to pay him."

"Surely to goodness," said the doctor, "they must have half a dozen tunes learned off by this time. Nobody'll know whether they play them right or wrong. Let them do the best they can, and make some sort of a noise anyway."

"I don't know," said the priest, "will they be fit to do that much itself. It was only last week they were telling me that the cornet's broke, and I'm thinking they'll do badly without it. What's more, I'm not sure but young Flaherty put the blade of his knife through the big drum."

"We'll have to get them some new instruments then," said the doctor. "The band we simply must have."

"You can't get new instruments, for there's no money, and I don't see where it's to be got after the way you've collected the whole district for the sports. There isn't one about the place has a shilling left in his pocket."

Dr. Whitty had, in fact, levied a sum of money very near the taxable capacity of the people. He recognised the impossibility of securing further contributions.

"I'll tell you what it is," he said. "We must get something out of Lord Allington. That man's as rich as a Jew."

"He never gives a penny," said the priest.

"He does. I happen to know that he gives twenty pounds a year to the Protestant Church on account of having property in the parish, though he doesn't live in it. I don't see why he shouldn't give the half of that amount to our band. You ought to try him anyway."

"I will not. I asked him for a subscription one time, and the way he refused me I swore I'd never ask him again. Do you go over to Allington Castle and ask him yourself."

"It wouldn't be a bit of good," said the doctor. "But I'll tell you what I'll do. I'll get the colonel to write. He'd give us something if the colonel asked him."

It took Dr. Whitty a long time to persuade Colonel Beresford to write the letter, but he succeeded in the end. By return of post a reply came from Lord Allington.

DEAR COLONEL BERESFORD,

I am always ready to support anything which is for the benefit of the tenants on my estate, and I should be perfectly willing to give a subscription to a band managed on non-political lines. Unfortunately, my experience of these local bands leads me to believe that they are nothing more or less than part of the machinery used by seditious persons for the inculcation of rebellious principles. On the only occasion on which I ever heard the Ballintra band play, the tune chosen was "God Save Ireland." I am sure you will understand that, in these circumstances, and in the absence of any express guarantee from some reasonable person that no Party tunes will be played, I cannot conscientiously support the band.

Thanks for your inquiry for Lady Allington. I am glad to say she is a great deal stronger than she was. The Irish air always sets her up.

I am, yours very sincerely,

ALLINGTON

The colonel handed the letter to Dr. Whitty.

"Do you think now," said the doctor, "that if the band was to play 'God Save the King' he'd give us a subscription?"

"I expect he would," said the colonel, smiling; "but you know as well as I do the band will do no such thing, and there'd be a riot if it did."

"Colonel," said the doctor, "do you write to Lord Allington and tell him you will send him a written undertaking from the parish priest—you can put in that the dispensary doctor will sign it, too, if you like—to the effect that the band will play 'God Save the King' in the middle of the afternoon on the day of the sports, and that Lord Allington can come over and hear it for himself so as to make sure that it's actually done."

"I don't believe you'll work it, doctor. Thady Glynn and the League boys would smash up every trumpet the band possessed if you did."

"You write the letter," said the doctor, "and leave the rest to me."

"If you do what you say," said the colonel, "I should think Lord Allington would give you twenty pounds with pleasure; and, what's more, I'll add two pounds to my own subscription if it's only for the sake of seeing the rage Thady Glynn will be in."

Dr. Whitty called on Father Henaghan at once.

"I've ten pounds," he said, "ten pounds at least, and maybe twenty pounds, got out of Lord Allington for the town band—at least I have it as good as got."

"Have you, then? I wouldn't have believed it possible. You're a wonderful man, doctor."

"All he wants," said the doctor, "is a written guarantee from you and me that the band will perform 'God Save the King' on the day of the sports. He says he objects to Party tunes."

"And is that what you call having the money as good as got? You know as well as I do the thing can't be done."

"It can. I'll get the music, and I'll teach it to the band myself. I'm not what you'd call practised in conducting an orchestra, but I have a middling good ear, and I could manage that much. Any new instruments wanted you can get, and pay for when Lord Allington's cheque comes."

"It's not the want of instruments would stop me," said the priest. "But the people would never stand it. There'd be the devil and all."

"You needn't appear in the matter," said the doctor. "Beyond writing the letter to Lord Allington, you've nothing to do. If there's a row, you can pretend to be as surprised as any one else. But there won't be a row."

"There will. There couldn't but be a row."

"There will not. There aren't ten men in Ballintra, barring the colonel, Mr. Jackson, and the police, that would know that tune from any other if they heard it. Would you know it yourself now, Father Henaghan? Tell the truth."

"I'm not sure that I would."

"And, if you wouldn't recognise it, how do you suppose that Thady Glynn will?—Thady that has no more ear for music than your cow. I'll tell you what I'll do. I'll drop into the hotel this evening, and I'll whistle it in the hearing of Thady. I'll call his attention to it, and I'll bet half a crown he hasn't the least notion what it is."

"Try it," said the priest. "But, mind you, I'll take no responsibility. If there's a row, I'll say you did the whole thing unknown to me."

Dr. Whitty strolled into the hotel at ten o'clock that night. There were five or six men drinking at the bar, all of them, he was pleased to see, prominent politicians and strong allies of Thady Glynn. He ordered a bottle of porter, and then, leaning against the bar, whistled "God Save the King" loudly and clearly. Then he drank half his porter and whistled the tune through again, throwing great spirit into the last few bars.

"That's a fine tune," he said when he had finished.

"It's good enough," said Thady.

"It's a tune I'm thinking of teaching the town band to play the day of the sports," said the doctor. "It's only the other day it was discovered, hid away in an old book that was buried in a bog in the neighbourhood of the hill of Tara. It turns out to be the ancient tune that was sung by Malachi, the High King of Ireland, at the time he was driving the English out of the country. There's great talk about it up in Dublin."

"It would be well," said Thady, "that the band would learn something new. We're tired of them old tunes they've been playing since the bandmaster was sent away."

Dr. Whitty, in order to make sure of getting the music in the most correct form possible, sent to Belfast for it. He had to copy it all out in manuscript when he got it, because the inconsiderate publisher had printed "God Save the King" at the top of every sheet of the score. Every sheet of Dr. Whitty's version had "The Song of King Malachi" written in large letters across the top. The members of the band made fair progress when the doctor took them in hand. He conducted on a system of his own: whistled shrilly, and flung himself into all sorts of grotesque attitudes, waving his arms, clenching his fists, and stamping violently with his feet. He succeeded in working up a most spirited performance of the tune.

The day of the sports was magnificently fine. The band was stationed in a prominent part of the grounds, and a space close beside it was reserved for Lord Allington's motor-car. Dr. Whitty asked Thady Glynn to act as judge and referee in all the races, an arrangement not altogether satisfactory to the competitors, but which he hoped would keep Thady from paying any attention to the band. With the same object he made the secretary and treasurer of the League starter and time-keeper, giving them a pistol, a supply of blank cartridges, and a stop-watch.

At four o'clock Colonel Beresford arrived in his dogcart. Lord Allington drove up in his motor-car at half-past four, and was shepherded by Dr. Whitty into the space reserved for him. He had Lady Allington with him and two strange gentlemen. The band, acting on instructions from Dr. Whitty, struck up "The Minstrel Boy." This is an Irish song, but quite unobjectionable because it is not stated in Moore's words what war the boy went to or on which side he fought.

After "The Minstrel Boy" had been played through four times, Dr. Whitty spoke earnestly to Flaherty, the cornet player, and to the man who managed the big drum. Then he strolled away from the band and engaged in conversation with Thady Glynn. A few minutes later the band struck up "God Save the King." Dr. Whitty looked round nervously. Thady Glynn took no notice of the tune. Most of the people seemed pleased to hear it. The reputation of "The Song of King Malachi" had been spread beforehand by the members of the band, and there was a good deal of curiosity about the remarkable tune. The only thing which disquieted Dr. Whitty was the behaviour of Lord Allington and his friends. The whole party stood up in the motor-car, and the three gentlemen took off their hats. Colonel Beresford, who was standing beside the car, stopped talking to Lady Allington and stood bareheaded.

Thady Glynn, fully occupied elsewhere, did not so much as glance at Lord Allington. Father Henaghan had disappeared from the seat he had occupied all the afternoon. Dr. Whitty made his way rapidly through the crowd towards the refreshment tent, an establishment run in connection with Thady Glynn's hotel. The band was beginning "God Save the King" for the second time when he reached it. He noticed with pleasure that the starter and timekeeper of the races were drinking whisky and water inside the tent, apparently unconscious of the band's performance. He ran round to the back of the tent. There, he felt sure, he would find Father Henaghan. He found the priest engaged in conversation with Mrs. Michael Geraghty, who was feeding her seven youngest children with biscuits and partially ripe apples.

"Come now, Father Henaghan," he said, "it's time you were going up to speak to Lord Allington to get that cheque out of him."

"Will you whisht," said the priest, with a glance at Mrs. Michael Geraghty.

"It's all right," said the doctor. "Mrs. Geraghty has a respect for the clergy, and wouldn't repeat what I'm saying to you, not that it would matter if she did, for we're talking no secrets."

"I'll go when the band stops playing that tune," said the priest.

"If you wait till then you'll wait too long, for Lord Allington will be gone, and it's ten to one you'll never see that cheque. I know the ways of people of his sort. They set up to be fonder of that tune than of anything else in heaven or earth; but there's no surer way of getting them out of a place than to play it. The minute they hear the first four notes they're streaming off for the door or the gate, as the case may be. What I'm wondering is that they've stood it as long as they have. Come on, now."

He took the priest by the arm and led him round the tent into the open. The band, very pleased with its own performance, had just begun to play the tune for the sixth time. Lord Allington was still standing bareheaded, but he was looking puzzled and a little annoyed. "God Save the King" is an excellent tune, but it is possible, even for an Irish peer, to get too much of it. There was not, so far as he could see, any sign of exhaustion about the band. Lady Allington, excusing herself on the ground of delicate health, sat down at the end of the fourth repetition of the tune.

"Go on now, Father Henaghan," said Dr. Whitty, pushing the priest towards the motor-car.

Lord Allington turned round.

"Ah," he said, "Father Henaghan, isn't it? I'm delighted to see you. Would you mind telling the band to stop playing for a moment? I can hardly hear myself speak."

Father Henaghan tapped the cornet player on the shoulder and gave his order. The music stopped abruptly in the middle of a bar. Lord Allington, with a sigh of relief, sat down and put on his hat.

"That's a capital band of yours," he said. "I don't know when I heard a better. All native talent, eh? That's right. Keep the young men out of mischief. By the way, I understand from my friend, Colonel Beresford, that it's dependent entirely on private contributions for its support. I shall have the greatest pleasure in sending you a cheque for fifteen guineas tonight when I go home. That will see you out of your difficulties, I hope. And you can count on me for the future for an annual five guineas. But no Party tunes now, remember that."

Father Henaghan bowed his thanks. Lord Allington, after a whisper from his wife, gave a signal to the chauffeur and drove off the ground.

Two days afterwards Dr. Whitty met Colonel Beresford in the street.

"Come into my house for two minutes, colonel," he said; "I've something to show you."

"Look here," he said, taking a letter from his desk, "read that":—

The Committee of the League (Ballintra Branch) having had under consideration at a special meeting the conduct of Dr. Whitty, Medical Officer of the Union, with reference to the band on the occasion of the recent Regatta and Athletic Sports, hereby allow Dr. Whitty an opportunity of defending himself at 8:15 sharp in the League rooms tomorrow evening.   Signed, on behalf of the Committee,
                                    THADDEUS GLYNN, President

"What do you think of that now?" said the doctor.

"It's—it's—the only words that seem to fit it at all are blasted insolence; but, of course, you'll take no notice of it."

"Oh yes, I shall. I'll make that League sit up. I shall have a glorious time with them if only they're sober enough to take in what I say."

"You'd better get Father Henaghan to quiet them," said the colonel.

"Not at all. I'm not going to hide behind the priest. I mean to see the thing through myself."

At the hour fixed for the trial Dr. Whitty stepped jauntily into the League rooms. He was received in gloomy silence, broken only by an order from Thady Glynn to stand at the end of the table. The doctor took a vacant chair and sat down. Thady Glynn scowled at him. Dr. Whitty smiled pleasantly by way of reply.

"Dr. Whitty," said Thady solemnly, "it has been reported to us that on the occasion of the recent sports, held in this town, you instigated the band to play a tune that can only be regarded as a deliberate insult to the Irish people. What have you to say for yourself?"

"What tune?" asked the doctor.

"I won't lower myself by naming it," said Thady; "but it was a tune that's seldom heard in this country outside of a music hall."

"If you mean the ancient 'Song of King Malachi,'" said the doctor, "I quite admit it's not often heard, but the reason of that is that it has only recently been discovered, as I told you and the rest of these gentlemen the night I first whistled it to you. If you had any objection to it you should have said so then."

"King Malachi be damned," said Thady Glynn.

"If you're prepared to let your temper run away with you," said the doctor, "to the extent of cursing one of the greatest heroes of ancient Ireland, of course I can't stop you. All I can do is to tell you that, if I repeat that last remark of yours outside this room, you'll never be able to hold up your head as a Nationalist again."

"Damn you and King Malachi both," said Thady Glynn.

"Very well," said the doctor, "if you're so drunk as to say a thing like that twice, there's no use my talking to you. Good night."

"Wait a minute," said Thady, "you'll not get off so easy as all that. We know well enough what the tune was, and we know why you had it played. You thought you'd make up to the colonel and Lord Allington by heaping insults on the people of this country. That's what you thought. But I may tell you it won't do. It's us and not them that's paying your salary. It's us and not them that's putting the bread and butter in your mouth, and I tell you it won't do. The tune you were the means of introducing into our midst is a tune that's well known. It's a Party tune, and we won't have it."

"What do you mean to do?" said the doctor.

"We've settled on a decision before you came in," said Thady, "and it's this: that if you don't offer an apology to the people of this neighbourhood, it'll be the worse for you."

"Listen to me now," said the doctor. "As a matter of fact, that tune was played over seven times and a half on the ground the other day, and not a single one of you cared a hang. The man that asked to have it stopped was Lord Allington. If it was the tune you think it was, would he have had it stopped? He would not. He'd have kept the band playing on at it the whole afternoon."

"It's a damned insult—" began Thady Glynn.

"Listen to me," said the doctor, "and don't interrupt. If you had as much real principle about you, Nationalist or any other kind, as would make a supper for a snipe, I'd have some pity for you. But you're the sort of man, Thady, that would sell his mother for the price of a pint of porter. I've let you down easy in the past, not telling the things I know about you; but if there's another word out of your head, I'll tell every man and woman in the place the dirty trick you tried to play on poor Michael Geraghty the time the inspector was down to give him the money for the pier; and, if that isn't enough, I'll buy a gramophone and set it playing the tune you don't like day and night outside the door of your beastly public-house, and, whenever it stops, I'll pay a boy to go and wind it up; and, what's more, the next time you're sick—and that won't be long if you go on drinking the way you do at present—I'll give you some medicine that'll twist you round and round the same way as your wife wrings out the clothes when she has them washed, and tie you up in knots, and, what's more, will turn you bright green from head to foot afterwards, so that your own children won't know you when they meet you in the street. After that, if there's any more fight left in you, I'll give word to the police about the Sunday drinking that goes on in your house, and I'll have your license taken away from you. And if that's not enough—"

Apparently it was enough. Thady Glynn was cowed by the extraordinary versatility of the doctor's threats. He waved his hand feebly towards the door. Dr. Whitty, after a cheerful good night to the other members of the committee, went home.

Logan Pearsall Smith

Though born in Millville, New Jersey, Logan Pearsall Smith belongs in a book of British humor. He moved to England because he found there more connoisseurs of the polished phrase than in America. Mr. Smith polishes a phrase until you can see your face in it, shuddering.

TRIVIA (Selection)

HIGH LIFE

Although that immense Country House was empty and for sale, and I had got an order to view it, I needed all my courage to walk through the lordly gates, and up the avenue, and then to ring the door-bell. And when I was ushered in, and the shutters were removed to let the daylight into those vast apartments, I sneaked through them, cursing the dishonest curiosity which had brought me into a place where I had no business. But I was treated with such deference, and so plainly regarded as a possible purchaser, that I soon began to believe in the opulence imputed to me. From all the novels describing the mysterious and glittering life of the Great which I had read (and I have read thousands), there came to me the vision of my own existence in this Palace. I filled those vast halls with the shine of jewels and stir of voices; I saw a vision of ladies sweeping in their tiaras down the splendid stairs.

But my Soul, in her swell of pride, soon outgrew these paltry limits. Oh, no! Never could I box up and house under that roof the Pomp, the Ostentation of which I was capable.

Then for one thing there was stabling for only forty horses; and this, of course, as I told them, would never do.

A FANCY

More than once, too, I have pleased myself with the notion that somewhere there is good Company which will like this small uncontemporaneous Book—these Thoughts (if I may call them so) dipped up from that phantasmagoria or phosphorescence which, by some unexplained process of combustion, flickers over the large lump of grey soft matter in the bowl of my skull.

HUMAN ENDS

I really was impressed, as we paced up and down the avenue, by the Vicar's words, and weighty, weighed advice. He spoke of the various professions; mentioned contemporaries of his own who had achieved success: how one had a Seat in Parliament, would be given a Seat in the Cabinet when his party next came in; another was a Bishop with a Seat in the House of Lords; a third was a Barrister who was soon, it was said, to be raised to the Bench.

But in spite of my good intentions, my real wish to find, before it is too late, some career or other for myself (and the question is getting serious), I am far too much at the mercy of ludicrous images. Front Seats, Episcopal, Judicial, Parliamentary Benches—were all the ends then, I asked myself, of serious, middle-aged ambition only things to sit on?

LORD ARDEN

"If I were Lord Arden," said the Vicar, "I would shut up that great House; it's too big—what can a young unmarried man ... ?"

"If I were Lord Arden," said the Vicar's wife (and Mrs. La Mountain's tone showed how much she disapproved of that young nobleman), "if I were Lord Arden, I would live there, and do my duty to my tenants and neighbours."

"If I were Lord Arden," I said; but then it flashed vividly into my mind, suppose I really were this Sardanapalian young Lord? I quite forgot to whom I was talking; the Moralist within ceased to function;

my memory was full with the names of people who had been famous for their enormous pleasures; who had filled their palaces with guilty revels, and built Pyramids, Obelisks, and half-acre Tombs, to soothe their pride. My mind kindled at the thought of these Audacities. "If I were Lord Arden!" I shouted ...

EDIFICATION

"I must really improve my mind," I tell myself, and once more begin to patch and repair that crazy structure. So I toil and toil on at the vain task of edification, though the wind tears off the tiles, the floors give way, the ceilings fall, strange birds build untidy nests in the rafters, and owls hoot and laugh in the tumbling chimneys.

SOCIAL SUCCESS

The servant gave me my coat and hat, and in a glow of self-satisfaction I walked out into the night. "A delightful evening," I reflected, "the nicest kind of people. What I said about finance and philosophy impressed them; and how they laughed when I imitated a pig squealing."

But soon after, "God, it's awful," I muttered, "I wish I was dead."

APOTHEOSIS

But oh, those heavenly moments when I feel this three-dimensioned universe too small to contain my Attributes; when a sense of the divine Ipseity invades me; when I know that my voice is the voice of Truth, and my umbrella God's umbrella!

THE GOAT

In the midst of my anecdote a sudden misgiving chilled me—had I told them about this Goat before? And then as I talked there gaped upon me—abyss opening beneath abyss—a darker speculation: when goats are mentioned, do I automatically and always tell this story about the Goat at Portsmouth?

LONGEVITY

"But when you are as old as I am!" I said to the young lady in pink satin.

"But I don't know how old you are," the young lady in pink answered almost archly. We were getting on quite nicely.

"Oh, I'm endlessly old; my memory goes back almost for ever. I come out of the Middle Ages. I am the primitive savage we are all descended from; I believe in Devil-worship and the power of the Stars; I dance under the new Moon, naked and tattooed and holy. I am a Cave-dweller, a contemporary of Mastodons and Mammoths; I am pleistocene and eolithic, and full of the lusts and terrors of the great pre-glacial forests. But that's nothing; I am millions of years older; I am an arboreal Ape, an aged Baboon, with all its instincts; I am a pre-simian quadruped, I have great claws, eyes that see in the dark, and a long prehensile tail."

"Good gracious!" said the terrified young lady in pink satin. Then she turned and talked in a hushed voice with her other neighbour.

GREEN IVORY

What a bore it is, waking up in the morning always the same person. I wish I were unflinching and emphatic, and had big, bushy eyebrows and a Message for the Age. I wish I were a deep Thinker, or a great Ventriloquist.

I should like to be refined-looking and melancholy, the victim of a hopeless passion; to love in the old, stilted way, with impossible Adoration and Despair under the pale-faced moon.

I wish I could get up; I wish I were the world's greatest living Violinist. I wish I had lots of silver, and first editions, and green ivory.

SHADOWED

I sometimes feel a little uneasy about that imagined self of mine—the Me of my daydreams—who leads a melodramatic life of his own, out of all relation with my real existence. So one day I shadowed him down the street. He loitered along for a while, and then stood at a shopwindow and dressed himself out in a gaudy tie and yellow waistcoat. Then he bought a great sponge and two stuffed birds and took them to lodgings, where he led a shady existence. Next he moved to a big house in Mayfair, and gave grand dinner-parties, with splendid service and costly wines. His amorous adventures among the High-up Ones of this Earth I pass over. He soon sold his house and horses, gave up his motors, dismissed his retinue of servants, and went—saving two young ladies from being run over on the way—to live a life of heroic self-sacrifice among the poor.

I was beginning to feel encouraged about him, when in passing a fishmonger's, he pointed at a great salmon and said, "I caught that fish."

REASSURANCE

I looked at my overcoat and my hat hanging in the hall with reassurance; for although I go out of doors with one individuality today, when yesterday I had quite another, yet my clothes keep my various selves buttoned up together, and enable all these otherwise irreconcilable aggregates of psychological phenomena to pass themselves off as one person.

IONS

"Self-determination," one of them insisted.

"Arbitration!" cried another.

"Co-operation?" suggested the mildest of the party.

"Confiscation!" answered an uncompromising female.

I, too, became slightly intoxicated by the sound of these vocables. And were they not the cure for all our ills?

"Inebriation!" I chimed in, "Inundation, Afforestation, Flagellation, Transubstantiation, Co-education!"

ABOVE THE CLOUDS

"I do so hate gossip," she murmured.

"How I hate it too!" I heard myself exclaim.

"There is so much that is good and noble in human nature; why not talk of that?"

"Why not indeed?" I sighed.

"I always feel that it is one's own fault if one dislikes people, or finds them boring."

"How I agree with you!" I cried, as Virtue crept like a guilty thing into my heart.

"But people are nowadays so cynical—they sneer at everything that makes life worth living—Love, Faith, Friendship—"

"And yet those very names are so lovely that even when used in mockery they shine like stars." (I should have died then; never again shall I be so fit for Heaven.)

"How beautifully you put it! I have so enjoyed our talk." I had enjoyed it too, and felt all the better for it; only a little giddy and out of breath, as if I had been up in a balloon.

THINGS TO SAY

"How did you get on with Mrs. Hearse? You didn't seem to have much to say!"

"Have you ever noticed," I asked, "how, when you are trying to talk to people, all sorts of inappropriate things to say float by with appealing faces?

"With me," I went on, "these ghosts of the unspoken are sometimes platitudes; sometimes dreadful facts; or I am deafened, as I was just now, by wicked, funny stories, which clamour like wild beasts behind the grating of my teeth."

NEWS-ITEMS

In spite of the delicacy of my moral feelings, and my unrelaxed solicitude for the maintenance of the right principles of conduct, I find I can read without tears of the retired Colonels who forge cheques, and the ladies of unexceptional position who are caught pilfering furs in shops. Somehow the sudden lapses of respected people, odd indecorums, backbitings, bigamies, embezzlements, and attempted chastities—the surprising leaps they make now and then out of propriety into the police-courts—somehow news-items of this kind do not altogether—how shall I put it?—well, they don't absolutely blacken the sunshine for me.

And Clergymen? If a Clergyman slips up, do not, I pray you, gentle Reader, grieve, on my account, too much—

WHISKERS

There was once a young man who thought he saw Life as it really is; who prided himself on looking at it grimly in the face without illusions. And he went on looking at it grimly, as he thought, for a good many years. This was his notion of himself; but one day, meeting some very young people, he saw, reflected as it were in their eyes, a bland old gentleman with a white waistcoat and Victorian whiskers, a lover of souls and sunsets, and noble solutions for all problems—

That was what he saw in the eyes of those atrocious young men.

AFTERTHOUGHTS ON LIFE AND HUMAN NATURE

That we should practise what we preach is generally admitted; but anyone who preaches what he and his hearers practise must incur the gravest moral disapprobation.

It is only those who can declare without guile that they are doing the very opposite of what they are really doing—meat-eating vegetarians for instance, and snob-hating snobs—who keep stainless their serene ideals, and walk the earth in white, like angels.

There are few sorrows, however poignant, in which a good income is of no avail.

AFTERTHOUGHTS ON AGE AND DEATH

We grow with the years more fragile in body, but morally stouter, and can throw off the chill of a bad conscience almost at once.

An evil name, which is a drawback at first, sheds a kind of lustre on old age.

What is more enchanting than the voices of young people, when you can't hear what they say?

Don't laugh at a youth for his affectations; he is only trying on one face after another to find his own.

AFTERTHOUGHTS ON OTHER PEOPLE

Don't tell your friends their social faults; they will cure the fault and never forgive you.

People have a right to be shocked; the mention of unmentionable things is a kind of participation in them.

AFTERTHOUGHTS ON THE WORLD

To suppose, as we all suppose, that we could be rich and not behave as the rich behave, is like supposing that we could drink all day and keep completely sober.

"When people say they hate gossip, remember," the son of a celebrated upholsterer once warned me, "that some of them do really hate it."

One can be bored until boredom becomes a mystical experience.

"O Joy!" sings a bird in the heart. "O Joy!" another bird answers; while the world, like a large, thoughtful cat, sits by and watches.

AFTERTHOUGHTS ON ART AND LETTERS

The test of a vocation is the love of the drudgery it involves.

We should nourish our souls on the dew of Poesy, and manure them as well.

Every author, however modest, keeps a most outrageous vanity chained like a madman in the padded cell of his breast.

AFTERTHOUGHTS ON MYSELF

When I come in talk on a blank wall of stupidity facing me, why do I go and break my bald head against it?

And what pursuit is more elegant than that of collecting the ignominies of our nature and transfixing them for show, each on the bright pin of a polished phrase?

People say that life is the thing, but I prefer reading.

How I should like to distil my disesteem of my contemporaries into prose so perfect that all of them would have to read it!

LAST WORDS

Don't let young people confide in you their aspirations; when they drop them they will drop you.

The denunciation of the young is a necessary part of the hygiene of older people, and greatly assists the circulation of their blood.

What with its crude awakenings can youth know of the rich returns of awareness to elderly people from their afternoon naps; of their ironic thoughts and long retrospections, and the sweetness they taste of not being dead?

All my life, as down an abyss without a bottom, I have been pouring van-loads of information into that vacancy of oblivion I call my mind.

H. G. Wells

The porter in the Sultan's palace, the churl in the château, is an ancient commonplace of farce. Wells' great innovation was to make his Kipps splendidly farcical, but nevertheless sympathetic, the hero. (Kipps invaded Society, of course, with the aid of a legacy.)

KIPPS IN THE ROYAL GRAND HOTEL

Kipps endured splendour at the Royal Grand Hotel for three nights and days, and then he retreated in disorder. The Royal Grand defeated and overcame and routed Kipps not of intention, but by sheer royal grandeur, combined with an organisation for his comfort carried to excess. On his return he came upon a difficulty, he had lost his circular piece of cardboard with the number of his room, and he drifted about the hall and passages in a state of perplexity for some time, until he thought all the porters and officials in gold lace caps must be watching him, and jesting to one another about him. Finally, in a quiet corner down below near the hairdresser's shop, he found a kindly-looking personage in bottle green, to whom he broached his difficulty. "I say," he said, with a pleasant smile, "I can't find my room nohow." The personage in bottle green, instead of laughing in a nasty way, as he might well have done, became extremely helpful, showed Kipps what to do, got his key, and conducted him by lift and passage to his chamber. Kipps tipped him half a crown.

Safe in his room, Kipps pulled himself together for dinner. He had learnt enough from young Walsingham to bring his dress clothes, and now he began to assume them. Unfortunately in the excitement of his flight from his Aunt and Uncle he had forgotten to put in his other boots, and he was some time deciding between his purple cloth slippers with a golden marigold and the prospect of cleaning the boots he was wearing with the towel, but finally, being a little footsore, he took the slippers.

Afterwards, when he saw the porters and waiters and the other guests catch sight of the slippers, he was sorry he had not chosen the boots.

However, to make up for any want of style at that end, he had his crush hat under his arm.

He found the dining-room without excessive trouble. It was a vast and splendidly decorated place, and a number of people, evidently quite *au fait,* were dining there at little tables lit with electric red-shaded candles, gentlemen in evening dress, and ladies with dazzling astonishing necks. Kipps had never seen evening dress in full vigour before, and he doubted his eyes. And there were also people not in evening dress, who no doubt wondered what noble family Kipps represented. There was a band in a decorated recess, and the band looked collectively at the purple slippers, and so lost any chance they may have had of a donation so far as Kipps was concerned. The chief drawback to this magnificent place was the excessive space of floor that had to be crossed before you got your purple slippers hidden under a table.

He selected a little table—not the one where a rather impudent-looking waiter held a chair, but another—sat down, and, finding his gibus in his hand, decided after a moment of thought to rise slightly and sit on it. (It was discovered in his abandoned chair at a late hour by a supper-party and restored to him next day.)

He put the napkin carefully on one side, selected his soup without difficulty, "Clear, please," but he was rather floored by the presentation of a quite splendidly bound wine-card. He turned it over, discovered a section devoted to whiskey, and had a bright idea.

" 'Ere," he said to the waiter, with an encouraging movement of the head; and then in a confidential manner, "You 'aven't any Old Methuselah Three Stars, 'ave you?"

The waiter went away to inquire, and Kipps went on with his soup with an enhanced self-respect. Finally, Old Methuselah being unattainable, he ordered a claret from about the middle of the list. "Let's 'ave some of this," he said. He knew claret was a good sort of wine.

"A half bottle?" said the waiter.

"Right you are," said Kipps.

He felt he was getting on. He leant back after his soup, a man of the world, and then slowly brought his eyes round to the ladies in evening dress on his right....

He couldn't have thought it!

They were scorchers. Jest a bit of black velvet over the shoulders!

He looked again. One of them was laughing with a glass of wine half-raised—wicked-looking woman she was; the other, the black velvet one, was eating bits of bread with nervous quickness and talking fast. He wished old Buggins could see them.

He found a waiter regarding him and blushed deeply. He did not look again for some time, and became confused about his knife and fork over the fish. Presently he remarked a lady in pink to the left of him eating the fish with an entirely different implement.

It was over the *vol au vent* that he began to go to pieces. He took a knife to it; then saw the lady in pink was using a fork only, and hastily put down his knife, with a considerable amount of rich creaminess on the blade, upon the cloth. Then he found that a fork in his inexperienced hand was an instrument of chase rather than capture. His ears became violently red, and then he looked up to discover the lady in pink glancing at him, and then smiling, as she spoke to the man beside her.

He hated the lady in pink very much.

He stabbed a large piece of the *vol au vent* at last, and was too glad of his luck not to make a mouthful of it. But it was an extensive fragment, and pieces escaped him. Shirt-front! "Desh it!" he said, and had resort to his spoon. His waiter went and spoke to two other waiters, no doubt jeering at him. He became very fierce suddenly. "'Ere!" he said, gesticulating; and then, "Clear this away!"

The entire dinner-party on his right, the party of the ladies in advanced evening dress, looked at him.... He felt that everyone was watching him and making fun of him, and the injustice of this angered him. After all, they had had every advantage he hadn't. And then, when they got him there doing his best, what must they do but glance and sneer and nudge one another. He tried to catch them at it, and then took refuge in a second glass of wine.

Suddenly and extraordinarily he found himself a Socialist. He did not care how close it was to the lean years when all these things would end.

Mutton came with peas. He arrested the hand of the waiter. "No peas," he said. He knew something of the danger and difficulty of eating peas. Then, when the peas went away, he was embittered again. ...Echoes of Masterman's burning rhetoric began to reverberate in his mind. Nice lot of people these were to laugh at anyone! Women half-undressed— It was that made him so beastly uncomfortable. How could one eat one's dinner with people about him like that? Nice lot they were. He was glad he wasn't one of them anyhow. Yes, they might look. He resolved, if they looked at him again, he would ask one of the men who he was staring at. His perturbed and angry face would have concerned anyone. The band, by an unfortunate accident, was playing truculent military music. The mental change Kipps underwent was, in its way, what psychologists call a conversion. In a few moments all Kipps' ideals were changed. He who had been "practically a gentleman," the sedulous pupil of Coote, the punctilious raiser of hats, was instantly a rebel, an outcast, the hater of everything "stuck up," the foe of Society and the social order of today. Here they were among the profits of their robbery, these people who might do anything with the world. . . .

"No, thenks," he said to a dish.

He addressed a scornful eye at the shoulders of the lady to his left.

Presently he was refusing another dish. He didn't like it—fussed-up food! Probably cooked by some foreigner. He finished up his wine and his bread. . . .

"No, thenks."

"No, thenks." . . .

He discovered the eye of a diner fixed curiously upon his flushed face. He responded with a glare. Couldn't he go without things if he liked?

"What's this?" said Kipps, to a great green cone.

"Ice," said the waiter.

"I'll 'ave some," said Kipps.

He seized fork and spoon and assailed the bombe. It cut rather stiffly. "Come up!" said Kipps, with concentrated bitterness, and the truncated summit of the bombe flew suddenly, travelling eastward with remarkable velocity. Flop, it went upon the floor a yard away, and for a while time seemed empty.

At the adjacent table they were laughing altogether.

Shy the rest of the bombe at them?

Flight?

At any rate, a dignified withdrawal.

"No!" said Kipps, "no more," arresting the polite attempt of the waiter to serve him with another piece. He had a vague idea he might carry off the affair as though he meant the ice to go on the floor— not liking ice, for example, and being annoyed at the badness of his dinner. He put both hands on the table, thrust back his chair, disengaged a purple slipper from his napkin, and rose. He stepped carefully over the prostrate ice, kicked the napkin under the table, thrust his hands deep into his pockets, and marched out—shaking the dust of the place as it were from his feet. He left behind him a melting fragment of ice upon the floor, his gibus hat, warm and compressed in his chair, and, in addition, every social ambition he had ever entertained in the world.

Kipps went back to Folkestone in time for the Anagram Tea. But you must not imagine that the change of heart that came to him in the dining-room of the Royal Grand Hotel involved any change of attitude towards this promised social and intellectual treat. He went back because the Royal Grand was too much for him.

Outwardly calm, or at most a little flushed and ruffled, inwardly Kipps was a horrible, tormented battleground of scruples, doubts, shames, and self-assertions during those days of silent, desperate grappling with the big hotel. He did not intend the monstrosity should beat him without a struggle; but at last he had sullenly to admit himself overcome. The odds were terrific. On the one hand himself—with, among other things, only one pair of boots; on the other a vast wilderness of rooms, covering several acres, and with over a thousand people, staff and visitors, all chiefly occupied in looking queerly at Kipps, in laughing at him behind his back, in watching for difficult corners at which to confront and perplex him and inflict humiliations upon him. For example, the hotel scored over its electric light. After the dinner the chambermaid, a hard, unsympathetic young woman with a superior manner, was summoned by a bell Kipps had rung under the impression the button was the electric-light switch. "Look 'ere," said Kipps, rubbing a shin that had suffered during his search in the dark, "why aren't there any candles or matches?" The hotel explained and scored heavily.

"It isn't everyone is up to these things," said Kipps.

"No, it isn't," said the chambermaid with ill-concealed scorn, and slammed the door at him.

"S'pose I ought to have tipped her," said Kipps.

After that Kipps cleaned his boots with a pocket-handkerchief and went for a long walk, and got home in a hansom; but the hotel scored again by his not putting out his boots, and so having to clean them again in the morning. The hotel also snubbed him by bringing him hot water when he was fully dressed and looking surprised at his collar, but he got a breakfast, I must admit, with scarcely any difficulty.

After that the hotel scored heavily by the fact that there are twenty-four hours in the day and Kipps had nothing to do in any of them. He was a little footsore from his previous day's pedestrianism, and he could make up his mind for no long excursions. He flitted in and out of the hotel several times, and it was the polite porter who touched his hat every time that first set Kipps tipping.

"What 'e wants is a tip," said Kipps.

So at the next opportunity he gave the man an unexpected shilling, and, having once put his hand in his pocket, there was no reason why he should not go on. He bought a newspaper at the bookstall and tipped the boy the rest of the shilling, and then went up by the lift and tipped the man sixpence, leaving his newspaper inadvertently in the lift. He met his chambermaid in the passage and gave her half a crown. He resolved to demonstrate his position to the entire establishment in this way. He didn't like the place; he disapproved of it politically, socially, morally; but he resolved no taint of meanness should disfigure his sojourn in its luxurious halls. He went down by the lift (tipping again), and, being accosted by a waiter with his gibus, tipped the finder half a crown. He had a vague sense that he was making a flank movement upon the hotel and buying over its staff. They would regard him as a "character"; they would get to like him. He found his stock of small silver diminishing and replenished it at a desk in the hall. He tipped a man in bottle green, who looked like the man who had shown him his room the day before; and then he saw a visitor eyeing him, and doubted whether he was in this instance doing right. Finally he went out and took chance buses to their destinations, and wandered a little in remote wonderful suburbs, and returned. He lunched at a chop-house in Islington, and found himself back in the Royal Grand, now unmistakably footsore and London-weary, about three. He was attracted to the drawing-room by a neat placard about afternoon tea.

It occurred to him that the campaign of tipping upon which he had embarked was, perhaps after all, a mistake. He was confirmed in this by observing that the hotel officials were watching him, not respectfully, but with a sort of amused wonder, as if to see whom he would tip next. However, if he backed out now, they would think him an awful fool. Everyone wasn't so rich as he was. It was his way to tip. Still—

He grew more certain the hotel had scored again.

He pretended to be lost in thought, and so drifted by, and having put hat and umbrella in the cloakroom, went into the drawing-room for afternoon tea.

There he did get what for a time he held to be a point in his favour. The room was large and quiet at first, and he sat back restfully until it occurred to him that his attitude brought his extremely dusty boots too prominently into the light, so instead he sat up, and then people of the upper and upper middle classes began to come and group themselves about him and have tea likewise, and so revive the class animosities of the previous day.

Presently a fluffy fair-haired lady came into prominent existence a few yards away. She was talking to a respectful low-voiced clergyman, whom she was possibly entertaining at tea. "No," she said; "dear Lady Jane wouldn't like that!"

"Mumble, mumble, mumble," from the clergyman.

"Poor dear Lady Jane was always so sensitive," the voice of the lady sang out clear and emphatic.

A fat, hairless, important-looking man joined this group, took a chair and planted it firmly with its back in the face of Kipps, a thing that offended Kipps, mightily. "Are you telling him," gurgled the fat, hairless man, "about dear Lady Jane's affliction?" A young couple, lady brilliantly attired, and the man in a magnificently cut frock-coat, arranged themselves to the right, also with an air of exclusion towards Kipps. "I've told him," said the gentleman in a flat abundant voice. "My!" said the young lady with an American smile. No doubt they all thought Kipps was out of it. A great desire to assert himself in some way surged up in his heart. He felt he would like to cut in on the conversation in some dramatic way. A monologue, something in the manner of Masterman? At any rate, abandoning that as impossible, he would like to appear self-centred and at ease. His eye, wandering over the black surfaces of a noble architectural mass close by, discovered a slot and an enamelled plaque of directions.

It was some sort of musical box!

It occurred to Kipps that he would like some music, that to inaugurate some would show him a man of taste and at his ease at the same time. He rose, read over a list of tunes, selected one haphazard, pressed his sixpence—it was sixpence!—home, and prepared for a confidential refined little melody.

Considering the high social tone of the Royal Grand, it was really a very loud instrument indeed. It gave vent to three deafening brays, and so burst the dam of silence that had long pent it in. It seemed to be chiefly full of the great-uncles of trumpets, megalo-trombones, and railway brakes. It made sounds like shunting trains. It did not so much begin as blow up your counterscarp and rush forward to storm under cover of melodious shrapnel. It had not so much an air as a *ricochette*. The music had in short the inimitable quality of Sousa. It swept down upon the friend of Lady Jane and carried away something socially striking into the eternal night of the unheard; the American girl to the left of it was borne off shrieking. "HIGH cockalorum Tootletootle tootle loo. HIGH cockalorum tootle loo. BUMP, bump, bump—BUMP," —Native American music, full of native American notes, full of the spirit of western college yells and election howls, joyous exorbitant music from the gigantic nursery of the Future, bearing the hearer along upon its torrential succession of sounds, as if he was in a cask on Niagara. Whiroo! Yah, Have at you! The Strenuous Life! Yaha! Stop! A Reprieve! A Reprieve! No! Bang! Bump!

Everybody looked round, conversation ceased and gave place to gestures.

The friend of Lady Jane became terribly agitated.

"Can't it be stopped?" she vociferated, pointing a gloved finger and saying something to the waiter about "that dreadful young man."

"Ought not to be working," said the clerical friend of Lady Jane.

The waiter shook his head at the fat, hairless gentleman.

People began to move away. Kipps leant back luxuriously, and then tapped with a half-crown to pay.

He paid, tipped like a gentleman, rose with an easy gesture, and strolled towards the door. His retreat evidently completed the indignation of the friend of Lady Jane, and from the door he could still discern her gestures as asking, "Can't it be stopped?" The music followed him into the passage and pursued him to the lift, and only died away completely in the quiet of his own room, and afterwards from his window he saw the friend of Lady Jane and her party having their tea carried out to a little table in the court.

Certainly that was a point to him. But it was his only score; all the rest of the game lay in the hands of the upper classes and the big hotel. And presently he was doubting whether even this was really a point. It seemed a trifle vulgar, come to think it over, to interrupt people when they were talking.

He saw a clerk peering at him from the office, and suddenly it occurred to him that the place might get back at him tremendously over the bill.

They would probably take it out of him by charging pounds and pounds.

Suppose they charged more than he had?

The clerk had a particularly nasty face, just the face to take advantage of a vacillating Kipps.

He became aware of a man in a cap touching it, and produced his shilling automatically, but the strain was beginning to tell. It was a deuce and all of an expense—this tipping.

If the hotel chose to stick it on to the bill something tremendous, what was Kipps to do? Refuse to pay? Make a row?

If he did he couldn't fight all these men in bottle green. . . .

He went out about seven and walked for a long time, and dined at last upon a chop in the Euston Road; then he walked along to the Edgeware Road and sat and rested in the Metropolitan Music Hall for a time, until a trapeze performance unnerved him, and finally he came back to bed. He tipped the lift-man sixpence and wished him good night. In the silent watches of the night he reviewed the tale of the day's tipping, went over the horrors of the previous night's dinner, and heard again the triumphant bray of the harmonicon devil released from its long imprisonment. Everyone would be told about him tomorrow. He couldn't go on! He admitted his defeat. Never in their whole lives had any of these people seen such a Fool as he! Ugh! . . .

His method of announcing his withdrawal to the clerk was touched with bitterness.

"I'm going to get out of this," said Kipps, blowing windily. "Let's see what you got on my bill."

"One breakfast?" asked the clerk.

"Do I *look* as if I'd ate two?" . . .

At his departure Kipps, with a hot face, convulsive gestures, and an embittered heart, tipped everyone who did not promptly and actively resist, including an absent-minded South African diamond merchant who was waiting in the hall for his wife. He paid his cabman a four-shilling piece at Charing Cross, having no smaller change, and wished he could burn him alive. Then in a sudden reaction of economy he refused the proffered help of a porter, and carried his bag quite violently to the train.

[From *Kipps*]

Archibald Marshall

The Birdikin Family is too delicate and low in key to be called a burlesque. Archibald Marshall imitates the style of an early nineteenth-century moral tale. He hardly exaggerates upon his originals, but by the mere placing of his epithets he reveals the cruelty of the early Victorian caste system. This is social criticism; it is also art.

A WALK WITH PAPA

"Come, children," said Mrs. Birdikin, entering the breakfast-parlour where the four young Birdikins were plying their tasks under the supervision of Miss Smith, "your good Papa is now able to resume walking exercise and wishes that you should all accompany him on this fine morning, if Miss Smith will kindly consent to release you half an hour earlier than customary."

Miss Smith, who occupied the position of governess at Byron Grove, the country seat of Mr. Birdikin, was a woman of decent but not lofty parentage, whom her employers treated almost as they would have done if her *birth* had been equal to her *integrity*. This toleration, which so well became persons of a superior station, was exhibited on this occasion by Mrs. Birdikin's asking *permission* of Miss Smith to cut short the hours devoted to study instead of issuing a *command*. Miss Smith was deeply conscious of the condescension thus displayed and replied in a respectful tone, "Indeed, ma'am, the advantages that my little charges will gain from the converse of my esteemed employer, while engaging in the healthful exercise of perambulation, would be beyond my powers to impart."

Mrs. Birdikin inclined her head in token of her appreciation of the propriety of Miss Smith's utterance and said, "Then go at once to your rooms, children, and prepare yourselves for the treat in store for you."

The four children trooped obediently out of the room, the two boys, Charles and Henry, politely making way for their sisters, Fanny and Clara; for, although their superiors in age, they had been taught to give place to the *weaker sex,* and invariably did so when either of their parents were by.

It did not take the little girls long to array themselves in their bonnets and tippets, nor their brothers to prepare themselves in a suitable manner for the excursion. When they were assembled in the hall Mr. Birdikin made his appearance from the library. John, the footman, who was in attendance, handed him his hat, gloves, and walking-cane, and the condescending word of thanks with which he was rewarded sent him back to the domestic quarters of the house in a thankful spirit at having taken service with so excellent a master, who seldom raised his hand in anger against a menial and had never been known to enforce his instructions by an *oath.* Small wonder then that Mr. Birdikin received willing service from those in his employ, who were assured of a comfortable home and such moral instruction as was suited to those of an inferior order, unless some serious delinquency should bring about their dismissal or illness render them no longer capable of performing the duties of their station.

It was Mr. Birdikin's custom in these delightful walks with his children to question them upon the course of study they were pursuing with Miss Smith and to distribute commendation or censure according as they acquitted themselves well or ill in his examination. But he was well aware that allowance must be made for the natural *exuberance* of young children, and that you could not expect *old* heads to grow on *young* shoulders. He was thus always ready to listen to *their* remarks as long as they were addressed to him in a proper and respectful manner.

"I am rejoiced, dear Papa," said Charles, a bright-faced lad of some eleven summers, whose natural high spirits caused him to leap and caper as they walked down the handsome carriage-drive, "that you are now able to use both your *feet.* At the same time I should prefer to keep one of my own feet on a rest rather than engage in uncongenial occupations."

"So would not I," said Henry, whose more thoughtful disposition seemed to mark him out even at that early age for the clerical profession, in which his maternal uncle held Episcopal office and had preferments of considerable emolument in his bestowal, to one of which Henry might well look forward. "To my mind a life of benevolent activity is preferable to one of idleness, and I would invite our dear Papa to judge between us in this matter."

"I have no hesitation, my dear Henry, in pronouncing in your favour," said Mr. Birdikin, "and if your brother will consent to use the *two* members of which he has so lightly expressed himself anxious to pretermit the use of *one,* instead of bounding about in what I can only refer to as a *caprine* manner, I will endeavour—"

'*I am rejoiced, dear Papa, that you are now able to use both your feet*'

Here he was interrupted by Fanny, a child of a somewhat sullen and intractable disposition, who inquired, "Is it true, Papa, that an attack of gout is brought on by over-indulgence in the pleasures of the table?"

"And pray where, Fanny," inquired Mr. Birdikin in his turn, "did you acquire an idea so unsuited to the intelligence of one of your years?"

His countenance displayed signs which Clara, who was known in the family as the Little Peacemaker, interpreted as indicative of annoyance. Anxious that the harmony of the expedition should be preserved, she hastened to say, "My sister inquired of Dr. Affable the cause of your ailment, dear Papa, and he informed her that it was *sometimes* brought on by partaking to an excessive extent of port wine; but—"

Here she was interrupted by Charles, who remarked, "When I grow to manhood I shall drink three bottles of port wine with my dinner every day."

"So shall not I," interpolated Henry, "for do we not read that wine is a mocker, strong drink is raging?"

This apposite remark caused Mr. Birdikin's brow to relax. "I am glad," he said, "that at least *one* of my children has learned to express himself with propriety on a question somewhat beyond childish intelligence. Our good Dr. Affable has no doubt had experience of ill-regulated lives where *excess* has led to bodily ailments. In *my* case the malady with which I have lately been visited is the result of a possibly *over*-anxious regard to the performance of my duties and a consequent *dis*regard for my own health.

"But, come, children, let not our walk be wasted in idle discourse. You have the advantage of the instructions of a preceptress whose lack of *breeding* must not blind you to the admirable use she has made of her *understanding*. You, Charles, subdue your spirits to a reasonable degree of quietude and inform me to what subject of study your attention was directed this morning."

Charles, thus admonished, put a curb upon his tendency to leap and curvet and replied with propriety that he and his brother and sisters had been instructed in the use of the Globes. This gave Mr. Birdikin the opportunity of putting various questions suited to the intelligence of his young hearers and administering correction and reproof in such a way that the limits of the walk were attained with profit to *all* and enjoyment to *some*.

Fanny, however, whose answers to her father's questions had betrayed a lack of application to the subject in hand that had brought her within measurable degree of a threat of punishment, did not show that spirit of gratitude for the condescension of a kind parent in devoting himself to the instruction and entertainment of his children that could have been wished. As she and Clara were removing their outer garments upon their return from the expedition, Clara said to her, "Are we not fortunate, sister, in the possession of a Papa who, with a mind so well stocked with knowledge, is anxious to put it at the disposal of his children?"

"I apprehend," replied Fanny, "that my Papa does not know so much as he thinks he does."

"Disrespectful child," ejaculated Clara, the blush of indignation mantling her cheek, "to speak thus of a kind and indulgent parent! Fie! For shame!"

"Fie to you!" replied the unrepentant Fanny.

And there we must leave our young friends for the present.

[From *The Birdikin Family*]

John Galsworthy

This is an example of introspective, or revelatory, humor. Galsworthy was not particularly known as a humorist, and, in fact, most of the Satires, *from which this item is taken, is not very funny. But* The Writer *is wonderful, if you can bear the steady drip of heart's blood.*

THE WRITER

Every morning when he awoke his first thought was: How am I? For it was extremely important that he should be well, seeing that when he was not well he could neither produce what he knew he ought, nor contemplate that lack of production with equanimity. Having discovered that he did not ache anywhere, he would say to his wife: "Are you all right?" and, while she was answering, he would think: "Yes—if I make that last chapter pass subjectively through Blank's personality, then I had better—" and so on. Not having heard whether his wife were all right, he would get out of bed and do that which he facetiously called "abdominable cult," for it was necessary that he should digest his food and preserve his figure, and while he was doing it he would partly think: "I am doing this well," and partly he would think: "That fellow in the *Parnassus* is quite wrong—he simply doesn't see—" And pausing for a moment with nothing on, and his toes level with the top of a chest of drawers, he would say to his wife: "What I think about that *Parnassus* fellow is that he doesn't grasp the fact that my books—" And he would not fail to hear her answer warmly: "Of course he doesn't; he's a perfect idiot." He would then shave. This was his most creative moment, and he would soon cut himself and utter a little groan, for it would be needful now to find his special cotton wool and stop the bleeding, which was a paltry business and not favourable to the flight of genius. And if his wife, taking advantage of the incident, said something which she had long been waiting to say, he would answer, wondering a little what it was she had said, and thinking: "There it is, I get no time for steady thought."

Having finished shaving he would bathe, and a philosophical conclusion would almost invariably come to him just before he douched himself with cold—so that he would pause, and call out through the door: "You know, I think the supreme principle—" And while his wife was answering, he would resume the drowning of her words, having fortunately remembered just in time that his circulation would suffer if he did not douse himself with cold while he was still warm. He would dry himself, dreamily developing that theory of the universe and imparting it to his wife in sentences that seldom had an end, so that it was not necessary for her to answer them. While dressing he would stray a little, thinking: "Why can't I concentrate myself on my work? it's awful!" And if he had by any chance a button off, he would present himself rather unwillingly, feeling that it was a waste of his time. Watching her frown from sheer self-effacement over her button-sewing, he would think: "She is wonderful! How can she put up with doing things for me all day long?" And he would fidget a little, feeling in his bones that the postman had already come.

He went down always thinking: "Oh, hang it! this infernal post taking up all my time!" And as he neared the breakfast-room, he would quicken his pace; seeing a large pile of letters on the table, he would say automatically: "Curse!" and his eyes would brighten. If— as seldom happened—there were not a green-coloured wrapper enclosing mentions of him in the press, he would murmur: "Thank God!" and his face would fall.

It was his custom to eat feverishly, walking a good deal and reading about himself, and when his wife tried to bring him to a sense of his disorder he would tighten his lips without a word and think: "I have a good deal of self-control."

He seldom commenced work before eleven, for, though he always intended to, he found it practically impossible not to dictate to his wife things about himself, such as how he could not lecture here; or where he had been born; or how much he would take for this; and why he would not consider that; together with those letters which began:

My Dear ——,
Thanks tremendously for your letter about my book, and its valuable criticism. Of course, I think you are quite wrong.... You don't seem to have grasped.... In fact, I don't think you ever quite do me justice....
Yours affectionately,

When his wife had copied those that might be valuable after he was dead, he would stamp the envelopes and, exclaiming: "Nearly eleven—my God!" would go somewhere where they think.

It was during those hours when he sat in a certain chair with a pen in his hand that he was able to rest from thought about himself; save, indeed, in those moments, not too frequent, when he could not help reflecting: "That's a fine page—I have seldom written anything better"; or in those moments, too frequent, when he sighed deeply and thought: "I am not the man I was." About half past one, he would get up, with the pages in his hand, and, seeking out his wife, would give them to her to read, remarking: "Here's the wretched stuff—no good at all"; and, taking a position where he thought she could not see him, would do such things as did not prevent his knowing what effect the pages made on her. If the effect were good he would often feel how wonderful she was; if it were not good he had at once a chilly sensation in the pit of his stomach, and ate very little lunch.

When, in the afternoons, he took his walks abroad, he passed great quantities of things and people without noticing, because he was thinking deeply on such questions as whether he were more of an observer or more of an imaginative artist; whether he were properly appreciated in Germany; and particularly whether one were not in danger of thinking too much about oneself. But every now and then he would stop and say to himself: "I really must see more of life, I really must take in more fuel"; and he would passionately fix his eyes on a cloud, or a flower, or a man walking, and there would instantly come into his mind the thought: "I have written twenty books—ten more will make thirty—that cloud is grey"; or: "That fellow X—— is jealous of me! This flower is blue"; or: "This man is walking very— very— D——n the *Morning Muff,* it always runs me down!" And he would have a sort of sore, beaten feeling, knowing that he had not observed those things as accurately as he would have wished to.

During these excursions, too, he would often reflect impersonally upon matters of the day, large questions, of art, public policy, and the human soul; and would almost instantly find that he had always thought this or that; and at once see the necessity for putting his conclusion forward in his book or in the press, phrasing it, of course, in a way that no one else could; and there would start up before him little bits of newspaper with these words on them: "No one, perhaps, save Mr. ——, could have so ably set forth the case for Baluchistan"; or,

"In the *Daily Miracle* there is a noble letter from that eminent writer, Mr. ——, pleading against the hyper-spiritualism of our age."

Very often he would say to himself, as he walked with eyes fixed on things that he did not see: "This existence is not healthy. I really must get away and take a complete holiday, and not think at all about my work; I am getting too self-centered." And he would go home and say to his wife: "Let's go to Sicily, or Spain, or somewhere. Let's get away from all this, and just live." And when she answered: "How jolly!" he would repeat, a little absently: "How jolly!" considering what would be the best arrangement for forwarding his letters. And if, as sometimes happened, they *did* go, he would spend almost a whole morning living, and thinking how jolly it was to be away from everything; but towards the afternoon he would feel a sensation as though he were a sofa that had been sat on too much, a sort of subsidence very deep within him. This would be followed in the evening by a disinclination to live; and that feeling would grow until on the third day he received his letters, together with a green-coloured wrapper enclosing some mentions of himself, and he would say: "Those fellows—no getting away from them!" and feel irresistibly impelled to sit down. Having done so he would take up his pen, not writing anything, indeed—because of the determination to "live," as yet not quite extinct—but comparatively easy in his mind. On the following day he would say to his wife: "I believe I can work here." And she would answer, smiling: "That's splendid"; and he would think: "She's wonderful!" and begin to write.

On other occasions, while walking the streets or about the countryside, he would suddenly be appalled at his own ignorance, and would say to himself: "I know simply nothing—I must read." And going home he would dictate to his wife the names of a number of books to be procured from the library. When they arrived he would look at them a little gravely and think: "By Jove! Have I got to read those?" and the same evening he would take one up. He would not, however, get beyond the fourth page, if it were a novel, before he would say: "Muck! He can't write!" and would feel absolutely stimulated to take up his own pen and write something that was worth reading. Sometimes, on the other hand, he would put the novel down after the third page, exclaiming: "By Jove! He can write!" And there would rise within him such a sense of dejection at his own inferiority that he would feel simply compelled to try to see whether he really was inferior.

But if the book were not a novel he sometimes finished the first chapter before one of two feelings came over him: Either that what he had just read was what he had himself long thought—that, of course, would be when the book was a good one; or that what he had just read was not true, or at all events debatable. In each of these events he found it impossible to go on reading, but would remark to his wife: "This fellow says what I've always said"; or, "This fellow says so and so, now I say—" and he would argue the matter with her, taking both sides of the question, so as to save her all unnecessary speech.

There were times when he felt that he absolutely must hear music, and he would enter the concert-hall with his wife in the pleasurable certainty that he was going to lose himself. Towards the middle of the second number, especially if it happened to be music that he liked, he would begin to nod; and presently, on waking up, would get a feeling that he really was an artist. From that moment on he was conscious of certain noises being made somewhere in his neighbourhood causing a titillation of his nerves favourable to deep and earnest thoughts about his work. On going out his wife would ask him: "Wasn't the Mozart lovely?" or, "How did you like the Strauss?" and he would answer: "Rather!" wondering a little which was which; or he would look at her out of the corner of his eye and glance secretly at the programme to see whether he had really heard them, and which Strauss it might be.

He was extremely averse to being interviewed, or photographed, and all that sort of publicity, and only made exceptions in most cases because his wife would say to him: "Oh! I think you ought"; or because he could not bear to refuse anybody anything; together, perhaps, with a sort of latent dislike of waste, deep down in his soul. When he saw the results he never failed to ejaculate: "Never again! No, really—never again! The whole thing is wrong and stupid!" And he would order a few copies.

For he dreaded nothing so much as the thought that he might become an egoist, and, knowing the dangers of his profession, fought continually against it. Often he would complain to his wife: "I don't think of you enough." And she would smile and say: "Don't you?" And he would feel better, having confessed his soul. Sometimes for an hour at a time he would make really heroic efforts not to answer her before having really grasped what she had said; and to check a tendency, that he sometimes feared was growing on him, to say: "What?" whether he had heard or no. In truth, he was not (as he often said) constitutionally given to small talk. Conversation that did not promise a chance of dialectic victory was hardly to his liking; so that he felt bound in sincerity to eschew it, which sometimes caused him to sit silent for "quite a while," as the Americans have phrased it. But once committed to an argument, he found it difficult to leave off, having a natural, if somewhat sacred, belief in his own convictions.

His attitude to his creations was, perhaps, peculiar. He either did not mention them, or touched on them if absolutely obliged, with a light and somewhat disparaging tongue; this did not, indeed, come from any real distrust of them, but rather from a superstitious feeling that one must not tempt Providence in the solemn things of life. If other people touched on them in the same way, he had, not unnaturally, a feeling of real pain, such as comes to a man when he sees an instance of cruelty or injustice. And, though something always told him that it was neither wise nor dignified to notice outrages of this order, he would mutter to his wife: "Well, I suppose it *is* true—I can't write"; feeling, perhaps, that—if *he* could not with decency notice such injuries, she might. And, indeed, she did, using warmer words than even he felt justified, which was soothing.

After tea it was his habit to sit down a second time, pen in hand; not infrequently he would spend those hours divided between the feeling that it was his duty to write something and the feeling that it was his duty not to write anything if he had nothing to say; and he generally wrote a good deal; for deep down he was convinced that if he did not write he would gradually fade away till there would be nothing left for him to read and think about, and, though he was often tempted to believe and even to tell his wife that fame was an unworthy thing, he always deferred that pleasure, afraid, perhaps, of too much happiness.

In regard to the society of his fellows he liked almost anybody, though a little impatient with those, especially authors, who took themselves too seriously; and there were just one or two that he really could not stand, they were so obviously full of jealousy, a passion of which he was naturally intolerant and had, of course, no need to indulge in. And he would speak of them with extreme dryness—nothing more, disdaining to disparage. It was, perhaps, a weakness in him that he found it difficult to accept adverse criticism as anything but an expression of that same yellow sickness; and yet there were moments when no words would adequately convey his low opinion of his own powers. At such times he would seek out his wife and confide to her his conviction that he was a poor thing, no good at all, without a thought in his head; and while she was replying: "Rubbish! You know there's nobody to hold a candle to you," or words to that effect, he would look at her tragically, and murmur: "Ah! you're prejudiced!" Only at such supreme moments of dejection, indeed, did he feel it a pity that he had married her, seeing how much more convincing her words would have been if he had not.

He never read the papers till the evening, partly because he had not time, and partly because he so seldom found anything in them. This was not remarkable, for he turned their leaves quickly, pausing, indeed, naturally, if there were any mention of his name; and if his wife asked him whether he had read this or that he would answer: "No," surprised at the funny things that seemed to interest her.

Before going up to bed he would sit and smoke. And sometimes fancies would come to him, and sometimes none. Once in a while he would look up at the stars, and think: "What a worm I am! This wonderful Infinity! I must get more of it—more of it into my work; more of the feeling that the whole is marvellous and great, and man a little clutch of breath and dust, an atom, a straw, a nothing!"

And a sort of exaltation would seize on him, so that he knew that if only he did get that into his work, as he wished to, as he felt just then that he could, he would be the greatest writer the world had ever seen, the greatest man, almost greater than he wished to be, almost too great to be mentioned in the press, greater than Infinity itself—for would he not be Infinity's creator? And suddenly he would check himself with the thought: "I must be careful—I must be careful. If I let my brain go at this time of night, I shan't write a decent word tomorrow!"

And he would drink some milk and go to bed.

Agnes Hunt

Agnes Hunt is the head of the Derwen Cripples' Training College in Shrewsbury. Herself crippled in youth, she became a nurse, and has devoted her life to the re-education of persons afflicted like herself. She wrote her This Is My Life *to be sold for the benefit of her school. Though most of her book deals with her labors in behalf of the crippled, she tells of her family with all a nurse's frankness. Her memories of her mother make what seems to me one of the finest character sketches in literature.*

MOTHER

I was born in 1867 of early Victorian parents. My poor mother disliked children intensely; she disliked them when they were coming, during their arrival, and most intensely after they had arrived. It seems, therefore, distinctly hard lines that between the ages of twenty-one and forty she was doomed to produce eleven children. At two weeks old we were consigned to the nursery and the bottle. In after years mother told me she had tried to nurse one of my elder brothers, but the little wretch had bitten her without a moment's hesitation, and so sealed the fate of his numerous brothers and sisters....

In 1883, my mother went to a lecture at the village hall, about Australia. She returned determined to take her family there. She explained the lecturer had said that an island off the coast of Queensland could be bought quite cheaply, and that the growing of angora goats was a most paying proposition; the goats would produce milk, their flesh was as good as mutton, they could be shorn and the children's clothes made from the hair; altogether a most admirable and economical scheme....

Eight berths were booked on the R. M. S. *Merkara,* a British-India liner, and on March 11, 1884, we had orders to report to various relations living in London, preparatory to departing two days later. Amy and I were billeted on some elderly cousins, who greatly disapproved of the whole proceeding. When we got to our bedroom we found a strange collection of hideous garments of all sizes. Mother had been round to the cheapest shops she could find and regardless of fit, had bought a job lot. We were also handed some labels marked "Cabin," "Wanted on the voyage," and "Not wanted." We felt at once that the last label applied to all the new clothes. . . .

The Bay of Biscay was not kind, mother's temper most uncertain, and arrangements for sea-sickness were primitive, consisting, in fact, of one basin, usually engaged. Life had suddenly become grim and hopeless. Our ship pitched and rolled. The screw, more often out of the water than in, shook the old ship till one wondered why she held together. All portholes were shut and, as there was practically no other ventilation, the air was horrible; imagination quailed at the thought of the emigrants' quarters. We had an ancient stewardess, who abstained as much as possible from giving assistance, and mother, being of a chaste disposition, would not allow the Lascar boys to come into the cabins unless we were all fully dressed, and even then she did not like it. . . .

[The *Merkara* is grounded for three weeks in the Suez Canal.]

Thereafter we went along peaceably until we came to the Torres Straits. The weather was terribly hot, and mother's little family was sleeping on deck. Suddenly the ship struck something, and we all shot into a sitting position. The next thing was rockets and blue flares. The captain and the doctor were standing close to us. The former gloomily remarked that there were not nearly enough boats to take the emigrants ashore, to which the doctor hopefully added, "No, and there are plenty of sharks in the sea." Finally, the order was given to parade the emigrants on deck, the women aft under the head steward; the doctor, complete with revolver, attended to the men; and the purser was to look after the saloon passengers, all of whom were sleeping on deck with the exception of my mother. We were tremendously thrilled, and in consequence very hungry; and, loudly demanding ham sandwiches, we induced the purser to raid the saloon pantry. He went, but returned rather quickly, very red in the face, and said hurriedly, "Look here, I think one of you had better go below and help your mother. She seems in difficulties." Down we went, and found mother firmly stuck in the doorway of my brother's cabin. She explained that the shock had awakened her, and, by the general commotion, she guessed we were about to be wrecked on a desert island. Whilst she had no objection to a desert island plus angora goats, she strongly objected to being stranded on one with seven children and no clothes. She therefore arose hurriedly and dressed herself in as many garments as possible, hanging numerous garments belonging to her progeny around her. All went well until she came to the last cabin, which belonged to my brothers, where she acquired two overcoats, some trousers, etc., only to find that she could not get through the cabin door. After a good deal of trouble we rescued her. By that time it was discovered that we were on a sandbank, and that the tide was coming in and we should float off in an hour or so.

We arrived at Brisbane after a voyage of nearly eleven weeks. This, however, was not the last my mother was to see of the old ship. Three years later she was returning to England on a P. and O. liner, which anchored off Aden, and mother, who was in her cabin, happened to look through the porthole and saw a ship apparently steering straight for them. When she saw the name *Merkara* she fled out of the cabin and went on deck, for she felt sure the old ship had come for her. Sure enough, without a moment's hesitation, the *Merkara's* bows crashed into mother's cabin and wrecked everything in it; no other part of the ship was touched. . . .

[The family returns to England. Mother gives her aid to the Charity Organisation Society, using for her transport a donkey-cart, with a donkey that stalls in traffic.]

At the same time the C. O. S. wished to palm off on mother an elderly hunchback of unprepossessing appearance but, so they said, of unblemished reputation. As the hunchback was by no means a light-weight, and had had no experience with asses, mother decided on a pony, but added that I must find her one and that it must not cost more than £5—at that time a ridiculously low price—also it must be small enough to fit the present cart and harness.

London was scoured, and produced many and various equine monstrosities. The last one was the sort of pony that one meets in a night-mare; it had only one side to its mouth and, as Lila remarked, only one rein was necessary. In order to give the animal a really good trial we took it into Hyde Park. Unfortunately, Rotten Row was on the wrong side, and twice a solemn Bobby explained to us that we must

NOT drive on Rotten Row, only Royalty was allowed that privilege. The third time the Bobby explained that he would be obliged to take us to the police station if it occurred again. Lila looked at him with a gleam of hope in her eye, and said, "Oh! could you really do that? It would be kind. And," she added thoughtfully, "we could give the police the pony for a pet if they would accept it."

That night I told mother I was through with five-pound ponies, and unless she was prepared to give a decent price, I would not try any more. Finally, for £14, I found a nice quiet and willing little beast. Two or three days after the hunchback was installed, mother came in and said she was pleased with the pony, but, she added gloomily, "I find it impossible for me to get a fair share of the seat unless I and the hunchback sit down together." Instantly the family had a vision of mother and the driver standing up in the pony cart together, whilst mother solemnly counted, "One, two, three—sit!" ...

One day whilst I was still in bed, mother arrived in my room with a large parcel, which she triumphantly dumped on my bed, and said, "I have solved the question of keeping dry in an open pony cart. An umbrella is an impossible thing; if there is wind it turns inside out, and anyway, it totally obscures the view of one's driver." I untied the parcel, and exposed a large mackintosh cape with two holes; proudly mother pointed to the large hole and said, "My hole, and the second, my driver's. The cape is made large enough to go over the back seat, so I shall not have to sit, as at present, in a pool of water." Vainly I tried to repress my giggles as in a strangled voice I said, "Won't you look rather odd, something like the Siamese twins?" "Nonsense," said my mother, undaunted, "no one could mistake my driver for my twin." The next day it was raining cats and dogs, and I put my head out of the window to see the start, a sight I shall never forget. The poor hunchback looked terribly self-conscious, but my mother's face was serene and calm. Mother returned about tea time and came into my room, looking somewhat coy; she told me the idea was very good, but, on reaching the C. O. S. office, she got out, entirely forgetting that she was attached to the driver, and only discovered the fact by the choking sounds which issued from the wretched Smith, who, once free from the cape, sternly refused to put his head into the noose again.

[In 1899 Agnes Hunt and her mother visit Tom in California.]

I don't think mother was really sorry to leave, but she said she must see something of America, and that we would break the journey at Utah, see the Great Salt Lake, go on to Chicago and Boston, and finally spend a week in New York. Personally, I hoped that the money would hold out, and that I should not have to pack and unpack mother's clothes too often. The first night on the train I had an awful time, as I had to share a bunk with mother, who insisted on the window being open, and all her clothes blew out. The black guard put his head through the curtains and woke mother up. She was furious, and said she would prefer to lose all her clothes than to be awakened by a horrid black man. I was relieved when we got to Utah.

The following morning mother and I sallied forth to view the Great Salt Lake. Nothing would induce her to ask the way; she said it was the Great Salt Lake City, and it would be impossible, therefore, to avoid finding the Great Salt Lake. After we had trudged many miles in many directions, we met a postman, and I asked mother if it would not be as well to ask him, but she replied, "Nonsense! There can be no difficulty in finding the way." I muttered that we had already been walking for an hour and seemed no nearer than when we started. Mother said I could do as I liked, but that she was going on. On enquiries, the postman said that we must go to such and such a station, that the Great Salt Lake was two hours away by train, and that there were only two trains in the day. I rushed after mother and told her, but all she said was that the postman was probably new to his round, and was not quite right in the head, and reiterated the maddening refrain that this was the Great Salt Lake City, and that, therefore, the aforesaid Great Salt Lake must be somewhere close. "Two hours by train indeed! Nonsense!" So we went on, but I was frankly getting to the end of my tether, and said, "Here's a big shop which must have been here long enough to know the whereabouts of this horrible lake." I stumped in, only to be told the same thing. The shopkeeper added that if we hurried we should just catch the 12:10 train. Mother was extremely annoyed, and explained what she thought of Americans in general and Mormons in particular, and decided she would have disliked to have married any of them. After two hours' jolting in a little train, we arrived. Mother wished to bathe in the lake, as she had been told that it was so salt that you could not possibly sink, but as she was unlikely to be able to hire a bathing dress to suit her portly figure I had been lugging her own vast serge suit round with me. The guard of the train told mother it was too early in the year to bathe, and that we must catch the train back, which was the last one in the day. He said a bell was rung ten minutes before the train started, and that we had about one hour and a half to see the sights, but added that the season did not begin for another month so there was not much to see.

Mother and I stood and gloomily meditated on a large lake to which there was apparently no access except down a long step-ladder. A number of men were working on this place, preparing it for the season; we agreed that the only place it reminded us of was Margate just before a Bank Holiday. Mother wandered about in a very much disgruntled frame of mind; she felt that the Great Salt Lake had let her down badly. Suddenly she espied a long ladder leading straight down into the lake, which did not look quite so steep, and had a shelf at the bottom. She said if she could get down that ladder she could at least put her feet in the lake. I firmly refused to go with her, and asked what would happen if she slipped and tumbled in. She replied it would not matter as you could not sink! Very slowly and carefully she went down the ladder, and finally sat upon the shelf, took off her shoes and stockings, and put her feet into the water, and at the same moment the bell rang! I shouted down to mother that she must put her stockings on again quickly, as it was some way to the train and we had not much time. Alas! She had forgotten her feet would want drying, and, after frantic efforts to wipe them with a handkerchief, she finally put on her shoes without any stockings, and called up to me to know if I thought any one would notice! Luckily, mother's skirts were long, but, even so, those were not the days when even young girls walked bare-legged, let alone aged and respectable ladies. Mother was cross with me because I could only giggle. She said it was no laughing matter, and what did I think the hotel people would say? We just managed to catch the train. Mother coyly tucked her feet under the seat and hoped for the best.

In due course we visited Chicago, Boston, and ended up in New York, where we went to the Zoo. We found a placard over the home of one of the elephants with a warning to the public not to feed this particular beast as it "spat." Mother said she had never heard such nonsense in her life, that it probably used to be where the llamas were kept, and that the notice had never been removed. She thereupon gave the animal a large bun. I made myself scarce, not feeling so sure about the llama idea. Mother stayed quite close, gazing fondly at the elephant, who, having well chewed the bun, thoughtfully returned it all over her.

We left New York and duly arrived in England without further adventures, and my wanderings over the globe ceased forever....

Early in March, 1914, I was hurriedly summoned by the housemaid to my mother's bedroom. I found her lying on the floor, where she had been for nearly two hours. When she saw me, she said, calmly, "I have been expecting this for seven years. Your grandfather had a stroke when he was seventy, I am now seventy-seven, so I'm luckier than he was." She grudgingly supposed Dr. Urwick would have to be sent for, but added that I had better warn him that he need not order a light diet, as there was no logical connection between her stomach, which had always been a good servant, and a stroke. Poor Dr. Urwick vainly tried to explain that for the next few days mother ought not to eat a great deal, and that she was not to touch meat or rich sauces. He suggested a little steamed fish. "Steamed fish!" exclaimed mother when he had gone. "Tush! Tell Aldis (our cook) that I will have fried fish with Hollandaise sauce for my luncheon, and beefsteak pudding for dinner followed by an omelette. And," she added firmly, "you need not think that just because I have a stroke, you are going to be allowed to order me about as your cousin, Jenny, does my poor sister, Annie."

Mother's right arm and leg were affected but, in a comparatively short time, she recovered the use of her arm. Her leg was always paralysed, though she managed to walk from room to room with the help of two sticks. For indomitable pluck I think in all my experience my mother stands supreme. She said to me one day, "Prop this wretched wheeled chair against the wall, and give me your arm. I am going to walk!" I began to expostulate, but she stopped me by replying that she had done as she liked all her life, and would certainly do so now. Leaning heavily on me, she took one step, and we both fell down together. As we lay on the floor, mother said placidly that it was all right as she now knew she could not walk, but, she added with some annoyance, "I thought you were supposed to be a trained nurse."

[From *This Is My Life*]

E. F. Benson

*The humor of this bit seems to lie wholly in the subjects, whom
the artist portrays with scrupulous candor. We think we are amused
by the Cambridge Dons, and not by E. F. Benson. This is excellent
art.*

CAMBRIDGE DONS

Then there was Mr. J. E. Nixon: though he was of the earlier day
and held a life-fellowship, he was no recluse but wildly sociable. He
had realised that the old order was changing and had enthusiastically
gone out to meet the new. He was Dean of the College, he was lecturer in Latin, and for sheer experimentalism he was further ahead
in the van of progress than the most extravagant of modern pioneers,
and had more new notions every day than most people have in a lifetime. He held glee-meetings once a week after Hall, at which he sang
Victorian catches and madrigals arranged for male voices. Dr. Ford,
the present Dean of York, sat by his elbow, and with him sang the
tenor part, while Nixon beat time (like my mother at Lincoln) with a
paper-knife. Faster and faster under the intoxication of the music rang
out our melodies, until the paper-knife flew from his hand, like Ex-
calibur, and crashed into the fender. Between the songs he handed
round hot buttered buns, anchovy-toast, Borneo cigars and Tintara
wine. In person he was small: a short honey-coloured beard framed his
chin, he had one glass eye, and only one hand: in place of the other he
had a tight black kid glove (I think pneumatic, for it sometimes
seemed to be deflated) which was attached to his wrist, and protruded
from the sleeve of his tail-coat. But these physical deficiencies were no
handicap to his activity: rather, they seemed to stimulate it, as if he
was gallantly bent on showing how much could be done with how
little. He rode a tricycle intrepidly about the traffic-crowded streets of
Cambridge, he played lawn tennis on fine summer afternoons in the
Fellows' Gardens, taking down there a small black bag containing
tennis-balls and sealing-wax, and pieces of string (for there was no
telling whether some emergency would not arise when string or seal-

ing-wax would be urgently required) and Borneo cigars. When he served he lodged a ball in the crook of his arm and by some unique jerk of his body, tossed it into the air and gave it a savage underhand blow. Everything he did was performed at top speed, and he generally dropped something. His mind whirled about incessantly in a maelstrom of new dodges for counting the attendance of the undergraduates in chapel, for registering votes at Fellows' meetings, for insuring regular supplies of toilet paper in such places as the dons needed them, or for ascertaining the speed of the train in which he was travelling. He was also (God knows how or why) a Gresham lecturer in London, and I once went up from Cambridge in order to attend one of these discourses. The subject was either "Poetry in Rhetoric" or "Rhetoric in Poetry," but the course of the lecture did not make it clear which it was, and there has been complete confusion in my mind about it ever since. On Sunday in May week at Cambridge, there was always an immense crush to get into King's Chapel for afternoon service, and in preparation for this, Nixon printed a small leaflet "On the Management of Large Crowds," which he distributed to the vergers, so that they should know what to do. The crowd this year was more unwieldy than ever, and Nixon popped out of the organ-loft where he had been observing the management of it, and cried in a lamentable voice, "If there is any more shoving, there will be no Divine Service at all." As a teacher of Latin prose he was chiefly remarkable for correcting the exercises shown up to him, partly in red and partly in purple ink. Red ink indicated grammatical errors, purple ink errors of construction, or something of the sort. But he was not very clear about it himself, and he could not always read what he had written, and sometimes he had evidently dipped his pen first in red ink and then in purple so that there was no clue to the nature of the correction, for it was of a rich lake tone, and denoted neither grammar nor construction. . . . I do not pretend to reproduce these details with literal accuracy, but I will vouch for their impressionistic truth. The world, to Mr. Nixon, consisted of Latin prose, lawn tennis and glee-singing, and contained besides numbers of problems to which he sought solution: how to turn envelopes inside out and use them again, how to cut pencils without blackening the forefinger, how to stop a draught from an ill-fitting window-sash. Each of these was as bright as a new pin, and he never succeeded in picking any of them up.

But the really outstanding figure of that time not among the dons of King's only, but of the whole of Cambridge, was Oscar Browning: he would have been notorious and absurd and remarkable anywhere, and if he had ever succeeded in getting into Parliament, he must have made a mark of some unusual kind there, as surely as he made it everywhere else. He was a tragic instance of such stupid jokes as Nature plays when, after she has formed by means of cosmic pressures and secular incandescences, some noble gem, she proceeds with a silly giggle to plant a fatal flaw in the very heart of it. He was a genius flawed by abysmal fatuity. No one had finer gifts than he, he could think on large lines, he could strike out great ideas, he had wit, he had the power of planning largely and constructively, he had courage and a high scorn of ridicule, it was impossible to come into contact with him without being conscious of great intellectual force. But it was impossible not to be aware that he was a buffoon. As an Eton master, before he came to take up his fellowship again and reside at King's, he had been the first to grasp the fact that boys had minds, and that public-school education should not merely consist of loading those minds with irrelevant knowledge about Greek particles, but of opening them to the reception of ideas, and of teaching them how to think. His colleagues of that day looked with traditional suspicion on such crazy notions, and instantly the flaw began to manifest itself, for he always took any opposition to his ideas as a personal attack, and instead of defending them, defended himself. He was immensely liked by his house and his pupils, he treated them with the warmest friendliness, he had Sunday concerts for them, he had social gatherings in which, without the least encouragement to priggishness, he interested them in topics of history and politics. But with a fatal silliness he made pets of those who were handsome and attractive, and the head master, Dr. Hornby, who looked with the darkest suspicion on everything he did, took advantage of a technical breach which he had committed in the school rules concerning the number of boys in his house, and dismissed him. He then took up residence at King's as a life-fellow, and became a unique institution. He was appointed a lecturer in history: probably there was no epoch on which he was not prepared to discourse without any preparation. He was very inaccurate, for he never was a scholar, nor took the trouble to learn anything thoroughly, but he had the superlative gift as a teacher of being interesting. Then, just as at Eton he had made social gatherings for his boys, so at Cambridge he opened his rooms every Sunday evening, to anybody who cared to come. The idea was excellent, for there poured into King's, still rather a close corporation, dons and undergraduates and general intelligentsia from other colleges. There were members of that mystic and elevated society called the Apostles who were supposed in their lighter moments to chat about Determinism: there were sporting gents from the Athenæum, which, in spite of its name, had nothing whatever to do with learning, there were lights from the University Musical Society. For these there was special provision, for O.B. had four instruments of the nature of harmoniums, popularly known as Obeophones, possessed of a pleasant buzzing tone, remotely resembling that of stringed instruments, and vividly that of combs wrapped in toilet paper. They were of different compasses, one had the compass of a 'cello, another of a viola, two others, one of an inconceivable shrillness, did duty for violins, and the quartettes of Mozart and Beethoven rent the air. But then that fatuous egotism came in: O.B. found the slow movement rather tedious, and said, "Ha, ha, isn't it awfully jolly? Let's stop." So instead he went to the piano and bellowed "Funiculi, funicula," or collected a group round him and gave them a curious pink liqueur tasting of furniture polish, and told them about the Empress of Austria's visit to Maloja, when, dressed like a Roman Emperor and attended by four youthful lictors, he went out to welcome her, and made her a speech in Latin. His snobbishness was of a really remarkable order: it was impossible not to respect a quality of such fire and purity, for, although already waddling with obesity, he took to playing hockey simply for the pleasure of being wiped over the shins by H.R.H. Prince Edward of Wales, when he was an undergraduate at Trinity.

Whatever he did was a matter that aroused attention and comment: that was because he was a great man. But whatever he did also aroused opposition and ridicule, and that was because he was such a silly ass. His facility and his exuberance in ideas made him indolent: he could not bother to work any of them out, because it was so much easier to think of fresh ones: besides there were so many small grudges which he cherished against those who had belittled him, and they must be dealt with before anything else was done. He must speak to the Provost about the conduct of the Classical Tutor, and when he had spoken he would certainly have to complain to someone else about the lack of sympathy the Provost had shown him. Then there were many diversions: it was a cold winter afternoon, and he would go after lunch to the Coffee Club in the College, always sociable, but always wanting to shine, and there one day he imprudently asked Jim Stephen what was the derivation of the word "microbe." Jim instantly replied: "It's derived from the Greek word, μιϰρὸς, meaning small, and O.B. meaning you. It's a little O.B." After that it would be pleasant to have a Turkish bath, and he tried to persuade some member of the Coffee Club to come with him. "Awfully jolly: you can't be healthy unless you sweat every day as the Greeks did. Hesiod says that Sweat is the threshold of many virtues." So he went off to the small hot closet which represented a Turkish bath, and after sitting copiously on the threshold of many virtues, he reclined in a small cool closet, wrapped in towels, and ate quantities of hot buttered toast. Or if it was summer he found it pleasant to have a bathe at the University sheds, on the upper river; some sort of Charley or Bobby would row him up there, and tie his shoe-laces for him when he had dressed again. Then came the end of term, and he went up to London for a month, taking lodgings as nearly as possible opposite Marlborough House. As he grew old he became impossible to work with: he quarrelled with everyone who was associated with him on board or committee, accusing them of plagiarising his ideas and organising them. He left Cambridge and went to live at Bexhill where he played golf in cap, coat and gloves of bright red, and became a Christian Scientist. After that he settled in Rome where with incredible fluency he engaged himself in writing a history of the world. He calculated that he wrote about a million words every year, and wondered that he could not get them all published, suspecting conspiracy: in the intervals of composition he learned Polish. Never was there a man of so much originality of mind who did less with it, or one of so much genuine kindliness which was so curdled by egotism.

O.B. became a legend in his lifetime, which is always a mark of distinction. He was a model for every sort of caricature, a constant subject for the invention of the quick-witted, and many of these items, though possibly fabulous, ring so true that it really does not much matter whether they are authentic or not. Internal evidence based on a thorough knowledge of the character to whom they are attributed is the only test which is worth anything: if they are really characteristic they should be accepted, and the story of O.B. returning to Cambridge after a delirious July in London among the eminent, and remarking quite casually that William II of Germany was one of the nicest Emperors he had ever met, is, by such a test, obviously authentic. Anyone who had known O.B. in moods when he was dead drunk with the strong wine of royalty, could not hesitate about passing it, and if it was not true, so much the worse for the truth. Indeed it is a tribute to his personality that so many tales were invented about him, for nobody troubles to make up stories about everyday people, nor would anyone listen to them if they did.

Of all the Classical Fellows of King's about this time there was just one, and he of a younger generation and not of Eton, who worked conformably to the spirit of the bounty of King Henry VI, for in return for his board and lodging and fellowship, he devoted himself entirely to the study of Greek. Those who lectured, those who taught, those who, like Mr. Nixon, looked over our weekly efforts in Latin prose or Greek Iambics were not scholars at all in any real sense of the word: their knowledge of these languages was of the same class as that of the twenty or twenty-five undergraduates who yearly took a first in the Classical Tripos. They knew the principal dates and main operations in the Peloponnesian war, they could translate passages of Greek and Latin into grammatical English, and they could turn passages of English prose into Greek that probably bore the same relation to classical Greek, as written in the age of Pericles, as the best Baboo does to plain decent English prose of the day. Like the Baboo clerk, who when asked by his employer for what reason he wanted a day's remission from office work, replied, "The hand that rocked the cradle has kicked the bucket" (the proper English for which is "my mother is dead"), so these admirable preceptors of ours would produce the most remarkable patchwork of recondite constructions and unusual words snipped from Thucydides and Plato and neatly stitched together, and hand them to their pupils as models for classical composition. Had any of them competed in the Classical Tripos of the year, they would probably have taken quite good degrees, but there their attainments ended, and their years of teaching had not taught them anything that differentiated them from their more intelligent pupils. Their knowledge of Greek ended just about where Walter Headlam's began: his mind was Greek, and he kept on learning the lore of its ancestors. The fragmentary mimes of Herondas had lately been discovered, and on this new text he poured out a knowledge which was as far beyond that of the accredited tutors of the College, as is some advanced treatise on mathematics beyond the scope of an ordinary school-teacher of algebra. Though he was of a rich and boyish humanity, he had also that queer aloof quality which develops in those whose life is centred on research, and he passed into regions where no calls or needs of the flesh could penetrate.

One morning, for instance, his water for shaving was not hot, so after breakfast he put a small kettle to boil over his spirit lamp, and as he waited for that, he sat down in the armchair where he worked and casually looked at a note he had made the evening before. It was about a change of rhythm in a Greek chorus, or perhaps it was a word in his Herondas, which occurred in no dictionary, but which he knew he had seen before in some scholiast on Aristophanes. But where was the particular book he wanted? His room was lined with book-shelves, books that he was using paved the floor round his chair, and the table was piled high with them. There it was underneath a heap of others on the table, and he pulled it out: those on the top of it tumbled to the ground. He put down his pipe on the edge of the table, and as he turned the leaves, he found not just that which he was looking for, but something else he had wanted yesterday. He made a note of this on a slip of paper and picked up his pipe, which had gone out. There were no matches, so he folded up the paper on which he had made his note, thrust it into the flame of the spirit-lamp and lit his pipe again. Then he found the passage he had originally started to hunt up. Awfully interesting: it was a slang word, not very polite, in use among the daughters of joy in Corinth during the fifth century B.C. These intelligent ladies seemed to have an argot of their own; there were several other words of the sort which he had come across. He became lost in this pursuit, his pipe had to be relit several times, and presently a smell of roasting metal brought him back for a brief moment to the surface of life. His shaving-water had all boiled away, and so he put out the spirit lamp. Later in the morning his gyp came to see if he wanted any lunch ordered for him: bread and butter and cheese would do, with a tankard of beer. These were laid and left in the next room, and he wandered there after another hour or two deep in his investigation. The sight of food aroused no association of desire, but he had a drink out of the tankard and carrying it back with him, put it in a nest of books on his table. Presently more books got piled up round the tankard; he absently laid a folio note-book on the top of it, and so it completely vanished. Then he wanted more books from his shelves, in one of these excursions he stepped on his pipe and broke the stem. It did not matter for there were others about, but he forgot to look for them in the heat of this diverting chase. "I shall write a monograph on the slang current in Corinthian brothels," he said to himself.

It began to grow dark on this early close of the autumn afternoon. There was no electric light in those days, and he fetched a couple of candles and put them on the edge of his table. He was hungry now, and he gobbled up his bread and cheese, wondering what time it was, for his watch had stopped. Beer too: he felt sure he had ordered some beer, but where the devil was it? It should have been on his table with the bread and cheese. He looked everywhere for it, even in his bedroom, but it was nowhere to be seen. Then his razor lying ready on his dressing-table reminded him that he had not yet shaved. It was true there was no hot water, but cold water would do, and though it was rapidly getting dark, he had not yet found any matches to light his candles. But one ought to be able to shave in the dark, he thought, for an action, often repeated, became, as Aristotle said, an instinctive process, and it would be interesting to see if he could not make quite a good job of it. He made a fair job of it, there were a few negligible cuts, and finding that he had a box of matches in his pocket all the time, he lit his candles and went back to the ladies of Corinth. Then his gyp came in to see if he would go into Hall for dinner, or dine in his room: he settled to have some cold meat here, but where was the beer he had ordered for lunch? The gyp felt sure he had brought it, but evidently he was mistaken for there was no sign of it. So he brought the cold meat and another tankard and with this comfortless refreshment Walter Headlam pursued the ladies of Corinth till the small hours of the morning. The missing tankard came to light the next day.

He would work like this for several days on end (the details of my description are in no way composed but actually and collectively true) and then he was drained of scholarly energy and emerging as from deep seas with some pearls of research, he busied himself with social concerns and diversions till he could dive again.

One day he fell in love with an intelligent young lady from Newnham, but he soon forgot about her, because he went to a concert where he heard Schubert's "Unfinished Symphony." Instantly all became dross except Schubert, and though he could not read a note of music, nor play a correct scale, he sat hour after hour at his piano, dabbing at single notes till out of them he had extricated a short melody of four bars, which I wrote down for him; it was to be the air in the slow movement of "Headlam Op. 1." Then he immersed himself in Greek again, and again rising to the surface came across a pseudo-medical primer. The study of this convinced him that he had diabetes, and so sure was he of this that he never consulted a doctor at all. He had a tragic collection of unmistakable insignia, headache, fitful appetite, fatigue, and so there was no doubt about it. He told me very seriously that he had not long to live, and when I asked what was the matter with him, he said in a hollow but resigned whisper, "Sugar." So we went to a race-meeting at Newmarket, and entirely bowled over with adoration for the splendour and the speed of the flying hooves and the rhythm of their galloping, he felt that he must instantly learn to ride: for the moment the whores of Corinth were pale to him. He ordered some elegant riding breeches and hired a horse, and we set out along the backs. One of his feet slipped out of its stirrup, but in these first moments of poise upon a horse's back, he did not think it wise, in spite of advice and proffered assistance, to imperil his balance by recovering it, and in consequence when his horse decided to walk into the shallow water of the Grantchester mill-pool and drink, he slipped gently out of the saddle and fell in. Then he thought he would like to go for a drive, as a less hazardous method of commerce with horses, and he asked a friend to come out for a spin with him. On arrival at the livery stables, a high dog-cart was made ready for them, and Walter Headlam asked his friend if he would do the driving. The friend very properly replied that he had never done such a thing in his life, and so he said, "Nor have I," and was instructed that the reins went in the left hand, and the whip in the right. A little way out of Cambridge, in trying to turn a corner, he drove up a bank at the side of the road, and the dog-cart upset. As he flew out of it (still with the reins in his left hand) he was heard to observe, "Damn: I shall never finish Herondas," and alighted unharmed in a hedge.

Mr. Charles Waldstein, Reader in Classical Archaeology, was another of these Fellows of King's who was not quite like other people: King's was rich in variations from type. By blood of birth he was German, American, and Jew, and Sir Charles Stanford at a musical rehearsal of a Greek play, at which he had been irritated to the verge of insanity by Waldstein's continually interrupting the chanting of Athenian elders, in order to show them how to stand and move in truly Pheidian attitudes, exclaimed in a highly injured brogue, "I wish that German-American-Jew would go back to his respective countries." There was a coolness in consequence, or you might call it a heat. He was one of those fortunate folk to whom for no particular reason, ludicrous things happen: thus he was a source of fearful joy as well as affection to his friends.

He belonged to an earnest and exclusive Literary Society called the "Chitchat." Both dons and undergraduates were among its members, and we assembled in each other's rooms in rotation every Saturday night during term time, on terms of equality. The host for the evening provided claret cup and hot buns and anchovy toast, and the Society owned a snuff-box from which, as a piece of ceremonial, we all took pinches. When the sneezing had died down, the secretary called upon the host to read a paper which he had written on some literary or ethical subject, and during the reading the claret cup went quietly round. On one memorable evening when Waldstein entertained the Society, he told us that he had not time to write down his lecture, and so he addressed his fellow-members instead, on the subject of "Manners." He stood in front of the fire in cap and gown, and was full of glorious gestures. He lit a cigarette and put it down on the chimney piece, he lit another and another and put them down on table-edge or chair-back. An eloquence of sentences, faintly Teutonic sometimes in construction, streamed from him, sometimes they contained rather exotic words like "cocksuredom" and no one as yet knew with any precision what he was talking about. The atmosphere grew a little tense, and the members of the Chitchat, sitting very demure and attentive, felt that it was not wise to catch each other's eyes. There came a pause: the lecturer slapped his forehead and confessed that he had forgotten exactly what he meant to say on that topic. So he launched out on something cognate, and then remembered what he had forgotten and went back to it. The exquisite grace of Greek sculpture— that was it: it reflected the charm and the urbanity and the breeding of that superlative race. Gentlemanly-ishness no less than genius was characteristic of sculptor and model alike. There was that statue of the Discobolus which illustrated what he meant as well as anything, and he threw himself into a semblance of the famous pose, and his mortar-board cap dropped off. He picked it up. "It's no use," he said, "you should see me naked." At that intense moment when everybody might have been statues too, so still they sat, Dr. Cunningham of

Trinity happened to be drinking claret cup, and he burst. The liquid squirted from his mouth and nose, he hooted with laughter, and seizing his cap and gown he hurried from the room. Through the open window he could be heard roaring and slapping his leg in the court below.

[From *As We Were*]

Norman Douglas

The scene of South Wind *is the Mediterranean island of Nepenthe, which has a close physical and spiritual resemblance to Capri. I have chosen the chapter about the Russian Messiah and his followers, the Little White Cows. Seekers for sources should consult Edwin Cerio's beautiful book,* Aria di Capri, *especially the chapters on August Weber, the Lunar Myth; Oscar Westergard, the Solar Myth; Miradois, the German Messiah; and Bludoir, the Provisional Messiah. Also the chapter on Norman Douglas, whom Cerio characterizes as the professional of imaginary sin. And Cerio quotes an anonymous poet.*

> "Was there a sin Tiberius committed
> Which might one moment find N. D. outwitted?
> No! cry the rocks and the reverberate caves;
> No! from their tombs proclaim a myriad slaves."

TROUBLE ON NEPENTHE

Both the old boatman and Mr. Keith were correct in their surmises. There was trouble in the market-place, serious trouble; so serious that for the first time in five years—ever since that deplorable scandal of the Irish lady and the poodle—the Militia were being called out. And it was entirely the fault of the Sacred Sixty-three.

The Messiah, personally, was not to blame. That poor old man had much declined of late; he was enfeebled in health and spirits. A French artist who was especially despatched from Paris to do an original sketch of him for the enterprising journal *L'Illustration* had, at the end of several sittings, uncharitably declared him to be "*complètement ga-ga.*" The voluptuous surroundings of Nepenthe, the abundant food, adoration of disciples, alcoholic and carnal debaucheries, had impaired his tough Moujik frame and blunted his wit, working havoc with that energy and peasant craftiness which once ruled an Emperor's Court. His body was obese. His mind was in a state of advanced putrefaction. Even his personal cleanliness left something to be desired. Sitting there, puffy and pasty, in a darkened room, he looked more than ever like some obscene vegetable that has grown up in the shade.

He moved seldom and with difficulty; he hardly ever opened his mouth save to eat—for his appetite, thanks to certain daily exertions on the part of the communal doctor, was still fairly satisfactory. When he spoke at all it was in scattered monosyllables which even the most devoted of his disciples were unable to arrange into such coherence as to justify their inclusion in the *Golden Book*. All this, though hidden from the world at large, had been observed with dismay by the initiated. It was an open secret among them that the last twenty-one sayings ascribed to him in that volume had never issued from his lips at all. They had been concocted by a clique of young extremists, who were now masters of the situation. These fanatics edited the *Golden Book* and held the old man completely in subjection, ousting his former and more moderate collaborators.

An ill-considered action on the part of this group led to the disaster and eclipsed the light of holiness on Nepenthe by bringing the Apostles into conflict with the secular arm of the law. Fretting at the Master's prolonged inactivity and eager, after the fashion of disciples, to improve on his maxims, they decided upon a bold step. They decided that the time was ripe for a new Revelation.

The Messiah's last authentic one, it will be remembered, ran to the effect that "flesh and blood of warm-blooded beasts is Abomination to Little White Cows." He had been inspired to insert the word *warm-blooded* because fish, for example, was an article of diet of which he was inordinately fond, and he could not bring himself to deprive the faithful of this gift of God.

With misplaced zeal, and little thinking that it would cost many of them their lives and liberties, these enthusiasts gave it out that the new Revelation ran as follows: "everything derivable from dead beasts is Abomination to Little White Cows." They had been inspired to insert the word *dead* because sheep's wool, for example, was an article of clothing in which they greatly delighted, and they could not bring themselves to deprive the faithful of this gift of God.

Even as it stood, the Commandment entailed severe sacrifices on the part of the Sacred Sixty-three. No bootleather, no picturesque belts, no bone knife-handles or combs, no tallow candles.... They were prepared, none the less, to carry out to the letter this injunction, since it gave them what all religious people require—something to torment themselves with; and this is how matters stood when, on that morning, a stalwart batch of newcomers from the wilds of Muscovy, burning with the ardour of abnegation and wholly ignorant of local laws and customs, sauntered across the market-place in freshly purchased hempen sandals.

Tobacco being derivable neither from warm-blooded beasts nor yet from dead ones, a member of the band bethought himself of the fact that he had run out of cigarettes. Knowing not a word of Italian, he entered the shop of a tobacconist and imitated the gesture of smoking with such success that the proprietor straightway understood and supplied him with a packet. Then he remembered that he also needed matches. This called for a gesture rather more complex; so complex, indeed, that perhaps nobody but a Nepenthean—gifted, as all his nation is, with alert intuition—could have divined the Apostle's want. The tobacconist was equal to the occasion. With a friendly smile of comprehension he laid on the counter a diminutive box of wax vestas, price two sous.

There the matter might have rested but for the new Revelation, which prompted the sturdy stranger to investigate the composition of the article tendered. He took out one match and examined it carefully. Then, triturating its substance between his fingers, he applied his nose to the product and sniffed critically. The outcome was suspicious in the highest degree. There was no perceptible odour of beeswax; the object had been compounded, only too plainly, of the fat of dead animals; it was the Abomination, the Unclean Thing. Devout, and gifted with the hot impulse of youth, he acted precisely as he would have acted in Russia under a similar provocation. With a third gesture, one of abhorrence and ungovernable fury, he threw the box in the tobacconist's face.

And there the matter, once more, might have rested, had the salesman been a Russian. Russians understand frank dealing.

He happened to be a native.

Fully to appreciate what followed, it is necessary to bear in mind that local tobacconists are in a somewhat anomalous position. They occupy a social status superior to those of many other countries. They are not private merchants or ordinary citizens; they are, in a manner, servants of the State. A native tobacconist is empowered to dispense *carta bollata,* which is the official stamped paper used for contracts and other legal documents requiring registration; he deals in tobacco and postage stamps—government monopolies; he sells, by special licence, wax vestas, on each box of which there is a duty so minute as not to be felt by the individual purchaser and yet, in its cumulative effect, so great as to enable the State to pay, out of this source of revenue alone, for the upkeep of all its colonial judges at a monthly salary of forty-five francs apiece. It is a reasonable tax. Don Francesco, who had notions of political economy and knew something of English life, having preached to thousands of Catholic miners in Wales and confessed hundreds of Catholic ladies in Mayfair—an occupation in which he might still be engaged, but for a little *contretemps* which brought him into collision with the Jesuits of Mount Street—Don Francesco, who could voice the Southerner's one-sided point of view, often adverted to this match-tax when proving the superiority of his country's administrative methods over those of England. This is what he would say to his intimate friends:

"The Russian has convictions but no principles. The Englishman has principles but no convictions—cast-iron principles, which save him the trouble of thinking out anything for himself. This is as much as anyone can ever hope to grasp concerning this lymphatic, unimaginative race. They obey the laws—a criminal requires imagination. They never start a respectable revolution—you cannot revolt without imagination. Among other things, they pride themselves on their immunity from vexatious imposts. Yet whisky, the best quality of which is worth tenpence a bottle, is taxed till it costs five shillings; ale, the life-blood of the people, would be dear at threepence a gallon and yet costs fivepence a pint; tobacco, which could profitably be sold at twopence a pound, goes for fivepence an ounce. They will submit to any number of these extortions, being persuaded, in the depths of their turbid intelligence, that such things are devised for the good of the nation at large. That is the Englishman's method of procuring happiness: to deny himself pleasure in order to save his neighbor's soul. Ale and tobacco are commodities out of which a man can extract pleasure. They are therefore appropriate objects for harassing restrictions. But nobody can extract pleasure out of lucifer matches. They are therefore pre-eminently unfitted for exploitation as a source of governmental revenue. So keen is their sense of pleasure and non-pleasure, and such is their *furor phlegmaticus* on this particular question, that when it is proposed to establish a tax on matches—an imperceptible duty which would enrich the Exchequer to a vast extent—they will form a procession ten miles long to protest against the outrage, and threaten to batter down the Houses of Parliament. Why? Because there is no ethical purpose to be served by taxing matches, seeing that only a madman would give himself the guilty pleasure of either drinking or smoking them. In short, these English reason after the fashion of paranoiacs—logically, but from a wrong premise. Not that I dislike their women...."

The action of the quick-tempered Apostle can now be appraised in its full enormity. A local tobacconist is a person in authority, a State official, and the nation safeguards the interests and the fair name of those who serve it faithfully. When it is remembered that according to No. 43 of the 16th Section of their Penal Code any person speaking disrespectfully to, or of, a Government official renders himself liable to a term of cellular confinement not exceeding thirty-one years, ten lunar months and eighteen days, it may be imagined what penalties are applicable to the crime of actual personal violence towards such a sacrosanct individual—a crime of which the Russian was unquestionably guilty.

Now this particular tobacconist, though tremendously sensitive, like all Southerners, on a point of honour, was as good-natured and forgiving as might be consistent with his rank of Government official. He passed for a respectable married man, with an eligible daughter and a taste for the quiet life; he did not want trouble. The purchase of an additional packet of cigarettes, accompanied or unaccompanied by a frank apology, would have more than satisfied his sense of honour.

There the matter might have rested. The second packet might have been bought and even the apology tendered, but for the ill-considered action of a young farmer who entered the shop at that moment to procure a couple of postcards. This worthy lad was one of several dozen aspirants to the hand of the tobacconist's daughter, whose dowry was reputed to be considerable. He witnessed the insult and, desirous of standing well in the graces of a prospective father-in-law, dealt the offending alien so masterly a punch in the region of the solar plexus that he not only doubled up, but forgot to straighten himself out again. Two or three lusty Apostles came to the rescue without delay. They threw the youth down, stamped on his face, pounded his abdomen, pulled his hair out in handfuls, and otherwise treated him exactly as if the thing were happening in Russia. This spectacle was too much for the tobacconist's sense of honour. With unwonted sprightliness he vaulted over the writhing cluster and summoned a municipal police-man. The officer was on the spot in a twinkling, sword and trumpet in hand. And there, in all conscience, the matter ought to have rested—with the identification and bestowal in custody of the turbulent parties.

But frenzy hung in the air; a red cloud of insanity was hovering over Nepenthe. Although the volcano continued to behave in exemplary fashion, although the clergy had done their utmost to allay popular apprehensions, the native mind had not calmed down since the news concerning the Saint Elias fountain and those other portents had been disseminated. The inhabitants were in a state of suppressed alarm and ready, at the least provocation, to burst out into some fiendish act of folly. And the Russians, especially those latest arrivals, could not withdraw themselves from the subtle influence of the south wind, the frank stimulation of a cloudless sky; it made them feel, after their gloomy forests and lowering horizons, like wild beasts that rush from darkened cages into some sunny arena. Everyone lost his wits. The appearance of a constable, far from restoring order, was the signal for an uproarious tumult; the *fracas,* as the French artist was heard to declare, promptly developed into a *mêlée.* Nobody troubled about the merits of the case further than that it was a question of Apostles *versus* Gentiles.

The former were in sad minority. But they constituted a serried rank of muscular Christians; they laid about them like those old monks of Alexandria. All Russians are born fighters—if not on the battlefield, then at least in the lanes and taverns of their natal villages. The Little White Cows, wholly ignorant of the difference between their own law and that of Italy on questions of assault and battery, used their fists with such success that thirty natives were stretched out in almost as few seconds. Their Faith was at stake; moreover, and as a matter of fact, they were enjoying themselves hugely. The occasion reminded them of a Sunday at home.

Then numbers began to tell—numbers and knives. For your sunscorched Nepenthean, when duly roused, confesses to an expert knowledge of anatomy; he can tell you, to the fraction of an inch, where the liver, the spleen, kidneys and various other coy organs of the human frame are located. Blood, the blood of the Sacred Sixty-three, began to flow. At that sight the women, as their manner is, set up a scream.

The Palace of Justice abutted on the market-place, and up to that moment His Worship Signor Malipizzo might have been lost to the world, so deeply immersed was he in threading the labyrinthine mazes of an exceptionally intricate affiliation case—a warm document, after his own heart. The sound of the scream suspended his labours. Like a gouty parrot he hopped down from his seat of judgment, spat on the floor, limped to the window and took in the situation at a glance. That is to say, he understood the cause of the disturbance as little as did anyone else; it would have required a divine inspiration to guess that a box of wax vestas was at the bottom of the affair; but he knew enough, quite enough, more than enough, for the purpose at hand. He knew, to begin with, that Apostles were involved in the brawl. He knew, what was equally important, the provisions of the Penal Code. It sufficed. His chance for dealing with the Russian colony had at last arrived. Allowing himself barely time to smack his lips at this providential interlude he gave orders for the great cannon of Duke Alfred to be sounded. It boomed once or twice over Nepenthe and reverberated among the rocks.

In times of yore a certain interval was wont to elapse before the Militia could be assembled, living as they did in distant regions of the island. But nowadays, as befitted a laborious rural population, they were spending their morning in the wine-shops of the town, gambling, drinking, or playing skittles. This enabled a sufficient number of them to forgather, in an incredibly short space of time, at the outskirts of the market-place (occupied by a seething, howling tangle of humanity)— there to receive the plainest of instructions. They were to quell the disorder and to single out for punishment, whenever possible, the strangers, the obvious authors of the rebellion, easily discernible by their scarlet blouses. Not that the judge was particular about the lives or deaths of a few natives; he knew that any injuries received by his countrymen would strengthen his case against the outsiders. But an order couched in such terms would look well in the records of the Court.

Within ten minutes the market-place was cleared. The Militia had used their weapons with such precision that four school children, seven women, eleven islanders, and twenty-six Apostles were wounded— about half of them, it was believed, mortally. Order reigned in Nepenthe.

The warm affiliation case having been laid on ice for the nonce, the next few minutes were occupied by His Worship in issuing warrants of arrest against the Messiah's followers. They were lodged by batches in gaol, and in supplementary gaols—disused cellars and so forth. Once under lock and key they were safe from mischief for an indefinite length of time, since according to the statutes of the Code of Criminal Procedure, there is no reason on earth why an Italian lawsuit should ever end, or indeed, why it should ever begin. They might, and probably would, remain incarcerated for life, pending the commencement of a trial which could only be set in motion by the judge himself—a most improbable conjuncture—or, failing that, by an extravagant bribe to his official superior, the President of the Court of Cassation. How were poor Apostles to find the necessary sixty or seventy francs for such a venture?

His Worship retired to luncheon, reasonably satisfied with the morning's work. And yet not altogether delighted. Both the Messiah and Peter the Great had eluded his wrath. Peter was able to prove, beyond the shadow of a doubt, that he had spent the last twenty-four hours on Madame Steynlin's premises and knew nothing whatever of occurrences in the outside world. In the face of such a fact—so conformable to common knowledge, so inherently probable—Malipizzo gave way. He was too good a lawyer to spoil his case. Sooner or later, he foresaw, that bird would be caged with the rest of them. Regarding the Messiah, an unexpected and breathless appeal for mercy was lodged by the Communal doctor, atheist and freemason like the judge, who implored, with tears in his eyes, that the warrant for his arrest should be rescinded. By means of a sequence of rapid and intricate Masonic signs, he explained that Bazhakuloff was a patient of his; that he was undergoing a daily treatment with the stomach-pump; that the prison diet being notoriously slender, he feared that if he, the Messiah, were confined in captivity, then it, the stomach-pump, would no longer be required and therefore he, the physician, a family man, would be deprived of a small but regular source of income. Again the astute judge relented. This is how the Messiah and his disciple escaped. They escaped, but not for long.

And all this happened while Mr. Keith and his companion, drowsily ensconced among the morocco cushions of their boat, were being wafted over the blue sea, far away, under the cliffs.

[From *South Wind*]

Ernest Bramah

THE STORY OF YUNG CHANG

Narrated by Kai Lung, in the open space of the tea-shop of the Celestial Principles, at Wu-Whei

"Ho, illustrious passers-by!" said Kai Lung, the story-teller, as he spread out his embroidered mat under the mulberry-tree. "It is indeed unlikely that you would condescend to stop and listen to the foolish words of such an insignificant and altogether deformed person as myself. Nevertheless, if you will but retard your elegant footsteps for a few moments, this exceedingly unprepossessing individual will endeavour to entertain you with the recital of the adventures of the noble Yung Chang, as recorded by the celebrated Pe-ku-hi."

Thus adjured, the more leisurely minded drew near to hear the history of Yung Chang. There was Sing You the fruit-seller, and Li Ton-ti the wood-carver; Hi Seng left his clients to cry in vain for water; and Wang Yu, the idle pipe-maker, closed his shop of "The Fountain of Beauty," and hung on the shutter the gilt dragon to keep away customers in his absence. These, together with a few more shop-keepers and a dozen or so loafers, constituted a respectable audience by the time Kai Lung was ready.

"It would be more seemly if this ill-conditioned person who is now addressing such a distinguished assembly were to reward his fine and noble-looking hearers for their trouble," apologised the story-teller. "But, as the Book of Verses says, 'The meaner the slave, the greater the lord'; and it is, therefore, not unlikely that this majestic concourse will reward the despicable efforts of their servant by hand-fuls of coins till the air appears as though filled with swarms of locusts in the season of much heat. In particular, there is among this august crowd of mandarins one Wang Yu, who has departed on three previous occasions without bestowing the reward of a single cash. If the feeble and covetous-minded Wang Yu will place in this very ordi-

449

nary bowl the price of one of his exceedingly ill-made pipes, this unworthy person will proceed."

"Vast chasms can be filled, but the heart of man never," quoted the pipe-maker in retort. "Oh, most incapable of story-tellers, have you not on two separate occasions slept beneath my utterly inadequate roof without payment?"

But he, nevertheless, deposited three cash in the bowl, and drew nearer among the front row of the listeners.

"It was during the reign of the enlightened Emperor Tsing Nung," began Kai Lung, without further introduction, "that there lived at a village near Honan a wealthy and avaricious maker of idols, named Ti Hung. So skillful had he become in the making of clay idols that his fame had spread for many li round, and idol-sellers from all the neighbouring villages, and even from the towns, came to him for their stock. No other idol-maker between Honan and Nankin employed so many clay-gatherers or so many modellers; yet, with all his riches, his avarice increased till at length he employed men whom he called 'agents' and 'travellers,' who went from house to house selling his idols and extolling his virtues in verses composed by the most illustrious poets of the day. He did this in order that he might turn into his own pocket the full price of the idols, grudging those who would otherwise have sold them the few cash which they would make. Owing to this he had many enemies, and his army of travellers made him still more; for they were more rapacious than the scorpion, and more obstinate than the ox. Indeed, there is still the proverb, 'With honey it is possible to soften the heart of the he-goat; but a blow from an iron cleaver is taken as a mark of welcome by an agent of Ti Hung.' So that people barred the doors at their approach, and even hung out signs of death and mourning.

"Now, among all his travellers there was none more successful, more abandoned, and more valuable to Ti Hung than Li Ting. So depraved was Li Ting that he was never known to visit the tombs of his ancestors; indeed, it was said that he had been heard to mock their venerable memories, and that he had jestingly offered to sell them to any one who should chance to be without ancestors of his own. This objectionable person would call at the houses of the most illustrious mandarins, and would command the slaves to carry to their masters his tablets, on which were inscribed his name and his virtues. Reaching their presence, he would salute them with the greeting of an equal, 'How is your stomach?' and then proceed to exhibit samples of his wares, greatly overrating their value. 'Behold!' he would exclaim, 'is not this elegantly-moulded idol worthy of the place of honour in this sumptuous mansion, which my presence defiles to such an extent that twelve basins of rose-water will not remove the stain? Are not its eyes more delicate than the most select of almonds? and is not its stomach rounder than the cupolas upon the high temple at Pekin? Yet, in spite of its perfections, it is not worthy of the acceptance of so distinguished a mandarin, and therefore I will accept in return the quarter-tael, which, indeed, is less than my illustrious master gives for the clay alone.'

"In this manner Li Ting disposed of many idols at high rates, and thereby endeared himself so much to the avaricious heart of Ti Hung that he promised him his beautiful daughter Ning in marriage.

"Ning was indeed very lovely. Her eyelashes were like the finest willow twigs that grow in the marshes by the Yang-tse-Kiang; her cheeks were fairer than poppies; and when she bathed in the Hoang Ho, her body seemed transparent. Her brow was finer than the most polished jade; while she seemed to walk, like a winged bird, without weight, her hair floating in a cloud. Indeed, she was the most beautiful creature that has ever existed."

"Now may you grow thin and shrivel up like a fallen lemon; but it is false!" cried Wang Yu, starting up suddenly and unexpectedly. "At Chee Chou, at the shop of 'The Heaven-sent Sugar-cane,' there lives a beautiful and virtuous girl who is more than all that. Her eyes are like the inside circles on the peacock's feathers; her teeth are finer than the scales on the Sacred Dragon; her—"

"If it is the wish of this illustriously endowed gathering that this exceedingly illiterate paper tiger should occupy their august moments with a description of the deformities of the very ordinary young person at Chee Chou," said Kai Lung imperturbably, "then the remainder of the history of the noble-minded Yung Chang can remain until an evil fate has overtaken Wang Yu, as it assuredly will shortly."

"A fair wind raises no storm," said Wang Yu sulkily; and Kai Lung continued:

"Such loveliness could not escape the evil eye of Li Ting, and, accordingly, as he grew in favour with Ti Hung, he obtained his consent to the drawing up of the marriage contracts. More than this, he had already sent to Ning two bracelets of the finest gold, tied together with a scarlet thread, as a betrothal present. But, as the proverb says, 'The good bee will not touch the faded flower,' and Ning, although compelled by the second of the Five Great Principles to respect her father, was unable to regard the marriage with anything but abhorrence. Perhaps this was not altogether the fault of Li Ting, for on the evening of the day on which she had received his present, she walked in the rice fields, and sitting down at the foot of a funereal cypress, whose highest branches pierced the Middle Air, she cried aloud:

" 'I cannot control my bitterness. Of what use is it that I should be called the "White Pigeon among Golden Lilies," if my beauty is but for the hog-like eyes of the exceedingly objectionable Li Ting? Ah, Yung Chang, my unfortunate lover! what evil spirit pursues you that you cannot pass your examination for the second degree? My noble-minded but ambitious boy, why were you not content with an agricultural or even a manufacturing career and happiness? By aspiring to a literary degree, you have placed a barrier wider than the Whang Hai between us.'

" 'As the earth seems small to the soaring swallow, so shall insuperable obstacles be overcome by the heart worn smooth with a fixed purpose,' said a voice beside her, and Yung Chang stepped from behind the cypress-tree, where he had been waiting for Ning. 'O one more symmetrical than the chrysanthemum,' he continued, 'I shall yet, with the aid of my ancestors, pass the second degree, and even obtain a position of high trust in the public office at Pekin.'

" 'And in the meantime,' pouted Ning, 'I shall have partaken of the wedding-cake of the utterly unpresentable Li Ting.' And she exhibited the bracelets which she had that day received.

" 'Alas!' said Yung Chang, 'there are times when one is tempted to doubt even the most efficacious and violent means. I had hoped that by this time Li Ting would have come to a sudden and most unseemly end; for I have drawn up and affixed in the most conspicuous places notifications of his character, similar to the one here.'

"Ning turned, and beheld fastened to the trunk of the cypress an exceedingly elegantly written and composed notice, which Yung read to her as follows:

"BEWARE OF INCURRING DEATH FROM STARVATION.

"Let the distinguished inhabitants of this district observe the exceedingly ungraceful walk and bearing of the low person who calls himself Li Ting.

Truthfully, it is that of a dog in the act of being dragged to the river because his sores and diseases render him objectionable in the house of his master. So will this hunchbacked person be dragged to the place of execution, and be bowstrung, to the great relief of all who respect the five senses: A Respectful Physiognomy, Passionless Reflection, Soft Speech, Acute Hearing, Piercing Sight.

"He hopes to attain to the Red Button and the Peacock's Feather; but the right hand of the Deity itches, and Li Ting will assuredly be removed suddenly.

"'Li Ting must certainly be in league with the evil forces if he can withstand so powerful a weapon,' said Ning admiringly, when her lover had finished reading. 'Even now he is starting on a journey, nor will he return till the first day of the month when the sparrows go to the sea and are changed into oysters. Perhaps the fate will overtake him while he is away. If not—'

"'If not,' said Yung, taking up her words as she paused, 'then I have yet another hope. A moment ago you were regretting my choice of a literary career. Learn, then, the value of knowledge. By its aid (assisted, indeed, by the spirits of my ancestors) I have discovered a new and strange thing, for which I can find no word. By using this new system of reckoning, your illustrious but exceedingly narrow-minded and miserly father would be able to make five taels where he now makes one. Would he not, in consideration for this, consent to receive me as a son-in-law, and dismiss the inelegant and unworthy Li Ting?'

"'In the unlikely event of your being able to convince my illustrious parent of what you say, it would assuredly be so,' replied Ning. 'But in what way could you do so? My sublime and charitable father already employs all the means in his power to reap the full reward of his sacred industry. His "solid household gods" are in reality mere shells of clay; higher-priced images are correspondingly constructed, and his clay-gatherers and modellers are all paid on a "profit-sharing system." Nay, further, it is beyond likelihood that he should wish for more purchasers, for so great is his fame that those who come to buy have sometimes to wait for days in consequence of those before them; for my exceedingly methodical sire entrusts none with the receiving of money, and the exchanges are therefore made slowly. Frequently an unnaturally devout person will require as many as a hundred idols, and so the greater part of the day will be passed.'

"'In what way?' inquired Yung tremulously.

"'Why, in order that the countings may not get mixed, of course it is necessary that when he has paid for one idol he should carry it to a place aside, and then return and pay for the second, carrying it to the first, and in such a manner to the end. In this way the sun sinks behind the mountains.'

"'But,' said Yung, his voice thick with his great discovery, 'if he could pay for the entire quantity at once, then it would take but a hundredth part of the time, and so more idols could be sold.'

"'How could this be done?' inquired Ning wonderingly. 'Surely it is impossible to conjecture the value of many idols.'

"'To the unlearned it would indeed be impossible,' replied Yung proudly, 'but by the aid of my literary researches I have been enabled to discover a process by which such results would be not a matter of conjecture, but of certainty. These figures I have committed to tablets, which I am prepared to give to your mercenary and slow-witted father in return for your incomparable hand, a share of the profits, and the dismissal of the uninventive and morally threadbare Li Ting.'

"'When the earth-worm boasts of his elegant wings, the eagle can afford to be silent,' said a harsh voice behind them; and turning hastily they beheld Li Ting, who had come upon them unawares. 'Oh, most insignificant of tablet-spoilers,' he continued, 'it is very evident that much over-study has softened your usually well-educated brains. Were it not that you are obviously mentally afflicted, I should unhesitatingly persuade my beautiful and refined sword to introduce you to the spirits of your ignoble ancestors. As it is, I will merely cut off your nose and your left ear, so that people may not say that the Dragon of the Earth sleeps and wickedness goes unpunished.'

"Both had already drawn their swords, and very soon the blows were so hard and swift that, in the dusk of the evening, it seemed as though the air were filled with innumerable and many-coloured fireworks. Each was a practised swordsman, and there was no advantage gained on either side, when Ning, who had fled on the appearance of Ti Ling, reappeared, urging on her father, whose usually leisurely footsteps were quickened by the dread that the duel must result in certain loss to himself, either of a valuable servant, or of the discovery which Ning had briefly explained to him, and of which he at once saw the value.

"'Oh, most distinguished and expert persons,' he exclaimed breathlessly, as soon as he was within hearing distance, 'do not trouble to give so marvellous an exhibition for the benefit of this unworthy individual, who is the only observer of your illustrious dexterity! Indeed, your honourable condescension so fills this illiterate person with shame that his hearing is thereby preternaturally sharpened, and he can plainly distinguish many voices from beyond the Hoang Ho, crying for the Heaven-sent representative of the degraded Ti Hung to bring them more idols. Bend, therefore, your refined footsteps in the direction of Poo Chow, O Li Ting, and leave me to make myself objectionable to this exceptional young man with my intolerable commonplaces.'

"'The shadow falls in such a direction as the sun wills,' said Li Ting, as he replaced his sword and departed.

"'Yung Chang,' said the merchant, 'I am informed that you have made a discovery that would be of great value to me, as it undoubtedly would if it is all that you say. Let us discuss the matter without ceremony. Can you prove to me that your system possesses the merits you claim for it? If so, then the matter of arrangement will be easy.'

"'I am convinced of the absolute certainty and accuracy of the discovery,' replied Yung Chang. 'It is not as though it were an ordinary matter of human intelligence, for this was discovered to me as I was worshipping at the tomb of my ancestors. The method is regulated by a system of squares, triangles, and cubes. But as the practical proof might be long, and as I hesitate to keep your adorable daughter out in the damp night air, may I not call at your inimitable dwelling in the morning, when we can go into the matter thoroughly?'

"I will not weary this intelligent gathering, each member of which doubtless knows all the books of mathematics off by heart, with a recital of the means by which Yung Chang proved to Ti Hung the accuracy of his tables and the value of his discovery of the multiplication table, which till then had been undreamt of," continued the story-teller. "It is sufficient to know that he did so, and that Ti Hung agreed to his terms, only stipulating that Li Ting should not be made aware of his dismissal until he had returned and given in his accounts. The share of the profits that Yung was to receive was cut down very low by Ti Hung, but the young man did not mind that, as he would live with his father-in-law for the future.

"With the introduction of this new system, the business increased like a river at flood-time. All rivals were left far behind, and Ti Hung put out this sign:

"No Waiting Here!

"Good-morning! Have you worshipped one of Ti Hung's refined ninety-nine cash idols?

"Let the purchasers of ill-constructed idols at other establishments, where they have grown old and venerable while waiting for the all-thumb proprietors to count up to ten, come to the shop of Ti Hung and regain their lost youth. Our ninety-nine cash idols are worth a tael a set. We do not, however, claim that they will do everything. The ninety-nine cash idols of Ti Hung will not, for example, purify linen, but even the most contented and frozen-brained person cannot be happy till he possesses one. What is happiness? The exceedingly well-educated Philosopher defines it as the accomplishment of all our desires. Every one desires one of Ti Hung's ninety-nine cash idols, therefore get one; but be sure that it is Ti Hung's.

"Have you a bad idol? If so, dismiss it, and get one of Ti Hung's ninety-nine cash specimens.

"Why does your idol look old sooner than your neighbour's? Because yours is not one of Ti Hung's ninety-nine cash marvels.

"They bring all delights to the old and the young,
    The elegant idols supplied by Ti Hung.

"N.B.—The 'Great Sacrifice' idol, forty-five cash; delivered, carriage free, in quantities of not less than twelve, at any temple, on the evening before the sacrifice."

"It was about this time that Li Ting returned. His journey had been more than usually successful, and he was well satisfied in consequence. It was not until he had made out his accounts and handed in his money that Ti Hung informed him of his agreement with Yung Chang.

"'Oh, most treacherous and excessively unpopular Ti Hung,' exclaimed Li Ting, in a terrible voice, 'this is the return you make for all my entrancing efforts in your service, then? It is in this way that you reward my exceedingly unconscientious recommendations of your very inferior and unendurable clay idols, with their goggle eyes and concave stomachs! Before I go, however, I request to be inspired to make the following remark—that I confidently predict your ruin. And now this low and undignified person will finally shake the elegant dust of your distinguished house from his thoroughly inadequate feet, and proceed to offer his incapable services to the rival establishment over the way.'

"'The machinations of such an evilly-disposed person as Li Ting will certainly be exceedingly subtle,' said Ti Hung to his son-in-law when the traveller had departed. 'I must counteract his omens. Herewith I wish to prophesy that henceforth I shall enjoy an unbroken run of good fortune. I have spoken, and assuredly I shall not eat my words.'

"As the time went on, it seemed as though Ti Hung had indeed spoken truly. The ease and celerity with which he transacted his business brought him customers and dealers from more remote regions than ever, for they could spend days on the journey and still save time. The army of clay-gatherers and modellers grew larger and larger, and the work-sheds stretched almost down to the river's edge. Only one thing troubled Ti Hung, and that was the uncongenial disposition of his son-in-law, for Yung took no further interest in the industry to which his discovery had given so great an impetus, but resolutely set to work again to pass his examination for the second degree.

" 'It is an exceedingly distinguished and honourable thing to have failed thirty-five times, and still to be undiscouraged,' admitted Ti Hung; 'but I cannot cleanse my throat from bitterness when I consider that my noble and lucrative business must pass into the hands of strangers, perhaps even into the possession of the unendurable Li Ting.'

"But it had been appointed that this degrading thing should not happen, however, and it was indeed fortunate that Yung did not abandon his literary pursuits; for after some time it became very apparent to Ti Hung that there was something radically wrong with his business. It was not that his custom was falling off in any way; indeed, it had lately increased in a manner that was phenomenal, and when the merchant came to look into the matter, he found to his astonishment that the least order he had received in the past week had been for a hundred idols. All the sales had been large, and yet Ti Hung found himself most unaccountably deficient in taels. He was puzzled and alarmed, and for the next few days he looked into the business closely. Then it was that the reason was revealed, both for the falling off in the receipts and for the increase in the orders. The calculations of the unfortunate Yung Chang were correct up to a hundred, but at that number he had made a gigantic error—which, however, he was never able to detect and rectify—with the result that all transactions above that point worked out at a considerable loss to the seller. It was in vain that the panic-stricken and infuriated Ti Hung goaded his miserable son-in-law to correct the mistake; it was equally in vain that he tried to stem the current of his enormous commercial popularity. He had competed for public favour, and he had won it, and every day his business increased till ruin grasped him by the pigtail. Then came an order from one firm at Pekin for five millions of the ninety-nine cash idols, and at that Ti Hung put up his shutters, and sat down in the dust.

"'Behold!' he exclaimed, 'in the course of a lifetime there are many very disagreeable evils that may overtake a person. He may offend the Sacred Dragon, and be in consequence reduced to a fine dry powder; or he may incur the displeasure of the benevolent and pure-minded Emperor, and be condemned to death by roasting; he may also be troubled by demons or by the disturbed spirits of his ancestors, or be struck by thunderbolts. Indeed, there are numerous annoyances, but they all become as Heaven-sent blessings in comparison to a self-opinionated and more than ordinarily weak-minded son-in-law. Of what avail is it that I have habitually sold one idol for the value of a hundred? The very objectionable man in possession sits in my delectable summer-house, and the unavoidable legal documents settle around me like a flock of pigeons. It is indeed necessary that I should declare myself to be in voluntary liquidation, and make an assignment of my book debts for the benefit of my creditors. Having accomplished this, I will proceed to the well-constructed tomb of my illustrious ancestors, and having kow-towed at their incomparable shrines, I will put an end to my distinguished troubles with this exceedingly well-polished sword.'

"'The wise man can adapt himself to circumstances as water takes the shape of the vase that contains it,' said the well-known voice of Li Ting. 'Let not the lion and the tiger fight at the bidding of the jackal. By combining our forces all may be well with you yet. Assist me to dispose of the entirely superfluous Yung Chang and to marry the elegant and symmetrical Ning, and in return I will allot to you a portion of my not inconsiderable income.'

"'However high the tree, the leaves fall to the ground, and your hour has come at last, O detestable Li Ting!' said Yung, who had heard the speakers, and crept upon them unperceived. 'As for my distinguished and immaculate father-in-law, doubtless the heat has affected his indefatigable brains, or he would not have listened to your contemptible suggestion. For yourself, draw!'

"Both swords flashed, but before a blow could be struck the spirits of his ancestors hurled Li Ting lifeless to the ground, to avenge the memories that their unworthy descendant had so often reviled.

"'So perish all the enemies of Yung Chang,' said the victor. 'And now, my venerated but exceedingly short-sighted father-in-law, learn how narrowly you have escaped making yourself exceedingly objectionable to yourself. I have just received intelligence from Pekin that I have passed the second degree, and have in consequence been appointed to a remunerative position under the Government. This will enable us to live in comfort, if not in affluence, and the rest of your engaging days can be peacefully spent in flying kites.'"

Stephen Leacock

Stephen Leacock, the Canadian Master, is Emeritus Professor of Political Economy in McGill University, Montreal. His wit is not, however, the quizzical, donnish irony of the scholarly tradition. Rather is it marked by gusto, by a magnificent boyish exuberance. By sheer force of character, he has been able to surmount the academic distrust which it has aroused.

SOAKED IN SEAWEED

It was in August in 1867 that I stepped on board the deck of the *Saucy Sally,* lying in dock at Gravesend, to fill the berth of second mate.

Let me first say a word about myself.

I was a tall, handsome young fellow, squarely and powerfully built, bronzed by the sun and the moon (and even copper-coloured in spots from the effect of the stars), and with a face in which honesty, intelligence, and exceptional brain power were combined with Christianity, simplicity, and modesty.

As I stepped on the deck I could not help a slight feeling of triumph, as I caught sight of my sailor-like features reflected in a tar-barrel that stood beside the mast, while a little later I could scarcely repress a sense of gratification as I noticed them reflected again in a bucket of bilge water.

"Welcome on board, Mr. Blowhard," called out Captain Bilge, stepping out of the binnacle and shaking hands across the taffrail.

I saw before me a fine sailor-like man of from thirty to sixty, clean-shaven, except for an enormous pair of whiskers, a heavy beard, and a thick moustache, powerful in build, and carrying his beam well aft, in a pair of broad duck trousers across the back of which there would have been room to write a history of the British Navy.

Beside him were the first and third mates, both of them being quiet men of poor stature, who looked at Captain Bilge with what seemed to me an apprehensive expression in their eyes.

The vessel was on the eve of departure. Her deck presented that scene of bustle and alacrity dear to the sailor's heart. Men were busy nailing up the masts, hanging the bowsprit over the side, varnishing the lee-scuppers and pouring hot tar down the companion-way.

Captain Bilge, with a megaphone to his lips, kept calling out to the men in his rough sailor fashion:

"Now, then, don't over-exert yourselves, gentlemen. Remember, please, that we have plenty of time. Keep out of the sun as much as you can. Step carefully in the rigging there, Jones; I fear it's just a little high for you. Tut, tut, Williams, don't get yourself so dirty with that tar, you won't look fit to be seen."

I stood leaning over the gaff of the mainsail and thinking—yes, thinking, dear reader, of my mother. I hope that you will think none the less of me for that. Whenever things look dark, I lean up against something and think of mother. If they get positively black, I stand on one leg and think of father. After that I can face anything.

Did I think, too, of another, younger than mother and fairer than father? Yes, I did. "Bear up, darling," I had whispered as she nestled her head beneath my oilskins and kicked out backward with one heel in the agony of her girlish grief, "in five years the voyage will be over, and after three more like it, I shall come back with money enough to buy a second-hand fishing-net and settle down on shore."

Meantime the ship's preparations were complete. The masts were all in position, the sails nailed up, and men with axes were busily chopping away the gangway.

"All ready?" called the Captain.

"Aye, aye, sir."

"Then hoist the anchor in board and send a man down with the key to open the bar."

Opening the bar! the last sad rite of departure. How often in my voyages have I seen it; the little group of men soon to be exiled from their home, standing about with saddened faces, waiting to see the man with the key open the bar—held there by some strange fascination.

Next morning with a fair wind astern we had buzzed around the corner of England and were running down the Channel.

I know no finer sight, for those who have never seen it, than the English Channel. It is the highway of the world. Ships of all nations are passing up and down, Dutch, Scotch, Venezuelan, and even American.

Chinese junks rush to and fro. Warships, motor yachts, icebergs, and lumber rafts are everywhere. If I add to this fact that so thick a fog hangs over it that it is entirely hidden from sight, my readers can form some idea of the majesty of the scene.

We had now been three days at sea. My first sea-sickness was wearing off, and I thought less of father.

On the third morning, Captain Bilge descended to my cabin.

"Mr. Blowhard," he said, "I must ask you to stand double watches."

"What is the matter?" I enquired.

"The two other mates have fallen overboard," he said uneasily, and avoiding my eye.

I contented myself with saying, "Very good, sir," but I could not help thinking it a trifle odd that both the mates should have fallen overboard in the same night.

Surely there was some mystery in this.

Two mornings later the Captain appeared at the breakfast-table with the same shifting and uneasy look in his eye.

"Anything wrong, sir?" I asked.

"Yes," he answered, trying to appear at ease and twisting a fried egg to and fro between his fingers with such nervous force as almost to break it in two—"I regret to say that we have lost the bosun."

"The bosun!" I cried.

"Yes," said Captain Bilge more quietly, "he is overboard. I blame myself for it, partly. It was early this morning. I was holding him up in my arms to look at an iceberg, and, quite accidentally, I assure you— I dropped him overboard."

"Captain Bilge," I asked, "have you taken any steps to recover him?"

"Not as yet," he replied uneasily.

I looked at him fixedly, but said nothing.

Ten days passed.

The mystery thickened. On Thursday two men of the starboard watch were reported missing. On Friday the carpenter's assistant disappeared. On the night of Saturday a circumstance occurred which, slight as it was, gave me some clue as to what was happening.

As I stood at the wheel about midnight, I saw the Captain approach in the darkness carrying the cabin-boy by the hind leg. The lad was a bright little fellow, whose merry disposition had already endeared him to me, and I watched with some interest to see what the Captain would do to him. Arrived at the stern of the vessel, Captain Bilge looked cautiously around a moment and then dropped the boy into the sea. For a brief instant the lad's head appeared in the phosphorus of the waves. The Captain threw a boot at him, sighed deeply, and went below.

Here then was the key to the mystery! The Captain was throwing the crew overboard. Next morning we met at breakfast as usual.

"Poor little Williams has fallen overboard," said the Captain, seizing a strip of ship's bacon and tearing at it with his teeth as if he almost meant to eat it.

"Captain," I said, greatly excited, stabbing at a ship's loaf in my agitation with such ferocity as almost to drive my knife into it—"You threw that boy overboard!"

"I did," said Captain Bilge, grown suddenly quiet, "I threw them all over and intend to throw the rest. Listen, Blowhard, you are young, ambitious, and trustworthy. I will confide in you."

Perfectly calm now, he stepped to a locker, rummaged in it a moment, and drew out a faded piece of yellow parchment, which he spread on the table. It was a map or chart. In the centre of it was a circle. In the middle of the circle was a small dot and a letter T, while at one side of the map was a letter N, and against it on the other side a letter S.

"What is this?" I asked.

"Can you not guess?" queried Captain Bilge. "It is a desert island."

"Ah!" I rejoined with a sudden flash of intuition, "and N is for North and S is for South."

"Blowhard," said the Captain, striking the table with such force as to cause a loaf of ship's bread to bounce up and down three or four times, "you've struck it. That part of it had not yet occurred to me."

"And the letter T?" I asked.

"The treasure, the buried treasure," said the Captain, and turning the map over he read from the back of it—"The point T indicates the spot where the treasure is buried under the sand; it consists of half a million Spanish dollars, and is buried in a brown leather dress-suit case."

"And where is the island?" I enquired, mad with excitement.

"That I do not know," said the Captain. "I intend to sail up and down the parallels of latitude until I find it."

"And meantime?"

"Meantime, the first thing to do is to reduce the number of the crew so as to have fewer hands to divide among. Come, come," he added in a burst of frankness which made me love the man in spite of his shortcomings, "will you join me in this? We'll throw them all over, keeping the cook to the last, dig up the treasure, and be rich for the rest of our lives."

Reader, do you blame me if I said yes? I was young, ardent, ambitious, full of bright hopes and boyish enthusiasm.

"Captain Bilge," I said, putting my hand in his, "I am yours."

"Good," he said, "now go forward to the forecastle and get an idea what the men are thinking."

I went forward to the men's quarters—a plain room in the front of the ship, with only a rough carpet on the floor, a few simple arm-chairs, writing desks, spittoons of a plain pattern, and small brass beds with blue-and-green screens. It was Sunday morning, and the men were mostly sitting about in their dressing-gowns.

They rose as I entered and curtseyed.

"Sir," said Tompkins, the bosun's mate, " I think it my duty to tell you that there is a great deal of dissatisfaction among the men."

Several of the men nodded.

"They don't like the way the men keep going overboard," he continued, his voice rising to a tone of uncontrolled passion. "It is positively absurd, sir, and if you will allow me to say so, the men are far from pleased."

"Tompkins," I said sternly, "you must understand that my position will not allow me to listen to mutinous language of this sort."

I returned to the Captain. "I think the men mean mutiny," I said.

"Good," said Captain Bilge, rubbing his hands, "that will get rid of a lot of them, and of course," he added musingly, looking out of the broad old-fashioned port-hole at the stern of the cabin, at the heaving waves of the South Atlantic, "I am expecting pirates at any time, and that will take out quite a few of them. However"—and here he pressed the bell for a cabin-boy—"kindly ask Mr. Tompkins to step this way."

"Tompkins," said the Captain as the bosun's mate entered, "be good enough to stand on the locker and stick your head through the stern port-hole, and tell me what you think of the weather."

"Aye, aye, sir," replied the tar with a simplicity which caused us to exchange a quiet smile.

Tompkins stood on the locker and put his head and shoulders out of the port.

Taking a leg each we pushed him through. We heard him plump into the sea.

"Tompkins was easy," said Captain Bilge. "Excuse me as I enter his death in the log."

"Yes," he continued presently, "it will be a great help if they mutiny. I suppose they will, sooner or later. It's customary to do so. But I shall take no step to precipitate it until we have first fallen in with pirates. I am expecting them in these latitudes at any time. Meantime, Mr. Blowhard," he said, rising, "if you can continue to drop overboard one or two more each week, I shall feel extremely grateful."

Three days later we rounded the Cape of Good Hope and entered upon the inky waters of the Indian Ocean. Our course lay now in zigzags and, the weather being favourable, we sailed up and down at a furious rate over a sea as calm as glass.

On the fourth day a pirate ship appeared. Reader, I do not know if you have ever seen a pirate ship. The sight was one to appall the stoutest heart. The entire ship was painted black, a black flag hung at the masthead, the sails were black, and on the deck people dressed all in black walked up and down arm-in-arm. The words "Pirate Ship" were painted in white letters on the bow. At the sight of it our crew were visibly cowed. It was a spectacle that would have cowed a dog.

The two ships were brought side by side. They were then lashed tightly together with bag string and binder twine, and a gang plank laid between them. In a moment the pirates swarmed upon our deck, rolling their eyes, gnashing their teeth and filing their nails.

Then the fight began. It lasted two hours—with fifteen minutes off for lunch. It was awful. The men grappled with one another, kicked one another from behind, slapped one another across the face, and in many cases completely lost their temper and tried to bite one another. I noticed one gigantic fellow brandishing a knotted towel, and striking right and left among our men, until Captain Bilge rushed at him and struck him flat across the mouth with a banana skin.

At the end of two hours, by mutual consent, the fight was declared a draw. The points standing at sixty-one and a half against sixty-two.

The ships were unlashed, and with three cheers from each crew, were headed on their way.

"Now, then," said the Captain to me aside, "let us see how many of the crew are sufficiently exhausted to be thrown overboard."

He went below. In a few minutes he reappeared, his face deadly pale. "Blowhard," he said, "the ship is sinking. One of the pirates (sheer accident, of course, I blame no one) has kicked a hole in the side. Let us sound the well."

We put our ear to the ship's well. It sounded like water.

The men were put to the pumps and worked with the frenzied effort which only those who have been drowned in a sinking ship can understand.

At 6 P.M. the well marked one-half an inch of water, at nightfall, three-quarters of an inch, and at daybreak, after a night of unremitting toil, seven-eighths of an inch.

By noon of the next day the water had risen to fifteen-sixteenths of an inch, and on the next night the sounding showed thirty-one thirty-seconds of an inch of water in the hold. The situation was desperate. At this rate of increase few, if any, could tell where it would rise to in a few days.

That night the Captain called me to his cabin. He had a book of mathematical tables in front of him, and great sheets of vulgar fractions littered the floor on all sides.

"The ship is bound to sink," he said, "in fact, Blowhard, she is sinking. I can prove it. It may be six months or it may take years, but if she goes on like this, sink she must. There is nothing for it but to abandon her."

That night, in the dead of darkness, while the crew were busy at the pumps, the Captain and I built a raft.

Unobserved we cut down the masts, chopped them into suitable lengths, laid them crosswise in a pile and lashed them tightly together with bootlaces.

Hastily we threw on board a couple of boxes of food and bottles of drinking fluid, a sextant, a chronometer, a gas-meter, a bicycle pump, and a few other scientific instruments. Then taking advantage of a roll in the motion of the ship, we launched the raft, lowered ourselves upon a line, and under cover of the heavy dark of a tropical night, we paddled away from the doomed vessel.

The break of day found us a tiny speck on the Indian Ocean. We looked about as big as this (.).

In the morning, after dressing, and shaving as best we could, we opened our box of food and drink.

Then came the awful horror of our situation.

One by one the Captain took from the box the square blue tins of corned beef which it contained. We counted fifty-two in all. Anxiously and with drawn faces we watched until the last can was lifted from the box. A single thought was in our minds. When the end came the Captain stood up on the raft with wild eyes staring at the sky.

"The can-opener!" he shrieked, "just Heaven, the can-opener." He fell prostrate.

Meantime, with trembling hands, I opened the box of bottles. It contained lager beer bottles, each with a patent tin top. One by one I took them out. There were fifty-two in all. As I withdrew the last one and saw the empty box before me, I shroke out—"The thing! the thing! oh, merciful Heaven! The thing you open them with!"

I fell prostrate upon the Captain.

We awoke to find ourselves still a mere speck upon the ocean. We felt even smaller than before.

Over us was the burnished copper sky of the tropics. The heavy, leaden sea lapped the sides of the raft. All about us was a litter of corn beef cans and lager beer bottles. Our sufferings in the ensuing days were indescribable. We beat and thumped at the cans with our fists. Even at the risk of spoiling the tins for ever we hammered them fiercely against the raft. We stamped on them, bit at them and swore at them. We pulled and clawed at the bottles with our hands, and chipped and knocked them against the cans, regardless even of breaking the glass and ruining the bottles.

It was futile.

Then day after day we sat in moody silence, gnawed with hunger, with nothing to read, nothing to smoke, and practically nothing to talk about.

On the tenth day the Captain broke silence.

"Get ready the lots, Blowhard," he said. "It's got to come to that."

"Yes," I answered drearily, "we're getting thinner every day."

Then, with the awful prospect of cannibalism before us, we drew lots.

I prepared the lots and held them to the Captain. He drew the longer one.

"Which does that mean," he asked, trembling between hope and despair. "Do I win?"

"No, Bilge," I said sadly, "you lose."

But I mustn't dwell on the days that followed—the long quiet days of lazy dreaming on the raft, during which I slowly built up my strength, which had been shattered by privation. They were days, dear reader, of deep and quiet peace, and yet I cannot recall them without shedding a tear for the brave man who made them what they were.

It was on the fifth day after that I was awakened from a sound sleep by the bumping of the raft against the shore. I had eaten perhaps over-heartily, and had not observed the vicinity of land.

Before me was an island, the circular shape of which, with its low, sandy shore, recalled at once its identity.

"The treasure island," I cried, "at last I am rewarded for all my heroism."

In a fever of haste I rushed to the centre of the Island. What was the sight that confronted me? A great hollow scooped in the sand, an empty dress-suit case lying beside it, and on a ship's plank driven deep into the sand, the legend, "*Saucy Sally,* October, 1867." So! the miscreants had made good the vessel, headed it for the island of whose existence they must have learned from the chart we so carelessly left upon the cabin table, and had plundered poor Bilge and me of our well-earned treasure!

Sick with the sense of human ingratitude I sank upon the sand.

The island became my home.

There I eked out a miserable existence, feeding on sand and gravel and dressing myself in cactus plants. Years passed. Eating sand and mud slowly undermined my robust constitution. I fell ill. I died. I buried myself.

Would that others who write sea stories would do as much.

WITH THE PHOTOGRAPHER

"I want my photograph taken," I said. The photographer looked at me without enthusiasm. He was a drooping man in a grey suit, with the dim eye of a natural scientist. But there is no need to describe him. Everybody knows what a photographer is like.

"Sit there," he said, "and wait."

I waited an hour. I read the *Ladies Companion* for 1912, the *Girls Magazine* for 1902 and the *Infants Journal* for 1888. I began to see that I had done an unwarrantable thing in breaking in on the privacy of this man's scientific pursuits with a face like mine.

After an hour the photographer opened the inner door.

"Come in," he said severely.

I went into the studio.

"Sit down," said the photographer.

I sat down in a beam of sunlight filtered through a sheet of factory cotton hung against a frosted skylight.

The photographer rolled a machine into the middle of the room and crawled into it from behind.

He was only in it a second—just time enough for one look at me,— and then he was out again, tearing at the cotton sheet and the window panes with a hooked stick, apparently frantic for light and air.

Then he crawled back into the machine again and drew a little black cloth over himself. This time he was very quiet in there. I knew that he was praying and I kept still.

When the photographer came out at last, he looked very grave and shook his head.

"The face is quite wrong," he said.

"I know," I answered quietly; "I have always known it."

He sighed.

"I think," he said, "the face would be better three-quarters full."

"I'm sure it would," I said enthusiastically, for I was glad to find that the man had such a human side to him. "So would yours. In fact," I continued, "how many faces one sees that are apparently hard, narrow, limited, but the minute you get them three-quarters full they get wide, large, almost boundless in—"

But the photographer had ceased to listen. He came over and took my head in his hands and twisted it sideways. I thought he meant to kiss me, and I closed my eyes.

But I was wrong.

He twisted my face as far as it would go and then stood looking at it.

He sighed again.

"I don't like the head," he said.

Then he went back to the machine and took another look.

"Open the mouth a little," he said.

I started to do so.

"Close it," he added quickly.

Then he looked again.

"The ears are *bad,*" he said; "droop them a little more. Thank you. Now the eyes. Roll them in under the lids. Put the hands on the knees, please, and turn the face just a little upward. Yes, that's better. Now just expand the lungs! So! And hump the neck—that's it—and just contract the waist—ha!—and twist the hip up toward the elbow— now! I still don't quite like the face, it's just a trifle *too* full, but—"

I swung myself round on the stool.

"Stop," I said with emotion but, I think, with dignity. "This face is *my* face. It is not yours, it is mine. I've lived with it for forty years and I know its faults. I know it's out of drawing. I know it wasn't made for me, but it's *my* face, the only one I have—" I was conscious of a break in my voice but I went on—"such as it is, I've learned to love it. And this is my mouth, not yours. These ears are *mine,* and if your machine is too narrow—" Here I started to rise from the seat.

Snick!

The photographer had pulled a string. The photograph was taken. I could see the machine still staggering from the shock.

"I think," said the photographer, pursing his lips in a pleased smile, "that I caught the features just in a moment of animation."

"So!" I said bitingly,—"features, eh? You didn't think I could animate them, I suppose? But let me see the picture."

"Oh, there's nothing to see yet," he said. "I have to develop the negative first. Come back on Saturday and I'll let you see a proof of it."

On Saturday I went back.

The photographer beckoned me in. I thought he seemed quieter and graver than before. I think, too, there was a certain pride in his manner.

He unfolded the proof of a large photograph, and we both looked at it in silence.

"Is it me?" I asked.

"Yes," he said quietly, "it is you," and we went on looking at it.

"The eyes," I said hesitatingly, "don't look very much like mine."

"Oh, no," he answered, "I've retouched them. They come out splendidly, don't they?"

"Fine," I said, "but surely my eyebrows are not like that?"

"No," said the photographer, with a momentary glance at my face, "the eyebrows are removed. We have a process now—the Delphide—for putting in new ones. You'll notice here where we've applied it to carry the hair away from the brow. I don't like the hair low on the skull."

"Oh, you don't, don't you?" I said.

"No," he went on, "I don't care for it. I like to get the hair clear back to the superficies and make out a new brow line."

"What about the mouth?" I said with a bitterness that was lost on the photographer; "is that mine?"

"It's adjusted a little," he said, "yours is too low. I found I couldn't use it."

"The ears, though," I said, "strike me as a good likeness; they're just like mine."

"Yes," said the photographer thoughtfully, "that's so; but I can fix that all right in the print. We have a process now—the Sulphide—for removing the ears entirely. I'll see if—"

"Listen!" I interrupted, drawing myself up and animating my features to their full extent and speaking with a withering scorn that should have blasted the man on the spot. "Listen! I came here for a photograph—a picture—something which (mad though it seems) would have looked like me. I wanted something that would depict my face as Heaven gave it to me, humble though the gift may have been. I wanted something that my friends might keep after my death, to reconcile them to my loss. It seems that I was mistaken. What I wanted is no longer done. Go on, then, with your brutal work. Take your negative, or whatever it is you call it,—dip it in sulphide, bromide, oxide, cowhide,—anything you like,—remove the eyes, correct the mouth, adjust the face, restore the lips, reanimate the necktie and reconstruct the waistcoat. Coat it with an inch of gloss, shade it, emboss it, gild it, till even you acknowledge that it is finished. Then when you have done all that—keep it for yourself and your friends. They may value it. To me it is but a worthless bauble."

I broke into tears and left.

Saki (H. H. Munro)

Saki's talent was one of the most original in English letters. He pretended to be a tea-table bloom, telling anecdotes of frivolity and quaint horror in a dainty chippendale style. But, though over age, he enlisted in August, 1914, refused every opportunity to gain a commission, and was killed in action in 1916.

TEA

James Cushat-Prinkly was a young man who had always had a settled conviction that one of these days he would marry; up to the age of thirty-four he had done nothing to justify that conviction. He liked and admired a great many women collectively and dispassionately without singling out one for especial matrimonial consideration, just as one might admire the Alps without feeling that one wanted any particular peak as one's own private property. His lack of initiative in this matter aroused a certain amount of impatience among the sentimentally minded women-folk of his home circle; his mother, his sisters, an aunt-in-residence, and two or three intimate matronly friends regarded his dilatory approach to the married state with a disapproval that was far from being inarticulate. His most innocent flirtations were watched with the straining eagerness which a group of unexercised terriers concentrates on the slightest movements of a human being who may be reasonably considered likely to take them for a walk. No decent-souled mortal can long resist the pleading of several pairs of walk-beseeching dog-eyes; James Cushat-Prinkly was not sufficiently obstinate or indifferent to home influences to disregard the obviously expressed wish of his family that he should ·become enamoured of some nice marriageable girl, and when his Uncle Jules departed this life and bequeathed him a comfortable little legacy it really seemed the correct thing to do to set about discovering someone to share it with him. The process of discovery was carried on more by the force of suggestion and the weight of public opinion than by any initiative of his own; a clear working majority of his female relatives and the

473

aforesaid matronly friends had pitched on Joan Sebastable as the most suitable young woman in his range of acquaintance to whom he might propose marriage, and James became gradually accustomed to the idea that he and Joan would go together through the prescribed stages of congratulations, present-receiving, Norwegian or Mediterranean hotels, and eventual domesticity. It was necessary, however, to ask the lady what she thought about the matter; the family had so far conducted and directed the flirtation with ability and discretion, but the actual proposal would have to be an individual effort.

Cushat-Prinkly walked across the Park towards the Sebastable residence in a frame of mind that was moderately complacent. As the thing was going to be done he was glad to feel that he was going to get it settled and off his mind that afternoon. Proposing marriage, even to a nice girl like Joan, was a rather irksome business, but one could not have a honeymoon in Minorca and a subsequent life of married happiness without such preliminary. He wondered what Minorca was really like as a place to stop in; in his mind's eye it was an island in perpetual half-mourning, with black or white Minorca hens running all over it. Probably it would not be a bit like that when one came to examine it. People who had been in Russia had told him that they did not remember having seen any Muscovy ducks there, so it was possible that there would be no Minorca fowls on the island.

His Mediterranean musings were interrupted by the sound of a clock striking the half-hour. Half-past four. A frown of dissatisfaction settled on his face. He would arrive at the Sebastable mansion just at the hour of afternoon tea. Joan would be seated at a low table, spread with an array of silver kettles and cream-jugs and delicate porcelain teacups, behind which her voice would tinkle pleasantly in a series of little friendly questions about weak or strong tea, how much, if any, sugar, milk, cream, and so forth. "Is it one lump? I forgot. You do take milk, don't you? Would you like some more hot water, if it's too strong?"

Cushat-Prinkly had read of such things in scores of novels, and hundreds of actual experiences had told him that they were true to life. Thousands of women, at this solemn afternoon hour, were sitting behind dainty porcelain and silver fittings, with their voices tinkling pleasantly in a cascade of solicitous little questions. Cushat-Prinkly detested the whole system of afternoon tea. According to his theory of life a woman should lie on a divan or couch, talking with incomparable charm or looking unutterable thoughts, or merely silent as a thing to be looked on, and from behind a silken curtain a small Nubian page should silently bring in a tray with cups and dainties, to be accepted silently, as a matter of course, without drawn-out chatter about cream and sugar and hot water. If one's soul was really enslaved at one's mistress's feet, how could one talk coherently about weakened tea? Cushat-Prinkly had never expounded his views on the subject to his mother; all her life she had been accustomed to tinkle pleasantly at tea-time behind dainty porcelain and silver, and if he had spoken to her about divans and Nubian pages she would have urged him to take a week's holiday at the seaside. Now, as he passed through a tangle of small streets that led indirectly to the elegant Mayfair terrace for which he was bound, a horror at the idea of confronting Joan Sebastable at her tea-table seized on him. A momentary deliverance presented itself; on one floor of a narrow little house at the noisier end of Esquimault Street lived Rhoda Ellam, a sort of remote cousin, who made a living by creating hats out of costly materials. The hats really looked as if they had come from Paris; the cheques she got for them unfortunately never looked as if they were going to Paris. However, Rhoda appeared to find life amusing and to have a fairly good time in spite of her straitened circumstances. Cushat-Prinkly decided to climb up to her floor and defer by half-an-hour or so the important business which lay before him; by spinning out his visit he could contrive to reach the Sebastable mansion after the last vestige of dainty porcelain had been cleared away.

Rhoda welcomed him into a room that seemed to do duty as workshop, sitting-room, and kitchen combined, and to be wonderfully clean and comfortable at the same time.

"I'm having a picnic meal," she announced. "There's caviare in that jar at your elbow. Begin on that brown bread-and-butter while I cut some more. Find yourself a cup; the teapot is behind you. Now tell me about hundreds of things."

She made no other allusion to food, but talked amusingly and made her visitor talk amusingly too. At the same time she cut the bread-and-butter with a masterly skill and produced red pepper and sliced lemon, where so many women would merely have produced reasons and regrets for not having any. Cushat-Prinkly found that he was enjoying an excellent tea without having to answer as many questions about it as a Minister for Agriculture might be called on to reply to during an outbreak of cattle plague.

"And now tell me why you have come to see me," said Rhoda suddenly. "You arouse not merely my curiosity but my business instincts. I hope you've come about hats. I heard that you had come into a legacy the other day, and, of course, it struck me that it would be a beautiful and desirable thing for you to celebrate the event by buying brilliantly expensive hats for all your sisters. They may not have said anything about it, but I feel sure the same idea has occurred to them. Of course, with Goodwood on us, I am rather rushed just now, but in my business we're accustomed to that; we live in a series of rushes —like the infant Moses."

"I didn't come about hats," said her visitor. "In fact, I don't think I really came about anything. I was passing and just thought I'd look in and see you. Since I've been sitting talking to you, however, a rather important idea has occurred to me. If you'll forget Goodwood for a moment and listen to me, I'll tell you what it is."

Some forty minutes later James Cushat-Prinkly returned to the bosom of his family, bearing an important piece of news.

"I'm engaged to be married," he announced.

A rapturous outbreak of congratulation and self-applause broke out. "Ah, we knew! We saw it coming! We foretold it weeks ago!"

"I'll bet you didn't," said Cushat-Prinkly. "If any one had told me at lunch-time today that I was going to ask Rhoda Ellam to marry me and that she was going to accept me, I would have laughed at the idea."

The romantic suddenness of the affair in some measure compensated James's women-folk for the ruthless negation of all their patient effort and skilled diplomacy. It was rather trying to have to deflect their enthusiasm at a moment's notice from Joan Sebastable to Rhoda Ellam; but, after all, it was James's wife who was in question, and his tastes had some claim to be considered.

On a September afternoon of the same year, after the honeymoon in Minorca had ended, Cushat-Prinkly came into the drawing-room of his new house in Granchester Square. Rhoda was seated at a low table, behind a service of dainty porcelain and gleaming silver. There was a pleasant tinkling note in her voice as she handed him a cup.

"You like it weaker than that, don't you? Shall I put some more hot water to it? No?"

THE RETICENCE OF LADY ANNE

Egbert came into the large, dimly lit drawing-room with the air of a man who is not certain whether he is entering a dovecote or a bomb factory, and is prepared for either eventuality. The little domestic quarrel over the luncheon-table had not been fought to a definite finish, and the question was how far Lady Anne was in a mood to renew or forgo hostilities. Her pose in the arm-chair by the tea-table was rather elaborately rigid; in the gloom of a December afternoon Egbert's pince-nez did not materially help him to discern the expression of her face.

By way of breaking whatever ice might be floating on the surface he made a remark about a dim religious light. He or Lady Anne were accustomed to make that remark between 4:30 and 6 on winter and late autumn evenings; it was a part of their married life. There was no recognised rejoinder to it, and Lady Anne made none.

Don Tarquinio lay astretch on the Persian rug, basking in the fire-light with superb indifference to the possible ill-humour of Lady Anne. His pedigree was as flawlessly Persian as the rug, and his ruff was coming into the glory of its second winter. The page-boy, who had Renaissance tendencies, had christened him Don Tarquinio. Left to themselves, Egbert and Lady Anne would unfailingly have called him Fluff, but they were not obstinate.

Egbert poured himself out some tea. As the silence gave no sign of breaking on Lady Anne's initiative, he braced himself for another Yermak effort.

"My remark at lunch had a purely academic application," he announced; "you seem to put an unnecessarily personal significance into it."

Lady Anne maintained her defensive barrier of silence. The bullfinch lazily filled in the interval with an Air from *Iphigénie en Tauride.* Egbert recognized it immediately, because it was the only air the bullfinch whistled, and he had come to them with the reputation for whistling it. Both Egbert and Lady Anne would have preferred something from *The Yeoman of the Guard,* which was their favourite opera. In matters artistic they had a similarity of taste. They leaned towards the honest and explicit in art, a picture, for instance, that told its own story, with generous assistance from its title. A rider-less warhorse with harness in obvious disarray, staggering into a courtyard full of pale swooning women, and marginally noted "Bad News," suggested to their minds a distinct interpretation of some military catastrophe. They could see what it was meant to convey, and explain it to friends of duller intelligence.

The silence continued. As a rule Lady Anne's displeasure became articulate and markedly voluble after four minutes of introductory muteness. Egbert seized the milk-jug and poured some of its contents into Don Tarquinio's saucer; as the saucer was already full to the brim an unsightly overflow was the result. Don Tarquinio looked on with a surprised interest that evanesced into elaborate unconsciousness when he was appealed to by Egbert to come and drink up some of the spilt matter. Don Tarquinio was prepared to play many roles in life, but a vacuum carpet-cleaner was not one of them.

"Don't you think we're being rather foolish?" said Egbert cheerfully.

If Lady Anne thought so she didn't say so.

"I dare say the fault has been partly on my side," continued Egbert, with evaporating cheerfulness. "After all, I'm only human, you know. You seem to forget that I'm only human."

He insisted on the point, as if there had been unfounded suggestions that he was built on Satyr lines, with goat continuations where the human left off.

The bullfinch recommenced its air from *Iphigénie en Tauride*. Egbert began to feel depressed. Lady Anne was not drinking her tea. Perhaps she was feeling unwell. But when Lady Anne felt unwell she was not wont to be reticent on the subject. "No one knows what I suffer from indigestion" was one of her favourite statements; but the lack of knowledge can only have been caused by defective listening; the amount of information available on the subject would have supplied material for a monograph.

Evidently Lady Anne was not feeling unwell.

Egbert began to think he was being unreasonably dealt with; naturally he began to make concessions.

"I dare say," he observed, taking as central a position on the hearth-rug as Don Tarquinio could be persuaded to concede him, "I may have been to blame. I am willing, if I can thereby restore things to a happier standpoint, to undertake to lead a better life."

He wondered vaguely how it would be possible. Temptations came to him, in middle age, tentatively and without insistence, like a neglected butcher-boy who asks for a Christmas box in February for no more hopeful reason than that he didn't get one in December. He had no more idea of succumbing to them than he had of purchasing the fish-knives and fur boas that ladies are impelled to sacrifice through the medium of advertisement columns during twelve months of the year. Still, there was something impressive in this unasked-for renunciation of possibly latent enormities.

Lady Anne showed no sign of being impressed.

Egbert looked at her nervously through his glasses. To get the worst of an argument with her was no new experience. To get the worst of a monologue was a humiliating novelty.

"I shall go and dress for dinner," he announced in a voice into which he intended some shade of sternness to creep.

At the door a final access of weakness impelled him to make a further appeal.

"Aren't we being very silly?"

"A fool," was Don Tarquinio's mental comment as the door closed on Egbert's retreat. Then he lifted his velvet forepaws in the air and leapt lightly on to a bookshelf immediately under the bullfinch's cage. It was the first time he had seemed to notice the bird's existence, but he was carrying out a long-formed theory of action with the precision of mature deliberation. The bullfinch, who had fancied himself something of a despot, depressed himself of a sudden into a third of his normal displacement; then he fell to a helpless wing-beating and shrill cheeping. He had cost twenty-seven shillings without the cage, but Lady Anne made no sign of interfering. She had been dead for two hours.

Hilaire Belloc

Many humorists get their effects by being dry, sardonic, pince-sans-rire; Hilaire Belloc, on the contrary, uses the exuberant method. He is in the noisy tradition of Rabelais; a very good tradition too. A sincere Catholic, he has developed a special kind of roaring Catholic comedy, which must seem irreverent even to his own side.

THE DRINKING SONG OF PELAGIUS

So we sat outside there upon the benches of the Crabtree Inn, eating bread and cheese.

Now when we had eaten our bread and cheese in that cold, still air, and overlooking so great a scene below us, and when we had drunk yet more of the ale, and also of a port called Jubilee (for the year of Jubilee was, at the time this walk was taken, not more than five years past), the Sailor said in a sort of challenging tone:

"You were saying, I think, that a man could only sing today in certain lonely places, such as all down that trim hedgerow, which is the roadside of Leonard's Lee, and when Grizzlebeard here asked whether a man might sing outside the Crabtree, you said no. But I will make the experiment; and by way of compromise, so that no one may be shocked, my song shall be of a religious sort, dealing with the great truths. And perhaps that will soften the heart of the torturers, if indeed they have orders, as you say, to persecute men for so simple a thing as a song."

GRIZZLEBEARD: "If your song is one upon the divinities, it will not go with ale and with wine, nor with the character of an inn."

THE SAILOR: "Do not be so sure. Wait until you have heard it. For this song that I am proposing to sing is of a good loud roaring sort, but none the less it deals with the ultimate things, and you must know that it is far more than one thousand years old. Now it cannot be properly sung unless the semi-chorus (which I will indicate by raising my hands) is sung loudly by all of you together, nor unless the chorus is bellowed by the lot of you for dear life's sake, until the windows rattle and the populace rise. Such is the nature of the song."

Having said so much then, the Sailor, leaning back, began in a very full and decisive manner to sing this

SONG OF THE PELAGIAN HERESY FOR THE STRENGTHENING OF MEN'S BACKS AND THE VERY ROBUST OUTTHRUSTING OF DOUBTFUL DOCTRINE AND THE UNCERTAIN INTELLECTUAL

Pelagius lived in Kardanoel,
   And taught a doctrine there,
How whether you went to Heaven or Hell,
   It was your own affair.
How, whether you found eternal joy
   Or sank forever to burn,
It had nothing to do with the Church, my boy,
   But was your own concern.

GRIZZLEBEARD: "This song is blasphemous."

THE SAILOR: "Not at all—the exact contrary, it is orthodox. But now I beg of you do not interrupt, for this is the semi-chorus."

SEMI-CHORUS:

Oh, he didn't believe
In Adam and Eve,
   He put no faith therein!
His doubts began
With the fall of man,
   And he laughed at original sin!

In this semi-chorus we all joined, catching it up as he went along, and then the Sailor, begging us to put all our manhood into it, launched upon the chorus itself, which was both strong and simple.

CHORUS:

With my row-ti-tow, ti-oodly-ow,
   He laughed at original sin!

When we had got as far as this, which was the end of the first verse, and defines the matter in hand, the very extravagant noise of it all brought out from their dens not a few of the neighbourhood, who listened and waited to see what would come. But the Sailor, not at all abashed, continued, approaching the second verse.

Whereat the Bishop of old Auxerre
   (Germanus was his name),

He tore great handfuls out of his hair,
    And he called Pelagius Shame:
And then with his stout Episcopal staff
    So thoroughly thwacked and banged
The heretics all, both short and tall,
    They rather had been hanged.

SEMI-CHORUS:

Oh, he thwacked them hard, and he banged them long,
    Upon each and all occasions,
Till they bellowed in chorus, loud and strong,
    Their orthodox persuasions!

CHORUS:

With my row-ti-tow, ti-oodly-ow,
    Their orthodox persu-a-a-sions!

At the end of this second verse the crowd had grown greater, and
not a few of them had dropped their lower jaws and stood with their
mouths wide open, never having heard a song of this kind before. But
the Sailor, looking kindly upon them, and nodding at them, as much
as to say, "You will understand it all in a minute," took on the third
verse, with still greater gusto, and sang:

Now the Faith is old and the Devil is bold,
    Exceedingly bold indeed;
And the masses of doubt that are floating about
    Would smother a mortal creed.
But we that sit in a sturdy youth,
    And still can drink strong ale,
Oh—let us put it away to infallible truth,
    Which always shall prevail!

SEMI-CHORUS:

And thank the Lord
For the temporal sword,
    And howling heretics too;
And whatever good things
Our Christendom brings,
    But especially barley brew!

CHORUS:

With my row-ti-tow, ti-oodly-ow,
    Especially barley brew!

When we had finished this last chorus in a louder mode than all the rest, you may say that half the inhabitants of that hill were standing round. But the Sailor, rising smartly and putting money down upon the table to pay for our fare and somewhat over, bade us all rise with him, which we did, and then he spoke thus to the assembly:

"Good people! I trust you clearly heard every word of what we have just delivered to you, for it is Government business, and we were sent to give it to you just as we had ourselves received it of the Cabinet, whose envoys we are. And let me add for your comfort that this same Government of our Lord the King (his crown and dignity), ever solicitous for the welfare of poorer folk, has given us monies wherewith to refresh all the people of Sussex all our way along. On which account I have left here upon the table, in the name of the aforesaid Right Honourables, a sum of five shillings, against which you may order ale to the breaking point, and so good-day to you. But you are strictly charged that you do not follow us or molest us in any fashion, to the offence of those good Ministers who lie awake at night, considering the good of the people, and the service of our Lord the King (his crown and dignity). *Oyez! Le Roi le veult!*"

And having said this he beckoned us to follow him, and as we strode down the road we heard them all cheering loudly, for they thought that time had come which is spoken of by the Prophet Habakkuk, "When the poor shall be filled and the rich shall be merry." A thing that never yet was since the beginning of the world.

[From *The Four Men*]

CHARLES AUGUSTUS FORTESCUE

Who always Did what was Right, and so accumulated an Immense Fortune

The nicest child I ever knew
Was Charles Augustus Fortescue.
He never lost his cap, or tore
His stockings or his pinafore:
In eating Bread he made no Crumbs,

He was extremely fond of sums,
To which, however, he preferred
The Parsing of a Latin Word—
He sought, when it was in his power,
For information twice an hour,
And as for finding Mutton-Fat
Unappetising, far from that!
He often, at his Father's Board,
Would beg them, of his own accord,
To give him, if they did not mind,
The Greasiest Morsels they could find—
His Later Years did not belie
The Promise of his Infancy.
In Public Life he always tried
To take a judgment Broad and Wide;
In Private, none was more than he
Renowned for quiet courtesy.
He rose at once in his Career,
And long before his Fortieth Year
Had wedded Fifi, Only Child
Of Bunyan, First Lord Aberfylde.
He thus became immensely Rich,
And built the Splendid Mansion which
Is called "The Cedars, Muswell Hill,"
Where he resides in Affluence still,
To show what Everybody might
Become by
                    SIMPLY DOING RIGHT.

LINES TO A DON

Remote and ineffectual Don
That dared attack my Chesterton,
With that poor weapon, half-impelled,
Unlearnt, unsteady, hardly held,
Unworthy for a tilt with men—
Your quavering and corroded pen;

Don poor at Bed and worse at Table,
Don pinched, Don starved, Don miserable;
Don stuttering, Don with roving eyes,
Don nervous, Don of crudities;
Don clerical, Don ordinary,
Don self-absorbed and solitary;
Don here-and-there, Don epileptic;
Don puffed and empty, Don dyspeptic;
Don middle-class, Don sycophantic,
Don dull, Don brutish, Don pedantic;
Don hypocritical, Don bad,
Don furtive, Don three-quarters mad;
Don (since a man must make an end),
Don that shall never be my friend.

Don different from those regal Dons!
With hearts of gold and lungs of bronze,
Who shout and bang and roar and bawl
The Absolute across the hall,
Or sail in amply billowing gown
Enormous through the Sacred Town,
Bearing from College to their homes
Deep cargoes of gigantic tomes;
Dons admirable! Dons of Might!
Uprising on my inward sight
Compact of ancient tales, and port
And sleep—and learning of a sort.
Dons English, worthy of the land;
Dons rooted; Dons that understand.
Good Dons perpetual that remain
A landmark, walling in the plain—
The horizon of my memories—
Like large and comfortable trees.

Don very much apart from these,
Thou scapegoat Don, thou Don devoted,
Don to thine own damnation quoted,
Perplexed to find thy trivial name
Reared in my verse to lasting shame.

Don dreadful, rasping Don and wearing,
Repulsive Don—Don past all bearing.
Don of the cold and doubtful breath,
Don despicable, Don of death;
Don nasty, skimpy, silent, level;
Don evil; Don that serves the devil.
Don ugly—that makes fifty lines.
There is a Canon which confines
A Rhymed Octosyllabic Curse
If written in Iambic Verse
To fifty lines. I never cut;
I far prefer to end it—but
Believe me I shall soon return.
My fires are banked, but still they burn
To write some more about the Don
That dared attack my Chesterton.

ON MUNDANE ACQUAINTANCES

Good morning, Algernon: Good morning, Percy.
Good morning, Mrs. Roebeck. Christ have mercy!

ON A GREAT ELECTION

The accursèd power which stands on Privilege
(And goes with Women, and Champagne and Bridge)
Broke—and Democracy resumed her reign:
(Which goes with Bridge, and Women and Champagne).

FATIGUED

I'm tired of Love: I'm still more tired of Rhyme.
But Money gives me pleasure all the time.

Max Beerbohm

Max Beerbohm is commonly referred to as "the Incomparable Max,"
although some sturdy souls, who prefer the pratfall to the ogle, prefer
"insufferable"; snorting at a fellow who says "for that" instead of
"because." But the stories in Seven Men *are magnificent; I would have*
put one of them here if they hadn't been so often reproduced before.
The parodies in A Christmas Garland *are fine, too, but I have a ruling*
against parodies. Here are a couple of his more robust pieces. Can you
identify the Good Prince?

A GOOD PRINCE

I first saw him one morning of last summer, in the Green Park.
Though short, even insignificant, in stature and with an obvious tendency to be obese, he had that unruffled, Olympian air, which is so sure
a sign of the Blood Royal. In a suit of white linen he looked serenely
cool, despite the heat. Perhaps I should have thought him, had I not
been versed in the *Almanach de Gotha,* a trifle older than he is. He did
not raise his hat in answer to my salute, but smiled most graciously
and made as though he would extend his hand to me, mistaking me, I
doubt not, for one of his friends. Forthwith, a member of his suite
said something to him in an undertone, whereat he smiled again and
took no further notice of me.

I do not wonder the people idolise him. His almost blameless life has
been passed among them, nothing in it hidden from their knowledge.
When they look upon his dear presentment in the photographer's window—the shrewd, kindly eyes under the high forehead, the sparse
locks so carefully distributed—words of loyalty only and of admiration
rise to their lips. For of all princes in modern days he seems to fulfil
most perfectly the obligation of princely rank.

He might have been called in the heroic age, when princes were
judged according to their mastery of the sword or of the bow, or have
seemed, to those mediæval eyes that loved to see a scholar's pate under
the crown, an ignoramus. We are less exigent now. We do but ask

of our princes that they should live among us, be often manifest to our
eyes, set a perpetual example of a right life. We bid them be the ornaments of our State. Too often they do not attain to our ideal. They
give, it may be, a half-hearted devotion to soldiering, or pursue pleasure merely—tales of their frivolity raising now and again the anger
of a public swift to envy them their temptations. But against this admirable Prince no such charges can be made. Never (as yet, at least)
has he cared to "play at soldiers." By no means has he shocked the
Puritans. Though it is no secret that he prefers the society of ladies,
not one breath of scandal has ever tinged his name. Of how many English princes could this be said, in days when Figaro, quill in hand, in-
clines his ear to every keyhole?

Upon one action that were well obliterated from his record I need
not long insist. It seems that the wife of an aged ex-Premier came to
have an audience and pay her respects. Hardly had she spoken when
the Prince, in a fit of unreasoning displeasure, struck her a violent
blow with his clenched fist. Had His Royal Highness not always
stood so far aloof from political contention, it had been easier to find
a motive for this unmannerly blow. The incident is deplorable, but it
belongs, after all, to an earlier period of his life; and, were it not that
no appreciation must rest upon the suppression of any scandal, I
should not have referred to it. For the rest, I find no stain, soever faint,
upon his life. The simplicity of his tastes is the more admirable for
that he is known to care not at all for what may be reported in the
newspapers. He has never touched a card, never entered a play-house.
In no stud of racers has he indulged, preferring to the finest blood-
horse ever bred a certain white and woolly lamb with a blue riband
to its neck. This he is never tired of fondling. It is with him, like the
roebuck of Henri Quatre, wherever he goes.

Suave and simple his life is! Narrow in range, it may be, but with
every royal appurtenance of delight, for to him Love's happy favours
are given and the tribute of glad homage, always, here and there and
every other where. Round the flower-garden at Sandringham runs an
old wall of red brick, streaked with ivy and topped infrequently with
balls of stone. By its iron gates, that open to a vista of flowers, stand
two kind policemen, guarding the Prince's procedure along that bright
vista. As his perambulator rolls out of the gate of St. James's Palace,
he stretches out his tiny hands to the scarlet sentinels. An obsequious
retinue follows him over the lawns of the White Lodge, cooing and

laughing, blowing kisses and praising him. Yet do not imagine his life has been all gaiety! The afflictions that befall royal personages always touch very poignantly the heart of the people, and it is not too much to say that all England watched by the cradle-side of Prince Edward in that dolorous hour, when first the little battlements rose about the rose-red roof of his mouth. I am glad to think that not one querulous word did His Royal Highness, in his great agony, utter. They only say that his loud, incessant cries bore testimony to the perfect lungs for which the House of Hanover is most justly famed. Irreiterate be the horror of that epoch!

As yet, when we know not even what his first words will be, it is too early to predict what verdict posterity will pass upon him. Already he has won the hearts of the people; but in the years which, it is to be hoped, still await him, he may accomplish more. *Attendons!* He stands alone among European princes—but, as yet, only with the aid of a chair.

A HOME-COMING

Belike, returning from a long pilgrimage, in which you have seen many strange men and strange cities, and have had your imagination stirred by marvellous experiences, you have never, at the very end of your journey, almost in sight of your home, felt suddenly that all you had been seeing and learning was as naught—a pack of negligible illusions, faint and forgotten. From me, however, this queer sensation has not been withheld. It befell me a few days ago; in a cold grey dawn, and in the Buffet of Dover Harbour.

I had spent two months far away, wandering and wondering; and now I had just fulfilled two thirds of the little tripartite journey from Paris to London. I was sleepy, as one always is after that brief and twice broken slumber. I was chilly, for is not the dawn always bleak at Dover, and perforated always with a bleak and drizzling rain? I was sad, for I had watched from the deck the white cliffs of Albion coming nearer and nearer to me, towering over me, and in the familiar drizzle looking to me more than ever ghastly for that I had been so long and so far away from them. Often though that harsh, chalky coast had thus borne down on me, I had never yet felt so exactly and lamentably like a criminal arrested on an extradition warrant.

In its sleepy, chilly shell my soul was still shuddering and whimpering. Piteously it conjured me not to take it back into this cruel humdrum. It rose up and fawned on me. "Down, Sir, down!" said I sternly. I pointed out to it that needs must when the devil drives, and that it ought to think itself a very lucky soul for having had two happy, sunny months of fresh and curious adventure. "A sorrow's crown of sorrow," it murmured, "is remembering happier things." I declared the sentiment to be as untrue as was the quotation trite, and told my soul that I looked keenly forward to the pleasure of writing, in collaboration with it, that book of travel for which I had been so sedulously amassing notes and photographs by the way.

This colloquy was held at a table in the Buffet. I was sorry, for my soul's sake, to be sitting there. Britannia owns nothing more crudely and inalienably Britannic than her Buffets. The barmaids are but incarnations of her own self, thinly disguised. The stale buns and the stale sponge-cakes must have been baked, one fancies, by her own heavy hand. Of her everything is redolent. She it is that has cut the thick stale sandwiches, bottled the bitter beer, brewed the unpalatable coffee. Cold and hungry though I was, one sip of this coffee was one sip too much for me. I would not mortify my body by drinking more of it, although I had to mortify my soul by lingering over it till one of the harassed waiters would pause to be paid for it. I was somewhat comforted by the aspect of my fellow-travellers at the surrounding tables. Dank, dishevelled, dismal, they seemed to be resenting as much as I the return to the dear homeland. I suppose it was the contrast between them and him that made me stare so hard at the large young man who was standing on the threshold and surveying the scene.

He looked, as himself would undoubtedly have said, "fit as a fiddle," or "right as rain." His cheeks were rosy, his eyes sparkling. He had his arms akimbo, and his feet planted wide apart. His grey bowler rested on the back of his head, to display a sleek coating of hair plastered down over his brow. In his white satin tie shone a dubious but large diamond, and there was the counter-attraction of geraniums and maidenhair fern in his button-hole. So fresh was the nosegay that he must have kept it in water during the passage! Or perhaps these vegetables had absorbed by mere contact with his tweeds, the subtle secret of his own immarcescibility. I remembered now that I had seen him, without realising him, on the platform of the Gare du Nord. "Gay Paree" was still written all over him. But evidently he was no repiner.

Unaccountable though he was, I had no suspicion of what he was about to do. I think you will hardly believe me when I tell you what he did. "A traveller's tale" you will say, with a shrug. Yet I swear to you that it is the plain and solemn truth. If you still doubt me, you have the excuse that I myself hardly believed the evidence of my eyes. In the Buffet of Dover Harbour, in the cold grey dawn, in the brief interval between boat and train, the large young man, shooting his cuffs, strode forward, struck a confidential attitude across the counter, and began to flirt with the barmaid.

Open-mouthed, fascinated, appalled, I watched this monstrous and unimaginable procedure. I was not near enough to overhear what was said. But I knew by the respective attitudes that the time-honoured ritual was being observed strictly by both parties. I could see the ice of haughty indifference thawing, little by little, under the fire of gallant raillery. I could fix the exact moment when "Indeed?" became "I daresay," and when "Well, I *must* say" gave place to "Go along," and when "Oh, *I* don't mind you—not particularly" was succeeded by "Who gave you them flowers?" ... All in the cold grey dawn....

The cry of "Take your places, please!" startled me into realisation that all the other passengers had vanished. I hurried away, leaving the young man still in the traditional attitude which he had assumed from the first—one elbow sprawling on the counter, one foot cocked over the other. My porter had put my things into a compartment exactly opposite the door of the Buffet. I clambered in.

Just as the guard blew his whistle, the young man or monster came hurrying out. He winked at me. I did not return his wink.

I suppose I ought really to have raised my hat to him. Pre-eminently, he was one of those who have made England what it is. But they are the very men whom one does not care to meet just after a long truancy in preferable lands. He was the backbone of the nation. But ought backbones to be exposed?

Though I would rather not have seen him then and there, I did realise, nevertheless, the overwhelming interest of him. I knew him to be a stranger sight, a more memorable and instructive, than any of the fair sights I had been seeing. He made them all seem nebulous and unreal to me. Beside me lay my despatch-box. I unlocked it, drew from it all the notes and all the photographs I had brought back with me. These, one by one, methodically, I tore up, throwing their fragments out of the window, not grudging them to the wind.

Harry Graham

Harry Graham carried the humor of heartlessness to a point beyond the reach of any of his predecessors. His monstrous babes started a reign of terror throughout the English-speaking world. Every college paper in the early 1900's was filled with monotonous savagery. Everyone remembers his "In the drinking-well, Which the plumber built her, Aunt Eliza fell; We must buy a filter." And his "Billy, in one of his nice new sashes..." Here are three which don't seem to be so well known.

INDIFFERENCE

When Grandmamma fell off the boat,
And couldn't swim (and wouldn't float),
Matilda just stood by and smiled.
I almost could have slapped the child.

COMPENSATION

Weep not for little Léonie
Abducted by a French *Marquis!*
Though loss of honour was a wrench,
Just think how it's improved her French!

WINTER SPORTS

The ice upon our pond's so thin
That poor Mamma has fallen in!
We cannot reach her from the shore
Until the surface freezes more.
Ah me, my heart grows weary waiting—
Besides, I want to have some skating.

G. K. Chesterton

Chesterton represents, to me, the best of the Tory tradition in humor. He attacked steadily, throughout his life, middle-class thought, middle-ground compromise, middle-everything. He could be extremely funny, but his comedy always had a basis of serious conviction. Conviction, of course, is prejudice to the unconvinced.

I have included the Ballade of Suicide, *well known as it is, because it is so beautiful.*

THE PERFECT GAME

We have all met the man who says that some odd things have happened to him, but that he does not really believe that they were supernatural. My own position is the opposite of this. I believe in the supernatural as a matter of intellect and reason, not as a matter of personal experience. I do not see ghosts; I only see their inherent probability. But it is entirely a matter of the mere intelligence, not even of the emotions; my nerves and body are altogether of this earth, very earthy. But upon people of this temperament one weird incident will often leave a peculiar impression. And the weirdest circumstance that ever occurred to me occurred a little while ago. It consisted in nothing less than my playing a game, and playing it quite well for seventeen consecutive minutes. The ghost of my grandfather would have astonished me less.

On one of these blue and burning afternoons I found myself, to my inexpressible astonishment, playing a game called croquet. I had imagined that it belonged to the epoch of Leach and Anthony Trollope, and I had neglected to provide myself with those very long and luxuriant side whiskers which are really essential to such a scene. I played it with a man whom we will call Parkinson, and with whom I had a semi-philosophical argument which lasted through the entire contest. It is deeply implanted in my mind that I had the best of the argument; but it is certain and beyond dispute that I had the worst of the game.

494

"Oh, Parkinson, Parkinson!" I cried, patting him affectionately on the head with a mallet, "how far you really are from the pure love of the sport—you who can play. It is only we who play badly who love the Game itself. You love glory; you love applause; you love the earth-quake voice of victory; you do not love croquet. You do not love croquet until you love being beaten at croquet. It is we the bunglers who adore the occupation in the abstract. It is we to whom it is art for art's sake. If we may see the face of Croquet herself (if I may so express myself) we are content to see her face turned upon us in anger. Our play is called amateurish; and we wear proudly the name of amateur, for amateurs is but the French for Lovers. We accept all adventures from our Lady, the most disastrous or the most dreary. We wait outside her iron gates (I allude to the hoops), vainly essaying to enter. Our devoted balls, impetuous and full of chivalry, will not be confined within the pedantic boundaries of the mere croquet ground. Our balls seek honour in the ends of the earth; they turn up in the flower-beds and the conservatory; they are to be found in the front garden and the next street. No, Parkinson! The good painter has skill. It is the bad painter who loves his art. The good musician loves being a musician, the bad musician loves music. With such a pure and hopeless passion do I worship croquet. I love the game itself. I love the parallelogram of grass marked out with chalk or tape, as if its limits were the frontiers of my sacred Fatherland, the four seas of Britain. I love the mere swing of the mallets, and the click of the balls is music. The four colours are to me sacramental and symbolic, like the red of martyrdom, or the white of Easter Day. You lose all this, my poor Parkinson. You have to solace yourself for the absence of this vision by the paltry consolation of being able to go through hoops and to hit the stick."

And I waved my mallet in the air with a graceful gaiety.

"Don't be too sorry for me," said Parkinson, with his simple sarcasm. "I shall get over it in time. But it seems to me that the more a man likes a game the better he would want to play it. Granted that the pleasure in the thing itself comes first, does not the pleasure of success come naturally and inevitably afterwards? Or, take your own simile of the Knight and his Lady-love. I admit the gentleman does first and foremost want to be in the lady's presence. But I never yet heard of a gentleman who wanted to look an utter ass when he was there."

"Perhaps not; though he generally looks it," I replied. "But the truth is that there is a fallacy in the simile, although it was my own. The happiness at which the lover is aiming is an infinite happiness, which can be extended without limit. The more he is loved, normally speaking, the jollier he will be. It is definitely true that the stronger the love of both lovers, the stronger will be the happiness. But it is not true that the stronger the play of both croquet players the stronger will be the game. It is logically possible—(follow me closely here, Parkinson!)—it is logically possible to play croquet too well to enjoy it at all. If you could put this blue ball through that distant hoop as easily as you could pick it up with your hand, then you would not put it through that hoop any more than you pick it up with your hand; it would not be worth doing. If you could play unerringly you would not play at all. The moment the game is perfect the game disappears."

"I do not think, however," said Parkinson, "that you are in any immediate danger of effecting that sort of destruction. I do not think your croquet will vanish through its own faultless excellence. You are safe for the present."

I again caressed him with the mallet, knocked a ball about, wired myself, and resumed the thread of my discourse.

The long, warm evening had been gradually closing in, and by this time it was almost twilight. By the time I had delivered four more fundamental principles, and my companion had gone through five more hoops, the dusk was verging upon dark.

"We shall have to give this up," said Parkinson, as he missed a ball almost for the first time, "I can't see a thing."

"Nor can I," I answered, "and it is a comfort to reflect that I could not hit anything if I saw it."

With that I struck a ball smartly, and sent it away into the darkness towards where the shadowy figure of Parkinson moved in the hot haze. Parkinson immediately uttered a loud and dramatic cry. The situation, indeed, called for it. I had hit the right ball.

Stunned with astonishment, I crossed the gloomy ground, and hit my ball again. I could not see the hoop; but it was the right hoop. I shuddered from head to foot.

Words were wholly inadequate, so I slouched heavily after that impossible ball. Again I hit it away into the night, in what I supposed was the vague direction of the quite invisible stick. And in the dead silence I heard the stick rattle as the ball struck it heavily.

I threw down my mallet. "I can't stand this," I said. "My ball has gone right three times. These things are not of this world."

"Pick your mallet up," said Parkinson, "have another go."

"I tell you I daren't. If I made another hoop like that I should see all the devils dancing there on the blessed grass."

"Why devils?" asked Parkinson; "they may be only fairies making fun of you. They are sending you the 'Perfect Game,' which is no game."

I looked about me. The garden was full of a burning darkness, in which the faint glimmers had the look of fire. I stepped across the grass as if it burnt me, picked up the mallet, and hit the ball somewhere—somewhere where another ball might be. I heard the dull click of the balls touching, and ran into the house like one pursued.

A BALLADE OF SUICIDE

The gallows in my garden, people say,
Is new and neat and adequately tall.
I tie the noose on in a knowing way
As one that knots his necktie for a ball;
But just as all the neighbours—on the wall—
Are drawing a long breath to shout "Hurray!"
The strangest whim has seized me . . . After all
I think I will not hang myself today.

Tomorrow is the time I get my pay—
My uncle's sword is hanging in the hall—
I see a little cloud all pink and grey—
Perhaps the Rector's mother will *not* call—
I fancy that I heard from Mr. Gall
That mushrooms could be cooked another way—
I never read the works of Juvenal—
I think I will not hang myself today.

The world will have another washing day;
The decadents decay; the pedants pall;
And H. G. Wells has found that children play,
And Bernard Shaw discovered that they squall;

Rationalists are growing rational—
And through thick woods one finds a stream astray,
So secret that the very sky seems small—
I think I will not hang myself today.

ENVOY

Prince, I can hear the trump of Germinal,
The tumbrils toiling up the terrible way;
Even today your royal head may fall—
I think I will not hang myself today.

THE SONG AGAINST GROCERS

God made the wicked Grocer
For a mystery and a sign,
That men might shun the awful shops
And go to inns to dine;
Where the bacon's on the rafter
And the wine is in the wood,
And God that made good laughter
Has seen that they are good.

The evil-hearted Grocer
Would call his mother "Ma'am,"
And bow at her and bob at her,
Her aged soul to damn,
And rub his horrid hands and ask
What article was next,
Though *mortis in articulo*
Should be her proper text.

His props are not his children,
But pert lads underpaid,
Who call out "Cash!" and bang about
To work his wicked trade;

He keeps a lady in a cage
Most cruelly all day,
And makes her count and calls her "Miss"
Until she fades away.

The righteous minds of innkeepers
Induce them now and then
To crack a bottle with a friend
Or treat unmoneyed men,
But who hath seen the Grocer
Treat housemaids to his teas
Or crack a bottle of fish-sauce
Or stand a man a cheese?

He sells us sands of Araby
As sugar for cash down;
He sweeps his shop and sells the dust
The purest salt in town,
He crams with cans of poisoned meat
Poor subjects of the King,
And when they die by thousands
Why, he laughs like anything.

The wicked Grocer groces
In spirits and in wine,
Not frankly and in fellowship
As men in inns do dine;
But packed with soap and sardines
And carried off by grooms,
For to be snatched by Duchesses
And drunk in dressing-rooms.

The hell-instructed Grocer
Has a temple made of tin,
And the ruin of good innkeepers
Is loudly urged therein;
But now the sands are running out
From sugar of a sort,
The Grocer trembles; for his time,
Just like his weight, is short.

Maurice Baring

Some humor is the direct criticism of life, while some is indirect, taking the form of criticism of literature, legend, or familiar history. The lowest manifestations of this indirect humor are the undergraduates' facetious renderings of old dignity in modern slang. The highest manifestations are Maurice Baring's revaluations of the past. His defense of the Lear girls, for instance, is more than comic casuistry, more than an illusive manipulation of moral values; it is real Shakespearean criticism.

KING LEAR'S DAUGHTER

Letter from Goneril, Daughter of King Lear, to her sister Regan

I have writ my sister.
King Lear, Act I, Scene iv.

The Palace, November.

DEAREST REGAN,

I am sending you this letter by Oswald. We have been having the most trying time lately with Papa, and it ended today in one of those scenes which are so painful to people like you and me, who *hate* scenes. I am writing now to tell you all about it, so that you may be prepared. This is what has happened.

When Papa came here he brought a hundred knights with him, which is a great deal more than we could put up, and some of them had to live in the village. The first thing that happened was that they quarrelled with our people and refused to take orders from them, and whenever one told anyone to do anything it was either—if it was one of Papa's men—"not his place to do it"; or if it was one of our men, they said that Papa's people made work impossible. For instance, only the day before yesterday I found that blue vase which you brought back from Dover for me on my last birthday broken to bits. Of course I made a fuss, and Oswald declared that one of Papa's knights had

500

knocked it over in a drunken brawl. I complained to Papa, who flew into a passion and said that his knights, and in fact all his retainers, were the most peaceful and courteous people in the world, and that it was my fault, as I was not treating him or them with the respect which they deserved. He even said that I was lacking in filial duty. I was determined to keep my temper, so I said nothing.

The day after this the chief steward and the housekeeper and both my maids came to me and said that they wished to give notice. I asked them why. They said they couldn't possibly live in a house where there were such "goings-on." I asked them what they meant. They refused to say, but they hinted that Papa's men were behaving not only in an insolent but in a positively outrageous manner to them. The steward said that Papa's knights were never sober, that they had entirely demoralised the household, and that life was simply not worth living in the house; it was *impossible* to get anything done, and they couldn't sleep at night for the noise.

I went to Papa and talked to him about it quite quietly, but no sooner had I mentioned the subject than he lost all self-control, and began to abuse me. I kept my temper as long as I could, but of course one is only human, and after I had borne his revilings for some time, which were monstrously unfair and untrue, I at last turned and said something about people of his age being trying. Upon which he said I was throwing up his old age at him, that I was a monster of ingratitude—and he began to cry. I cannot tell you how painful all this was to me. I did everything I could to soothe him and quiet him, but the truth is, ever since Papa has been here he has lost control of his wits. He suffers from the oddest kind of delusions. He thinks that for some reason he is being treated like a beggar; and although he has a hundred knights—a hundred, mind you! (a great deal more than we have)—in the house, who do nothing but eat and drink all day long, he says he is not being treated like a King! I do hate unfairness.

When he gave up the crown he said he was tired of affairs, and meant to have a long rest; but from the very moment that he handed over the management of affairs to us he never stopped interfering, and was cross if he was not consulted about everything, and if his advice was not taken.

And what is still worse is this: ever since his last illness he has lost not only his memory but his control over language, so that often when he wants to say one thing he says just the opposite, and sometimes when he wishes to say some quite simple thing he uses *bad* language quite unconsciously. Of course we are used to this, and *we* don't mind, but I must say it is very awkward when strangers are here. For instance, the other day before quite a lot of people, quite unconsciously, he called me a dreadful name. Everybody was uncomfortable and tried not to laugh, but some people could not contain themselves. This sort of thing is constantly happening. So you will understand that Papa needs perpetual looking after and management. At the same time, the moment one suggests the slightest thing to him he boils over with rage.

But perhaps the most annoying thing which happened lately, or, at least, the thing which happens to annoy me most, is Papa's Fool. You know, darling, that I have always hated that kind of humour. He comes in just as one is sitting down to dinner, and beats one on the head with a hard, empty bladder, and sings utterly idiotic songs, which make me feel inclined to cry. The other day, when we had a lot of people here, just as we were sitting down in the banqueting-hall, Papa's Fool pulled my chair from behind me so that I fell sharply down on the floor. Papa shook with laughter, and said: "Well done, little Fool," and all the courtiers who were there, out of pure snobbishness, of course, laughed too. I call this not only very humiliating for me, but undignified in an old man and a king; of course Albany refused to interfere. Like all men and all husbands, he is an arrant coward.

However, the crisis came yesterday. I had got a bad headache, and was lying down in my room, when Papa came in from the hunt and sent Oswald to me, saying that he wished to speak to me. I said that I wasn't well, and that I was lying down—which was perfectly true— but that I would be down to dinner. When Oswald went to give my message Papa beat him, and one of his men threw him about the room and really hurt him, so that he has now got a large bruise on his forehead and a sprained ankle.

This was the climax. All our knights came to Albany and myself, and said that they would not stay with us a moment longer unless Papa exercised some sort of control over his men. I did not know what to do, but I knew the situation would have to be cleared up sooner or later. So I went to Papa and told him frankly that the situation was intolerable; that he must send away some of his people, and choose for the remainder men fitting to his age. The words were scarcely out of my mouth than he called me the most terrible names, ordered his horses to be saddled, and said that he would shake the dust from his feet and not stay a moment longer in this house. Albany tried to calm him, and begged him to stay, but he would not listen to a word, and said he would go and live with you.

So I am sending this by Oswald, that you may get it before Papa arrives and know how the matter stands. All I did was to suggest he should send away fifty of his men. Even fifty is a great deal, and puts us to any amount of inconvenience, and is a source of waste and extravagance—two things which I cannot bear. I am perfectly certain you will not be able to put up with his hundred knights any more than I was. And I beg you, my dearest Regan, to do your best to make Papa listen to sense. No one is fonder of him than I am. I think it would have been difficult to find a more dutiful daughter than I have always been. But there is a limit to all things, and one cannot have one's whole household turned into a pandemonium, and one's whole life into a series of wrangles, complaints, and brawls, simply because Papa in his old age is losing the control of his faculties. At the same time, I own that although I kept my temper for a long time, when it finally gave way I was perhaps a little sharp. I am not a saint, nor an angel, nor a lamb, but I do hate unfairness and injustice. It makes my blood boil. But I hope that you, with your angelic nature and your tact and your gentleness, will put everything right and make poor Papa listen to reason.

Let me hear at once what happens.

Your loving

GONERIL

P.S.—Another thing Papa does which is most exasperating is to throw up Cordelia at one every moment. He keeps on saying: "If only Cordelia were here," or "How unlike Cordelia!" And you will remember, darling, that when Cordelia was here Papa could not endure the sight of her. Her irritating trick of mumbling and never speaking up used to get terribly on his nerves. Of course, I thought he was even rather unfair on her, trying as she is. We had a letter from the French Court yesterday, saying that she is driving the poor King of France almost mad.

P.P.S.—It is wretched weather. The poor little ponies on the heath will have to be brought in.

CATHERINE PARR

London. Breakfast chamber in the palace. KING HENRY VIII *and* CATHERINE PARR *are discovered sitting opposite to each other at the breakfast table.* THE KING *has just cracked a boiled egg.*

KING HENRY: My egg's raw. It really is too bad.

CATHERINE: Yesterday you complained of their being hard.

KING HENRY: And so they were. I don't want a hard egg, and I don't want a raw egg. I want them to be cooked just right.

CATHERINE: You are very difficult to please. The egg was in boiling water for three minutes and a half. I boiled it myself. But give it me. I like them like that. I will boil you another.

KING HENRY: No, it's too late now. But it is a fact that you have no idea how to boil an egg. I wish you'd let them do them in the kitchen.

CATHERINE: If they're done in the kitchen you complain because they're not here when you come down, and if they are here, you say they're cold.

KING HENRY: I never say anything of the kind. The cook boils eggs beautifully.

CATHERINE: She shall boil them tomorrow.

KING HENRY: One would have thought that a woman of your experience might at least know how to boil an egg. I hate a watery egg. (*Pensively*) Poor dear Katie used to boil eggs beautifully.

CATHERINE: Do you mean Catherine Howard or Katharine of Aragon?

KING HENRY: I was alluding to poor, dear, misguided Katie Howard. Katharine of Aragon never was my wife. The marriage was not valid.

CATHERINE: Well, Catherine Howard ought to have known how to boil eggs, considering her mother was a kitchenmaid.

KING HENRY: That is utterly untrue. Her mother was a Rochford.

CATHERINE: You're thinking of Anne Bullen.

KING HENRY: Yes, yes, to be sure, Katie's mother was a Somerset.

CATHERINE: You're thinking of Jane Seymour.

KING HENRY: Not at all. Jane Seymour was a sister of Somerset's.

CATHERINE: All I know is that Catherine Howard's mother was a kitchenmaid. And I think it's very unkind of you to mention her to me. I suppose you mean that you wish she were alive, and that you loved her better than you love me.

KING HENRY: I never said anything of the kind. All I said was that she knew how to boil eggs.

CATHERINE: You clearly meant to say that she had all the qualities which I lack.

KING HENRY: You are most unfair. I never meant to hint at any such thing. All I said was that I hate a watery egg, and my egg this morning was raw.

CATHERINE (*rising and going to the door in a temper*): Well, the best thing you can do is to get rid of me, and to marry someone who knows how to boil an egg.

KING HENRY: Catherine, come back! I really didn't mean to offend you. You know how to boil eggs very well.

CATHERINE (*sitting down*): One takes an endless amount of trouble, and that's all the thanks one gets. Don't think that I shall ever boil your eggs for you again, because I shan't.

KING HENRY: I was thinking we might have a little music this morning. I have composed a new ballad which I should like to try over with you. It's for viol and lute and voice. We might try it.

CATHERINE: I'm not sure if I have time. What is it called?

KING HENRY: It's called "The Triumph of Love," and it begins:

"Come list to Alexander's deed,
　　Great Jove's immortal son,
Who, riding on a snow-white steed,
　　To Babylon did come."

CATHERINE: "Son" doesn't rhyme with "come."

KING HENRY: It's not meant to. It's assonance.

CATHERINE: Do you mean Alexander the Great?

KING HENRY: Yes, of course.

CATHERINE: The only thing is, his horse was black.

KING HENRY: No, my dear, you're mistaken; his horse was white.

CATHERINE: Black—black as jet.

KING HENRY: But I know for a fact it was white.

CATHERINE: Alexander's horse was black. Everybody knows it was black.

KING HENRY: It was white. You can ask anyone you like.

CATHERINE: It was black. He was famous for his black horse. There are hundreds of pictures of him on his *black* horse—my father has got one.

KING HENRY: Then the painter made a mistake. Plutarch, Xenophon, Aristotle all mention his *white* horse.

CATHERINE: Black.

KING HENRY: But, my dear, how obstinate you are! I *know* it is white—

CATHERINE: Black, *coal*-black.

KING HENRY: Have you read Xenophon?

CATHERINE: You are thinking of something else. Even when we were children my father always showed us the picture of Alexander's *black* horse.

KING HENRY: Well, I can easily prove it to you. There's a Plutarch here in the bookcase. (*He goes to the bookcase and takes out a book.*)

CATHERINE: I remember it particularly well, because my brother had a black horse and we called it "Bucephalus," after Alexander's *black* horse.

KING HENRY (*turning over the leaves of the book*): If it had been black it would never have been called Bucephalus—it would be absurd to call a black horse Bucephalus.

CATHERINE: Not so absurd as calling a white horse Bucephalus.

KING HENRY: He would never have chosen a black horse. He was superstitious—

CATHERINE: Just because you're superstitious and believe in saints, and worship images, you think everyone else is. As a matter of fact, he chose a black horse on purpose to show he didn't care a pin about superstitions—

KING HENRY: Here it is—χαλεπὸς εἶναι καὶ κομιδῇ δύσχρηστος—"The horse was wild and extremely difficult to manage." In fact, he had all the characteristics of the white Thessalian horses of that day.

CATHERINE: But it doesn't say it was white. And Thessalian horses are famous for being black.

KING HENRY: You really are too obstinate for words. I will find you the proofs in Xenophon. It is distinctly stated that the horse is *white*. It is an historical fact. Nobody has ever disputed it.

CATHERINE: But Plutarch, you see, practically says it was black.

KING HENRY: Plutarch says nothing of the kind. Besides, I now remember talking about this with Wolsey, who was an excellent scholar. I distinctly remember his saying one day: "As white as Bucephalus." It's quite a common phrase among scholars.

CATHERINE: He must have said, "As black as Bucephalus."

KING HENRY: Of course, if you mean to say I tell lies—

CATHERINE: I don't mean that you tell lies, but you are mistaken—that's all.

KING HENRY: But I tell you that there is no mistake possible. I know it as well as I know my own name.

CATHERINE: Your memory plays you tricks. Just now you couldn't remember Catherine Howard's mother's name.

KING HENRY: That's nothing to do with it. Besides, I did remember it. I made a slip, that's all. But this is an historical fact which I've known all my life.

CATHERINE: I quite understand your memory failing you. You have so many names to remember. I expect you were confusing Alexander's black horse with King Alfred's white horse—the white horse of Wantage.

KING HENRY: Good gracious! If you had a smattering of education you wouldn't say such things! It comes of having no religion and no education, and of not knowing Latin. A Lutheran education is worse than none. Even Anne of Cleves knew Latin.

CATHERINE: Thank Heavens, I don't know Latin! Stupid, superstitious language, fit only for bigots and monks!

KING HENRY: I suppose you mean I am a bigot.

CATHERINE: You can turn what one says into meaning anything you like. As a matter of fact, all I said was that the horse was black.

KING HENRY: I'd rather be a bigot than a Lutheran heretic.

CATHERINE: You know you're wrong and you try to escape the point. That's just like a Tudor. No Tudor could ever listen to reason.

KING HENRY: I must ask you not to insult my family.

CATHERINE: You've insulted mine, which is a far older one. My family has no blood on its escutcheon.

KING HENRY: I won't stand this any longer. (*He gets up, opens the door, and calls*) Denny, Butts, Page, who is there?

    (*Enter a* PAGE.)

PAGE: Your Majesty.

KING HENRY: Go and tell the Lord Chamberlain to make the necessary arrangements for transporting the ex-Queen to the Tower.

PAGE (*puzzled*): Yes, your Majesty. Does your Majesty mean the late Queen's remains?

KING HENRY: I said the *ex*-Queen, you stupid boy—Queen Catherine Parr.

PAGE: Yes, your Majesty.

KING HENRY: And tell him to give orders to the Governor of the Tower to have everything ready for the ex-Queen's execution.

PAGE: Is the same ceremonial to be observed as in the case of Queen Catherine Howard, your Majesty?

KING HENRY: Yes; only there need only be one roll of drums instead of two—at the end. (*The* PAGE *goes to the door.*) And on the way ask Dr. Butts whether Alexander the Great's horse was black or white.

CATHERINE: It was black. (*The* PAGE *bows and goes out.*) Well, since I'm to be executed, I daresay you will allow me to go and pack up my things. By the way, you left your lute in my sitting-room yesterday. I will bring it down.

KING HENRY: Wait a minute, there's no hurry.

CATHERINE: I beg your pardon, I have very little time, and a great many letters to write.

KING HENRY (*hesitating*): And I wanted to have some music.

CATHERINE: You don't expect me to accompany you now, I suppose? You had better find someone else. I have got other things to think about during my last moments on earth.

KING HENRY (*laughing uneasily*): I was only joking, of course, my dear. You don't mean to say you took it seriously.

CATHERINE: I am afraid I don't appreciate that kind of joke.

KING HENRY: Come, come; let bygones be bygones, and let us have some music. I want to play you my ballad.

    (*Enter the* PAGE.)

PAGE: If you please, your Majesty, I can't find the Lord Chamberlain, and Dr. Butts says your Majesty was quite correct as to the colour of Alexander the Great's horse.

KING HENRY (*beaming*): Very good; you can go. You need not deliver the message to the Lord Chamberlain. (*The* PAGE *bows and retires*.) And now, my dear, we'll go and play. You see, I knew I was right.

(*The* KING *opens the door with a bow*.)

CATHERINE: It was black, all the same.

KING HENRY (*indulgently, as if speaking to a child*): Yes, yes, my dear, of course it was black, but let's go and have some music.

(*They go out*.)

CURTAIN

Lord Dunsany

There is a hint of eternity about almost everything that Lord Dunsany writes. His wild, soaring Irish imagination has created a humor of his own, to be classed as a subhead under Transcendental Humor.

THE TRUE HISTORY OF THE HARE AND THE TORTOISE

For a long time there was doubt with acrimony among the beasts as to whether the Hare or the Tortoise could run the swifter. Some said the Hare was the swifter of the two because he had such long ears, and others said that the Tortoise was the swifter because anyone whose shell was so hard as that should be able to run hard too. And lo, the forces of estrangement and disorder perpetually postponed a decisive contest.

But when there was nearly war among the beasts, at last an arrangement was come to and it was decided that the Hare and the Tortoise should run a race of five hundred yards so that all should see who was right.

"Ridiculous nonsense!" said the Hare, and it was all his backers could do to get him to run.

"The contest is most welcome to me," said the Tortoise. "I shall not shirk it."

Oh, how his backers cheered.

Feeling ran high on the day of the race; the goose rushed at the fox and nearly pecked him. Both sides spoke loudly of the approaching victory up to the very moment of the race.

"I am absolutely confident of success," said the Tortoise. But the Hare said nothing, he looked bored and cross. Some of his supporters deserted him then and went to the other side, who were loudly cheering the Tortoise's inspiriting words. But many remained with the Hare. "We shall not be disappointed in him," they said. "A beast with such long ears is bound to win."

"Run hard," said the supporters of the Tortoise.

And "run hard" became a kind of catch-phrase which everybody repeated to one another. "Hard shell and hard living. That's what the country wants. Run hard," they said. And these words were never uttered but multitudes cheered from their hearts.

Then they were off, and suddenly there was a hush.

The Hare dashed off for about a hundred yards, then he looked around to see where his rival was.

"It is rather absurd," he said, "to race with a Tortoise." And he sat down and scratched himself. "Run hard! Run hard!" shouted some.

"Let him rest," shouted others. And "let him rest" became a catch-phrase too.

And after a while his rival drew near to him.

"There comes that damned Tortoise," said the Hare, and he got up and ran as hard as he could so that he should not let the Tortoise beat him.

"Those ears will win," said his friends. "Those ears will win; and establish upon an incontestable footing the truth of what we have said." And some of them turned to the backers of the Tortoise and said: "What about your beast now?"

"Run hard," they replied. "Run hard."

The Hare ran on for nearly three hundred yards, nearly in fact as far as the winning-post, when it suddenly struck him what a fool he looked running races with a Tortoise who was nowhere in sight, and he sat down again and scratched.

"Run hard. Run hard," said the crowd, and "Let him rest."

"Whatever is the use of it?" said the Hare, and this time he stopped for good. Some say he slept.

There was desperate excitement for an hour or two, and then the Tortoise won.

"Run hard. Run hard," shouted his backers. "Hard shell and hard living: that's what has done it." And then they asked the Tortoise what his achievement signified, and he went and asked the Turtle. And the Turtle said: "It is a glorious victory for the forces of swiftness." And then the Tortoise repeated it to his friends. And all the beasts said nothing else for years. And even to this day "a glorious victory for the forces of swiftness" is a catch-phrase in the house of the snail.

And the reason that this version of the race is not widely known is that very few of those that witnessed it survived the great forest-fire that happened shortly after. It came up over the weald by night with a great wind. The Hare and the Tortoise and a very few of the beasts saw it far off from a high bare hill that was at the edge of the trees, and they hurriedly called a meeting to decide what messenger they should send to warn the beasts in the forest.

They sent the Tortoise.

A. E. Coppard

The simple villager, with his funny speech and customs, has always amused the refined. A good part of the amusement proceeds from the patronizing air of the writer and reader. "Thank Heaven," they chorus, "that we are not as they are!" A. E. Coppard has found the means to be truthful, poetic, and humorous about simple people without being patronizing. "It would be rather nice," he makes us feel, "to be a simple villager...."

WILLIE WAUGH

On a fine afternoon in April a man is sitting at the foot of an ash-tree beside the pool of water on Peck Common. Twelve tiny ducklings on the water belong to him, and he is admiring them. There are four ash-trees there, growing out of the tenderest turf and spreading over the pool; the bright air seems to swim visibly around their bare grey limbs. A carrier this man is, a little man with an old conical hat, his coat sleeves coming down over his knuckles, his hat coming down over his ears, and he is the masterpiece of the whole district for trapping a mole. Beside him a sallow bush, richly embowered, also stretches out above the pool, every twig of it bearing a ball of blossom covered with yellow dust, whereon fat bees are mumbling and clinging. But the day's air comes coldly from the east, and at intervals the bees, so chilled, tumble into the pool. The man takes a branch he has broken from the palm tree and drags them to earth again, where they dry their wings and crawl into the grass for comfort. "Lend us your saw, Willie Waugh," said Peter Finch, coming suddenly upon him.

"Good evening," said the man in the funny hat, without looking up. He had not noticed Peter's approach, for the grass was quiet under his footfall, and then his ducklings had just paddled to the shore and one of them was behaving queerly. It would not follow his friends, it just kept turning round and turning round, squealing all the time.

Peter Finch asked again: "Will you lend me your saw for a few nights, Willie?"

"Look at that duckling," Waugh indicated the creature with his pipe; "do you know what the matter is with that duckling?"

"I only waunts to borrow it for a few nights," continued Peter Finch, a tall man, a thin man, who shaved in vain so blue was his sharp chin. "The old keeper asked me to fell some trees arter I done my daily work, so it's for a bit of overtime, you see. Your big saw, if you're not a-using of it."

"It's blind, that duckling is," explained the other, "blind."

"I ain't got a saw of my own, Willie, or I wouldn't ask ye,"—Peter was not to be diverted—"I'll take care of it, you knows that, I'll take care of it well."

"I shan't kill it for a day or two, not yet I shan't. I'll see how it gets on. It eats like a blam young tiger," commented Waugh.

"Dan'l Gunn," pursued Peter, "ask me and Hoppy Marlow to fell they trees. We'em a-going to do it between us, overtime work. It'll put three or four pounds apiece in our pockets. If so be as you'd lend us your big saw."

"Blind as a bat," Willie Waugh continued, "that's why he keeps on turning round. It ain't got no tail now, neither."

"I thought Hoppy had got one, but he ain't. He used to have a big saw, I thought; I quite thought that, but he says as how he didn't."

"That foal in Casby's paddock," cried Waugh, "picked it up in its mouth last night and started chawing of it like a wisp of hay. That little duck! That's a fine caper, an' it? I collared that duckling away just in time, but his tail was gone." As disgust and indignation mounted within him, Willie turned and looked Peter Finch fiercely in the eyes. "An I gin him a kick in the stomach as cured him o' duck hunting, I warrant!"

"So I'll send my young Tommy," said Peter, "round for it tomorrow, after tea-time. Right-o." And off went Peter.

Next evening little Tom Finch came to the carrier's door to fetch the saw for his father to fell the trees along of Hoppy Marlow.

"I've changed my mind," declared Willie Waugh, "I can't lend him, tell your father."

"Our father sent me for the saw, please," repeated the child.

"And I tell you I ain't a-going to lend him. Can't you hear? I told you once and now I tell you twice. Tell your father I've changed my mind."

Away went little Tom, and soon afterwards Peter Finch appeared at the door of Waugh's cottage, which was No. 93, Peck Common, although if you took a spyglass, even, you would not, and could not, see more than ten or a dozen cottages there. Willie had crept away to the pool, but Peter saw him and went after him.

"Lend us your saw, Willie Waugh," begged Peter, "I've a job of overtime to do."

"I can't lend you," Willie said.

"Why can't you lend me your big saw?" There was a sharpish note in Peter's voice.

"I've changed my mind."

"And why for have you changed your mind?"

Willie meditated, stared at his interrogator's chest, removed his pipe with his right hand, and with the forefinger of his left he tapped the arm of Peter Finch, and began:

"I'll tell you for why, I'll diagonise it for you. You're a man in full heart of work, from Monday morning to Saturday arternoon; a full week's work, and a full week's pay you draws."

"Ah?"

'Well, there's a-plenty men roundabout here's not doing more than two or three days' work instead of a week, and they's the ones as ought to be set to do this overtime job. When you be in full heart o' work and they be not, you to go and work overtime for another man does them out of the chance."

"Ho, that's how it runs, is it?" commented Peter.

"That's it an' all. Several there be. Two of 'em I knows for certain at Creevey Lane—Moby Colfax for one—and there's Topper Oakes over at Firebrass Hill, and some more I knows. And that's why I shan't a-lend 'ee my saw."

"Topper Oakes! He couldn't fell a nut tree! Look here, did I ever do you a bad turn, Willie Waugh?"

Willie began to fill his pipe. "No, not to my knowledge, I can't say you ever did that."

"Treat me as a neighbour, then, as a neighbour should. Do me no harm. Do me no harm, and I'll do none. Only man I ever harmed is myself. Full work and full pay, says you; but you knows you can put that thirty shillings in your eye and sneeze on it—and *then* it wouldn't choke you."

"I understands all that...."

"Eight young uns I got, a wife, and a cripple mother...."

"Well, that's your look-out, it's your luck. I understands all that. But if you doos this overtime job you're depriving another man of his just dues, and if I lends you my saw I be just as bad."

"How d'ye make that out?"

"Stands to reason. You be a-taking the bread out of a man's mouth. That's truth and sound sense."

Peter Finch stared at him as if he were an absurd phenomenon—an ox with a hat on, perhaps, or a pig with a toothbrush. "You're chattering as if you was the lord mayor of this parish."

"Sound truth and sound sense," repeated Willie, "sound as a bell."

"Ah, and hard as a ram's horn," quoth Peter. "There's many a man as wouldn't ever speak to you again for this, Willie Waugh. You talk of robbing men of their bread: tell me this—Would you lend e'er a one of 'em your big saw?"

"If they asked me," replied Waugh imperturbably, "I might."

"Then wouldn't you be a-robbing me and mine, and Hoppy Marlow and his'n?"

"No!"

"Course you would. Come on, I'll pay you a crown for the use of that saw."

"I couldn't take it," said Waugh, "my conscience wouldn't let me."

"Bah! If I harboured a thing like that I wouldn't call it a conscience! You're a sour neighbour, Willie Waugh, sour as varjuice. I've done a good deed to you, more than once I have, and known you all my life."

"The same to you, many a time!" ejaculated Willie. Then he lit his pipe that he always smoked with the bowl upside down.

"When the wheel of your cart come off on Cadmer Hill," continued Finch, "and we had to unempty it 'cause of a storm coming on..."

"I unemptied it myself," cried the carrier.

"Didn't I carry four sacks of meal home for you? On my back? Half a mile each time, and rain and sweat sopping me through?"

"Who was it drove your missus to the 'firmary when she had her breast off for cancer, eh? A day's journey, that were, free and for nothing!"

"Well, and when you and your wife was down with fever, and no one come near you for fear of catching it, not even the parson, eh? Said he never knew about it...."

"Ah, the Peter!"

"Who looked after you then, Willie Waugh, and your stock, Willie Waugh, and emptied your slops, Willie Waugh?"

"And who collected a subscription for you when your sow died?" rejoined the carrier. "Seven pounds fourteen shillin's and ninepence ha'penny for a pig as warn't worth half that money."

"That's right enough," Peter agreed. "You been a good neighbour, good as a man ever knowed. But why do you round on me now?"

"I've not rounded on you, I'm only telling you."

"A neighbour," Peter Finch observed, "should stand *by* his neighbour, turn and turn about. I've lived next or nigh you all my life. You riz in the world, you've prospered, but I haven't."

"God bless me," cried Waugh, "when I started out to work I got three and six a week and a pound at Michaelmas. My old dad would give me a penny out of that on Saturdays."

"Oh, I knows. I knowed you, Willie Waugh, ever since you was a nipper; I knowed you when you put the tadpoles in the font at Farmer Fescot's christening."

"Five o'clock we had to get up then, and work till dark. None of this 'ere starting at seven and leaving off at five, and football, and crickets, and God knows what all! They *was* some farmers in those days, but if their old corpses could come out of their holes and see what goes on now, why, they ... they ... they'd go mad—it 'ud kill 'em!"

Peter was unmoved, a very unfeeling, unprincipled man.

"Too many holidays in this country," Willie rambled moodily on, "that's what there is. I'd sooner work seven days a week than six, for I don't know what to be at a' Sundays."

"We was at school then," mused Peter, "I caught the tadpoles, a tin-full, and you tipped 'em in the font water. There was a racket about that."

"Ah," commented Willie, "you was afraid to do it of yourself."

"I bet you once as you couldn't swallow a butterfly...."

"Ah, and I ate four of 'em at once," interrupted Willie.

"But you was sick arterwards."

"Nor you didn't pay up, by dam." Waugh, leaning against one of the ash-trees, smiled into the pool. "That Farmer Fescot was a good old farmer as ever was, a thoroughbred 'un."

"Thoroughly thoroughbred," granted Peter. "We cooked the liver of his piebald nag when it died, you and me!"

"His wife warn't much," declared Willie.

"No. She ought to have had her head shook. Do you recollect that circus as come by here one evening? Going out west somewheres. They pasted up bills on the barns and walls as they went along, and we dogged 'em and turned their bills all upsy down. Miles we followed that circus, and it wasn't half late when we got home!"

"Ah," chortled Willie, "I 'members you falling over the elephant's dung in the dark."

"That's a few years ago," sighed Peter, "a few years ago, thirty, forty. Ah!" He turned and sauntered away, plucking as he did so a blade of grass and chewing it as he went.

Willie called after him. "Aren't you going to take that saw?"

"If you like, Willie," Peter turned, "if you don't mind obliging me for a few nights."

"Well, take the blam saw," said Willie gruffly. "Think I'm going to run about arter you with it!"

So they went back to the cottage, and Peter got the saw and took it home. When he had gone Willie Waugh came and leaned over his garden gate, staring across the common at the four ash-trees by the pond where the grass was so very green. The trees were budding; the sky beyond them was glassy blue, with a cusp of new white moon, and clouds with fiery fringes hovering on the borders of everywhere. Long shadows slanted from the ash-trees, and long smoke twirled from the village chimneys. Tir-a-loo sang the birds, and the eyes of the playing children shone with a golden light.

"I never see," grumbled Willie to himself, "never in all my days—such a pack of fools—as there be in this world. And," he added, "they be all alike."

ALAS, POOR BOLLINGTON!

"I walked out of the hotel, just as I was, and left her there. I never went back again. I don't think I intended anything quite so final, so dastardly; I had not intended it, I had not thought of doing so, but that is how it happened. I lost her, lost my wife purposely. It was heartless, it was shabby, for she was a nice woman, a charming woman, a good deal younger than I was, a splendid woman, in fact she was very beautiful, and yet I ran away from her. How can you explain that, Turner?"

Poor Bollington looked at Turner, who looked at his glass of whiskey, and that looked irresistible—he drank some. Bollington sipped a little from his glass of milk.

I often found myself regarding Bollington as a little old man. Most of the club members did so too, but he was not that at all, he was still on the sunny side of fifty, but *so* unassertive, no presence to speak of, no height, not enough hair to mention—if he had had it would surely have been yellow. So mild and modest he cut no figure at all, just a man in glasses that seemed rather big for him. Turner was different, though he was just as bald; he had stature and bulk, his very pince-nez seemed twice the size of Bollington's spectacles. They had not met each other for ten years.

"Well, yes," Turner said, "but that was a serious thing to do."

"Wasn't it!" said the other, "and I had no idea of the enormity of the offence—not at the time. She might have been dead, poor girl, and her executors advertising for me. She had money, you know, her people had been licensed victuallers, quite wealthy. Scandalous!"

Bollington brooded upon his sin until Turner sighed: "Ah well, my dear chap."

"But you have no idea," protested Bollington, "how entirely she engrossed me. She was twenty-five and I was forty when we married. She was entrancing. She had always lived in a stinking hole in Balham, and it is amazing how strictly some of those people keep their children; licensed victuallers, did I tell you? Well, I was forty, and she was twenty-five; we lived for a year dodging about from one hotel to another all over the British Isles, she was a perfect little nomad. Are you married, Turner?"

No, Turner was not married, he never had been.

"Oh, but you should be," cried little Bollington. "It's an extraordinary experience, the real business of the world is marriage, marriage. I was deliriously happy and she was learning French and Swedish— that's where we were going later. She was an enchanting little thing, fair, with blue eyes; Phoebe her name was."

Turner thoughtfully brushed his hand across his generous baldness, then folded his arms.

"You really should," repeated Bollington, "you ought to, really. But I remember we went from Killarney to Belfast, and there something dreadful happened. I don't know, it had been growing on her, I suppose, but she took a dislike to me there, had strange fancies, thought I was unfaithful to her. You see, she was popular wherever we went, a lively little woman, in fact she wasn't merely a woman, she was a little magnet, men congregated and clung to her like so many tacks and nails and pins. I didn't object at all—on the contrary, 'Enjoy yourself, Phoebe,' I said, 'I don't expect you always to hang around an old fogey like me.' Fogey was the very word I used; I didn't mean it, of course, but that was the line I took, for she was so charming until she began to get so bad-tempered. And believe me, that made her angry, furious. No, not the fogey, but the idea that I did not object to her philandering. It was fatal, it gave colour to her suspicions of me—Turner, I was as innocent as any lamb—tremendous colour. And she had such a sharp tongue! If you ventured to differ from her—and you couldn't help differing sometimes—she'd positively bludgeon you, and you couldn't help being bludgeoned. And she had a passion for putting me right, and I always seemed to be so very wrong, always. She would not be satisfied until she had proved it, and it was so monstrous to be made to feel that because you were rather different from other people you were an impertinent fool. Yes, I seemed at last to gain only the pangs and none of the prizes of marriage. Now there was a lady we met in Belfast to whom I paid some attention..."

"Oh, good Lord!" groaned Turner.

"No, but listen," pleaded Bollington, "it was a very innocent friendship—nothing was further from my mind—and she was very much like my wife, very much, it was noticeable, everybody spoke of it— I mean the resemblance. A Mrs. Macarthy, a delightful woman, and Phoebe simply loathed her. I confess that my wife's innuendoes were so mean and persistent that at last I hadn't the strength to deny them, in fact at times I wished they were true. Love is idolatry if you like, but it cannot be complete immolation—there's no such bird as the phoenix, is there, Turner?"

"What, what?"

"No such bird as the phoenix."

"No, there is no such bird, I believe."

"And sometimes I had to ask myself quite seriously if I really hadn't been up to some infidelity! Nonsense, of course, but I assure you that was the effect it was having upon me. I had doubts of myself, frenzied doubts! And it came to a head between Phoebe and me in our room one day. We quarrelled. Oh, dear, how we quarrelled! She said I was sly, two-faced, unfaithful, I was a scoundrel, and so on. Awfully untrue, all of it. She accused me of dreadful things with Mrs. Macarthy and she screamed out: 'I hope you will treat her bettter than you have treated me.' Now what did she mean by that, Turner?"

Bollington eyed his friend as if he expected an oracular answer, but just as Turner was about to respond, Bollington continued: "Well, I never found out, I never knew, for what followed was too terrible. 'I shall go out,' I said, 'it will be better, I think.' Just that, nothing more. I put on my hat and I put my hand on the knob of the door when she said most violently: 'Go with your Macarthys, I never want to see your filthy face again!' Extraordinary you know, Turner. Well, I went out, and I will not deny I was in a rage, terrific. It was raining but I didn't care, and I walked about in it. Then I took shelter in a bookseller's doorway opposite a shop that sold tennis rackets and tobacco, and another one that displayed carnations and peaches on wads of coloured wool. The rain came so fast that the streets seemed to empty, and the passers-by were horribly silent under their umbrellas, and their footsteps splashed so dully, and I tell you I was very sad, Turner, there. I debated whether to rush across the road and buy a lot of carnations and peaches and take them to Phoebe. But I did not do so, Turner, I never went back, never."

"Why, Bollington, you, you were a positive ruffian, Bollington."

"Oh, scandalous," rejoined the ruffian.

"Well, out with it, what about this Mrs. Macarthy?"

"Mrs. Macarthy? But, Turner, I never saw her again, never, I ... I forgot her. Yes, I went prowling on until I found myself at the docks and there it suddenly became dark; I don't know, there was no evening, no twilight, the day stopped for a moment—and it did not recover. There were hundreds of bullocks slithering and panting and steaming in the road, thousands; lamps were hung up in the harbour, cabs and trollies rattled round the bullocks, the rain fell dismally and everybody hurried. I went into the dock and saw them loading the steamer, it was called s. s. *Frolic,* and really, Turner, the things they put into the belly of that steamer were rather funny: tons and tons of monstrous big chain, the links as big as soup plates, and two or three pantechnicon vans. Yes, but I was anything but frolicsome, I assure you, I was full of misery and trepidation and the deuce knows what. I did not know what I wanted to do, or what I was going to do, but I found myself buying a ticket to go to Liverpool on that steamer, and, in short, I embarked. How wretched I was, but how determined. Everything on board was depressing and dirty, and when at last we moved off the foam slewed away in filthy bubbles as if that dirty steamer had been sick and was running away from it. I got to Liverpool in the early morn, but I did not stay there, it is such a clamouring place, all trams and trollies and teashops. I sat in the station for an hour, the most miserable man alive, the most miserable ever born. I wanted some rest, some peace, some repose, but they never ceased shunting an endless train of goods trucks, banging and screeching until I almost screamed at the very porters. Criff was the name on some of the trucks, I remember, Criff, and everything seemed to be going criff, criff, criff. I haven't discovered to this day what Criff signifies, whether it's a station or a company, or a manufacture, but it was Criff, I remember. Well, I rushed to London and put my affairs in order. A day or two later I went to Southampton and boarded another steamer and put to sea, or rather we were ignominiously lugged out of the dock by a little rat of a tug that seemed all funnel and hooter. I was off to America, and there I stopped for over three years."

Turner sighed. A waiter brought him another glass of spirit.

"I can't help thinking, Bollington, that it was all very fiery and touchy. Of course, I don't know, but really it was a bit steep, very squeamish of you. What did your wife say?"

"I never communicated with her, I never heard from her, I just dropped out. My filthy face, you know, she did not want to see it again."

"Oh, come, Bollington! And what did Mrs. Macarthy say?"

"Mrs. Macarthy! I never saw or heard of her again. I told you that."

"Ah, yes, you told me. So you slung off to America."

"I was intensely miserable there for a long while. Of course I loved Phoebe enormously, I felt the separation, I . . . Oh, it is impossible to describe. But what was worst of all was the meanness of my behaviour, there was nothing heroic about it, I soon saw clearly that it was a shabby trick, disgusting, I had bolted and left her to the mercy of . . .

well, of whatever there was. It made such an awful barrier—you've
no idea of my compunction—I couldn't make overtures—'Let us forgive and forget.' I was a mean rascal, I *was* filthy. That was the
barrier—myself; I was too bad. I thought I should recover and enjoy
life again, I began to think of Phoebe as a cat, a little cat. I went
everywhere and did everything. But America is a big country, I
couldn't get into contact, I was lonely, very lonely, and although two
years went by I longed for Phoebe. Everything I did I wanted to do
with Phoebe by my side. And then my cousin, my only relative in
the world—he lived in England—he died. I scarcely ever saw him,
but still he was my kin. And he died. You've no comprehension,
Turner, of the truly awful sensation such a breavement brings. Not a
soul now would have the remotest interest in my welfare. Oh, I tell
you, Turner, it was tragic, tragic, when my cousin died. It made my
isolation complete. I was alone, a man who had made a dreadful
mess of life. What with sorrow and remorse I felt that I should soon
die, not of disease, but disgust."

"You were a great ninny," ejaculated his friend. "Why the devil
didn't you hurry back, claim your wife, bygones be bygones; why,
bless my conscience, what a ninny, what a great ninny!"

"Yes, Turner, it is as you say. But though conscience is a good
servant it is a very bad master, it overruled me, it shamed me, and
I hung on to America for still another year. I tell you my situation
was unbearable, I was tied to my misery, I was a tethered dog, a duck
without water—even dirty water. And I hadn't any faith in myself or
in my case; I knew I was wrong, had always been wrong, Phoebe had
taught me that. I hadn't any faith, I wish I had had. Faith can move
mountains, so they say, though I've never heard of it actually being
done."

"No, not in historical times," declared Turner.

"What do you mean by that?"

"Oh, well, time is nothing, it's nothing, it comes and off it goes.
Has it ever occurred to you, Bollington, that in 5,000 years or so there
will be nobody in the world speaking the English language, our very
existence even will be speculated upon, as if we were the Anthropo-
phagi? Oh, good lord, yes."

And another whiskey.

"You know, Bollington, you were a perfect fool. You behaved
liked one of those half-baked civil service hounds who lunch in a

dairy on a cup of tea and a cream horn. You wanted some beef, some ginger. You came back, you must have come back because there you are now."

"Yes, Turner, I came back after nearly four years. Everything was different, ah, how strange! I could not find Phoebe, it is weird how people can disappear. I made enquiries, but it was like looking for a lost umbrella, fruitless after so long."

"Well, but what about Mrs. Macarthy?"

Mr. Bollington said, slowly and with the utmost precision: "I did not see Mrs. Macarthy again."

"Oh, of course, you did not see her again, not ever."

"Not ever. I feared Phoebe had gone abroad too, but at last I found her in London..."

"No," roared Turner, "why the devil couldn't you say so and done with it? I've been sweating with sympathy for you. Oh, I say, Bollington!"

"My dear Turner, listen. Do you know, she was delighted to see me, she even kissed me, straight off, and we went out to dine and had the very deuce of a spread and we were having the very deuce of a good time. She was lovelier than ever, and I could see all her old affection for me was returning, she was so... well, I can't tell you, Turner, but she had no animosity whatever, no grievance, she would certainly have taken me back that very night. Oh, dear, dear ... and then! I was anxious to throw myself at her feet, but you couldn't do that in a public café, I could only touch her hands, beautiful, as they lay on the white linen cloth. I kept asking: 'Do you forgive me?' and she would reply: 'I have nothing to forgive, dear, nothing.' How wonderful that sounded to my truly penitent soul—I wanted to die.

" 'But you don't ask me where I've been!' she cried gaily, 'or what I've been doing, you careless old Peter. I've been to France, and Sweden too!'

"I was delighted to hear that, it was so very plucky.

" 'When did you go?' I asked.

" 'When I left you,' she said.

" 'You mean when I went away?'

" 'Did you go away? Oh, of course, you must have. Poor Peter, what a sad time he has had.'

"I was a little bewildered, but I was delighted; in fact, Turner, I was hopelessly infatuated again, I wanted to wring out all the dregs of my detestable villainy and be absolved. All I could begin with was: 'Were you not very glad to be rid of me?'

" 'Well,' she said, 'my great fear at first was that you would find me again and make it up. I didn't want that then, at least, I thought I didn't.'

" 'That's exactly what I felt,' I exclaimed, 'but how could I find you?'

" 'Well,' Phoebe said, 'you might have found out and followed me. But I promise never to run away again, Peter dear, never.'

"Turner, my reeling intelligence swerved like a shot bird.

" 'Do you mean, Phoebe, that you ran away from *me?*'

" 'Yes, didn't I?' she answered.

" 'But I ran away from *you,*' I said. 'I walked out of the hotel on that dreadful afternoon we quarrelled so, and I never went back. I went to America. I was in America nearly four years.'

" 'Do you mean you ran away from me?' she cried.

" 'Yes,' I said, 'didn't I?'

" 'But that is exactly what I did—I mean, I ran away from you. *I* walked out of the hotel directly you had gone—*I* never went back, and I've been abroad thinking how tremendously I had served you out, and wondering what you thought of it all and where you were.'

"I could only say, "Good God, Phoebe, I've had the most awful four years of remorse and sorrow, all vain, mistaken, useless, thrown away.' And she said: 'And I've had four years—living in a fool's paradise after all. How dared you run away, it's disgusting!'

"And, Turner, in a moment she was at me again in her old dreadful way, and the last words I had from her were: 'Now I *never* want to see your face again, never, this *is* the end!'

"And that's how things are now, Turner. It's rather sad, isn't it?"

"Sad! Why you chump, when was it you saw her?"

"Oh, a long time ago, it must be nearly three years now."

"Three years! But you'll see her again!"

"Tfoo! No, no, no, Turner. God bless me, no, no, no!" said the little old man.

Robert Lynd ("Y. Y.")

The intimate, engaging essay does not thrive in America. Plenty of people write them, but the magazines always send them back. "No intimate, engaging essays!" the magazine editor snarls out of the side of his mouth, with a casual cuff at his secretary. In England, however, the little essay is held in much honor. The average Englishman reads an essay a week by his favorite essayist in his favorite review. The difficulty about supplying this demand is that the writer has to have a good 1500-word idea every week. I hope no one thinks this is easy.

Robert Lynd, who writes over the signature "Y. Y." in the New Statesman and Nation, *has had a good idea every week for about forty years. Well, almost every week.*

THE VICE OF PUNCTUALITY

"Punctuality with the Englishman," says M. André Maurois, "is more than a habit. It is a vice." This is a severe judgment, but, from a strictly moral point of view, it is probably a true one. To the strict moralist—at least, to the Puritan—every form of self-indulgence is a vice, and undoubtedly punctuality is a form of self-indulgence. It is rooted in laziness and a desire to avoid trouble. The Englishman, being one of the laziest of men, was the first to discover the fact that, if he were habitually punctual, he would be spared a great deal of superfluous work and worry, and so he set about preaching the gospel of punctuality, which is merely a branch of the gospel of the higher selfishness. Needless to say, he lauded his vice as a virtue, and it is only the more logical moralists of the Continent who have seen through his pretences.

It is useless to deny that the unpunctual man excels the punctual both in energy and endurance. Even the unpunctual schoolboy is a model to his punctual coeval in these respects. How smoothly the day passes for the punctual fourteen-year-old! He glides through the day as easily as a tram along its lines! Sitting down in good time to break-

526

fast, he has leisure to practise the art of gluttony almost before the sun is warm. Rising seasonably from the table, he sets off for school under no shadow of fear of an irate master's reproof. He saunters into school in the mood of Pippa, and is in his seat in class before the bell has rung and in time to receive his by-no-means-easy-to-placate master's glance of approval. And so he passes through the day, effortless, careless, and, I cannot help thinking, spiritually idle.

Compare with his the lot of the unpunctual boy, whose day is one long series of strenuous efforts. First, he has to make an effort to get out of bed, expending energy on what his punctual fellow had accomplished with lazy ease. At the breakfast-table, again, his brain is working hard, calculating exactly how many seconds he can afford in which to bolt his food before rushing off to an institution in which he is almost sure to be received, not with commendation, but with frowns. Only half-fed—for the unpunctual boy of necessity eats sparingly, like the saints and the ascetics—he tumbles out of the house, banging the door after him with the energy of a gymnast. See him running along the street, and you will note in him none of those marks of indolence which were all too conspicuous in the deportment of his punctual predecessor. His breath comes fast; his face is flushed; every step he takes is that of a boy doing his utmost, like a hero trying to score a try for the honour of his school. He is so bent on doing his best and arriving at his school in good time that, when he mounts a tram, he finds that, in his absorption in duty, he has not even had leisure to tie his shoe-laces. At the school gates the empty playing-fields tell him that the bell has already rung and that he will have to face a reception in the schoolroom that only the bravest can face with equanimity. He braces himself for the ordeal; and the acute observer will perceive that the unpunctual schoolboy has to brace himself a score of times in the course of the day for once that this is required of the punctual. He lives in a fury of moral energy, indeed, that ought to have received, but did not receive, the approbation of Samuel Smiles. My own schoolmaster agreed with Samuel Smiles. He did not even look up from his desk as he thought out words withering enough to discourage all moral effort on my part in the future. "Y," he said coldly, "if you cannot arrive in class in time, you will kindly stay away altogether." Such was the reward of virtue, of an output of energy of which no other boy in the class was capable or, at least, which no other boy in the class dreamed of emulating.

I doubt whether the punctual have the slightest conception of what the unpunctual go through—of their exhausting labours, of their endless tribulations. They seem to think that other people like being late for the sake of being late, whereas there is no one who suffers more from being late than the late-comer. There is very little fun for a middle-aged man in bolting half an egg and running a quarter of a mile to catch a morning train to town. No one, intent on his own comfort and eager to get through a day as lazily as possible, would think of doing such a thing. It is a form of penance that the unpunctual have to go through for not having been ease-loving enough in childhood to discover the art of living with a minimum of effort.

The unpunctual, again, are accused of selfishness. Theatre-goers are continually complaining of the selfishness of those who arrive late in the stalls. The accusation is false. I know, for, being one of the most selfish of men, I always make a point of arriving at the theatre in time for purely selfish reasons. I have not the courage to endure the miseries of being late—to face the silent hatred of women whom there is no room to pass without crushing their knees or treading on their feet and the fury of fat men whom there is scarcely room to pass at all. To arrive in time at a theatre or a football match I regard as one of the luxuries of life. If I have to choose between disturbing other people and being disturbed myself, I prefer—for purely selfish reasons—being disturbed myself. For, since I am naturally unpunctual, I can make allowances for the late-comers and understand what they are suffering. Some of them, I tell myself, have been held up in traffic blocks. Others have been kept fuming in the hall, while their wives and daughters were held prisoners upstairs by their mirrors. Others are the victims of slow clocks and watches. Every man who has ever been late knows that there are twenty good reasons for being late, whereas there is only one good reason for being punctual—self-love.

Our hatred of unpunctuality is, I think it can be shown, mainly a selfish hatred and, therefore, a vicious hatred. It is not from virtue, for example, that we object to being kept late for dinner. I have heard a fussily punctual fellow, after he had been kept waiting twenty minutes for dinner, saying: "My God, I could kill that cook." It was scarcely a Christian sentiment. Yet even I, who am frequently late for meals, hate to be kept waiting for one. I remember spending a summer holiday in a cottage on an estuary in which breakfast was never on the table before eleven. In London, I have no objection to an eleven-o'clock breakfast, but on a holiday I like to be up early and am ready for breakfast by ten. The woman who looked after us, however, lacked the art of doing things easily, and, morning after morning, we hung about, famished, clamouring for food like young birds in a nest. Self, self, self—we thought nothing of the woman and the desperate efforts she was making in the kitchen. We were equally self-centred when, arriving back for lunch at half-past one, we were kept waiting for it till four. It was not that, after our late breakfast, we were starving, but that the woman by her unpunctuality was interfering with our time-table. The whole day seemed to be wasted in waiting for meals that did not come. There is a kind of false gnawing that afflicts the body—or is it the soul?—when cooks are unpunctual. I used to feel it in the cottage about a quarter-past ten at night when dinner had not appeared.

The truth is, in a selfish world, we feel that other people should always be punctual. Imagine the effect of short-tempered egotists, as most of us are, if the morning papers were constantly delivered late, if the first post arrived according to the caprice of an unpunctual postman, if no milk arrived for breakfast and the only explanation were the moral grandeur of the milkman. Italy, it is commonly said, went through a revolution largely in order to ensure the punctuality of trains. The wise men of the past said: "Better late than never"; but who nowadays echoes the ancient philosophy when the fish is not delivered in time for lunch? In a mechanized world, we insist that life must imitate the smoothness of a machine, and that other people must live, not according to their temperament, but in obedience to a time-table. This, it must be admitted, is for a highly organized society a convenience, but it is also a pursuit of the line of least resistance. There is nothing noble about it: it is merely Epicureanism on a practical plane. In demanding punctuality from others, we primarily seek, not their good, but our own happiness and comfort. Is that vicious? The Puritans, and M. Maurois among them, would say, "Yes." I cannot quite agree with them. I like other people to be punctual. As for myself, however, unpunctuality happens to be one of the things that have given me such character as I possess.

THE LION AND THE SHEEP
(1933)

"It is better," Mussolini has been assuring his followers, "to live as a lion for a day, than as a sheep for a hundred years." This seems to me to be highly improbable. I have never heard anything about the lion that has made it seem worth while being a lion even for a single day. It is a beast that cannot compromise with civilisation. Certain scholars believe that it survived in Greece till fairly civilised times, but the Greeks apparently thought poorly of it, since they got rid of it before the great days of Pericles. Europe, indeed, scarcely began to be civilised till the last lion had been killed or captured. It is only as a slave beast that it has been allowed to exist in Europe for the last two thousand years and more. The Romans found lions entertaining animals to throw Christians to, but they did not let lions loose in their fields. Today the best use to which Europeans can put lions is to imprison them in a cage in a zoo. There is a lion in the Roman Zoo with an inscription on the cage announcing that it is the gift of Mussolini. Is it worth while being a lion in order to be presented to a zoo even by a statesman of genius? Does Mussolini really regard it as the lordliest life to prowl and growl in a cage and to be stared at by trippers? Better than that, surely, even to be a clergyman exhibiting himself in a barrel at Blackpool for gain. The clergyman at least is free outside his working hours, and does not live under the domination of a keeper. On the whole, the caged lion's life seems little superior to that of a convict, except for the fact that it is pampered at meal-times.

As for the lion in its native haunts, what qualities has it that should make human beings envy it? According to the *Encyclopaedia Britannica,* "the accounts of early writers as to courage, nobility, and magnanimity have led to a reaction, causing some modern writers to accuse it of cowardice and meanness." Livingstone denied that it was either as ferocious or as noble as its reputation. At best it is a sneaking sort of animal. It is a beast of prey that does not like to be seen about in daylight, an assassin that strikes in the dark. It has no sense of honour and seldom attacks its victim openly. "For the most part he steals upon it in the manner of a cat, or ambushes himself near to the water or a pathway frequented by game." We need not be over-censorious of him, for he is no more than a beast; but he is no model for young men in the twentieth century.

True, he is strong and good-looking, and he can gallop for short distances almost as fast as a horse. Also he has a most impressive roar. The *Encyclopaedia* quotes an admirable description by Gordon-Cumming of the roaring of lions at its best. "On no occasion," he declares, "are their roars to be heard in such perfection, and so intensely powerful, as when two or three troops of strange lions approach a fountain to drink at the same time. When this occurs, every member of each troop sounds a bold roar of defiance at the opposite parties, and, when one roars, all roar together, and each seems to vie with his comrades in the intensity and power of his voice. The power and grandeur of these nocturnal concerts is inconceivably striking and pleasing to the hunter's ear."

That, I think, is the secret of the lion's charm for human beings. He is no use except for killing Christians, but he can roar magnificently. Every normal human being longs to be able to roar, to "sound a bold roar of defiance at the opposite parties." There are few greater luxuries known to men than that. We like even to hear other people roaring: it convinces us of their sincerity. We are spellbound if the roar is loud enough.

I remember how a clergyman, returning from a holiday too late to have time to prepare his Sunday sermon, once borrowed a manuscript sermon of my father's and took it into the pulpit with him on the following morning. To his consternation he found that there were words and phrases in the manuscript which, when he came on them, he could not make head or tail of, owing to the difficulty of the handwriting. He afterwards described how he triumphed over circumstances. "When I came to a sentence that I could not read," he said, "I simply beat the cushion and roared as loud as I could." After the service people came round and congratulated him with shining eyes on having performed the greatest feat of oratory of his life. There is music in a roar, as the greatest street-corner orators know. Anybody can talk sense, but hardly anybody will listen to it; roar the greatest nonsense at the top of your voice, however, and a crowd will be listening openmouthed before the end of two minutes.

Hence it is not surprising that the art of roaring is being more and more widely practised in Europe every day. Reason is for the moment dethroned, not being sensational enough for the age of the film; instinct has taken its place; and instinct bids men roar. The politics of roaring have captured some of the leading countries of Europe, and roaring has even spread to literature. I have read several works by young writers lately which were little more than roaring at the opposite parties. Let the roarers not deceive themselves, however, into imagining that one has only to roar like a lion in order to be a lion. According to Livingstone, the roar of a lion is indistinguishable from that of an ostrich. Possibly, a good deal of roaring that is going on in Europe today is the roaring not of lions but of ostriches.

Even so, the roar of a lion is terrifying to most human beings, and it is natural to wish to strike terror into one's fellow-men. That, no doubt, is why the British adopted the lion as their patron animal. All these national animals imply challenge and hostility. The Scots even chose the most minatory of plants as a patriotic emblem. The Americans and Germans symbolized their nationality with that not very useful bird of prey, the eagle. The French made a more civilized choice in the farmyard cock, but it must be remembered that the cock is the most pugnacious of domestic birds. It seems to me that we shall never have peace in the world till we have got rid of all these fighting beasts and birds as emblems of patriotism. Can the League of Nations not appoint a committee to investigate the matter? It would need only a few sittings to abolish the whole menagerie of pugnacity, and to assign to each nation a symbolic animal denoting peace and goodwill. Germany might become dove-like if only she got accustomed to thinking of herself as a dove. America might forget her debt if she saw herself admiringly as the milch-cow of Europe. Italy might become even more lovable than she remains under all her rulers if she adopted as her patron animal the harmless ortolan. Russia might become the pet of Europe if everybody got to associate her with some household pet— say, a kitten. England, I am sure, would be glad to get rid of her leonine reputation. It is obviously already her intention, if she remains a lion at all, to become more and more like the lion who refused to eat Androcles. That is what makes Lord Rothermere so impatient. If he had seen the lion making friends with Androcles in the arena, he would have cried out angrily to it: "What do you think lions are for? Get on with your job, and none of this white-flaggery." Yet Androcles's lion is the only lion I ever heard of that everybody loves. That, it may be retorted, is because we are getting soft. The truth is, we were always soft. Nobody ever liked the idea of being eaten by a wild beast.

The theory, then, that it would be a fine thing to live like a lion for a day does not seem to hold water. If the life of a lion were so deserving of praise men would not for centuries have been doing their best to exterminate him. The sheep, on the other hand—*there* is an animal that all human beings, except vegetarians, admire and do their utmost to keep alive. We rent fields and mountain-sides for the sheep's exclusive use. We pay shepherds to look after him as we pay nursemaids to look after our children. We buy sheep-dip to keep him clean, and feed him in winter, and cut his hair, and, in fact, treat him more or less as one of ourselves. It is true that in the end we kill him, but we kill him, not as we kill a lion, because we dislike him, but because we like him. Meanwhile, he can live with a good conscience. He is no nocturnal skulker preying on his fellow-creatures. He is not the terror of the community, but its generous servant. Why should he not be happy, even if he lived for a hundred years? I should have thought that in almost every respect the sheep was the pattern of the good citizen. He helps to clothe and feed us as no lion ever did; and scarcely ever does a sheep die without leaving the world a better place than he found it. And what a life he has while it lasts—those skippings of infancy, that endless sociability, that perpetual holiday among some of the finest scenery on the planet! The lion in his cage has no life comparable to this. Even the poor hunted lion in the jungle, roar as he will, can never enjoy the free life of the sheep. Mussolini should think again. I cannot see a single ground, apart from the roar, on which it is not infinitely better to be a sheep than a lion.

A. Neil Lyons

*Though A. Neil Lyons was born in Cape Colony, he became a
master of the English genre-picture in prose. No one had a more sensitive ear for the speech of the London Cockney and the Sussex villager, and no one had a more affectionate understanding of their character. He lived at Old Blacksmith, Wisborough Green, Sussex, which
certainly seems as right as his favorite recreation: waggoning.*

JENNER

The author of this work has already hinted that he inhabits a picturesque cottage, situated in Sussex. It is not generally known, however, that his enjoyment of this property is shared in perpetuity by a
Mr. Jenner. By an awful, ceaseless Mr. Jenner, who is a sort of un-
holy ghost—invisible, inaudible; the whole incomprehensible.

My original introduction to Jenner was performed by Mr. Tracey—
a local horticulturist of some standing who, having represented in convincing terms his ability to convert the wilderness attached to this cottage into a "proper, antikew, le'l genelman's garden," was engaged,
for an indefinite period, to perform that miracle. Mr. Tracey, during
his first day's work and whilst occupied in disinterring pot-lids and kettles from a tin-mine which then existed on the property, thus broached
the subject of Jenner.

"I wonder," said Mr. Tracey, "what old Jenner would think of all
this?"

"Ah!" I murmured, not wishing to display my ignorance of local
history.

"Not much, I expect," continued Mr. Tracey.

"Oh!" I exclaimed, with anxious wonder.

" 'Twas old Jenner," exclaimed Mr. Tracey, "as made this garden
what it be."

What this garden at the moment be was an unsightly and extensive refuse-heap, adorned in places by parched, neglected, blighted fruit
trees. Even the elaborately organised kettle-beds were mildewed and

534

weed-bound. A prolonged survey of old Jenner's performance left me quite without enthusiasm.

"Old Jenner," mused Mr. Tracey, "was the sort of good old gardener they don't make these days. 'E on'y got one eye. A most respectable man in every way. 'E built this cottage. I knowed 'im well."

"But this cottage," I pointed out, "was built in the reign of Queen Anne."

"Ah!" said Mr. Tracey, "very likely."

"In that case," I urged, "Mr. Jenner would have to be about one hundred and eighty years old when you knew him."

"He was very old," said Mr. Tracey.

"So old as all that, do you think?" I submitted.

"Well," observed Mr. Tracey, " 'is son died on'y the other day, and 'e was nigh sixty. Per'aps, when you come to think it over, I be got confused in me mind, and 'twas the son as built this place. That would bring it back to about the time you mention."

I did not see by what process of reasoning Mr. Tracey arrived at this result. But I preferred to leave his arithmetic as I found it, rather than to institute a propaganda at that moment. For, mind you, I employed this person: why should he study arithmetic in *my* time?

Nothing more was heard of Mr. Jenner for the rest of that day; but he reappeared again the following afternoon, when a small, red-whiskered man accosted me on the high road, saying:

"I beg ye're pardon, young man, but be you the party what have rented Jenner's?"

"No," I replied.

"Well, now," commented Whiskers, "then I bin told a lie. And yet —and yet you be surely the party what was pointed out to me: the same funny walk and all. 'Tis the le'l old cottage 'long in Sludge Lane what I speak of. Ain't you rented that, young man?"

"Sir," I replied, "it is true that I have acquired Stone Cottage in Sludge Lane. But I do not call it by the name of 'Jenner's.' What has Jenner to do with me?"

" 'E got this much to do with you, young man," responded Whiskers: "There wouldn't be no le'l old cottage 'long in Sludge Lane, save for this Jenner what rooted it all with 'is own 'and and planted the medlar tree. What would Jenner's be without the medlar tree?"

"But there is not a medlar tree," I protested.

"There is, then," said Whiskers. " 'Cos ole Jenner, 'e planted it, and me own old father 'e *seed* 'im plant it. That was afore *your* time, young man."

"At any rate, I have never seen the medlar tree."

"I'll lay you *'ave*, then," responded Whiskers; "on'y more than likely you took it for a quince. 'Tisn't everybody as know a medlar tree when they see one. I don't believe there be a finer crop of medlars in the parish than them what old Jenner raises. Well I remember 'im in 'is old blue coat. 'E was lame of one leg."

"And partially blind?" I hazarded.

"Not 'im!" responded Whiskers hotly. " 'Tis the son you be a-thinkin' of, unless it be the uncle. Jenner 'isself could see as well as me. 'Twas 'im what planted the medlar: *that* was never planted by no blind man. But the son—or else the uncle—'e *was* blind, for many's the time I've heard my father speak of it, 'e 'avin' blinded 'im 'is very own self, crossing Potter's stile with a shot-gun. But whether 'twas the son or whether 'twas the uncle I don't exackly know: but whichever that be, 'twas the same as put in they winter apple trees."

"But," I submitted, "those winter apples are said to be as old as the cottage."

"Ah!" said Whiskers; "and older!"

" 'Tis a good job I met you," continued Whiskers: "for I was goin' along to 'Jenner's' in the 'opes I *should* meet you: in the matter of your 'edges and ditches. You be recommended to me as 'avin arst for a good 'edger and ditcher."

"Go along to 'Johnson's,' " I responded, "and ask for Mr. Tracey. Tell him that if he sees fit to employ you he has my permission to do so."

"Ah," said Whiskers, "old Tom Tracey. I know. 'Tis 'Jenner's,' I suppose, you mean. I'll say 'so long!' till then."

I went about my business in the village calmly and without fear. It had not yet occurred to me that I was haunted. This knowledge came to me that very morning: for I was waited upon by a Mrs. Pett, who came to seek the office of "housekeeper." Having made certain inquiries, Mrs. Pett appointed herself to the post in these words: "Five shillings, eh? Ah well; I daresay I can oblige." Then, with wet eyes and a faltering accent, she made the following speech:

" 'Tis a funny le'l old place, to be sure. I could almost fancy, comin' up the road, as I seed old Jenner 'isself a-standin' at the gate. 'E made that gate 'isself with some wood what my old father give 'im."

"On the contrary," I asserted, "that is a brand-new gate, made to my order by a steam engine in Norway."

Mrs. Pett inspected the gate. "I see, now," she said at last, "as this be new. 'Tis a flimsy sort of thing, don't you think, sir? But, then, they don't make gates at all in these days, not to say gates. My man is allus saying as nobody can make a gate same as old Jenner could. Sich a nice old man that be: a great chapel-goer, and stone-deaf."

I peremptorily closured Mrs. Pett, and strode into the garden, hoping to encounter just cause for having a row with Mr. Tracey, but Mr. Tracey was peaceably lunching off bread and cucumber. With him was Whiskers similarly occupied. And Whiskers was relating a sad incident from the life of Mr. Jenner.

Mr. Jenner, it seems, had disinherited a son—or else it was a nephew —who had revenged himself by stealing into the garden at dead of night and "barking" the old man's favourite fruit trees, with the result that they wilted and died. Whiskers, I believe, had recollected this story in order to explain the evident absence of the medlar tree; but to me the history was interesting, as proving that Mr. Jenner—or somebody else of the same name—had really existed. It was so obviously a true story, so thoroughly in accord with the fine old English ideal of "the family."

Not wishing to obtrude upon the well-earned repose of these worthy men, I retreated to the house; but was soon fetched back again by the sound of a violent altercation.

Whiskers, who had risen to his feet, was threatening Mr. Tracey with a formidable length of cucumber. "I tell you 'twas old Jenner 'isself," cried Whiskers.

"And I tell *you* 'twas 'is son," retorted Mr. Tracey.

"I suppose my father never went to school with Jenner, then? Nor went a-courtin' with 'im? Nor stood as a witness to the first boy's christening? I tell you 'twas *old* Jenner as built the place; and likewise put the trees in—at least they *was* trees them days, afore any novices 'ad the prunin' of 'em."

" 'Twas his son," repeated Mr. Tracey. "And if you call me ere another name I'll knock ye're ribs in!"

" 'Twas old Jenner, I tell you," persisted Whiskers.

"I say 'twas Jenner's son," said Mr. Tracey. "If 'twas old Jenner, same as you will 'ave it, he would have to be a hunderd and eighty year old day of 'is death. I be surprised a man o' your schooling don't see that for 'isself."

"I don't care nothing about old Jenner's age," responded Whiskers. "You can call 'im any age you like. All I tell you is this: old Jenner built that cottage. Aye," added Whiskers, warming to his theme, "and I'll tell you somethink else: old Jenner 'e likewise built the first cottage what stood on this spot: the old original cottage. When that wore out, 'e put up this one. If anybody arst who tell you that, let you say as 'Arry 'Opkins tell you, what knowed old Jenner well—'im and 'is old blue coat."

I had had a surfeit of Jenner by this time. I went for a walk on the Downs. I walked all night. When, at the first sign of dawn, I staggered home, who should accost me but the ancient postman.

"Ah, now," pipes this dotard, "you be making things shipshape up at 'Jenner's,' I see. What with they arches and the pleasure-lawn and that, 'tis the same as if Jenner 'isself was come back."

"You are mistaken," I said. "Old Jenner grew cabbages and pigs."

"That's right," assented the postman; "and pleasure lawns and arches also. That pear tree of 'is be the first in the village to this day."

I crawled on home to bed. At noon I got up. I stood at my gate of Norway deal and was greeted by an offensive tax-collector, who was riding by on a fat pony. The tax-collector, mind you: a greasy rascal who levies a lamp and pavement rate, but gives me neither lamp nor pavement. This person waved an oily palm at me and said:

"Good morning, Mr. Jenner."

A NATURALIST

"I shall be late for me tea agin," said Mr. Green. "Not that *moi* tea matter. I got a lot o' work to do this evenin'—wroitin' out accounts and that. Not that *moi* work matter to anybody."

"You are a Pessimist, Mr. Green," I observed.

"No," said Mr. Green; "a Plumber."

"You look at the sad side of things," I explained; "you undervalue your own happiness."

"Look what a miserable, muddy world it is," responded Mr. Green.

"Look how people put on you. That don't 'arf 'old some water, this blessed well. I never reckoned on all this water when I put the job at seven shillin'."

"Have you heard the nightingale yet, Mr. Green?" I inquired hastily.

"That I 'ave," said Mr. Green. " 'Eard the blighter three week agoo."

"You *were* in luck!" I exclaimed admiringly. "Sure it was the nightingale?"

"That I be," asserted Mr. Green. " 'Im what say 'Pewee! Pewee!' all the bloody night."

I dissembled my surprise. "Most people," I pointed out, "speak well of the nightingale."

"Ugly great beast," said Mr. Green—"flappin' 'is white wings were 'e beant wanted. 'Pewee! *Pew*-ee! Pe-*wee!*' 'e say, same's if anybody was took ill. Meself, I never did ownerstand why so much fuss be made about 'im."

"The note, or sound, which you describe," I said, "is not altogether characteristic of the nightingale. He does not always imitate the plover."

"That *be* the plover," stated Mr. Green, greatly to my surprise. "Nightingale, plover, or peweet, 'tis one and the same bird. They put it in the story books where a woman are got the nightingale's sweet voice. 'Tis true enough, I will allow, though where the sweetness of it come in I never *did* see. Screechin' passel o' monkeys—"

"It is curious," I reflected, "that different men should derive such different emotions from the same experiences."

"Say it slower, sir," suggested Mr. Green.

"Many people like the nightingale better than any other bird," I said.

"They're the sort," responded Mr. Green, "as like women."

"Don't you like women?" I inquired.

"Screechin' passel o' monkeys," repeated Mr. Green.

"Some men like the sound of women's voices," I submitted.

"They be the sort," said Mr. Green, "as would like the screechin' of a nightingale."

"Ah well," I mused, "it is a question of temperament, I suppose."

"Of what?" said Mr. Green.

"Temperament," I repeated.

"I donno narthin' about temper meant," quoth Mr. Green. "Temper meant or not, they be for ever screechin'."

"Which—the nightingales?"

"Or the women," said Mr. Green. " 'Tis the same thing. A nightingale aren't got narthin' better to do, on'y cry out 'Pewee—Pe-wee' all the blessed night, and a woman aren't got narthin' better to do on'y carry on the same infernal tune."

"But nightingales sing pleasantly at times."

"Never to moi 'earin'," said Mr. Green. " 'Tis a scattle-tongued bird."

"Beauty," I murmured, "is in the eye of the beholder; and music, I suppose, is—"

"Music!" echoed Mr. Green. "D'ye call that music?"

"Which?"

"The screechin' of women," said Mr. Green; "or nightingales. 'Tis the same thing. They be for ever 'ollerin'. Whether you 'it 'em or whether you don't."

"But people don't hit nightingales," I objected.

"Only for want o' the chanst," responded Mr. Green. " 'Oo wouldn't 'it a plaguesome creeter same's that be? 'Pe-wee! Pew-ee!' 'e cry out all the bloody night. Puts a man in mind of 'is wife."

"Do you believe in hitting wives?" I suggested, with an air of pleasantry.

"No doubt I should," assented Mr. Green, "on'y I aren't possessed of no sich thing—on'y a old aunt. She be nightingale enough for me.

" 'Pewee!' she says: 'Pe-wee! Pew-ee!' all the jolly day, and 'arf the bloody night. 'Pewee! Pe-wee! Pe-wee!'—jus' the same as a ugly ole nightingale."

Adrian Porter

THE PERFECT CHILD

It asked for bread and butter first,
It ceased to eat before it burst.
It kept its clothing clean and neat,
It blew its nose, it wiped its feet.
Meekly repentant when it erred,
Was seldom seen and never heard.
Ordered itself with zeal intense
To those of riper years and sense.
It walked demurely through the land
With governesses hand in hand.
It fled from rowdy little boys,
It turned from vulgar books and toys,
From pantomimes and such distractions,
And gave its time to vulgar fractions.
But when it takes to married life
I shall be sorry for its wife!

P. G. Wodehouse

I dare not assert that this is the noblest story Wodehouse ever wrote. Who could choose the one most perfect rose displayed at the Royal Horticultural Society, or the finest vegetable marrow ever grown at Blandings Castle? It is, in any case, a rich and vibrant tale, and typical of Wodehouse at his most typical. It will inspire in many readers a tragic fear that the Drones Club has been bombed beyond hope of resurrection in the better world to be. All, all are gone, the old familiar Crumpets.

TRIED IN THE FURNACE

The annual smoking-concert of the Drones Club had just come to an end, and it was the unanimous verdict of the little group assembled in the bar for a last quick one that the gem of the evening had been item number six on the programme, the knockabout cross-talk act of Cyril ("Barmy") Fotheringay-Phipps and Reginald ("Pongo") Twistleton-Twistleton. Both Cyril, in the red beard, and Reginald, in the more effective green whiskers, had shown themselves, it was agreed, at the very peak of their form. With sparkling repartee and vigorous byplay they had gripped the audience from the start.

"In fact," said an Egg, "it struck me that they were even better than last year. Their art seemed to have deepened somehow."

A thoughtful Crumpet nodded.

"I noticed the same thing. The fact is, they passed through a soul-testing experience not long ago and it has left its mark upon them. It also dashed nearly wrecked the act. I don't know if any of you fellows are aware of it, but at one time they had definitely decided to scratch the fixture and not give a performance at all."

"What!"

"Absolutely. They were within a toucher of failing to keep faith with their public. Bad blood had sprung up between them. Also pique and strained relations. They were not on speaking terms."

His hearers were frankly incredulous. They pointed out that the

542

friendship between the two artistes had always been a byword or whatever you called it. A well-read Egg summed it up by saying that they were like Thingummy and What's-his-name.

"Nevertheless," insisted the Crumpet, "what I am telling you is straight, official stuff. Two weeks ago, if Barmy had said to Pongo: 'Who was that lady I saw you coming down the street with?' Pongo would not have replied: 'That was no lady, that was my wife,'— he would simply have raised his eyebrows coldly and turned away in a marked manner."

It was a woman, of course (proceeded the Crumpet), who came between them. Angelica Briscoe was her name, and she was the daughter of the Rev. P. P. Briscoe, who vetted the souls of the local peasantry at a place called Maiden Eggesford down in Somersetshire. This hamlet is about half-a-dozen miles from the well-known resort, Bridmouth-on-Sea, and it was in the establishment of the Messrs. Thorpe and Widgery, the popular grocers of that town, that Barmy and Pongo first set eyes on the girl.

They had gone to Bridmouth partly for a splash of golf, but principally to be alone and away from distractions, so that they would be able to concentrate on the rehearsing and building up of this cross-talk act which we have just witnessed. And on the morning of which I speak they had strolled into the Thorpe and Widgery emporium to lay in a few little odds and ends, and there, putting in a bid for five pounds of streaky bacon, was a girl so lovely that they congealed in their tracks. And as they stood staring she said to the bloke behind the counter:

"That's the lot. Send them to Miss Angelica Briscoe, the Vicarage, Maiden Eggesford."

She then pushed off, and Barmy and Pongo, feeling rather as if they had been struck by lightning, bought some sardines and a segment of certified butter in an overwrought sort of way and went out.

They were both pretty quiet for the rest of the day, and after dinner that night Pongo said to Barmy:

"I say, Barmy."

And Barmy said:

"Hullo?"

And Pongo said:

"I say, Barmy, it's a bally nuisance, but I'll have to buzz up to London for a day or two. I've suddenly remembered some spots of business that call for my personal attention. You won't mind my leaving you?"

Barmy could scarcely conceal his bracedness. Within two minutes of seeing that girl, he had made up his mind that somehow or other he must repair to Maiden Eggesford and get to know her, and the problem which had been vexing him all day had been what to do with the body—viz., Pongo's.

"Not a bit," he said.

"I'll be back as soon as I can."

"Don't hurry," said Barmy heartily. "As a matter of fact, a few days' layoff will do the act all the good in the world. Any pro. will tell you that the worst thing possible is to over-rehearse. Stay away as long as you like."

So next morning—it was a Saturday—Pongo climbed onto a train, and in the afternoon Barmy collected his baggage and pushed off to the Goose and Grasshopper at Maiden Eggesford. And, having booked a room there and toddled into the saloon bar for a refresher with the love light in his eyes, the first thing he saw was Pongo chatting across the counter with the barmaid.

Neither was much bucked. A touch of constraint about sums it up.

"Hullo!" said Barmy.

"Hullo!" said Pongo.

"You here?"

"Yes. You here?"

"Yes."

"Oh."

There was a bit of a silence.

"So you didn't go to London?" said Barmy.

"No," said Pongo.

"Oh," said Barmy.

"And you didn't stick on at Bridmouth?" said Pongo.

"No," said Barmy.

"Oh," said Pongo.

There was some more silence.

"You came here, I see," said Pongo.

"Yes," said Barmy. "I see *you* came here."

"Yes," said Pongo. "An odd coincidence."

"Very odd."

"Well, skin off your nose," said Pongo.

"Fluff in your latchkey," said Barmy.

He drained his glass and tried to exhibit a lighthearted nonchalance, but his mood was sombre. He was a chap who could put two and two together and sift and weigh the evidence and all that sort of thing, and it was plain to him that love had brought Pongo also to this hamlet, and he resented the fact. Indeed, it was at this instant, he tells me, that there came to him the first nebulous idea of oiling out of that cross-talk act of theirs. The thought of having to ask a beastly, butting-in blighter like Reginald Twistleton-Twistleton if he was fond of mutton broth and being compelled to hit him over the head with a rolled-up umbrella when he replied, "No, Mutt and Jeff," somehow seemed to revolt his finest feelings.

Conversation languished after this, and presently Pongo excused himself in a somewhat stiff manner and went upstairs to his room. And it was while Barmy was standing at the counter listening in a distrait kind of way to the barmaid telling him what cucumber did to her digestive organs that a fellow in plus fours entered the bar and Barmy saw that he was wearing the tie of his old school.

Well, you know how it is when you're in some public spot and a stranger comes in wearing the old school tie. You shove a hasty hand over your own and start to sidle out before the chap can spot it and grab you and start gassing. And Barmy was just doing this when the barmaid uttered these sensational words:

"Good evening, Mr. Briscoe."

Barmy stood spellbound. He turned to the barmaid and spoke in a hushed whisper.

"Did you say 'Briscoe'?"

"Yes sir."

"From the Vicarage?"

"Yes sir."

Barmy quivered like a jelly. The thought that he had had the amazing luck to find in the brother of the girl he loved an old schoolmate made him feel boneless. After all, he felt, as he took his hand away from his tie, there is no bond like that of the old school. If you meet any of the dear old school in a public spot, he meant to say, why, you go straight up to him and start fraternizing.

He made a beeline for the chap's table.

"I say," he said, "I see you're wearing a ..."

The chap's hand had shot up to his tie with a sort of nervous gesture, but he evidently realized that the time had gone by for protective measures. He smiled a bit wryly.

"Have a drink," he said.

"I've got one, thanks," said Barmy. "I'll bring it along to your table, shall I? Such a treat meeting someone from the dear old place, what?"

"Oh, rather."

"I think I'd have been a bit after your time, wouldn't I?" said Barmy, for the fellow was well stricken in years—twenty-eight if a day. "Fotheringay-Phipps is more or less my name. Yours is Briscoe, what?"

"Yes."

Barmy swallowed a couple of times.

"Er . . . Ah . . . Um. . . . I think I saw your sister yesterday in Bridmouth," he said, blushing prettily.

So scarlet, indeed, did his countenance become that the other regarded him narrowly, and Barmy knew that he had guessed his secret.

"You saw her in Bridmouth yesterday, eh?"

"Yes."

"And now you're here."

"Er—yes."

"Well, well," said the chap, drawing his breath in rather thoughtfully.

There was a pause, during which Barmy's vascular motors continued to do their bit.

"You must meet her," said the chap.

"I should like to," said Barmy. "I only saw her for a moment buying streaky bacon, but she seemed a charming girl."

"Oh, she is."

"I scarcely noticed her, of course, but rather attractive she struck me as."

"Quite."

"I gave her the merest glance, you understand, but I should say at a venture that she has a great white soul. In fact," said Barmy, losing his grip altogether, "you wouldn't be far out in describing her as divine."

"You must certainly meet her," said the chap. Then he shook his head. "No, it wouldn't be any good."

"Why not?" bleated Barmy.

"Well, I'll tell you," said the chap. "You know what girls are. They have their little enthusiasms and it hurts them when people scoff at them. Being a parson's daughter, Angelica is wrapped up at present in the annual village School Treat. I can see at a glance the sort of fellow you are—witty, mordant, ironical. You would get off one of your devastating epigrams at the expense of the School Treat, and, while she might laugh at the wit, she would be deeply wounded by the satire."

"But I wouldn't dream ..."

"Ah, but if you didn't, if you spoke approvingly of the School Treat, what then? The next thing that would happen would be that she would be asking you to help her run it. And that would bore you stiff."

Barmy shook from stem to stern. This was better even than he had hoped.

"You don't mean she would let me help her with the School Treat?"

"Why, you wouldn't do it, would you?"

"I should enjoy it above all things."

"Well, if that's the way you feel, the matter can easily be arranged. She will be here any moment now to pick me up in her car."

And, sure enough, not two minutes later there floated through the open window a silvery voice, urging the fellow, who seemed to answer to the name of "Fathead," to come out quick, because the voice did not intend to remain there all night.

So the fellow took Barmy out, and there was the girl, sitting in a two-seater. He introduced Barmy. The girl beamed. Barmy beamed. The fellow said that Barmy was anxious to come and help with the School Treat. The girl beamed again. Barmy beamed again. And presently the car drove off, the girl's last words being a reminder that the binge started at two sharp on the Monday.

That night, as they dined together, Barmy and Pongo put in their usual spot of rehearsing. It was their practice to mould and shape the act during meals, as they found that mastication seemed to sharpen their intellect. But tonight it would have been plain to an observant spectator that their hearts were not in it. There was an unmistakable coolness between them. Pongo said he had an aunt who complained of rheumatism, and Barmy said, "Well, who wouldn't?" And Barmy said his father could not meet his creditors, and Pongo said, "Did he want to?" But the old fire and sparkle were absent. And they had relapsed into a moody silence when the door opened and the barmaid pushed her head in.

"Miss Briscoe just sent over a message, Mr. Phipps," said the barmaid. "She says she would like you to be there a little earlier than two, if you can manage it. One-fifteen if possible, because there's always so much to do."

"Oh, right," said Barmy, a bit rattled, for he had heard the sharp hiss of his companion's indrawn breath.

"I'll tell her," said the barmaid.

She withdrew, and Barmy found Pongo's eyes resting on him like a couple of blobs of vitriol.

"What's all this?" asked Pongo.

Barmy tried to be airy.

"Oh, it's nothing. Just the local School Treat. The vicar's daughter here—a Miss Briscoe—seems anxious that I should drop round on Monday and help her run it."

Pongo started to grind his teeth, but he had a chunk of potato in his mouth at the moment and was hampered. But he gripped the table till his knuckles stood out white under the strain.

"Have you been sneaking round behind my back and inflicting your beastly society on Miss Briscoe?" he demanded.

"I do not like your tone, Reginald."

"Never mind about my tone. I'll attend to my tone. Of all the bally low hounds that ever stepped you are the lowest. So this is what the friendship of years amounts to, is it? You crawl in here and try to cut me out with the girl I love."

"Well, dash it ..."

"That is quite enough."

"But, dash it ..."

"I wish to hear no more."

"But, dash it, I love her, too. It's not my fault if you happen to love her, too, is it? I mean to say, if a fellow loves a girl and another fellow loves her, too, you can't expect the fellow who loves the girl to edge out because he happens to be acquainted with the fellow who loves her, too. When it comes to love, a chap has got to look out for his own interests, hasn't he? You didn't find Romeo or any of those chaps easing away from the girl just to oblige a pal, did you? Certainly not. So I don't see ..."

"Please!" said Pongo.

A silence fell.

"Might I trouble you to pass the mustard, Fotheringay-Phipps?" said Pongo coldly.

"Certainly, Twistleton-Twistleton," replied Barmy, with equal hauteur.

It is always unpleasant not to be on speaking terms with an old friend. To be cooped up alone in a mouldy village pub with an old friend with whom one has ceased to converse is simply rotten. And this is especially so if the day happens to be a Sunday.

Maiden Eggesford, like so many of our rural hamlets, is not at its best and brightest on a Sunday. When you have walked down the main street and looked at the Jubilee Watering-Trough, there is nothing much to do except go home and then come out again and walk down the main street once more and take another look at the Jubilee Watering-Trough. It will give you some rough idea of the state to which Barmy Fotheringay-Phipps had been reduced by the end of the next day when I tell you that the sound of the church bells ringing for evensong brought him out of the Goose and Grasshopper as if he had heard a fire engine. The thought that at last something was going to happen in Maiden Eggesford in which the Jubilee Watering-Trough *motif* was not stressed, stirred him strangely. He was in his pew in three jumps. And as the service got under way he began to feel curious emotions going on in his bosom.

There is something about evening church in a village in the summertime that affects the most hard-boiled. They had left the door open, and through it came the scent of lime trees and wallflowers and the distant hum of bees fooling about. And gradually there poured over Barmy a wave of sentiment. As he sat and listened to the First Lesson he became a changed man.

The Lesson was one of those chapters of the Old Testament all about how Abimelech begat Jazzbo and Jazzbo begat Zachariah. And, what with the beauty of the words and the peace of his surroundings, Barmy suddenly began to become conscious of a great remorse.

He had not done the square thing, he told himself, by dear old Pongo. Here was a chap, notoriously one of the best, as sound an egg as ever donned a heliotrope sock, and he was deliberately chiselling him out of the girl he loved. He was doing the dirty on a fellow whom he had been pally with since their Eton-jacket days—a bloke who time and again had shared with him his last bar of almond rock. Was this right? Was this just? Would Abimelech have behaved like that to Jazzbo or—for the matter of that—Jazzbo to Zachariah? The answer, he could not disguise it from himself, was in the negative.

It was a different, stronger Barmy, a changed, chastened Cyril Fotheringay-Phipps, who left the sacred edifice at the conclusion of the vicar's fifty-minute sermon. He had made the great decision. It would play the dickens with his heart and probably render the rest of his life a blank, but nevertheless he would retire from the unseemly struggle and give the girl up to Pongo.

That night, as they cold-suppered together, Barmy cleared his throat and looked across at Pongo with a sad, sweet smile.

"Pongo," he said.

The other glanced distantly up from his baked potato.

"There is something you wish to say to me, Fotheringay-Phipps?"

"Yes," said Barmy, "a short while ago I sent a note to Miss Briscoe, informing her that I shall not be attending the School Treat and mentioning that you will be there in my stead. Take her, Pongo, old man. She is yours. I scratch my nomination."

Pongo stared. His whole manner changed. If was as if he had been a Trappist monk who had suddenly decided to give Trappism a miss and become one of the boys again.

"But, dash it, this is noble!"

"No, no."

"But it is! It's ... Well, dash it, I hardly know what to say."

"I hope you will be very, very happy."

"Thanks, old man."

"Very, very, very happy."

"Rather! I should say so. And I'll tell you one thing. In the years to come there will always be a knife and fork for you at our little home. The children shall be taught to call you Uncle Barmy."

"Thanks," said Barmy. "Thanks."

"Not at all," said Pongo. "Not at all."

At this moment the barmaid entered with a note for Barmy. He read it and crumpled it up.

"From her?" asked Pongo.

"Yes."

"Saying she quite understands, and so forth?"

"Yes."

Pongo ate a piece of cheese in a meditative manner. He seemed to be pursuing some train of thought.

"I should think," he said, "that a fellow who married a clergyman's daughter would get the ceremony performed at cut rates, wouldn't he?"

"Probably."

"If not absolutely on the nod?"

"I shouldn't wonder."

"Not," said Pongo, "that I am influenced by any consideration like that, of course. My love is pure and flamelike, with no taint of dross. Still in times like these, every little helps."

"Quite," said Barmy. "Quite."

He found it hard to control his voice. He had lied to his friend about that note. What Angelica Briscoe had really said in it was that it was quite all right if he wanted to edge out of the School Treat, but that she would require him to take the Village Mothers for their Annual Outing on the same day. There had to be some responsible person with them, and the curate had sprained his ankle tripping over a footstool in the vestry.

Barmy could read between the lines. He saw what this meant. His fatal fascination had done its deadly work, and the girl had become infatuated with him. No other explanation would'fit the facts. It was absurd to suppose that she would lightly have selected him for this extraordinarily important assignment. Obviously it was the big event of the village year. Anyone would do to mess about at the School Treat, but Angelica Briscoe would place in charge of the Mothers' Annual Outing only a man she trusted...respected...loved.

He sighed. What must be, he felt, must be. He had done his conscientious best to retire in favour of his friend, but Fate had been too strong.

I found it a little difficult (said the Crumpet) to elicit from Barmy exactly what occurred at the annual outing of the Village Mothers of Maiden Eggesford. When telling me the story, he had the air of a man whose old wound is troubling him. It was not, indeed, till the fourth cocktail that he became really communicative. And then, speaking with a kind of stony look in his eye, he gave me a fairly comprehensive account. But even then each word seemed to hurt him in some tender spot.

The proceedings would appear to have opened in a quiet and orderly manner. Sixteen females of advanced years assembled in a motor coach, and the expedition was seen off from the vicarage by the Rev. P. P. Briscoe in person. Under his eye, Barmy tells me, the Beauty Chorus was demure and docile. It was a treat to listen to their murmured responses. As nice and respectable a bunch of mothers, Barmy says, as he had ever struck. His only apprehension at this point, he tells me, was lest the afternoon's proceedings might possibly be a trifle stodgy. He feared a touch of ennui.

He needn't have worried. There was no ennui.

The human cargo, as I say, had started out in a spirit of demureness and docility. But it was amazing what a difference a mere fifty yards of the high road made to these Mothers. No sooner were they out of sight of the vicarage than they began to effervesce to an almost unbelievable extent. The first intimation Barmy had that the binge was going to be run on lines other than those which he had anticipated was when a very stout Mother in a pink bonnet and a dress covered with bugles suddenly picked off a passing cyclist with a well-directed tomato, causing him to skid into a ditch. Upon which, all sixteen Mothers laughed like fiends in hell, and it was plain that they considered that the proceedings had now been formally opened.

Of course, looking back at it now in a calmer spirit, Barmy tells me that he can realise that there is much to be said in palliation of the exuberance of these ghastly female pimples. When you are shut up all the year round in a place like Maiden Eggesford, with nothing to do but wash underclothing and attend Divine Service, you naturally incline to let yourself go a bit at times of festival and holiday. But at the moment he did not think of this, and his spiritual agony was pretty pronounced.

If there's one thing Barmy hates it's being conspicuous, and conspicuous is precisely what a fellow cannot fail to be when he's in a motor coach with sixteen women of mature ages who alternate between singing ribald songs and hurling volleys of homely chaff at passers-by. In this connection, he tells me, he is thinking particularly of a Mother in spectacles and a Homburg hat, which she had pinched from the driver of the vehicle, whose prose style appeared to have been modelled on that of Rabelais.

It was a more than usually penetrating sally on the part of this female which at length led him to venture a protest.

"I say! I mean, I say. I say, dash it, you know. I mean, dash it," said Barmy, feeling even as he spoke, that the rebuke had not been phrased as neatly as he could have wished.

Still, lame though it had been, it caused a sensation which can only be described as profound. Mother looked at Mother. Eyebrows were raised, breath drawn in censoriously.

"Young man," said the Mother in the pink bonnet, who seemed to have elected herself forewoman, "kindly keep your remarks to yourself."

Another Mother said: "The idea!" and a third described him as a kill-joy.

"We don't want none of *your* impudence," said the one in the pink bonnet.

"Ah!" agreed the others.

"A slip of a boy like that!" said the Mother in the Homburg hat, and there was a general laugh, as if the meeting considered that the point had been well taken.

Barmy subsided. He was wishing that he had yielded to the advice of his family and become a curate after coming down from the University. Curates are specially trained to handle this sort of situation. A tough, hard-boiled curate, spitting out of the corner of his mouth, would soon have subdued these Mothers, he reflected. He would have played on them as on a stringed instrument—or, rather, as on sixteen stringed instruments. But Barmy, never having taken Orders, was helpless.

So helpless, indeed, that when he suddenly discovered that they were heading for Bridmouth-on-Sea, he felt that there was nothing he could do about it. From the vicar's own lips he had had it officially that the programme was that the expedition should drive to the neighbouring village of Bottsford Mortimer, where there were the ruins of an old abbey, replete with interest; lunch among these ruins; visit the local museum (founded and presented to the village by the late Sir Wandesbury Pott, J.P.); and, after filling in with a bit of knitting, return home. And now the whole trend of the party appeared to be towards the Amusement Park on the Bridmouth pier. And, though Barmy's whole soul shuddered at the thought of these sixteen Bacchantes let loose in an Amusement Park, he hadn't the nerve to say a word.

It was at about this point, he tells me, that a vision rose before him of Pongo happily loafing through the summer afternoon amid the placid joys of the School Treat.

Of what happened at the Amusement Park Barmy asked me to be content with the sketchiest of outlines. He said that even now he could not bear to let his memory dwell upon it. He confessed himself perplexed by the psychology of the thing. These Mothers, he said, must have had mothers of their own and at those mothers' knees must have learned years ago the difference between right and wrong, and yet... Well, what he was thinking of particularly, he said, was what occurred on the Bump the Bumps apparatus. He refused to specify exactly, but he said that there was one woman in a puce mantle who definitely seemed to be living for pleasure alone.

It was a little unpleasantness with the proprietor of this concern that eventually led to the expedition leaving the Amusement Park and going down to the beach. Some purely technical point of finance, I understand—he claiming that a Mother in bombazine had had eleven rides and only paid once. It resulted in Barmy getting lugged into the brawl and rather roughly handled—which was particularly unfortunate, because the bombazined Mother explained on their way down to the beach that the whole thing had been due to a misunderstanding. In actual fact, what had really happened was that she had had twelve rides and paid twice.

However, he was so glad to get his little troupe out of the place that he counted an eye well blacked as the price of deliverance, and his spirits, he tells me, had definitely risen when suddenly the sixteen Mothers gave a simultaneous whoop and made for a sailing-boat which was waiting to be hired, sweeping him along with them. And the next moment they were off across the bay, bowling along before a nippy breeze which, naturally, cheesed it abruptly as soon as it had landed them far enough away from shore to make things interesting for the unfortunate blighter who had to take to the oars.

This, of course, was poor old Barmy. There was a man in charge of the boat, but he, though but a rough, untutored salt, had enough sense not to let himself in for a job like rowing this Noah's Ark home. Barmy did put it up to him tentatively, but the fellow said that he had to attend to the steering, and when Barmy said that he, Barmy, knew how to steer, the fellow said that he, the fellow, could not entrust a valuable boat to an amateur. After which, he lit his pipe and lolled

back in the stern sheets with rather the air of an ancient Roman ban-
queter making himself cosy among the cushions. And Barmy, attach-
ing himself to a couple of oars of about the size of those served out to
galley slaves in the old trireme days, started to put his back into it.

For a chap who hadn't rowed anything except a light canoe since
he was up at Oxford, he considers he did dashed well, especially when
you take into account the fact that he was much hampered by the
Mothers. They would insist on singing that thing about "Give yourself
a pat on the back," and, apart from the fact that Barmy considered
that something on the lines of the Volga Boat Song would have been
far more fitting, it was a tune it was pretty hard to keep time to. Seven
times he caught crabs, and seven times those sixteen Mothers stopped
singing and guffawed like one Mother. All in all, a most painful experience. Add the fact that the first thing the females did on hitting
the old homeland again was to get up an informal dance on the
sands and that the ride home in the quiet evenfall was more or less
a repetition of the journey out, and you will agreee with me that
Barmy, as he eventually tottered into the saloon bar of the Goose and
Grasshopper, had earned the frothing tankard which he now proceeded
to order.

He had just sucked it down and was signalling for another, when the
door of the saloon bar opened and in came Pongo.

If Barmy had been less preoccupied with his own troubles he would
have seen that Pongo was in poorish shape. His collar was torn, his
hair dishevelled. There were streaks of chocolate down his face and
half a jam sandwich attached to the back of his coat. And so moved was
he at seeing Barmy that he started ticking him off before he had
so much as ordered a gin and ginger.

"A nice thing you let me in for!" said Pongo. "A jolly job you
shoved off on me!"

Barmy was feeling a little better after his ingurgitations, and he was
able to speak.

"What are you talking about?"

"I am talking about School Treats," replied Pongo with an intense
bitterness. "I am talking about seas of children, all with sticky hands,
who rubbed those hands on me. I am talking.... Oh, it's no good your
gaping like a diseased fish, Fotheringay-Phipps. You know dashed
well that you planned the whole thing. Your cunning fiend's brain
formulated the entire devilish scheme. You engineered the bally out-

rage for your own foul purposes, to queer me with Angelica. You thought that when a girl sees a man blindfolded and smacked with rolled-up newspapers by smelly children she can never feel the same to him again. Ha!" said Pongo, at last ordering his gin and ginger.

Barmy was stunned, of course, by this violent attack, but he retained enough of the nice sense of propriety of the Fotheringay-Phippses to realize that this discussion could not be continued in public. Already the barmaid's ears had begun to work loose at the roots as she pricked them up.

"I don't know what the dickens you're talking about," he said, "but bring your drink up to my room and we'll go into the matter there. We cannot bandy a woman's name in a saloon bar."

"Who's bandying a woman's name?"

"You are. You bandied it only half a second ago. If you don't call what you said bandying, there are finer-minded men who do."

So they went upstairs, and Barmy shut the door.

"Now, then," he said. "What's all this drivel?"

"I've told you."

"Tell me again."

"I will."

"Right ho. One moment."

Barmy went to the door and opened it sharply. There came the unmistakable sound of a barmaid falling downstairs. He closed the door again.

"Now, then," he said.

Pongo drained his gin and ginger.

"Of all the dirty tricks one man ever played on another," he began, "your sneaking out of that School Treat and letting me in for it is one which the verdict of history will undoubtedly rank the dirtiest. I can read you now like a book, Fotheringay-Phipps. Your motive is crystal clear to me. You knew at what a disadvantage a man appears at a School Treat, and you saw to it that I and not you should be the poor mutt to get smeared with chocolate and sloshed with newspapers before the eyes of Angelica Briscoe. And I believed you when you handed me all that drip about yielding your claim and what not. My gosh!"

For an instant, as he heard these words, stupefaction rendered Barmy speechless. Then he found his tongue. His generous soul was seething with indignation at the thought of how his altruism, his great sacrifice, had been misinterpreted.

"What absolute rot!" he cried. "I never heard such bilge in my life. My motives in sending you to that School Treat instead of me were unmixedly chivalrous. I did it simply and solely to enable you to ingratiate yourself with the girl, not reflecting that it was out of the question that she could ever love a popeyed, pimply-faced poop like you."

Pongo started.

"Popeyed?"

"Popeyed was what I said."

"Pimply-faced?"

"Pimply-faced was the term I employed."

"Poop?"

"Poop was the expression with which I concluded. If you want to know the real obstacle in the way of any wooing you may do now or in the years to come, Twistleton-Twistleton, it is this—that you entirely lack sex appeal and look like nothing on earth. A girl of the sweet, sensitive nature of Angelica Briscoe does not have to see you smeared with chocolate to recoil from you with loathing. She does it automatically, and she does it on her head."

"Is that so?"

"That is so."

"Oh? Well, let me inform you that in spite of what has happened, in spite of the fact that she has seen me at my worst, there is something within me that tells me that Angelica Briscoe loves me and will one day be mine."

"Mine, you mean. I can read the message in a girl's shy, drooping eyes, Twistleton-Twistleton, and I am prepared to give you odds of eleven to four that before the year is out I shall be walking down the aisle with Angelica Fotheringay-Phipps on my arm. I will go further. Thirty-three to eight."

"What in?"

"Tenners."

"Done."

It was at this moment that the door opened.

"Excuse me, gentlemen," said the barmaid.

The two rivals glared at the intruder. She was a well-nourished girl with a kind face. She was rubbing her left leg, which appeared to be paining her. The staircases are steep at the Goose and Grasshopper.

"You'll excuse me muscling in like this, gentlemen," said the barmaid, or words to that effect, "but I happened inadvertently to overhear your conversation, and I feel it my duty to put you straight on an important point of fact. Gentlemen, all bets are off. Miss Angelica Briscoe is already engaged to be married."

You can readily conceive the effect of this announcement. Pongo biffed down into the only chair, and Barmy staggered against the washhand stand.

"What!" said Pongo.

"What!" said Barmy.

The barmaid turned to Barmy.

"Yes sir. To the gentleman you were talking to in my bar the afternoon you arrived."

Her initial observation had made Barmy feel as if he had been punched in the wind by sixteen Mothers, but at this addendum he was able to pull himself together a bit.

"Don't be an ass, my dear old barmaid," he said. "That was Miss Briscoe's brother."

"No sir."

"But his name was Briscoe, and you told me he was at the vicarage."

"Yes sir. He spends a good deal of his time at the vicarage, being the young lady's second cousin, and engaged to her since last Christmas!"

Barmy eyed her sternly. He was deeply moved.

"Why did you not inform me of this earlier, you chump of a barmaid? With your gift for listening at doors you must long since have become aware that this gentleman here and myself were deeply enamoured of Miss Briscoe. And yet you kept these facts under your hat, causing us to waste our time and experience the utmost alarm and despondency. Do you realise, barmaid, that, had you spoken sooner, my friend here would not have been subjected to nameless indignities at the School Treat? ..."

"Yes sir. It was the School Treat that Mr. Briscoe was so bent on not having to go to, which he would have had to have done, Miss Angelica insisting. He had a terrible time there last year, poor gentleman. He was telling me about it. And that was why he asked me as a particular favour not to mention that he was engaged to Miss Briscoe, because he said that, if he played his cards properly and a little secrecy and silence were observed in the proper quarters, there was a mug staying at the inn that he thought he could get to go instead of him. It would have done you good, sir, to have seen the way his face lit up as he said it. He's a very nice gentleman, Mr. Briscoe, and we're all very fond of him. Well, I mustn't stay talking here, sir. I've got my bar to see to."

She withdrew, and for some minutes there was silence in the room. It was Barmy who was the first to break it.

"After all, we still have our Art," said Barmy.

He crossed the room and patted Pongo on the shoulder.

"Of course, it's a nasty knock, old man ..."

Pongo had raised his face from his hands and was fumbling for his cigarette case. There was a look in his eyes as if he had just wakened from a dream.

"Well, *is* it?" he said. "You've got to look at these things from every angle. Is a girl who can deliberately allow a man to go through the horrors of a School Treat worth bothering about?"

Barmy started.

"I never thought of that. Or a girl, for that matter, who could callously throw a fellow to the Village Mothers."

"Remind me some time to tell you about a game called 'Is Mr. Smith At Home?' where you put your head in a sack and the younger generation jab you with sticks."

"And don't let me forget to tell you about that Mother in the puce mantle on the Bump the Bumps."

"There was a kid called Horace ..."

"There was a Mother in a Homburg hat ..."

"The fact is," said Pongo, "we have allowed ourselves to lose our sober judgment over a girl whose idea of a mate is a mere 'Hey, you,' to be ordered hither and thither at her will, and who will unleash the juvenile population of her native village upon him without so much as a pang of pity—in a word, a parson's daughter. If you want to know the secret of a happy and successful life, Barmy, old man, it is this: Keep away from parsons' daughters."

"Right away," agreed Barmy. "How do you react to hiring a car and pushing off to the metropolis at once?"

"I am all for it. And if we're to give of our best on the evening of the eleventh *prox.* we ought to start rehearsing again immediately."

"We certainly ought."

"We haven't any too much time, as it is."

"We certainly haven't. I've got an aunt who complains of rheumatism."

"Well, who wouldn't? My father can't meet his creditors."

"Does he want to? My uncle Joe's in very low water just now."

"Too bad. What's he doing?"

"Teaching swimming. Listen, Pongo," said Barmy, "I've been thinking. You take the green whiskers this year."

"No, no."

"Yes, really. I mean it. If I've said it to myself once, I've said it a hundred times—good old Pongo simply must have the green whiskers this year."

"Barmy!"

"Pongo!"

They clasped hands. Tried in the furnace, their friendship had emerged strong and true. Cyril Fotheringay-Phipps and Reginald Twistleton-Twistleton were themselves again.

E. V. Knox ("Evoe")

E. V. Knox, the present editor of Punch, *is the greatest living continuer of the Calverley tradition in verse. No one is more impregnated than he with the rhythms of English poetry; no one is such a master of the change of pace, the cunning discord. No one can make so much of so little; such was the immortal art of Racine.*

A POLITE PROTEST

(Dedicated Respectfully to the Owner of the Animal Next Door)

Dear Sir, when several weeks ago
  The perfect orb in heaven was hung
Of Dian wandering to and fro
    Thessalian woods among,
      When fast by many a forest glade
      The hunt was up, and hounds obeyed
      The horn-blast of the buskined maid,
      I did not weep when your decayed
    Old rag-bag too gave tongue.

I flung my window casement wide:
  O'er flood and fen, o'er field and bog
I seemed to see the huntress stride,
    Her silvery rout agog,
      Through beech and fir and pine-wood stem,
      And though the time was 2 A.M.
      I listed powerless to condemn
      A beast howe'er so slightly rem-
    Iniscent of a dog.

"Poor chap," I thought, "it well may be
  Some shadowy vision stirs within,
Some memory of the upland free
    And copses loud with din,

561

Of sires who from some moated grange
Would sally forth the woods to range:
He quests: there is a longing strange
Enkindled underneath the mange
That pies his odorous skin.

"Some strain perhaps of many strains
    That bids him bay the virgin moon,
Some atavistic dream remains,
    He will be silent soon:
        His ardour is a sign of grace,
        I will not mash that upturned face
        So filled with fever for the chase."
        These thoughts induced me to replace
The bootjack in my shoon.

Since then, through many midnights wrapped
    In darkness, when the Queen was dim,
Your mouldy hybrid still has yapped,
    It makes no odds to him.
        It does to me. I am a bard,
        And so I send this little card
        To say your Ponto will be marred
        By something heavy, thrown quite hard,
Unless you change his whim.

THE OLD SILENT HOUSE

I find that we have not had any poem yet about an old silent deserted house with nobody in it. This is a very serious omission, for
almost all modern poets write poems about this kind of house, possibly because the shortage of new houses is so great. Not that one
alludes to any such consideration in a poem about an old house. One
does not ask what the rent is, or discuss the difficulty of keeping up
the house, what with servants and one thing and another in these
terrible days. No, one simply stands and looks at the house and thinks

sad thoughts about it—how silent it is and how empty and how old. In order to catch the right spirit I went to look at an old house myself, so you may be quite sure there is no artifice whatever in these lines. I ought to have said that a poem about an old house should never be divided into stanzas, but run straight on; that the length of the lines should vary in order to increase the sadness, and that by the end of it the reader should be in tears. All right. Play:—

Nobody comes to the old house,
   It is so old and still;
The weeds have grown in the garden,
   The steps are damp and chill;
There is rust on the old gate-hinges
   And never a song of a bird
From any bush in the garden
   Or from any tree is heard.
Not an eye peeps out of the windows;
   Shuttered and fast as tombs
Are the ample bed, reception,
   Billiard and servants' rooms.
The rose-bloom falls in the long grass
   Gold-starred with the buttercup;
There is no sound in the pantry
   Of anyone washing up;
But the creeping mouse in the wainscot
   Rustles with paws like silk,
And the spider spins uncaring;
   No one with milk
Opens the gate of the garden
   Or knocks at the old side-door,
Or pushes under the front one
   Circulars any more.
Only Silence, she only
   Over the grass and stones
Creeps, and a little whisper
   And a little wind that moans.
She only touches the threshold
   With shadowy light footfalls,

564 A TREASURY OF BRITISH HUMOR

But nobody answers the front-door
    When Silence calls.
She treads on the musty landings,
    She mounts the echoless stair,
But nobody welcomes Silence,
    For no one is there.
Only invisible watchers
    With sightless eyes regard
The coming and going of Silence—
    She leaves no card;
She passes out through the great hall,
    Seeing no coat nor hat;
The house is entirely empty—
    You all grasp that.
Oh where, oh where are the people
    Whose voices, echoing gay,
Once made the old house cheerful?
    Why have they gone away?
Do they know that the lawn is stifled
    With the buttercups' starry gold,
And the bath-room taps are mildewed,
    Hot and cold?
Sorrowful is this old house
    That holds me here with the spell
Of all sad things and all old things
    Too sad to tell.
For not only the house is empty
    And seems to dream,
But down in the old still garden
    Strangely there gleam
The lid of a metal saucepan
    And a broken china vase
And a couple of disused kettles
    In the long rank grass;
And hard by the moss-damp doorstep
    Is a tin that once held fruit,
And under the rhododendrons
    Someone has thrown a boot.

Sadder to me seems an old house
Where memory walks and weeps,
And out of the darkened windows
No eye of watcher peeps,
When men cast forth disused things
Out of the next-door plot,
And in the old silent garden
Rubbish is being shot.

WHITE SOX VS. GIANTS
An Hour at Stamford Bridge

At either end of the ground stood the goal-posts and nets which were used last year (they tell me) by the opponents of the Chelsea Football Club. Somewhere in the middle of the field a man dressed in a sort of humorous golfing-suit and a jockey cap went through the complicated motions of a new dance. He raised one knee, put his clasped hands above his head, spun round and turned his back to the audience. I thought for a moment that he was overcome by pain. Then he faced round and imitated the action of a man throwing a ball; but I could not see any ball.

Whuck! Oh, there *was* a ball, then. It was hit by that man holding a ninepin in front of those two men with masks. It went high up into the air, descended and was caught with consummate ease. Another gentleman jockey took the ninepin and there was another step-dance.

Whuck! And the ball came like a stone from a catapult before the gentleman jockey, who had thrown away his ninepin, had time to reach the canvas pad.

Amidst the pile of peanut shells which grew round my feet—I was sitting between two Americans—I peered through the netting which protected the unmasked spectators from the mishits. And the most astonishing part of the performance was certainly this: that half those human catapults seemed to be hurling badinage at each other.

"No, no, no," I said to myself, "these Americans don't understand the Idea of a Game. They confuse it with fun. They think it is a merry romping affair. Far otherwise is the truth. We were not surely sent into the world to take our pastimes lightly. No decent English boy after the age of eight will permit himself to see any fun in a game. Consider the noise and laughter of 'Here we go gathering nuts and may' in the years of original sin, and compare it with the solemnity of a private school cricket-match. Fun, by that time, is relegated to the form room; it is not allowed to intrude on the serious business of life. At the age of forty to take a light view of a mashie-shot is little better than Bolshevism...."

Whuck! A good hit that. Several people running. The jabbering among the players grew fiercer still.

"This is terrible," I said to myself again. "Is there no sense of reverence in America? These gibes, these repartees might be all very well on the Stock Exchange, in the House of Commons or in the Upper House of Convocation, but try to imagine them at Twickenham or at Lord's."

Nevertheless I did my utmost to find excuses for these Americans. Things might not be so bad as they seemed. This hilarity, after all, might not be wholly spontaneous. It might be a part of the rules.... And I attempted, whilst the whucking and jabbering went on, to imagine a conversation between two proud American parents, whose boys might eventually, if Heaven prospered them, rise to be pitchers or catchers for their native town.

They meet—shall we say? at the Rotary Club. They talk first of all, as in duty bound, in a shamefaced manner about little Willie's and little Tommy's place in school, which is possibly top of the form. But they soon glide from this unpleasant topic to a consideration of their sons' chances in the great game of life.

"I am a good deal worried," says the one, "about my Willie."

"Why?" says the other. "He pitches beautifully. Can't he fox a base?"

"Yes." (Or "Yep," or "Yeh," or "Yeah." I am not very good, you know, on the niceties of American dialogue.)

"What's the matter, then? Can't he throw? Can't he catch?"

"Like sin, sir."

"What's worrying you, then? Can he bunt?" (I believe that when an American baseball player hits the invisible ball with his ninepin, he calls it a bunt.)

"Sure thing. He's the cutest bunter in his class, is my little Willie."

"What's biting you, then?"

At that the American father heaves a long sigh, the wrinkles gather on his forehead and a shadow passes over his fine proud face.

"Persiflage," he says. "The boy makes no headway with his persiflage. I tell you, my Willie can't root worth a row of beans."

Here again my phraseology may be wrong. I am trying to give you a general human picture, you understand, so that you may see the intolerable pathos of the thing. If you want mere pep in dialogue you must go elsewhere.

And then the other American parent, pretending sorrow for his old friend, but secretly elated because his own boy, Tommy, is one of the cutest vituperators for his age (Yes, Sir) that the school has ever known, recommends a persiflage coach for the holidays to put little Willie through an examination course in back answers and bring his chipping and chaffing into line with the rest of his scholastic work.

And in the end little Willie becomes the catcher of his college team, wearing a mask and pads and gauntlets as he crouches on his hams behind the base-plate (?) and never missing the invisible ball.... But is it for his looks that he wins the smile from Maisie's bright eyes? Not on your life. It is because he can sass the unfortunate batter who is bobbing about in front of him with such a stream of well-chosen invective that the poor fellow makes a half-hearted bunt and dashes blindly and vainly to the first base to hide his grief and despair.

Meanwhile the pile of peanut shells about my feet grew deeper still. The Giants seemed to be winning. The *facetiæ* of the catcher became excruciatingly funny. The Americans on either side of me were getting excited. They were rooting, I supposed, like the players on the field. They appeared to be fans. I wished to be a fan too. I wished I had some elementary notion of the rules, and turned with a faint hope to the large free pamphlet which had been pressed upon me at the gate.

I found nothing about the rules there, but I found enough to assure me that America was sound-hearted after all. Her levity about the national pastime, as I had already begun to hope, was assumed. The photographs of the men in the book were not the photographs of *flâneurs,* but of men who understand Reality, as we understand it over here.

"Charles A. Comiskey," I read, "known all over the baseball world as 'The Old Roman,' is the popular owner of the White Sox...John J. Evers is widely known in song and story as the pivot of the Tinker to Evers to Chance combination of the old Club machine...John J. McGraw takes full responsibility on the field, and does not hesitate to bear the blame if one of his pet plays turns out badly"...(How unlike our mere Premiers over here!)..."while Hugh Jennings, the man who made famous the great coaching cry of 'E—e—e—eah,' starting as a player in Louisville, Ky., in 1891, was traded to Baltimore in 1893."

And then there was "The Man of the Hour—Judge Kenesaw M. Landis, High Commissioner of Baseball, who was elected to the new and highest position in baseball by unanimous vote of the sixteen Major League Clubs for seven years. He was also endowed with absolute power without appeal." (Hear, hear.)

I gathered also that the object of these gentlemen in undertaking the present tour was to popularise baseball throughout the world, "as the foreign world in the last fifty years has been taking and adopting America's inventions for their commercial progress, beginning with steam as a motive-power, then to telegraphy, sewing-machines and farming implements, and last, but not least, the inventions of the electric wizard of the world, Tom Edison."

Whuck!

"See that guy over there?" said the American on my left, touching my arm and pointing to one of the gentleman jockeys. "He's one of your Britishers. He comes from Quee-bec."

Rising triumphantly amongst the peanut shells I made a feeble attempt to root.

Daisy Ashford

The Young Visiters *appeared in 1919. It was credited to Daisy Ash-*
ford, alleged to be a woman, then mature, who had written the novel
at the age of nine. James M. Barrie wrote a preface, and later drama-
tized the story, so everyone smiled knowingly and said, "You can't
fool us, you old pixy!" But Daisy Ashford was and is real.

THE YOUNG VISITERS

(Selection)

CHAPTER I

QUITE A YOUNG GIRL

Mr. Salteena was an elderly man of 42 and was fond of asking people
to stay with him. He had quite a young girl staying with him of 17
named Ethel Monticue. Mr. Salteena had dark short hair and mustache
and wiskers which were very black and twisty. He was middle sized
and he had very pale blue eyes. He had a pale brown suit but on Sundays he had a black one and he had a topper every day as he thorght
it more becoming. Ethel Monticue had fair hair done on the top and
blue eyes. She had a blue velvit frock which had grown rarther short
in the sleeves. She had a black straw hat and kid gloves.

One morning Mr. Salteena came down to brekfast and found Ethel
had come down first which was strange. Is the tea made Ethel he said
rubbing his hands. Yes said Ethel and such a quear shaped parcel has
come for you. Yes indeed it was a quear shape parcel it was a hat box
tied down very tight and a letter stuffed between the string. Well well
said Mr. Salteena parcels do turn quear I will read the letter first and
so saying he tore open the letter and this is what it said

MY DEAR ALFRED.

I want you to come for a stop with me so I have sent you a top hat
wraped up in tishu paper inside the box. Will you wear it staying with

me because it is very uncommon. Please bring one of your young ladies
whichever is the prettiest in the face.

I remain Yours truely

BERNARD CLARK

Well said Mr. Salteena I shall take you to stay Ethel and fancy him
sending me a top hat. Then Mr. S. opened the box and there lay the
most splendid top hat of a lovely rich tone rarther like grapes with a
ribbon round compleat.

Well said Mr. Salteena peevishly I dont know if I shall like it the
bow of the ribbon is too flighty for my age. Then he sat down and
eat the egg which Ethel had so kindly laid for him. After he had finished his meal he got down and began to write to Bernard Clark he
ran up stairs on his fat legs and took out his blotter with a loud sniff
and this is what he wrote

My DEAR BERNARD

Certinly I shall come and stay with you next Monday I will bring Ethel
Monticue commonly called Miss M. She is very active and pretty. I do hope
I shall enjoy myself with you. I am fond of digging in the garden and I
am parshial to ladies if they are nice I suppose it is my nature. I am not
quite a gentleman but you would hardly notice it but cant be helped anyhow. We will come by the 3-15.

Your old and valud friend

ALFRED SALTEENA

Perhaps my readers will be wondering why Bernard Clark had
asked Mr. Salteena to stay with him. He was a lonely man in a remote
spot and he liked peaple and partys but he did not know many. What
rot muttered Bernard Clark as he read Mr. Salteenas letter. He was
rarther a presumshious man.

CHAPTER II

STARTING GAILY

When the great morning came Mr. Salteena did not have an egg for
his brekfast in case he should be sick on the jorney.

What top hat will you wear asked Ethel.

I shall wear my best black and my white alpacka coat to keep off the
dust and flies replied Mr. Salteena.

I shall put some red ruge on my face said Ethel because I am very pale owing to the drains in this house.

You will look very silly said Mr. Salteena with a dry laugh.

Well so will you said Ethel in a snappy tone and she ran out of the room with a very superier run throwing out her legs behind and her arms swinging in rithum.

Well said the owner of the house she has a most idiotick run.

Presently Ethel came back in her best hat and a lovly velvit coat of royal blue. Do I look nice in my get up she asked.

Mr. Salteena survayed her. You look rarther rash my dear your colors dont quite match your face but never mind I am just going up to say good-bye to Rosalind the housemaid.

Well dont be long said Ethel. Mr. S. skipped upstairs to Rosalinds room. Good-bye Rosalind he said I shall be back soon and I hope I shall enjoy myself.

I make no doubt of that sir said Rosalind with a blush as Mr. Salteena silently put 2/6 on the dirty toilet cover.

Take care of your bronkitis said Mr. S. rarther bashfully and he hastilly left the room waving his hand carelessly to the housemaid.

Come along cried Ethel powdering her nose in the hall let us get into the cab. Mr. Salteena did not care for powder but he was an unselfish man so he dashed into the cab. Sit down said Ethel as the cabman waved his whip you are standing on my luggage. Well I am paying for the cab said Mr. S. so I might be allowed to put my feet were I like.

They traveled 2nd class in the train and Ethel was longing to go first but thought perhaps least said soonest mended. Mr. Salteena got very excited in the train about his visit. Ethel was calm but she felt excited inside. Bernard has a big house said Mr. S. gazing at Ethel he is inclined to be rich.

Oh indeed said Ethel looking at some cows flashing past the window. Mr. S. felt rarther disheartened so he read the paper till the train stopped and the porters shouted Rickamere station. We had better collect our traps said Mr. Salteena and just then a very exalted footman in a cocked hat and olive green uniform put his head in at the window. Are you for Rickamere Hall he said in impressive tones.

Well yes I am said Mr. Salteena and so is this lady.

Very good sir said the noble footman if you will alight I will see to your luggage there is a convayance awaiting you.

Oh thankyou thankyou said Mr. S. and he and Ethel stepped along the platform. Outside they found a lovely cariage lined with olive green cushions to match the footman and the horses had green bridles and bows on their manes and tails. They got gingerly in. Will he bring our luggage asked Ethel nervously.

I expect so said Mr. Salteena lighting a very long cigar.

Do we tip him asked Ethel quietly.

Well no I dont think so not yet we had better just thank him per-litely.

Just then the footman staggered out with the bagage. Ethel bowed gracefully over the door of the cariage and Mr. S. waved his hand as each bit of luggage was hoisted up to make sure it was all there. Then he said thankyou my good fellow very politely. Not at all sir said the footman and touching his cocked hat he jumped actively to the box.

I was right not to tip him whispered Mr. Salteena the thing to do is to leave 2/6 on your dressing table when your stay is over.

Does he find it asked Ethel who did not really know at all how to go on at a visit. I beleeve so replied Mr. Salteena anyhow its quite the custom and we can't help it if he does not. Now my dear what do you think of the sceenery.

Very nice said Ethel gazing at the rich fur rug on her knees. Just then the cariage rolled into a beautifull drive with tall trees and big red flowers growing amid shiny dark leaves. Presently the haughty coachman pulled up with a great clatter at a huge front door with tall pillers each side a big iron bell and two very clean scrapers. The doors flung open as if by majic causing Ethel to jump and a portly butler appeared on the scene with a very shiny shirt front and a huge pale face. Welcome sir he exclaimed good naturedly as Mr. Salteena alighted rarther quickly from the viacle and please to step inside.

Mr. Salteena stepped in as bid followed by Ethel. The footman again struggled with the luggage and the butler Francis Minnit by name kindly lent a hand. The hall was very big and hung round with guns and mats and ancesters giving it a gloomy but a grand air. The butler then showed them down a winding corridoor till he came to a door which he flung open shouting Mr. Salteena and a lady sir.

A tall man of 29 rose from the sofa. He was rarther bent in the middle with very nice long legs fairish hair and blue eyes. Hullo Alf old boy he cried so you have got here all safe and no limbs broken.

None thankyou Bernard replied Mr. Salteena shaking hands and let me introduce Miss Monticue she is very pleased to come for this visit. Oh yes gasped Ethel blushing through her red ruge. Bernard looked at her keenly and turned a dark red. I am glad to see you he said I hope you will enjoy it but I have not arranged any partys yet as I dont know anybody.

Dont worry murmered Ethel I dont mix much in Socierty and she gave him a dainty smile.

I expect you would like some tea said Bernard I will ring.

Yes indeed we should said Mr. Salteena egerly. Bernard pealed on the bell and the butler came in with a stately walk.

Tea please Minnit cried Bernard Clark. With pleshure sir replied Minnit with a deep bow. A glorious tea then came in on a gold tray two kinds of bread and butter a lovly jam role and lots of sugar cakes. Ethels eyes began to sparkle and she made several remarks during the meal. I expect you would now like to unpack said Bernard when it was over.

Well yes that is rarther an idear said Mr. Salteena.

I have given the best spare room to Miss Monticue said Bernard with a gallant bow and yours turning to Mr. Salteena opens out of it so you will be nice and friendly both the rooms have big windows and a handsome view.

How charming said Ethel. Yes well let us go up replied Bernard and he led the way up many a winding stairway till they came to an oak door with some lovly swans and bull rushes painted on it. Here we are he cried gaily. Ethels room was indeed a handsome compartment with purple silk curtains and a 4 post bed draped with the same shade. The toilit set was white and mouve and there were some violets in a costly varse. Oh I say cried Ethel in suprise. I am glad you like it said Bernard and here we have yours Alf. He opened the dividing doors and portrayed a smaller but dainty room all in pale yellow and wild primroses. My own room is next the bath room said Bernard it is deccrated dark red as I have somber tastes. The bath room has got a tip up bason and a hose thing for washing your head.

A good notion said Mr. Salteena who was secretly getting jellus.

Here we will leave our friends to unpack and end this Chapter.

Herbert Farjeon

In England writing is largely performed by families. All the Far-jeons write, each in his or her own field. Put them all together, they make a Literature. Herbert does the theater; his revues are incomparable.

OUR BRITISH PASTIMES

LAWN TENNIS

ANNOUNCER: Our British Pastimes, and What Really Happens. First, just a nice little Lawn Tennis Party.

> (*Tabs part. Garden seat.* THREE GIRLS *and* TWO MEN *with rackets.* MRS. PARKER, *past her tennis days, presides. Chatter and laughter.*)

MRS. PARKER (*clapping hands and rising*): Come, come, we're wasting valuable daylight. Now, then—who's in the next set? You'll play for one, Elsie, won't you?

ELSIE: Oh, really, Mrs. Parker, I'd just as lief stand out—

ERNEST: No, don't you stand out, I'll stand out—

PAM: Well, if anyone ought to stand out, I ought, I'm so bad—

DORA: Oh, you're not. I'd *much* better stand out—

ALL: *I'll stand out, Mrs. Parker, I'd quite like to....*

MRS. PARKER (*clapping hands*): Dear, dear, everybody can't stand out. The point is, who's going to *play?* You're willing to play, aren't you, Pam?

PAM: Ra-*ther.* I'm *willing* to—

FRED: I'd *love* to, I mean, if no one else wants to—

ERNEST: Oh, I *want* to—

ALL: *I'll play, Mrs. Parker, I'd quite like to—*

MRS. PARKER: Dear, dear! How difficult! I know. We'll toss.

ERNEST: That's right. Rough or smooth.

ALL: Rough or smooth, rough or smooth. (*They spin their rackets.*)

ELSIE: Rough.

DORA: Rough.

ERNEST: Rough.

FRED: Rough.

PAM: Rough...

MRS. PARKER: What a nuisance! Never mind. Try again. (*They spin their rackets.*)

ELSIE: Rough.

DORA: Rough.

ERNEST: Rough.

FRED: *Smooth!*

PAM: Smooth—no, rough—no, smooth....

MRS. PARKER (*after a pause*): Well, where are we now?

PAM: I can't think, can you?...

MRS. PARKER: Well, I'll *arrange* the next set. Pam and Ernest *v.* Elsie and Fred. There!

ERNEST: That's what we played last set!

FRED: I think they ought to play a Ladies' Four.

ELSIE: Yes, only there aren't four ladies.

PAM (*brightly*): If there were four men, they could have a Men's Four.

ELSIE: I think Fred and Dora ought to play Pam and Ernest.

ERNEST: I think Pam and Fred against Elsie and Dora.

PAM: I think Elsie and Ernest—no, Elsie and Fred—no, Elsie...

MRS. PARKER: I know! Men *v.* Girls.

ALL: Men *v.* Girls, Men *v.* Girls.

MRS. PARKER: Fred and Ernest *v.* Dora and Pam. Now then, girls!

ALL FOUR (*divesting themselves*): All right, Mrs. Parker.

VOICE (*off stage*): Mrs. Parker!

(*Enter* MR. FISHLOCK)

MRS. PARKER: Oh, *there* you are, Mr. Fishlock. We'd quite given you up.

MR. FISHLOCK: Fearfully sorry, Mrs. Parker, I just couldn't make it.

FRED: Well, now he has come, he *must* have one set.

ALL: Yes, Mr. Fishlock *must* have one set.

MRS. PARKER: Of course he must. Now—who's going to stand out?

FRED: I'll stand out, Mrs. Parker.

ELSIE: No, let *me* stand out, Mrs. Parker.

PAM: I don't see why *I* shouldn't stand out, Mrs. Parker.

ALL: Really, Mrs. Parker, I'll stand out, I'd quite like to...

BRIDGE

ANNOUNCER: Next, just a quiet little rubber. Have you ever noticed how cards induce a kind of hypnotic trance, in which trance the players descend to the most abysmal depths of imbecility? Well, here's a game of Bridge, played not by the Culbertsons, but by any average after-dinner four. Quite intelligent people really, though they may not sound it.

> (*Tabs part. Four players at card table:* Two MEN, Two WOMEN. *The last cards are being dealt as lights go up. The players examine their hands. When they talk, they do not look at each other, but concentrate entirely on their cards.*)

FIRST MAN (*humming softly as he sorts*): Pom-pom-pom-pom, pom-pom-pom, pom-pom-pom-pom, pom-pom-pom, pom-pom-pom-pom—

SECOND MAN (*whistling through his teeth*): Ss, ss-ss-ss-ss, ss-ss—ss, ss-ss-ss-ss, ss-ss—ss, ss-ss-ss-ss—

FIRST LADY: Bub-bub-bub-bub, bub-bub-bub-bub, bub-bub-bub, bub-bub-bub-bub—whose call?

SECOND LADY: Your callikins.

FIRST LADY (*still engrossed in her cards*): My little callikins, well, well, well—*my* little callikins, well, well, well. Let me see, then, let me see—I think—I think—I think-a-pink-a-pink—No bid.

SECOND LADY: Tch-tch-tch, tch-tch-tch, tch-tch, tch-tch, tch-tch-tch, tch-tch-tch—no bid.

FIRST MAN: One cloob.

SECOND MAN (*dropping into Irish*): Did ye say one cloob?

FIRST MAN (*ditto*): I did that.

SECOND MAN: *Er hat ein cloob gesagen.* (*Singing.*) *Er hat ein cloob gesagen, er hat ein cloob....* One hearty-party.

FIRST LADY: Two diminx.

SECOND LADY: No bid, no bid.

FIRST MAN: No bid-a-bid-bid.

SECOND MAN: Two diminx, is it? Two naughty leetle diminx. This, I think, demands a certain amount of *considération.* (*Drums fingers on table.*) Yes, yes, my friends, *beaucoup de considération.*

SECOND LADY (*after a pause*): Your *call,* partner.

SECOND MAN: I know it, I know it, I know it, I know it, I know it, indeed, indeed, I know it. (*Clacks tongue.*) Clack-clack-clack,

clack, clack, clack-clack-clack, clack, clack. I know it, I know it,
I double two diminx.

SECOND LADY: He doubles two diminx.

FIRST MAN: He doubles two diminx.

SECOND MAN: I double, I double, I double two diminx.

FIRST LADY: Very well, then, have at you. Two no trumpets.

FIRST MAN: Ha, ha!

SECOND MAN: Ho, ho!

FIRST LADY: He, he!

SECOND LADY: H'm, h'm!

(*They revert to their pet noises as they consider their hands.*)

MUSICAL CHAIRS

ANNOUNCER: So much for Bridge-players and their vocal doodles.
That's quite enough of that. To conclude, the game we all begin
young, and never quite give up—dear old Musical Chairs.

(*Piano music. Tabs part. Six people playing Musical Chairs.
OLD MAN with long grey beard. YOUNG MAN, MAMA, FIRST
LADY, SECOND LADY, and DUCKY (little girl) with doll. Music
stops. All get seats except DUCKY, whose features, when she
grasps the catastrophe, compose themselves for a howl. MAMA
jumps up and hastens over to her.*)

MAMA: Look, Ducky, look, *there's* a chair!

DUCKY (*still on verge of tears*): Where's a chair?

MAMA: Quick, Ducky, quick. (DUCKY *begins running in wrong direction.*) *This* way, Ducky. (MAMA *bundles* DUCKY *into chair, whereupon she perks up and bounces up and down.*)

DUCKY (*to* FIRST LADY): It's my birfday today.

FIRST LADY: I know, dear.

DUCKY: I been sick twiced.

FIRST LADY: I know, dear.

SECOND LADY: *Isn't* she sweet?

ALL: Isn't she?

(*Music again. Five players left.* OLD MAN *sits down and gets up.*
DUCKY *touches seats as she passes.*)

OLD MAN (*sharply*): You mustn't touch the chairs.

DUCKY: Wasn't!

OLD MAN: You were!

DUCKY (*making a face*): Gnyar!

>   (*Music stops. All get seats except* DUCKY, *who lets out prelude
>   to a howl.*)

SECOND LADY (*jumping up*): Where's that chair? I can't find that chair! Where *is* that chair?

MAMA: Hurry up, Ducky. (*Pushes* DUCKY *into chair.*) *There* we are!

DUCKY (*jeering at* SECOND LADY): You're out, sil-lee!

FIRST LADY: Isn't she *sweet*?

MAMA (*to* SECOND LADY): I think she's a little over-excited.

SECOND LADY: No wonder—after *such* a booful birfday!

>   (*Music again. Four players left.* OLD MAN *sits down and gets
>   up.* DUCKY *hovers.*)

OLD MAN (*sharply*): You mustn't hover.

DUCKY: Mustn't say mustn't! Boo!

OLD MAN: Don't say boo to me.

DUCKY (*stepping out of line and facing audience*): Boo, boo, boo, boo, boo ...

>   (*Music stops.* DUCKY *as before.* FIRST LADY *gets up, catches*
>   DUCKY *roughly by the hand, and drags her into seat.*)

FIRST LADY: *What* a clever girlie!

DUCKY (*holding doll against* OLD MAN'S *mouth*): Kiss my dolly! I love my dolly. (*Wipes doll's mouth with her skirt.*)

>   (*Music again. Three players left.* OLD MAN *sits down and gets
>   up.* DUCKY *sits down.*)

OLD MAN (*sharply*): Get up, get up!

DUCKY (*getting up*): I am up!

OLD MAN: You *weren't* up!

DUCKY: Who weren't up?

OLD MAN: *You* weren't!

DUCKY: I weren't what?

>   (*Music stops.* DUCKY *as before.*)

SECOND LADY (*severely*): George!

YOUNG MAN (*getting up*): Sorry!

>   (*All rush for* DUCKY *and dump her into chair.*)

DUCKY: My dolly's going to win, my dolly's going to win!

MAMA: Doesn't she love her dolly?

ALL: *Doesn't* she!

    (*Music again.* OLD MAN *and* DUCKY *left.* OLD MAN *sits down and gets up.* DUCKY *sits down and gets up.* OLD MAN *sits down and gets up.* DUCKY *sits down and gets up. Music stops.* OLD MAN *sits down.* DUCKY *glares at him.*)

OLD MAN (*triumphantly*): I've won!

DUCKY (*smashing her doll across his head*): You bloody old cheat!

BLACK OUT

Katherine Mansfield

GERMANS AT MEAT

Bread soup was placed upon the table.

"Ah," said the Herr Rat, leaning upon the table as he peered into the tureen, "that is what I need. My 'magen' has not been in order for several days. Bread soup, and just the right consistency. I am a good cook myself"—he turned to me.

"How interesting," I said, attempting to infuse just the right amount of enthusiasm into my voice.

"Oh, yes—when one is not married it is necessary. As for me, I have had all I wanted from women without marriage." He tucked his napkin into his collar and blew upon his soup as he spoke. "Now at nine o'clock I make myself an English breakfast, but not much. Four slices of bread, two eggs, two slices of cold ham, one plate of soup, two cups of tea—that is nothing to you."

He asserted the fact so vehemently that I had not the courage to refute it.

All eyes were suddenly turned upon me. I felt I was bearing the burden of the nation's preposterous breakfast—I who drank a cup of coffee while buttoning my blouse in the morning.

"Nothing at all," cried Herr Hoffmann from Berlin. "Ach, when I was in England in the morning I used to eat."

He turned up his eyes and his moustache, wiping the soup drippings from his coat and waistcoat.

"Do they really eat so much?" asked Fraulein Stiegelauer. "Soup and baker's bread and pig's flesh, and tea and coffee and stewed fruit, and honey and eggs, and cold fish and kidneys, and hot fish and liver? All the ladies eat, too, especially the ladies?"

"Certainly. I myself have noticed it, when I was living in a hotel in Leicester Square," cried the Herr Rat. "It was a good hotel, but they could not make tea—now—"

"Ah, that's one thing I *can* do," said I, laughing brightly. "I can make very good tea. The great secret is to warm the teapot."

"Warm the teapot," interrupted the Herr Rat, pushing away his soup plate. "What do you warm the teapot for? Ha! ha! that's very good! One does not eat the teapot, I suppose?"

He fixed his cold blue eyes upon me with an expression which suggested a thousand premeditated invasions.

"So that is the great secret of your English tea? All you do is to warm the teapot."

I wanted to say that was only the preliminary canter, but could not translate it, and so was silent.

The servant brought in veal, with sauerkraut and potatoes.

"I eat sauerkraut with great pleasure," said the Traveller from North Germany, "but now I have eaten so much of it that I cannot retain it. I am immediately forced to—"

"A beautiful day," I cried, turning to Fraulein Stiegelauer. "Did you get up early?"

"At five o'clock I walked for ten minutes in the wet grass. Again in bed. At half-past five I fell asleep, and woke at seven, when I made an 'overbody' washing! Again in bed. At eight o'clock I had a cold-water poultice, and at half-past eight I drank a cup of mint tea. At nine I drank some malt coffee, and began my 'cure.' Pass me the sauerkraut, please. You do not eat it?"

"No, thank you. I still find it a little strong."

"Is it true," asked the Widow, picking her teeth with a hairpin as she spoke, "that you are a vegetarian?"

"Why, yes; I have not eaten meat for three years."

"Im-possible! Have you any family?"

"No."

"There now, you see, that's what you're coming to! Who ever heard of having children upon vegetables? It is not possible. But you never have large families in England now; I suppose you are too busy with your suffragetting. Now I have had nine children, and they are all alive, thank God. Fine healthy babies—though after the first one was born I had to—"

"How *wonderful!*" I cried.

"Wonderful," said the Widow contemptuously, replacing the hairpin in the knob which was balanced on the top of her head. "Not at all! A friend of mine had four at the same time. Her husband was so pleased he gave a supper-party and had them placed on the table. Of course she was very proud."

"Germany," boomed the Traveller, biting round a potato which he had speared with his knife, "is the home of the Family."

Followed an appreciative silence.

The dishes were changed for beef, red currants and spinach. They wiped their forks upon black bread and started again.

"How long are you remaining here?" asked the Herr Rat.

"I do not know exactly. I must be back in London in September."

"Of course you will visit München?"

"I am afraid I shall not have time. You see, it is important not to break into my 'cure.'"

"But you *must* go to München. You have not seen Germany if you have not been to München. All the Exhibitions, all the Art and Soul life of Germany are in München. There is the Wagner Festival in August, and Mozart and a Japanese collection of pictures—and there is the beer! You do not know what good beer is until you have been to München. Why, I see fine ladies every afternoon, but fine ladies, I tell you, drinking glasses so high." He measured a good washstand pitcher in height, and I smiled.

"If I drink a great deal of München beer I sweat so," said Herr Hoffmann. "When I am here, in the fields or before my baths, I sweat, but I enjoy it; but in the town it is not at all the same thing."

Prompted by the thought, he wiped his neck and face with his dinner napkin and carefully cleaned his ears.

A glass dish of stewed apricots was placed upon the table.

"Ah, fruit!" said Fraulein Stiegelauer, "that is so necessary to health. The doctor told me this morning that the more fruit I could eat the better."

She very obviously followed the advice.

Said the Traveller: "I suppose you are frightened of an invasion, too, eh? Oh, that's good. I've been reading all about your English play in a newspaper. Did you see it?"

"Yes." I sat upright. "I assure you we are not afraid."

"Well, then, you ought to be," said the Herr Rat. "You have got no army at all—a few little boys with their veins full of nicotine poisoning."

"Don't be afraid," Herr Hoffmann said. "We don't want England. If we did we would have had her long ago. We really do not want you."

He waved his spoon airily, looking across at me as though I were a little child whom he would keep or dismiss as he pleased.

"We certainly do not want Germany," I said.

"This morning I took a half bath. Then this afternoon I must take a knee bath and an arm bath," volunteered the Herr Rat; "then I do my exercises for an hour, and my work is over. A glass of wine and a couple of rolls with some sardines—"

They were handed cherry cake with whipped cream.

"What is your husband's favourite meal?" asked the Widow.

"I really do not know," I answered.

"You really do not know? How long have you been married?"

"Three years."

"But you cannot be in earnest! You would not have kept house as his wife for a week without knowing that fact."

"I really never asked him; he is not at all particular about his food."

A pause. They all looked at me, shaking their heads, their mouths full of cherry stones.

"No wonder there is a repetition in England of that dreadful state of things in Paris," said the Widow, folding her dinner napkin. "How can a woman expect to keep her husband if she does not know his favourite food after three years?"

"Mahlzeit!"

"Mahlzeit!"

I closed the door after me.

THE MODERN SOUL

"Good-evening," said the Herr Professor, squeezing my hand; "wonderful weather! I have just returned from a party in the wood. I have been making music for them on my trombone. You know, these pine-trees provide most suitable accompaniment for a trombone! They are sighing delicacy against sustained strength, as I remarked once in a lecture on wind instruments in Frankfort. May I be permitted to sit beside you on this bench, gnädige Frau?"

He sat down, tugging at a white-paper package in the tail pocket of his coat.

"Cherries," he said, nodding and smiling. "There is nothing like cherries for producing free saliva after trombone playing, especially after Grieg's 'Ich Liebe Dich.' Those sustained blasts on 'liebe' make my throat as dry as a railway tunnel. Have some?" He shook the bag at me.

"I prefer watching you eat them."

"Ah, ha!" He crossed his legs, sticking the cherry bag between his knees, to leave both hands free. "Psychologically I understood your refusal. It is your innate feminine delicacy in preferring etherealised sensations.... Or perhaps you do not care to eat the worms. All cherries contain worms. Once I made a very interesting experiment with a colleague of mine at the university. We bit into four pounds of the best cherries and did not find one specimen without a worm. But what would you? As I remarked to him afterwards—dear friend, it amounts to this: if one wishes to satisfy the desires of nature one must be strong enough to ignore the facts of nature.... The conversation is not out of your depth? I have so seldom the time or opportunity to open my heart to a woman that I am apt to forget."

I looked at him brightly.

"See what a fat one!" cried the Herr Professor. "That is almost a mouthful in itself; it is beautiful enough to hang from a watch-chain." He chewed it up and spat the stone an incredible distance—over the garden path into the flower bed. He was proud of the feat. I saw it. "The quantity of fruit I have eaten on this bench," he sighed; "apricots, peaches, and cherries. One day that garden bed will become an orchard grove, and I shall allow you to pick as much as you please, without paying me anything."

I was grateful, without showing undue excitement.

"Which reminds me"—he hit the side of his nose with one finger—"the manager of the pension handed me my weekly bill after dinner this evening. It is almost impossible to credit. I do not expect you to believe me—he has charged me extra for a miserable little glass of milk I drink in bed at night to prevent insomnia. Naturally, I did not pay. But the tragedy of the story is this: I cannot expect the milk to produce somnolence any longer; my peaceful attitude of mind towards it is completely destroyed. I know I shall throw myself into a fever in attempting to plumb this want of generosity in so wealthy a man as the manager of a pension. Think of me to-night"—he ground the empty bag under his heel—"think that the worst is happening to me as your head drops asleep on your pillow."

Two ladies came on the front steps of the pension and stood, arm in arm, looking over the garden. The one, old and scraggy, dressed almost entirely in black bead trimming and a satin reticule; the other, young and thin, in a white gown, her yellow hair tastefully garnished with mauve sweet peas.

The Professor drew in his feet and sat up sharply, pulling down his waistcoat.

"The Godowskas," he murmured. "Do you know them? A mother and daughter from Vienna. The mother has an internal complaint and the daughter is an actress, Fräulein Sonia is a very modern soul. I think you would find her most sympathetic. She is forced to be in attendance on her mother just now. But what a temperament! I have once described her in her autograph album as a tigress with a flower in the hair. Will you excuse me? Perhaps I can persuade them to be introduced to you."

I said, "I am going up to my room." But the Professor rose and shook a playful finger at me. "Na," he said, "we are friends, and, therefore, I shall speak quite frankly to you. I think they would consider it a little 'marked' if you immediately retired to the house at their approach, after sitting here alone with me in the twilight. You know this world. Yes, you know it as I do."

I shrugged my shoulders, remarking with one eye that while the Professor had been talking the Godowskas had trailed across the lawn towards us. They confronted the Herr Professor as he stood up.

"Good-evening," quavered Frau Godowska. "Wonderful weather! It has given me quite a touch of hay fever!" Fräulein Godowska said nothing. She swooped over a rose growing in the embryo orchard, then stretched out her hand with a magnificent gesture to the Herr Professor. He presented me.

"This is my little English friend of whom I have spoken. She is the stranger in our midst. We have been eating cherries together."

"How delightful," sighed Frau Godowska. "My daughter and I have often observed you through the bedroom window. Haven't we, Sonia?"

Sonia absorbed my outward and visible form with an inward and spiritual glance, then repeated the magnificent gesture for my benefit. The four of us sat on the bench, with that faint air of excitement of passengers established in a railway carriage on the qui vive for the train whistle. Frau Godowska sneezed. "I wonder if it is hay fever," she remarked, worrying the satin reticule for her handkerchief, "or would it be the dew? Sonia, dear, is the dew falling?"

Fräulein Sonia raised her face to the sky, and half closed her eyes. "No, mamma, my face is quite warm. Oh, look, Herr Professor, there are swallows in flight; they are like a little flock of Japanese thoughts— nicht wahr?"

"Where?" cried the Herr Professor. "Oh, yes, I see, by the kitchen chimney. But why do you say 'Japanese'? Could you not compare them with equal veracity to a little flock of German thoughts in flight?" He rounded on me. "Have you swallows in England?"

"I believe there are some at certain seasons. But doubtless they have not the same symbolical value for the English. In Germany—"

"I have never been to England," interrupted Fräulein Sonia, "but I have many English acquaintances. They are so cold!" She shivered.

"Fish-blooded," snapped Frau Godowska. "Without soul, without heart, without grace. But you cannot equal their dress materials. I spent a week in Brighton twenty years ago, and the travelling cape I bought there is not yet worn out—the one you wrap the hot-water bottle in, Sonia. My lamented husband, your father, Sonia, knew a great deal about England. But the more he knew about it the oftener he remarked to me, 'England is merely an island of beef flesh swimming in a warm gulf sea of gravy.' Such a brilliant way of putting things. Do you remember, Sonia?"

"I forget nothing, mamma," answered Sonia.

Said the Herr Professor: "That is the proof of your calling, gnädiges Fräulein. Now I wonder—and this is a very interesting speculation—is memory a blessing or—excuse the word—a curse?"

Frau Godowska looked into the distance, then the corners of her mouth dropped and her skin puckered. She began to shed tears.

"Ach Gott! Gracious lady, what have I said?" exclaimed the Herr Professor.

Sonia took her mother's hand. "Do you know," she said, "tonight it is stewed carrots nut tart for supper. Suppose we go in and take our places," her sidelong, tragic stare accusing the Professor and me the while.

I followed them across the lawn and up the steps. Frau Godowska was murmuring, "Such a wonderful, beloved man"; with her disengaged hand Sonia was arranging the sweet pea "garniture."

A concert for the benefit of afflicted Catholic infants will take place in the salon at 8:30 P.M. Artists: Fräulein Sonia Godowska, from Vienna; Herr Professor Windberg and his trombone; Frau Oberlehrer Weidel, and others.

The notice was tied round the neck of the melancholy stag's head in the dining-room. It graced him like a red and white dinner bib for days before the event, causing the Herr Professor to bow before it and say "good appetite" until we sickened of his pleasantry and left the smiling to be done by the waiter, who was paid to be pleasing to the guests.

On the appointed day the married ladies sailed about the pension dressed like upholstered chairs, and the unmarried ladies like draped muslin dressing-table covers. Frau Godowska pinned a rose in the centre of her reticule; another blossom was tucked in the mazy folds of a white antimacassar thrown across her breast. The gentlemen wore black coats, white silk ties and ferny buttonholes tickling the chin.

The floor of the salon was freshly polished, chairs and benches arranged, and a row of little flags strung across the ceiling—they flew and jigged in the draught with all the enthusiasm of family washing. It was arranged that I should sit beside Frau Godowska, and that the Herr Professor and Sonia should join us when their share of the concert was over.

"That will make you feel quite one of the performers," said the Herr Professor genially. "It is a great pity that the English nation is so unmusical. Never mind! Tonight you shall hear something—we have discovered a nest of talent during the rehearsals."

"What do you intend to recite, Fräulein Sonia?"

She shook back her hair. "I never know until the last moment. When I come on the stage I wait for one moment and then I have the sensation as though something struck me here"—she placed her hand upon her collar brooch—"and ... words come!"

"Bend down a moment," whispered her mother. "Sonia, love, your skirt safety-pin is showing at the back. Shall I come outside and fasten it properly for you, or will you do it yourself?"

"Oh, mamma, please don't say such things." Sonia flushed and grew very angry. "You know how sensitive I am to the slightest unsympathetic impression at a time like this. . . . I would rather my skirt dropped off my body—"

"Sonia—my heart!"

A bell tinkled.

The waiter came in and opened the piano. In the heated excitement of the moment he entirely forgot what was fitting, and flicked the keys with the grimy table napkin he carried over his arm. The Frau Oberlehrer tripped on the platform followed by a very young gentleman, who blew his nose twice before he hurled his handkerchief into the bosom of the piano.

> "Yes, I know you have no love for me,
> And no forget-me-not.
> No love, no heart, and no forget-me-not,"

sang the Frau Oberlehrer, in a voice that seemed to issue from her forgotten thimble and have nothing to do with her.

"Ach, how sweet, how delicate," we cried, clapping her soothingly. She bowed as though to say, "Yes, isn't it?" and retired, the very young gentleman dodging her train and scowling.

The piano was closed, an arm-chair was placed in the centre of the platform. Fräulein Sonia drifted towards it. A breathless pause. Then, presumably, the winged shaft struck her collar brooch. She implored us not to go into the woods in trained dresses, but rather as lightly draped as possible, and bed with her among the pine needles. Her loud, slightly harsh voice filled the salon. She dropped her arms over the back of the chair, moving her lean hands from the wrists. We were thrilled and silent. The Herr Professor, beside me, abnormally serious, his eyes bulging, pulled at his moustache ends. Frau Godowska adopted that peculiarly detached attitude of the proud parent. The only soul who remained untouched by her appeal was the waiter, who leaned idly against the wall of the salon and cleaned his nails with the edge of a programme. He was "off duty" and intended to show it.

"What did I say?" shouted the Herr Professor under cover of tumultuous applause, "tem-per-ament! There you have it. She is a flame in the heart of a lily. I know I am going to play well. It is my turn now. I am inspired. Fräulein Sonia"— as that lady returned to us, pale and draped in a large shawl—"you are my inspiration. Tonight you shall be the soul of my trombone. Wait only."

To right and left of us people bent over and whispered admiration down Fräulein Sonia's neck. She bowed in the grand style.

"I am always successful," she said to me. "You see, when I act I *am*. In Vienna, in the plays of Ibsen we had so many bouquets that the cook had three in the kitchen. But it is difficult here. There is so little magic. Do you not feel it? There is none of that mysterious perfume which floats almost as a visible thing from the souls of the Viennese audiences. My spirit starves for want of that." She leaned forward, chin on hand. "Starves," she repeated.

The Professor appeared with his trombone, blew into it, held it up to one eye, tucked back his shirt cuffs and wallowed in the soul of Sonia Godowska. Such a sensation did he create that he was recalled to play a Bavarian dance, which he acknowledged was to be taken as a breathing exercise rather than an artistic achievement. Frau Godowska kept time to it with a fan.

Followed the very young gentleman who piped in a tenor voice that he loved somebody, "with blood in his heart and a thousand pains." Fräulein Sonia acted a poison scene with the assistance of her mother's pill vial and the arm-chair replaced by a "chaise longue"; a young girl scratched a lullaby on a young fiddle; and the Herr Professor performed the last sacrificial rites on the altar of the afflicted children by playing the National Anthem.

"Now I must put mamma to bed," whispered Fräulein Sonia. "But afterwards I must take a walk. It is imperative that I free my spirit in the open air for a moment. Would you come with me, as far as the railway station and back?"

"Very well, then, knock on my door when you're ready."

Thus the modern soul and I found ourselves together under the stars.

"What a night!" she said. "Do you know that poem of Sappho about her hands in the stars...I am curiously sapphic. And this is so remarkable—not only am I sapphic, I find in all the works of all the greatest writers, especially in their unedited letters, some touch, some sign of myself—some resemblance, some part of myself, like a thousand reflections of my own hands in a dark mirror."

"But what a bother," said I.

"I do not know what you mean by 'bother'; is it rather the curse of my genius...." She paused suddenly, staring at me. "Do you know my tragedy?" she asked.

I shook my head.

"My tragedy is my mother. Living with her I live with the coffin of my unborn aspirations. You heard that about the safety-pin tonight. It may seem to you a little thing, but it ruined my three first gestures. They were—"

"Impaled on a safety-pin," I suggested.

"Yes, exactly that. And when we are in Vienna I am the victim of moods, you know. I long to do wild, passionate things. And mamma says, 'Please pour out my mixture first.' Once I remember I flew into a rage and threw a washstand jug out of the window. Do you know what she said? 'Sonia, it is not so much throwing things out of windows, if only you would—"

"Choose something smaller?" said I.

"No . . . 'tell me about it beforehand.' Humiliating! And I do not see any possible light out of this darkness."

"Why don't you join a touring company and leave your mother in Vienna?"

"What! Leave my poor, little, sick, widowed mother in Vienna! Sooner than that I would drown myself. I love my mother as I love nobody else in the world—nobody and nothing! Do you think it is impossible to love one's tragedy? 'Out of my great sorrows I make my little songs,' that is Heine or myself."

"Oh, well, that's all right," I said cheerfully.

"But it is not all right!"

I suggested we should turn back. We turned.

"Sometimes I think the solution lies in marriage," said Fräulein Sonia. "If I find a simple, peaceful man who adores me and will look after mamma—a man who would be for me a pillow—for genius cannot hope to mate—I shall marry him. . . . You know the Herr Professor has paid me very marked attentions."

"Oh, Fräulein Sonia," I said, very pleased with myself, "why not marry him to your mother?" We were passing the hairdresser's shop at the moment. Fräulein Sonia clutched my arm.

"You, you," she stammered. "The cruelty. I am going to faint. Mamma to marry again before I marry—the indignity. I am going to faint here and now."

I was frightened. "You can't," I said, shaking her.

"Come back to the pension and faint as much as you please. But you can't faint here. All the shops are closed. There is nobody about. Please don't be so foolish."

"Here and here only!" She indicated the exact spot and dropped quite beautifully, lying motionless.

"Very well," I said, "faint away; but please hurry over it."

She did not move. I began to walk home, but each time I looked behind me I saw the dark form of the modern soul prone before the hairdresser's window. Finally I ran, and rooted out the Herr Professor from his room. "Fräulein Sonia has fainted," I said crossly.

"Du lieber Gott! Where? How?"

"Outside the hairdresser's shop in the Station Road."

"Jesus and Maria! Has she no water with her?" he seized the carafe —"nobody beside her?"

"Nothing."

"Where is my coat? No matter, I shall catch a cold on the chest. Willingly, I shall catch one.... You are ready to come with me?"

"No," I said; "you can take the waiter."

"But she must have a woman. I cannot be so indelicate as to attempt to loosen her stays."

"Modern souls oughtn't to wear them," said I. He pushed past me and clattered down the stairs.

When I came down to breakfast next morning there were two places vacant at table. Fräulein Sonia and the Herr Professor had gone off for a day's excursion in the woods.

I wondered.

A. P. Herbert

A. P. Herbert is the Leonardo da Vinci of the Humor world. He can do everything, and does everything well. A man of conviction, he has even succeeded in being elected to Parliament, the only humorist, I think, whom the people have ever really trusted. To be sure, he was elected from Oxford. Happily, he has not been sobered by the House of Commons. See his speech on the Population Bill, reproduced in the Everyman's Library volume of Modern Humor. It contains his memorandum in verse with the refrain, "And everybody wondered why the population fell."

JUNGLE ENGLISH

"Jungle. Fig., A wild, tangled mass."—S.O.E.D.

There is here, I repeat, brothers, no Belgravian attack upon the lowly born and poorly educated. Most of my horrible examples are taken from *The Times,* from the speeches of statesmen, the letters of philanthropists, or business men. We denounce, not honest slang, but fraudulent pomposity. For this jungle grows most richly in high places, though the fringes of it are beginning to creep into the valleys, which is a sad thing. It does not shock me to hear Bill say, "You've got a nerve, you 'ave"; it would shock me grievously to hear him say, "You've got a redundant inferiority complex." But that kind of vegetation is already taking root in the valleys where the simple people dwell. Modern communications, as we are fond of remarking, are rapid: and the corrupt phrase passes easily from the pompous letter in *The Times* to the Front Opposition Bench, and so to the street-corner orator, the public-house, and the home.

Today, instead of "fun," we learn to speak of "entertainment-value"; instead of Tories we have "the forces of reaction"; instead of games, "recreational facilities." Instead of swords and guns there are "casualty-producing weapons." We no longer work together: we co-operate according to a co-ordinated plan. We do not work whole-time, but "on a whole-time basis."

We do not hunger or starve; we exhibit evidences of malnutrition, or our diet is characterized by protein deficiency. A book is not instructive; it has a high education content. We say not "What is wanted is..." but "The requisites desiderated consist in...." (And requisite, I see, in *The Times Literary Supplement,* has grown to "prerequisite," though in the particular sentence the "pre" adds nothing.) A frontier is not "defined," nor "fixed," nor even "determined," but "delimited" or "demarcated"; and it will not be long, I suppose, before it is "delimitated."

Now, not all these expressions are base of origin or bad by themselves. Human life today is so complex that it is often difficult to discuss it in simple language. We cannot, obviously, explain the wireless, or the cinema, or an Unemployment Insurance Bill, in honest Anglo-Saxon. We invent new words or give a twist to old ones; we run for help, and rightly, to ancient Latin and Greek. (It is amusing to note that all the "live" modern devices get their names from the "dead" languages. Even in politics the latest thing is always Latin—a "quota," or a "moratorium," a "referendum," or "propaganda.")

Not everything in the jungle is unpleasant. There are noble trees and beautiful flowers. The Greek and Latin roots, though exotic, may flourish and do good service in our soil. But the forces which control them are too generous and powerful for orderly growth—free, but brief, education, the "popular" Press, the cinema, the wireless, "democratic" politics; the rain is too kind, the sun is too fierce, and the wind of communication that carried the seed too wild. There is neither the discipline of the English garden nor the decent profusion of the English wood. There is a jungle—a wild, tangled mass. The fine trees crowd together and their branches mingle without beauty or profit. And over all climb the horrid creepers, making the confusion worse— the clinging, choking "in view of's" and "with respect to's"—the "from the standpoint (or viewpoint) of's"—and "in connexion with's."

Is that clear?

No? Then we will give you an illustrative

EXERCISE

Translate into modern Jungle English the following passage from the Shorter Catechism:

"*My duty towards my Neighbour,* is to love him as myself, and to do to all men, as I would they should do unto me: To love, honour and succour my father and mother: To honour and obey the King, and all that are put in authority under him: To submit myself to all my governours, teachers, and spiritual pastors and masters: To order myself lowly and reverently to all my betters: To hurt nobody by word nor deed: To be true and just in all my dealing: To bear no malice nor hatred in my heart: To keep my hands from picking and stealing, and my tongue from evil-speaking, lying and slandering: To keep my body in temperance, soberness, and chastity: Not to covet nor desire other men's goods; but to learn and labour truly to get mine own living, and to do my duty in that state of life, unto which it shall please God to call me."

Answer

My duty towards my Neighbor, is to love him as myself, and to do to all men, as I would they should do unto me:

In connexion with my co-citizens a general standard of mutual good-will and reciprocal non-aggression is obviously incumbent upon me; but a comprehensive delimitation of my obligations might be grouped under four categories:

(A) *Relations involving the subordination of the individual.*

To love, honour and succour my father and mother.

To honour and obey the King, and all that are put in authority under him:

Among these must be listed the observance of Statutory and Common Law demands with regards to (a) parents and (b) the Monarchy (including here a co-operative attitude towards commissioned members of the armed forces and/or responsible civil servants, administrators, local government bodies, judges, and police officers) together with a measure of deference towards non-official authority (e.g. teachers, clergy, etc.) in so far as the same is com-

To submit myself to all my governours, teachers, spiritual pastors and masters: To order myself lowly and reverently to all my betters:

To hurt nobody by word nor deed:

To be true and just in all my dealing:

To bear no malice nor hatred in my heart:

To keep my hands from picking and stealing:

and my tongue from evil-speaking, lying, and slandering:

To keep my body in temperance, soberness, and chastity:

Not to covet nor desire other men's goods:

patible with an unfettered development of the personality.

(B) *Sociological relations not involving subordination.*

Abstention from personal injury in any shape or form, whether verbal or otherwise, is the first *desideratum* under this head, while hardly less important is the need for high integrity and veracity-values in all commercial and business contacts, coupled with, from the social standpoint, a non-provocative and community-conscious mentality.

(*C*) *Limits of criminal responsibility.*

Pending the eventual abolition of private property it is necessary to deprecate any active violation of the legal code by which that institution is buttressed: and some attention to the capitalist laws relating to defamation, sedition, blasphemy, etc., will be found advisable.

(D) *Personal hygiene, purity, etc.*

Of paramount importance, but at this date need hardly be stressed.

(E) *Miscellaneous.*

Subject to the reference to private property under (C) (above) the but to learn and labour truly to get mine own living, and to do my duty in that state of life unto which it shall please God to call me.

natural craving of the wealth-starved sections of the population for augmented material posses-sions should be kept in check; and in the interim the main issue for the individual seems to lie in some degree of concentration upon the securing of economic independ-ence and an adequate standard of life by means of intensive educa-tion and 100 per cent efficiency in the trade or industry adopted, as the case may be, respectively.

[From *What a Word!*]

MRS. MOLE

"This is the garden. I can see
You're fond of gard'ning—so are we.
A pity it is winter still,
You ought to see our daffodil.
We had some snowdrops in this bed,
I wish you'd seen them, but they're dead;
And in this other one we grow
Those What-d'-you-call-'ems in a row,
Of course you know the ones I mean,
Such pretty flowers, red and green—
Well, not exactly red, but pink,
Some funny foreign name, I think,
You know, they have those pointed leaves,
Not *Cattlecrop*, not *Widows' Eaves*,
Not *Alpigloss*, not *Bishop's Hat*,
But something similar to that—
I've got it! *Poly-something Pride!*
No, those are on the other side.

Well, did you ever? What a shame!
I never do forget a name.
Well, anyhow, it's here they grow,
And really it's a splendid show,
You cannot think how fine they are!
Don't put your foot in that—it's tar.
And in this pond Tom keeps his newts,
The most attractive little brutes!
Of course, they won't come out today,
You'll have to come again in May.
Last Whitsuntide we had a frog,
But it was eaten by the dog.

"And here we have the tennis-court,
It's narrow, yes, and rather short;
But still it is the same for all—
The Vicar says he *likes* it small.
You're sure you're not too tired, my dear?
We mean to put the chickens here.
But if we put the chickens there,
The hammock has to go elsewhere;
You see the difficulty, dear?
We've always had the hammock here.
Of course, it isn't used a lot,
We have the hammock when it's hot.
They say that chickens must have air,
And so we couldn't put them *there*.
You see, whichever way one tries,
It's awkward—what do *you* advise?
I think we'll put the hammock *here*.
You'll tell me when you're tired, my dear?

"Yes, that's my Milly, playing scales.
We suffer very much from snails.
It's odd we have so many more
Than Mrs. Hickory next-door.
I dare say Algernon is right—
She throws them over in the night.
I shouldn't be surprised—would you?
It's wonderful what people do.

My neighbour on the other side
Has just committed suicide.
A pity. Such a pleasant man!
We used to share a watering-can.
There'll be an inquest, I suppose.
And now I'll have to buy a hose.
That's our laburnum. That's a pear.
It's pretty, but it doesn't bear.
Now tell me, which do you prefer,
The smell of mint, or lavender?
I never know. They're both so sweet.
We have the two. It's quite a treat.
What, going, dear? Not tired, I trust?
Well, if you must, of course you must.
A pity. For you ought to see
My Milly imitate a bee.
But tell me, dear, before you go,
Can you get arrowroot to grow?
It wants a gravel soil, they say.
I've tried and tried. But this is clay.
The hens will be a worry too.
I really don't know *what* to do.
You see the difficulty, dear?
We've *always* had the hammock here.
I doubt if Algernon could bear
To see the hammock over there.
But there it is. One has to change.
But still, it will seem *very* strange.
Do say you haven't walked too far.
Mud on your skirt? No, dear, it's tar.
And there's a little on your hat!
How did you ever manage that?
Oh, well, a little turpentine—
You see? there's not a drop on mine.
Yes, isn't it a pretty hall?
I am so glad you liked it all.
Good-bye, my dear. Somehow I knew
That you were fond of gardens too.
It's raining, yes. Excuse me, dear,

You have some tar behind the ear.
Yes, that's the way—across the stile—
And then the tram is half a mile.
Yes, you'll be home in half a tick,
You'll miss the thunder if you're quick.
Good-bye! *Good*-bye! Now come again!
Of course, if you are off to Spain,
You'll miss the garden. Anyhow,
You've seen a little of it now.
But still, it's never quite the same
Without the flowers. Glad you came.
Well, that's for dinner. I must fly!
Good-bye again. *Good*-bye! Good-bye!"

I CAN'T THINK WHAT HE SEES IN HER

Jealousy's an awful thing and foreign to my nature;
I'd punish it by law if I was in the Legislature.
One can't have all of any one, and wanting it is mean,
But still, there is a limit, and I speak of Miss Duveen.

> *I'm not a jealous woman,*
> *But I can't see what he sees in her,*
> *I can't see what he sees in her,*
> *I can't see what he sees in her!*
> *If she was something striking*
> *I could understand the liking,*
> *And I wouldn't have a word to say to that;*
> *But I can't see why he's fond*
> *Of that objectionable blonde—*
> *That fluffy little, stuffy little, flashy little, trashy little, creepy-crawly,*
> *music-hally, horrid little CAT!*

I wouldn't say a word against the girl—be sure of that;
It's not the creature's fault she has the manners of a rat.
Her dresses may be dowdy, but her hair is always new,
And if she squints a little bit—well, many people do.

I'm not a jealous woman,
  But I can't *see what he sees in her,*
    I can't see what he sees in her,
      I can't see what he sees in her!
He's absolutely free—
There's no bitterness in me,
Though an ordinary woman would explode;
  I'd only like to know
  What he sees in such a crow
As that insinuating, calculating, irritating, titivating, sleepy little,
  creepy little, sticky little TOAD!

————

UNCOMMON LAW

Rex v. *Haddock*
Is a Golfer a Gentleman?

This case, which raised an interesting point of law upon the meaning of the world "gentleman," was concluded at the Truro Assizes today.

Mr. Justice Trout (giving judgment): In this case the defendant, Mr. Albert Haddock, is charged under the Profane Oaths Act, 1745, with swearing and cursing on a Cornish golf-course. The penalty under the Act is a fine of one shilling for every day-labourer, soldier, or seaman, two shillings for every other person under the degree of gentleman, and five shillings for every person of or above the degree of gentleman—a remarkable but not unique example of a statute which lays down one law for the rich and another (more lenient) for the poor. The fine, it is clear, is leviable not upon the string or succession of oaths, but upon each individual malediction (see *Reg.* v. *Scott* (1863) 33 L.J.M. 15).The curses charged, and admitted, in this case, are over four hundred in number, and we are asked by the prosecution to inflict a fine of one hundred pounds, assessed on the highest or gentleman's rate at five shillings a swear. The defendant admits the offences, but contends that the fine is excessive and wrongly calculated, on the curious ground that he is not a gentleman when he is playing golf.

He has reminded us in a brilliant argument that the law takes notice, in many cases, of such exceptional circumstances as will break down the normal restraint of a civilised citizen and so powerfully inflame his passions that it would be unjust and idle to apply to his conduct the ordinary standards of the law; as, for example, where without warning or preparation he discovers another man in the act of molesting his wife or family. Under such provocation the law recognises that a reasonable man ceases for the time being to be a reasonable man; and the defendant maintains that in the special circumstances of his offence a gentleman ceases to be a gentleman and should not be judged or punished as such.

Now, what were these circumstances? Broadly speaking, they were the 12th hole on the Mullion golf-course, with which most of us in this Court are familiar. At that hole the player drives (or does not drive) over an inlet of the sea which is enclosed by cliffs some sixty feet high. The defendant has told us that he never drives over, but always into, this inlet, or Chasm, as it is locally named. A steady but not sensational player on other sections of the course, he says that before this obstacle his normal powers invariably desert him. This has preyed upon his mind; he has registered, it appears, a kind of vow, and year after year, at Easter and in August, he returns to this county determined ultimately to overcome the Chasm.

Meanwhile, unfortunately, his tenacity has become notorious. The normal procedure, it appears, if a ball is struck into the Chasm, is to strike a second, and, if that should have no better fate, to abandon the hole. The defendant tells us that in the past he has struck no fewer than six or seven balls in this way, some rolling gently over the cliff and some flying far and high out to sea. But recently, grown fatalistic, he has not thought it worth while to make even a second attempt, but has immediately followed his first ball into the Chasm and there, among the rocks, small stones, and shingle, has hacked at his ball with the appropriate instrument until some lucky blow has lofted it onto the turf above, or in the alternative, until he has broken his instruments or suffered some injury from flying fragments of rock. On one or two occasions a crowd of holiday-makers and local residents have gathered on the cliff and foreshore to watch the defendant's indomitable struggles and to hear the verbal observations which have accompanied them. On the date of the alleged offences a crowd of un-precedented dimensions collected, but so intense was the defendant's concentration that he did not, he tells us, observe their presence. His ball had more nearly traversed the gulf than ever before; it struck the opposing cliff but a few feet from the summit; and nothing but an adverse gale of exceptional ferocity prevented success. The defendant therefore, as he conducted his customary excavations among the boulders of the Chasm, was possessed, he tells us, by a more than customary fury. Oblivious of his surroundings, conscious only of the will to win, for fifteen or twenty minutes he lashed his battered ball against the stubborn cliffs, until at last it triumphantly escaped. And before, during, and after every stroke he uttered a number of imprecations of a complex character which were carefully recorded by an assiduous caddie and by one or two of the spectators. The defendant says that he recalls with shame a few of the expressions which he used, that he has never used them before, and that it was a shock to him to hear them issuing from his own lips; and he says quite frankly that no gentleman would use such language.

Now, this ingenious defence, whatever may be its legal value, has at least some support in the facts of human experience. I am a golf-player myself—(*laughter*)—but, apart from that, evidence has been called to show the subversive effect of this exercise upon the ethical and moral systems of the mildest of mankind. Elderly gentlemen, gentle in all respects, kind to animals, beloved by children, and fond of music, are found in lonely corners of the downs, hacking at sand-pits or tussocks of grass, and muttering in a blind, ungovernable fury elaborate maledictions which could not be extracted from them by rob-bery or murder. Men who would face torture without a word become blasphemous at the short fourteenth. It is clear that the game of golf may well be included in that category of intolerable provocations which may legally excuse or mitigate behaviour not otherwise ex-cusable, and that under that provocation the reasonable or gentle man may reasonably act like a lunatic or lout respectively, and should legally be judged as such.

But then I have to ask myself, What does the Act intend by the words "of or above the degree of gentleman"? Does it intend a fixed social rank or a general habit of behaviour? In other words, is a gentleman legally always a gentleman, as a duke or solicitor remains unalterably a duke or solicitor? For if this is the case the defendant's argument must fail. The prosecution says that the word "degree" is used in the sense of "rank." Mr. Haddock argues that it is used in the sense of a university examination, and that, like the examiners, the Legislature divides the human race, for the purpose of swearing, into three vague intellectual or moral categories, of which they give certain rough but not infallible examples. Many a first-class man has "taken a third," and many a day-labourer, according to Mr. Haddock, is of so high a character that under the Act he should rightly be included in the first "degree." There is certainly abundant judicial and literary authority for the view that by "gentleman" we mean a personal quality and not a social status. We have all heard of "Nature's gentlemen." "Clothes do not make the gentleman," said Lord Mildew in *Cook v. The Mersey Docks and Harbour Board* (1896) 2 A.C., meaning that a true gentleman might be clad in the foul rags of an author. In the old maxim "Manners makyth man" (see *Charles v. The Great Western Railway*) there is no doubt that by "man" is meant "gentleman," and that "manners" is contrasted with wealth or station. Mr. Thomas, for the prosecution, has quoted against these authorities an observation of the poet Shakespeare that

"The Prince of Darkness is a gentleman,"

but quotations from Shakespeare (in Court) are generally meaningless and always unsound. This one, in my judgment, is both. I am more impressed by the saying of another author (whose name I forget) that the King can make a nobleman, but he cannot make a gentleman.

I am satisfied therefore that the argument of the defendant has substance. Just as the reasonable man who discovers his consort in the embraces of the supplanter becomes for the moment a raving maniac, so the habitually gentle man may become in a bunker a violent, unmannerly oaf. In each case the ordinary sanctions of the law are suspended; and while it is right that a normally gentle person should in normal circumstances suffer a heavier penalty for needless imprecations than a common seaman or cattle-driver, for whom they are part of the tools of his trade, he must not be judged by the standards of the gentle in such special circumstances as provoked the defendant.

That provocation was so exceptional that I cannot think that it was contemplated by the framers of the Act; and had golf at that date been a popular exercise I have no doubt that it would have been dealt with under a special section. I find therefore that this case is not governed by the Act. I find that the defendant at the time was not in law responsible for his actions or his speech and I am unable to punish him in any way. For his conduct in the Chasm he will be formally convicted of Attempted Suicide while Temporarily Insane, but he leaves the court without a stain upon his character. (*Applause*)

E. M. Delafield

Women are the particular partisans of E. M. Delafield (Mrs. Arthur Dashwood, by rights). Men find her revelations of the feminine mind almost too brutal to bear. Her Diary of a Provincial Lady *was very popular here, but I like better* As Others Hear Us, *from which these hatpin-thrusts are taken.*

WITH THE DIFFICULT GUEST

"Won't you change your mind? I'm afraid there's nothing much else coming."

"No, really, thank you so much. I really hardly ever touch eggs."

"I'm so sorry. I know some people never do. I do so wish I'd *thought*. (The chicken straight away please, Edith.) I think you know some neighbours of ours, the MacGoverns?"

"No, I don't think I do."

"I thought they said they'd met you in Wales or somewhere?"

"I was *in* Wales, a good many years ago. At least, it was really Monmouthshire, just motoring through."

"This was a place in Pembrokeshire."

"Oh yes."

"I don't know whether you remember them at all. He has rather a moustache."

"Mackintosh, did you say the name was?"

"Well, no. Their name is really MacGovern. With a capital G, you know."

"Oh, then I'm sure I don't know them. I once knew some people called Mackintosh, but that was in Scotland."

"Yes, I see. I suppose they— Well, anyhow, they're coming to lunch tomorrow."

"Oh yes."

"Now do have some chicken, won't you? I do hope you like *fried* chicken. The American way."

"Oh, really? It looks wonderful. Just a very, very little."

605

"Oh, but you've hardly got anything there. (Edith, just take back—) Do have a little more, I'm afraid there's nothing else coming."

"No, thanks, really. I always find I'm better without much meat at night."

"Oh, but do let me send— (Edith, find out if there are any sardines.) And what will you drink? A little white wine?"

"Just water, thank you."

"Cider? We've got it here, in the room. Or a whiskey and soda?"

"No, really; water, thank you."

"There's lemonade, if you like that better."

"I always drink water."

"Well, if you really. (Oh, that's right, Edith.) Now *do* let her change your plate, and try the sardines, if you don't care about chicken."

"Really not, thank you."

"Are you sure? (All right, Edith. The water jug.) I was wondering if you'd care to drive into Salisbury tomorrow, and take a look at the Cathedral."

"Thank you, that sounds delightful. I know Salisbury rather well, in fact I was staying there only last week."

"Oh—then perhaps you've seen the Cathedral?"

"Oh dear yes. We went over it very thoroughly, with the Guide. Still, it would be very nice to do it all over again, of course."

"Well, we might anyway just poke about, looking at shop windows and things. I don't know if you're interested in antiques at all? And of course there are one or two nice old book-shops."

"I always think the Americans have ruined all that, don't you? I mean, one knows so well that everything is just faked, nowadays. Still, I'm sure it would be delightful just to *look* at all the things."

"Do you ever patronize the cinema?"

"Quite often."

"Oh, good. I believe there's a marvellous film showing this week— *The Murder at South Molton* it's called."

"Oh, it's excellent. I saw it twice, in London. Not that I should in the very *least* mind seeing it again."

"Still, perhaps. That's chocolate soufflé. Or fruit salad?"

"Thank you so much. Just a very little fruit salad if I may."

"(Edith, the fruit salad.) I wonder if the wireless—"

"—I wonder if I might change my mind, and say soufflé after all?"

"Of course. (Edith!)"

"You were saying something about the wireless. I always think it is such a nuisance, don't you? It interferes with conversation so."

"Well, in a way. Though. But still, you can always turn it off."

"I never like doing that, somehow. I'm very funny in that way."

"Are you sure you won't have a little more?"

"No, really, thank you. I wonder if I might have *hot* water instead of cold?"

"I'm *so* sorry. I ought to have thought. (Edith! Will you please bring a glass of *hot* water.) Would you rather have it in a jug?"

"I'm afraid I'm giving a great deal of trouble. Perhaps I might have it when I go to bed."

"*Certainly* not. Of course you can have it in a moment—no trouble at all—"

"No, really, when I go upstairs."

"No, no. Certainly not."

"I oughtn't to have said anything."

"Oh, but *please.*"

"It would really do quite well at bedtime."

"It'll be here in one minute. And I'm sure you're tired, after your journey. You *will* say if you'd like to go upstairs early, won't you?"

"Thanks very much, but I'm one of those people who never go to bed until after twelve. I find I sleep better that way."

"Do you really? But I'm sure you *must* be tired. After dinner you must just lie on the sofa, or read, or do whatever rests you most."

"Thank you so much, but I always find it does me good to *talk.*"

DISCUSSING THE FIANCÉE

"Well, what did you think of her?"

"Of course, they've all got this terrific poise nowadays, haven't they?"

"Yes, I noticed that too. But I quite *liked* her."

"Oh, I quite liked her too. The hat was a mistake."

"The hat was a mistake but the frock was good. Would you say it was a perm, or natural, when she took off her hat?"

"A frightfully good perm."

"Well, dear, I can only say that poor Tony won't be able to afford things of that kind when they're married, and I only hope she understands it, that's all."

"Oh, Aunt Catherine, did you hate her?"

"Aunt Catherine thought she was utterly mouldy. I'm certain she did."

"No, dear, I haven't said I didn't like her. On the contrary. I daresay she's a very nice girl indeed, though I think she looks a good deal older than dear Tony."

"Six months."

"Is that what she says, dear? I hope she'll lose that irritating little *cough* of hers. It quite got on my nerves."

"It would be a great mistake if she were delicate. Poor darling Tony isn't at all strong, and I never think it does for husband and wife *both* to be delicate."

"Mother, Tony's *perfectly* strong."

"Darling, you're too young to remember what a time I had with him when he was cutting his second teeth."

"I must say, I never thought Tony would choose that *kind* of wife, did you? I mean—well—she's so sort of tall, isn't she?"

"Oh, huge. Though I must say, she's got good eyes. Did you hear what she said?"

"Which?"

"About wanting to be near the fire. I thought that was rather funny, I must say. Tony does so hate a hot room."

"I'm thankful to say that I brought up *all* my children to like the fresh air."

"She wasn't an only child or anything, was she?"

"No, because she said 'My little niece' or something. I didn't much like her voice, did you?"

"Oh my dear, they all talk like that nowadays. In that sort of voice, I mean, so that you can't hear a single word, and when you do it's all American slang."

"What's that, what's that? Don't tell me Tony's going to be married to an American!"

"Oh, Uncle Tom, are you awake? No, it's all right—we're only talking about Tony's *fiancée.*"

"Is that the girl he used to go to all those concerts with before Christmas?"

"No, no, no. That was all over *ages* ago, Uncle Tom. Besides, there was nothing in that at all. This one is terrifically good at games. Nothing to do with concerts."

"Oh. Nothing to do with concerts. Well, that's a good thing, anyhow. Where's the newspaper, somebody?"

"Naturally, Tony's my only son, and I feel very, very anxious about the future. I've always said that my children must go their own way; no one can ever say I've interfered with them, and I'm not going to say *one word* now."

"Mother, d'you think she's frightful?"

"No, dear, I don't want to say that. I'm old-fashioned, I suppose. To my mind, a man must choose his wife for himself, without advice from anybody. As I said to Tony before he ever proposed to this girl: Make sure that she's *good,* and a *lady,* and *healthy,* and *intelligent,* and that she's going to get on with your friends and relations, and you with hers—and then, my dear boy, if you feel that you can afford to marry—then, I suppose, there's no help for it."

"Well, they won't have a bean between them, that's one thing."

"I shouldn't have thought—I daresay I'm quite wrong—but I shouldn't have *thought,* somehow, that this was quite the kind of girl to manage on a very small income."

"Oh, she doesn't know a thing about house-keeping. She said so. I must say, I thought it was frightfully funny."

"Oh, the whole thing's *funny.*"

"Yes, that's what I thought. I thought it was funny altogether."

"Well, dears, we may not quite understand what poor dear Tony *sees* in this poor girl, but at least we can welcome her and make her feel how ready we all are to make the best of it."

THE UNSELFISH HOSTESS

"Do take that chair, dear—it's the only really comfortable one in the room."

"But what about you?"

"Oh, I'm quite all right—really I am. You see, I'm *used* to it. I'm just going to get you a cushion."

"Please don't bother."

"It's no bother at all. Wait a minute—there's a nicer one in the next room—I'll just get it—"

"No, no—please—"

"Yes, really—I like it. I *love* running about and waiting on people—I'm quite funny, like that. There! That's better."

"Thank you so much. Now, do tell me all your news."

"No, no, I want to hear yours. But you'd like a fire-screen—"

"No, thanks."

"Sure? It's no trouble. I can move that big one in from the dining-room in a minute. It isn't nearly as heavy as it looks."

"Honestly, I don't want a screen."

"Just exactly as you like, dear. It's so nice to have you here at last. Tell me, do you still like peppermints? I remember you always used to like my home-made peppermint creams."

"Of course I do! How kind of you to—"

"I said, 'Never mind whether I've got time or not, I *must* make some of my peppermint creams for Elizabeth.' I'm afraid I didn't get to bed till long after twelve last night."

"Oh dear—what a shame."

"No, no. I was up at seven just the same—or a little bit earlier, really, because I was *determined* to have plenty of spare time while you were here. It just meant a little reorganising, that was all."

"I know how busy you must be."

"I suppose I am, really. There always seems to be *something* to do for *somebody*. But then, as I always say, 'What are we here for, except to help one another?'"

"I'm sure you do a great deal."

"Ah well, I'm afraid I'm one of those silly people who *like* working for others. Now look here, I'm just going to pop into the next room and bring you that screen. Yes, really . . ."

"Please . . ."

"It's all right, it's quite all right. . . ."

"Let me . . ."

"I can manage. Yes, really, I can do it better by myself, I know just how to . . . was that your foot, dear? I'm so dreadfully sorry. . . . I hope it didn't hurt you. There! Isn't that better, keeping the fire off your face?"

"Well, thank you—"

"Now, tell me all about yourself. Or wait one second—I'm just going to give you that footstool. It's one I always use myself, it makes all the difference."

"Please, please keep it."

"No, no—I'd rather you had it. I know how miserably uncomfortable one can be without it. Now, I want you to tell me just what you'd like to do tomorrow. I've kept the day entirely free."

"How very kind of you. But what about your own plans?"

"No, dear, don't give them a thought. I said only this morning: 'Now whatever happens, I'm going to sacrifice *everything* while Elizabeth's here, I can make up for lost time *somehow,* afterwards.'"

"I'd so much rather you didn't bother about me. I can be quite happy with a book."

"My dear, what an idea! I shouldn't dream of it. Now do, do be perfectly honest. Isn't there somewhere you'd like to go, or someone you'd like to see, while you're in the neighbourhood?"

"I should very much like to have a look at Stonehenge, if that's at all possible. It isn't very far away, is it?"

"*Quite* near. Of course you shall. Now, let me see how we can possibly manage it. I could put off seeing the District Nurse in the morning, and try and get through my letters by eleven, and if we had lunch half an hour later than—no, no, that won't do. It's Cook's afternoon out. Still, I daresay I could—"

"No, no, please don't think of it. Really, I don't care—it isn't at all important."

"But, dear, of *course* it is! I know it can be done somehow, if I think it out. It's only just that the car— But perhaps I could hire the village car."

"No, no, no!"

"Or I daresay we could manage it in the afternoon. I'm not really supposed to be out late at this time of year, because of my wretched throat—but I daresay it wouldn't hurt me for once. I could risk it."

"I shouldn't dream of letting you, I don't really want to see Stonehenge at all—I can't think what made me say I did—I should *hate* it."

"That screen isn't really shielding you—I'll just move it. It doesn't matter about me— I never mind getting my face scorched. So long as *you're* all right. Now, we simply *must* find out how to get you to Stonehenge, if that's what you've set your heart on."

"I haven't—really and truly."

"Yes, dear, you have—and I'm determined to get you there, by hook or by crook, even if it means sacrificing an entire day. I'd half thought we might go and—but it doesn't matter."

"Oh, what?"

"Nothing, dear, nothing at all. Just a little scheme of my own. Don't give it a thought."

"But I'd so much rather you told me."

"No, no—it doesn't matter. I can probably manage it some other way—and if I can't, what does it matter? I want *you* to enjoy yourself. That's what you're here for."

Rose Macaulay

Miss Macaulay has written some of the wittiest novels of our time, but they don't seem to break up into lengths for an Anthology. Anyway, here is a pleasant example of her observant satire.

THE CONTINENTAL BOAT TRAIN

The people of Great Britain have always a passionate desire to travel
    by a boat train;
Partly because they believe that in the places to which such a train
    will convey them there will be less rain,
But chiefly because Britons who stay long in one country have always
    got bored,
So from the earliest centuries onwards they have gone in for paying
    visits abroad.
Regard us now, as we board the train at Victoria for one of those
    sea-side towns beyond which Britain ceases;
Mark with what eagerness we rummage in pockets, rucksacks and
    valises,
Hoping that the indispensable objects left behind
Do not include our passports, those ultimate imbecilities of the lost
    idiot official mind.
Observe our furtive concentration as we open little phrase books and
    brood
Over remarks so essential to international intercourse as, *"Get me a
    better portion. Don't give me the outside cut. This is overdone,
    underdone, too fat, too lean, take it away. Of course the portions
    can be divided? Now bring us an entree, it does not matter what,
    provided that it is good."*
Oh, marvellous continental meals! Oh, course following course of
    succulent foreign fare!
Maccaroni, tortillas, wienerschnitzel, poulet and haricots verts!
Oh, plump little Gauls, oh, beautiful Latins, oh, touching and bun-fed
    Teutons! Oh, poplars, oh, cafés on pavements, oh, futbal in plazas,
    oh, ravishing, noisy Neapolitan nights!

613

Oh, snows of Andorra and scorched Andalusian cities and Switzerland's shocking heights!

Wild and bright are our dreams of you as we sit tight and reserved in our tight reserved places—

Lunn's tourists, family parties, young men and maidens with rucksacks, large ladies with eau-de-cologne and mothersill in dressing-cases,

Cool and cosmopolitan bachelors and spinsters with travelled and worldly faces.

Lo, mark how, on sighting the ocean, these are transformed into a wild and sea-faring horde

Who leap from the train and run, each striving desperately to arrive first abroad.

(And they hope, oh they hope, fond romantics, that in no pension, albergo, fonda, café, piazza, casino, tramvía, Biergarten, musée, Alp, or Haute Pyrénée will they have the misfortune to encounter again

Any one of those mild British faces which they have viewed with such natural distaste for two hours on the Continental Boat Train.)

J. B. Morton ("Beachcomber")

One of the most significant literary innovations of the twentieth century has been the creation of a brave new form of humor, a super-or surhumor, of which the American masters are Frank Sullivan and S. J. Perelman. These intrepid pioneers, no doubt influenced by a profound study of Mallarmé, Rimbaud, and other symbolists, dare to dispense with many of the usual aids to the reader. Humor, like all other forms of thought, is a matter of associations. Logical thought proceeds by leaps, from premise to conclusion, in as straight a line as possible. Humor likewise leaps, but sometimes sidewise, to floating cakes of associations. Sullivan and Perelman, with their new barrel-roll technique of leaping, doubled the humorist's normal leap. They sometimes surprise by leaping directly upward, sometimes by sullenly sitting down. They may consider themselves successful if they force the reader to alight with them on the same association-cake. If the reader flies loosely through the air, the surhumorist may be said to lose a point, which he usually sacrifices with good humor.

Surhumor has sprung up independently in other countries. In Spain there is Ramón Gómez de la Serna, in Italy the incomparable Achille Campanile. The greatest English surhumorist is J. B. Morton, the "Beachcomber" of the Daily Express. Let us take an example of his thought. It happened, a few years ago, that the runners in some trans-Europe run for some high purpose carried a torch, each delivering it to the next relay. Morton, oppressed by the tiresomeness of carrying a torch all this distance, proposed that the runners should carry Marlene Dietrich. Now this proposal, while obviously impracticable, was entirely logical. His reader jumped and landed with him, though he didn't get much of anywhere.

In the following selections, the reader may notice a certain lack of design. Remember that they appeared from day to day in a newspaper, and that when they began "Beachcomber" certainly had not the faintest idea what was going to happen to his characters.

HOW TO GROW FLAX

Come hither, idiot reader,
And you shall have today
A pennyworth of poppycock
To pass the time away.
Upstairs and downstairs,
And in my lady's chamber,
And wha shall hauld the bridle-rein
At Lord Fitzronald's wedding?

A FOUL INNUENDO

There have lately been complaints in the newspapers, from Civil Servants, that lodging-house keepers show favouritism to their regular clientèle. The accusation roused that well-known seaside landlady, Mrs. McGurgle.

DEAR SIR,

I treat civil servants just like my other lodgers. No better and no worse. It is rapid eating and not social status that gets a second helping. If I see an empty plate, I fill it, be its owner a big panjandrum in Government circles or only a humble traveller in biscuits. Snobbery, I am thankful to say, has never cast its foul shadow across the threshold of Marine House. For though the late Mr. McGurgle, by whom I had the honour to be led to the altar at St. Philip's in this very resort, held an important position in a warehouse, he never to his dying day set up to be better than his fellows. An early decease, due to tainted cocoa partaken of at a French watering-place during a well-earned holiday, robbed me of my guide, philosopher and friend, but I flatter myself that Marine House is run today as it was in his lifetime, without fear or favour.

All are welcome, from dukes to dustmen.

Yours faithfully,

FLORENCE MCGURGLE

THE BOARDING-HOUSE ROW

DEAR SIR,

As one who has had a long experience of lodging-houses by the sea, may I hasten to support Mrs. McGurgle's contention that civil servants are human beings, and must be treated as such? But they are bad mixers. It takes the old habitué to come into the landlady's private sitting-room with a bit of a swagger, and maybe to pinch her ear in sheer camaraderie. Landladies don't like being treated as stand-off ogres, and are as susceptible to a spot of flattery as the rest of us. What some of these establishments where there are civil servants need is a bit of rough-and-tumble to break the ice—blind man's buff or something of that sort. That is the rule we have adopted at Beach View, and already it is no uncommon sight to see a gentleman from the Board of Works on all fours in the passage, begging a piece of kipper from one of the young ladies touring in "Atta Girl!"

Yours truly,

HERBERT CLEFT

MRS. MCGURGLE AGAIN

DEAR SIR,

I can well imagine what the late Mr. McGurgle—him that I have said fell a victim to tainted Continental cocoa and should have known better than to tempt fate by ordering it so far from home—would have had to say of a proprietress who graded her helpings according to the birth and education of the clientèle. Why, I remember once it was our privilege to receive as a paying guest at Marine House a very high official of the gas company. It is true we gave him a big room, him having so much luggage, but when it came to mealtimes, I can hear my late husband saying, as though it was yesterday, "Flo, put the gentleman between the insurance clerk and the piano-tuner. He is only one of us while he enjoys the shelter of the McGurgle roof." And I flatter myself that when I stood up to help the gravy, gas company or no gas company, his portion did not outweigh that of his neighbours, nor was the smile I directed to the least of our patrons, Miss Ansper, the orphan of a night-watchman whom diphtheria and complications carried to a premature burial in the north corner of St. Oswith's cemetery, any less friendly than that reserved for the official who, be it added, for all his luggage and fine airs, knew no better than to stove his morning egg in at a blow with his thumb.

Yours truly,

FLORENCE McGURGLE

MCGURGLE'S SENSITIVENESS

DEAR SIR,

Barbed tongues, vicious as the serpent's tooth, are saying that my communications to you are only a vulgar attempt to advertise Marine House. Let me say at once that the late Mr. McGurgle so detested even well-merited fame that on the occasion of his winning second prize in a South of England vegetable show, his entry being a gigantic turnip which he did my sister, Mrs. Cage, the honour of presenting to her afterwards, when the local newspaper sent a young man to interview him he refused to allow his photograph to be published, since he said he was not going to compete with film-stars for the public applause. Would such a man's widow be likely to go in for vulgar advertisement? On another occasion the late Mr. McGurgle, a horticulturist if there ever was one, called a peony which he exhibited at Bognor the Mrs. McGurgle, in compliment to me. But at the last moment he told me he could not bring himself to expose even so much as my married name to the sensation-mongers of today. So he changed the peony's name to Robinson, after a long-dead grand-uncle of his mother's. Perhaps I have said enough to defend myself from foul innuendo.

Yours truly,

FLORENCE McGURGLE

SUNDAY SUPPER AT MARINE HOUSE

DEAR SIR,

It is difficult for a mere member of the public to fathom what is behind your extraordinary attempt to deify the late Mr. McGurgle. I knew him quite well, when we were both with Clipper and Radlett. He was a very ordinary man, and had an annoying habit of cracking his fingers while he talked. Mrs. McGurgle, for whose feelings as a bereaved widow I have every respect, is, I think, idealising her late consort. I only once met her, being bidden to Sunday supper at Marine House. It was a gloomy meal, relieved only by the senseless giggling of a young lady, who appeared to be a filing clerk in the office of a hop factor. The food was terrible and scanty. I was allowed one glass of stout, and the whole time I was drinking it Mrs. McGurgle kept on saying that, though she had never succumbed to the demon drink, she had no objection to others wrecking their insides and their morals by wallowing in alcohol. We broke up early, because the very silent sister of a commissionaire suddenly went into screaming hysterics.

Yours truly,

OSCAR SUGGRIDGE

SHE IS HURT

DEAR SIR,

Mr. Suggridge's letter is merely vulgar. When he complains that Sunday suppers were gloomy at Marine House, I will ask him to remember that this establishment is not a cabaray. Almost my mother's last words to me, as she lay a-dying in Hampshire, were, "Flo, never let the French Sunday get a grip on your establishment." As to the clicking of the late Mr. McGurgle's fingers which so irritated this so-called Mr. Suggridge, may I hasten to assert that my late consort only clicked them when he desired to emphasise a point? The giggling lady he refers to was my niece, who has been nervous ever since she was jilted by a man who sold scissors and knives at a booth at Hexham. I hope I have said more than enough to demonstrate that Mr. Suggridge, whom I scarcely have the honour to recollect, is hardly what respectable people would call comeelfo. If one glass of stout on a Sunday night is not enough, his spiritual home is the bodeega.

Yours truly,

FLORENCE MCGURGLE

THE LATE MCGURGLE

DEAR SIR,

If the Mrs. McGurgle who writes to you is the Mrs. McGurgle whose husband tried to get my brother Alfred to join the Lamplight League of Sunday Silence, she must have married a tartar. McGurgle used to come to our house gassing about the beauty of contemplation, and he always left leaflets urging us all to link our thoughts in a chain of pure gold to the Infinite. I never heard a man talk so much about silence, and I often wondered how the lodgers at Marine House took his jabbering. He gave my brother a snapshot of his wife when she was Miss Palmer. He said she was the ray of sunshine which filled the boarding-house with singing birds. I told him to save me a chaffinch, and he left off bothering us.

Yours truly,

E. N. SPILLMAN

A NOBLE DEFENCE

DEAR SIR,

There appears to be a conspiracy to malign the late Mr. McGurgle, even by those who, baser than the serpent's tooth, mark their ingratitude by attempting to bite the hand of the deceased man who fed and boarded them in the early days of Marine House. If stout did not flow like water at our table, is that not to the credit of the establishment? There are doubtless boarding-houses which cater for such as cannot pass a public-house without darting in to the detriment of their characters. Mr. McGurgle used to say that his home was his public-house, and water his tipple, and that he required no bar in *his* front parlour. But I venture to reassert that he was no less gay and sporty than they whose veins run with distilled poison, whose eyes are bloodshot and restless, and whose limbs tremble at breakfast like the proverbial aspen. He is not likely to turn in his grave at the mud-slinging of mean natures.

Yours truly,

FLORENCE McGURGLE

ANOTHER SUPPORTER

DEAR SIR,

As sister to the late Mr. McGurgle, I protest against this bandying of his name, as though he were a Casanova always diving into public-houses frequented by what my sainted mother used to designate harpies of the underworld. Mr. McGurgle always abhorred strong drink, as exemplified on the 4:52 from Waterloo to Epsom one day, when a stranger changed hats with him unasked. My brother gave him a stare that would have turned a basilica to stone. The sot got out at Raynes Park, still reeking of the demon alcohol. My brother merely wiped his hat on his knee and began to hum nonchalantly. A fine example of manners and self-control.

Yours truly,

Freda Rumteigh

MORE GHOSTS FROM THE PAST

Dear Sir,

Florrie Palmer that was has certainly sobered up a bit, no offence. My word! There were evenings at the Magpie which would have made her future lord's hair stand on end. Florrie used to sing, "Tap, tap, tap! It's not the postman!" and then she and Fred Townham would do a Russian dance, splits and all, with two kitchen knives between their teeth. Ah, well! It's a far call from the Magpie to Marine House, which sounds to yours truly about as gay and giddy as a morgue. I wonder if Flo recalls the evening when Capper put a bloater down her back?

Yours truly,

Syd Telgrove

THE EXCELLENT COG

Dear Sir,

Your correspondent who claims to have known me in my courting days seems to be surprised that I have not remained a giddy young girl whose god was pleasure. It is one thing to stand on the threshold of life's doorway and raise the bubbling cup of youth to inexperienced lips. It is another thing to be the chosen consort of a serious-minded warehouse overseer and to have an old-established boarding-house to manage. Of course, I take my work seriously, and proud of it. Success in the boarding-house world is the guerdon of hard work and nothing la-di-da about it. We landladies are but small cogs in the vast machine of the lodgers' world, but as one of the least of those cogs permit me to say that without cogs where would you get to?

Yours truly,

FLORENCE McGURGLE

———

A TOUCHING TRIBUTE

DEAR SIR,

I hasten to corroborate all that my old and esteemed friend and landlady says of her deceased consort, the late lamented Stephen McGurgle. I had many occasions, while on tour, to use Marine House as my peadertair, and I can say, with my hand on my heart, that the excellence of the grub and the downy softness of the beds were only exceeded to by the human warmth and benignity of the welcome voochsaved to all by that charming host and hostess. Only a very brave woman could have kept the flag flying after the untimely removal of such a skipper as Stephen McGurgle. May I add that by a happy dispensation of his will and testament, when his anniversary comes round there is not a dry mouth in the King's Arms!

Yours truly,

EDMUND PILLINGER

———

SHE REMEMBERS MR. PILLINGER

DEAR SIR,

Mr. Pillinger's tribute to the late Mr. McGurgle is very handsome. I wonder whether he is the Mr. Pillinger who boarded at Marine House while playing the miser in *The Aftermath.* If so, I well remember him helping the late Mr. McGurgle to add a few twirls to the "Welcome" which was such a prominent feature of our door-mat. I fear we used to make a good deal of fun of him, as he was very much attracted to one of our patrons, a Miss Gowle, who afterwards married into a Steam Carpet Beating business, and only once returned to our humble Marine House, in a solid silver motor car with the flags of all the nations tacked onto the bonnet. I understand that her stepson was a bit of a racer and covered even the furniture with plaques and medals. I wonder if Mr. Pillinger ever married. He would have made a fine, steady mate for some decent girl who could appreciate art and culture, and though I was never a matchmaker, I tried to encourage a friendship between him and a girl who typed dramas. Nothing came of it as both became involved in a row about a loose board on the landing, and she left in a huff.

Yours truly,

FLORENCE McGURGLE

BREATHE ON HADDOCK

(For Voice, Flute, and Viola)

Breathe on haddock while you may,
See the smoke up-wreathing,
Nymphs and shepherds, come away
(This is Flora's holiday),
Cool it with your breathing.
Hoard not your little store of breath
Which shall be quenched, I ween, in death.

ADVTS.

If you collect string, communicate with Mrs. Reefer-Wright, Honey-cloves, Bigstead, who has some amusing odds and ends.

Will the old sailor who looked through the vacuum flask and cried, "A sail, a sail!" communicate with Miss Olga Reeves, Tredwych Manor, Gorsehill?

Wanted, by wealthy gentleman, fishmonger to sell fish at a concert, as a kind of joke. All fish supplied. Bring own apron and state size of slab required.

Dearest, do you remember Southall Gasworks? I have not forgotten.—H. L.

Headmaster, famous school, would exchange 12 barrels Cox's orange pippins for letter stolen by beautiful dark girl in private bar of Eight Bells last Monday.

NOSTRIL-FITNESS

Are your nostrils exhausted? Famous physicians have computed that owing to excitement and anxiety we are all breathing more than in normal times. Our breaths are shorter, and therefore more frequent. This imposes an additional strain on the nostrils, the second most important breath-duct. The man with weary nostrils soon becomes unfit. How can this be counteracted? Only by smearing the nostrils with TIMBALINE, the innocuous reagent vouched for by 32,981 physicians and surgeons.

At the dance:

MURIEL: Why does nobody ever dance with Joan?

TOM (*contemptuously*): Oh, Joan? She's—

MURIEL: She's awfully pretty, Tom.

TOM: I know. But—well, frankly, her nostrils are weary. Too much breathing, you know.

MURIEL: But, Tom! Has nobody ever told her about TIMBALINE?

TOM: By Jove! That's an idea! Mother swears by it. I'll go and tell her at once!

    (*A week later.*)

JOAN: Of course I'll marry you, Tom, dear.

COUNTRY IDYLL

O thrush in the copse,
What is it you sing?
Each sharp note drops
With a poignant "ping."

I said to the thrush,
"Sing on, sweet bird."
In the twilight hush
Not an elm-bough stirred.

O thrush on the bough,
And lamb on the lea,
And the farmer's cow,
And the pigs—and me!

MR. THAKE (Selection)

380a Jermyn Street,
London, W.

MY DEAR BEACHCOMBER,

As you will see from the above address, I am back in Jermyn Street once more. My return was rather rapid. The oil business turned out badly, and also I wanted to be back for the Season in London. It seems as though I had been away a long time, and yet it doesn't, if you know what I mean. I found an enormous mass of correspondence awaiting me, including a letter from Mrs. Hawkley telling me that the Colonel is in Scotland—no, it was Ireland. I think you met their boys once—darkish hair, and rather tall for twins. One of them, I forget which, either the younger or the elder, is going up to Woolwich (or Sandhurst) and then into the Army. It will be rather nice for him, won't it?

It is good to be home, in a way. It is like coming back to everything. It's hard to express. What I mean is, it's a sort of return to things, don't you think? I always feel like that about it, somehow. Saunders, with all his failings, is most efficient. I find everything in order, even the saucer of milk for Freckles in the sitting-room, by the revolving bookcase; and this morning he brought my tea, and said, "A fine day, sir," just as if nothing had happened. It wasn't—but that's his way. He tells me the Wansgroves have bought a house called Bewick somewhere near some Welsh place, and that the banging in the street is not as bad as it was before I left. That is good news. He has even fed the canary, which looks fatter than ever. Cause and effect; food makes fatness, eh? Upon my soul, that's almost a slogan, what?

Yours ever,

O. THAKE

P.S.—It's too bad. I find that all those things I wrote to Saunders for, from America, went out there after I had left for home. I must write and get them back, if I can remember what they were.

380a Jermyn Street,
London, W.

I am settling down again. I find a number of invitations awaiting me, including one from a Mrs. Thallett, a relative, I believe, of the Thallett who invented electric harpoons. You know, there's nothing like London. It's so *big*. It's somehow built on a grand scale—so many buildings and people, more than anywhere else. I suppose I'm what the world calls a Londoner—at heart. I love the bustle and the crowds. I shall never forget Mrs. Fume saying to me once, "London, my dear Mr. Thake, is England in miniature." Well, if you think that out, you will find it is true. And again, London is, after all, the very heart of our great Empire, with its dominions, protectorates and dependencies. One blood, one flag. One hates to boast, but really, I think we are "It," as young Pollington always says. (Not Edgar, his brother.) You remember he was one of the first to wear Oxford trousers, which I really could never understand. I think the best thing said about them was by Lady Flogge. She said, "The further, the broader." Good, eh? She is a most witty woman, and her collection of third century amber is most remarkable. I am dining with her on Tuesday—next Tuesday, I mean. Which reminds me, will you come and dine one day next week? We have much to discuss, and I will show you some photographs taken during my travels. I must end now, as I am expecting old Thistle any minute. Such a nice man, but obstinate.

By the way, a soup tureen has arrived from America. Saunders knows nothing about it.

380a Jermyn Street,
W.

I was at the opera the other night, and I must say the German atmosphere surprised and rather disgusted me. I had no idea they were going to sing in German. Of course, one is prepared to make allow-ances—I mean, one is ready to forgive them their music—(not that it isn't beautiful music)—but I do think it should be conducted and sung in the mother tongue. With representatives from all quarters of our vast Empire constantly visiting here, it is surely important to create a good impression among the English-speaking races. One South African I know quite well expressed his surprise at the German sing-ing. Let us forgive and forget, by all means, let bygones be bygones, but let us keep that sense of proportion which is, as Gladstone well recognised, one of our most valuable assets.

If people cannot be found to translate the German, could it not be sung in Italian or Belgian or French? This, I am certain, would bring us and our allies nearer together, and produce a feeling of mutual esteem and love. Not only would it be a compliment, but it would avoid giving offence to the millions comprising this great British Empire. Besides, the German language is not as beautiful as others, and "Tristram and Iseult," for instance, would be far more intelligible, at any rate, in England, if sung in English. I feel confident that I am voicing the opinion of the vast majority of Britishers in this matter. Tom Watson is writing a letter to the Press about it.

Yours ever,

O. THAKE

P.S.—In any case, why not play "Pinafore" or "The Gondoliers" at Covent Garden? Is English opera dead?

380a Jermyn Street,
W.

What a relief an English dinner-party is after foreign ones! For-eigners, like all commercial-minded people, talk of politics and religion and other serious things. It is such a strain. Last night I was at the Bunnards'—Cecil Bunnard, you know, the collector. We had a most enjoyable evening. Lady Porringer was there with Myrtle, and old Fenchurch, still grousing, and Mabel Weald and Dr. Flaring. I sat next to Barbara Bagge. She tells me her Sealyham has got synovitis, but she has built one of the new hygienic kennels for it, and hopes for the best. I asked the doctor what he thought of it, and he said that disease in men and animals varies considerably. Old Fenchurch said that it was a disgrace that medical science was powerless against mange. Bunnard retorted, "It depends what you call mange." Then a bishop said with a laugh, "It depends what you call medical science." The talk then turned on Tony Monteith's will. Somebody said he had left a lot to his dentist.

Mabel Weald said how brave it was of men to swim in the Serpentine in this weather, and Flaring pooh-poohed the suggestion that cold water cured liver complaints. He then told a long story about a man who had never been cured after years of cold water. After which some one remarked on the trouble the Horse Guards must take to keep spotless.

After we joined the ladies, Mrs. Bunnard's niece played a piece of Rachmaninoff, called, I think, "Prologue," and, as an encore, Hoffmann's "Barcarolle." Her touch is very good indeed. Lady Porringer has asked me to dinner next week, to meet Witham, the inventor.

The "Sandford and Merton" I asked Saunders for, and which he sent too late, has just returned from America. Unfortunately Saunders returned it again, without consulting me, so I must get it back again.

380a Jermyn Street,
W.

It was with feelings of some surprise (excuse this scrawl, but Freckles is perched on my shoulder, and is mewing) that I read your last letter about the young woman who wishes to meet me. I suppose I am rather out of date in my notions of propriety—but really! It takes my breath away. You withhold, quite rightly, her name, and I cannot think who she can be. It could not—no, it could not be that Miss Paddell I met at the Corringtons'. Really you will think me vain, but Tom Watson told me she was evidently trying to vampire me, as the Americans say. She asked me for my photograph, but I am sure she intended to stop at that. Besides, I know her brother in the Navy. Could it be the Fidge girl? Surely not. Of course, I am merely speculating. I would not for worlds pursue the matter in these days. Paula-Hicks-Gobble? The widow? Don't tell me that! But wait! It is clearly some one I have never met, as she desires, you say, to be introduced to me. I had forgotten that. It's no good my puzzling any more.

Did you see Lady P——'s portrait in the "Gabbler" last week? I was at the theatre with her the other night. I forget what it was called, but the jokes—well, I hope none of the women present understood them. I fear they did, as Constantia P——, who sat beside me, kept nudging me and saying, "Do you see the point?" "Did you get that?" Of course, she only wanted me to explain the jokes, so I said, sternly, I fear, "No, I do not get any of them. Dull, I assure you." She winked, and her mother rebuked her. Rather awkward, what? To appease the girl, I delved into my playgoing memories, and told her one or two lines from "Little Lord Fauntleroy" and "East Lynne." She said she preferred "Piff-Poff," and her mother again rebuked her. A dear, good woman, Lady P——.

Saunders will drive me mad. He has now returned to America the stamp album that was returned from there to me here, after he had sent it there. What is one to do?

380a Jermyn Street,
W.

If there is one thing I like about the Academy, it is the, as it were, social aspect of it. One meets everybody there, and it isn't necessary to be a highbrow to go there. I mean they are not all experts, and they don't talk all the time about the technique of the pictures. In fact, many people I know keep off the subject of painting altogether, and treat the occasion as purely social, which is rather a relief. The Relfs are like that. To meet them, you'd never think they'd know a good picture from a bad one, or vice versa. Yet he, I believe, once studied art, and she has written a guide to the Prado at Madrid.

I struck a good day at the Academy, and bumped into a lot of friends. We all went round together—"as if it was golf," as Percy said. Though I pointed out that we were too many for golf.

There was some trouble over Mrs. Bowley. She is so short sighted, and would insist on reading out from the catalogue. Of course, she confused portraits with cabbage, and generals with bridges, and so on. There was much laughter, but old age will be served. And anyhow, one can generally tell roughly what a picture is meant to be.

There are not enough seats, I think. It is so inconvenient to have to carry on a conversation standing up. But, on the whole, it was a good show, except that the Pargetters were away in Hampshire. They are usually the life and soul of such occasions. However, we laughed a lot, and swapped holiday news. I enclose a snapshot of myself taken by Myrtle in the Sculpture Room. It was signed by her brother, in a playful moment.

380a Jermyn Street,
W.

I had tea at Colonel Farley's yesterday, and played my first tennis of the season. I think one's first game is somehow different from the rest, don't you? I suppose the reason is simply that it is the first game—I mean, one is out of practice more than afterwards, and consequently cannot get the grip of things. After, of course, it is different. I played with Miss Paxted—you remember her cousin, who wrote the novel called "Dripping"—well, she (I mean that cousin) is some sort of a relation of Maude Farley's. I got one or two good shots in, but Sybil Paxted will run after the balls between strokes, which is most irritating. We played the Pinkwater girl and her brother, and beat them as far as we got. It was too dark to finish. Pinkwater told me a good budget story, which I forget. You know what a wag he is.

During tea Cyril Blankett arrived. He's got some new idea about planting delphiniums, all rather technical. The Colonel collared him and told him to try it on the pansies. Cyril was furious, and pointed out, half in fun, that a delphinium and a pansy are very different affairs. "Both flowers," snorted the Colonel. It was most amusing. Maude Farley can't stand Cyril. I think it's his red moustache. You never know, do you? As I was helping to roll up the net, the rain began. So we were just in time. By the way, do you remember Olive Watts? Well, she didn't go to Finland after all. She may later, according to Molly. But you know Molly!

The Towers,
Westborough.

I am at the Towers, as you will notice, for the week-end. Today being Sunday, we are all more or less doing nothing. Madge is here, and is reading rather a good leader from one of the Sunday papers. There will be church later on, and young Effington is to read the lessons. After that we shall probably chat with Sopwith, the vicar. Then home to lunch. In the afternoon—I don't quite know. We are divided. My host and hostess rather want to sleep. Some of the rest of us suggest going on the lawn to read, while others favour a walk to the Arnolds' next door, to hear about Walter Arnold's new car. One way, of course, and I have suggested as much, would be to send a note by one of the maids to the Arnolds asking them round. Which course will be adopted one can hardly say as yet. I do not much care myself. Anyhow, I've half promised to go and see Tony's rabbits.

Later.

It rained after lunch, so I suggested a rubber. To my surprise, our host said that he loathed playing bridge in the rain. He said bridge was depressing enough without that. Madge then suggested the gramophone, but no one could find a needle. I offered to give them my talk on America, the one that I gave at the Wilmington's garden party, but it appears that our host loathes Americans. Fortunately it stopped raining, and we were able to go to call on the Arnolds. They were out. You will remember that Arnold and I were at Oxford the same time as Tom Watson. By that time it was raining hard again, and we returned. Our host had gone to sleep by the fire, so I read the life of Charles Dickens until tea. A remarkable man.

Later.

Madge says she will drop in on you on her return. She is motoring home early on account of the serious illness of her aunt. When I asked the name of her aunt, she said, "Banbury," but I know no one of that name. Perhaps her aunt has married since then, however.

380a Jermyn Street,
W.

Each year the Glorious Fourth of June finds me a little older, a little further on the way to old age, a little further, too, from youth. But what a fine thing it is to go back to one's old school, to the buildings and fields one knew so well. All the faces, of course, are different, since those who were boys with us are boys no longer, but men, according to the inexorable decrees of fate. Yet these boys of today are boys like us—that is, as we used to be before we became men. And who can hear the old school songs without choking? They are like nothing on earth to one who revisits the scenes of his boyhood. Then, again, it is so fine to see the thing going on like a tree. Boys leave, but other boys take their places. Thus the thing goes on. Dear me, I am becoming quite sentimental.

I met a bishop I knew, a former schoolmate of mine, and he chaffed me about my inky fingers, and I reminded him that he used to say "damn" when his shins were kicked. He laughingly denied this, but all in the best-humoured way. He was not at all offended, which is proof that the Church is broader-minded than some people seem to think. Lady —— was there. One of her boys is quite a swell—Pop, and all that. As long as England can breed this kind of stuff nobody need fear for the future of our Empire. I tell you what's wrong with France. *She's got no Eton.* A Fourth of June would do her no end of good, and stop all the nonsense. I'd like to see the Wall Game in their dreadful Latin Quarter. You, as a writer, ought to be able to get an article out of this idea.

Well, another Fourth is over, and here I am again. Floreat Etona! Yes, indeed!

P.S.—Tom, of course, to the everlasting regret of his family, went to Harrow—good in its way, of course—but—well—you know.

Aldous Huxley

These are examples of the young Aldous Huxley, who typifies the intellectual development of the generation which came of age at the time of the first World War. He has now become a mystic, in tune with the infinite. This is of course splendid, but it does seem sad that we won't have another Crome Yellow.

JONAH

A cream of phosphorescent light
Floats on the wash that to and fro
Slides round his feet—enough to show
Many a pendulous stalactite
Of naked mucus, whorls and wreaths
And huge festoons of mottled tripes
And smaller palpitating pipes
Through which a yeasty liquor seethes.

Seated upon the convex mound
Of one vast kidney, Jonah prays
And sings his canticles and hymns,
Making the hollow vault resound
God's goodness and mysterious ways,
Till the great fish spouts music as he swims.

FIFTH PHILOSOPHER'S SONG

A million million spermatozoa,
    All of them alive:
Out of their cataclysm but one poor Noah
    Dare hope to survive.

And among that billion minus one
Might have chanced to be
Shakespeare, another Newton, a new Donne—
But the One was Me.

Shame to have ousted your betters thus,
Taking ark while the others remained outside!
Better for all of us, froward Homunculus,
If you'd quietly died!

———

CROME YELLOW
(Selection)

Mr. Wimbush had taken them to see the sights of the Home Farm, and now they were standing, all six of them—Henry Wimbush, Mr. Scogan, Denis, Gombauld, Anne, and Mary—by the low wall of the piggery, looking into one of the styes.

"This is a good sow," said Henry Wimbush. "She had a litter of fourteen."

"Fourteen?" Mary echoed incredulously. She turned astonished blue eyes towards Mr. Wimbush, then let them fall on to the seething mass of *élan vital* that fermented in the sty.

An immense sow reposed on her side in the middle of the pen. Her round, black belly, fringed with a double line of dugs, presented itself to the assault of an army of small, brownish-black swine. With a frantic greed they tugged at their mother's flank. The old sow stirred sometimes uneasily or uttered a little grunt of pain. One small pig, the runt, the weakling of the litter, had been unable to secure a place at the banquet. Squealing shrilly, he ran backwards and forwards, trying to push in among his stronger brothers or even to climb over their tight little black backs towards the maternal reservoir.

"There *are* fourteen," said Mary. "You're quite right. I counted. It's extraordinary."

"The sow next door," Mr. Wimbush went on, "has done very badly. She only had five in her litter. I shall give her another chance. If she does no better next time, I shall fat her up and kill her. There's the boar," he pointed towards a farther sty. "Fine old beast, isn't he? But he's getting past his prime. He'll have to go too."

"How cruel!" Anne exclaimed.

"But how practical, how eminently realistic!" said Mr. Scogan. "In this farm we have a model of sound paternal government. Make them breed, make them work, and when they're past working or breeding or begetting, slaughter them."

"Farming seems to be mostly indecency and cruelty," said Anne.

With the ferrule of his walking-stick Denis began to scratch the boar's long bristly back. The animal moved a little so as to bring himself within easier range of the instrument that evoked in him such delicious sensations; then he stood stock still, softly grunting his contentment. The mud of years flaked off his sides in a grey powdery scurf.

"What a pleasure it is," said Denis, "to do somebody a kindness. I believe I enjoy scratching this pig quite as much as he enjoys being scratched. If only one could always be kind with so little expense of trouble. . . ."

A gate slammed; there was a sound of heavy footsteps.

"Morning, Rowley!" said Henry Wimbush.

"Morning, sir," old Rowley answered. He was the most venerable of the labourers on the farm—a tall, solid man, still unbent, with grey side-whiskers and a steep dignified profile. Grave, weighty in his manner, splendidly respectable, Rowley had the air of a great English statesman of the mid-nineteenth century. He halted on the outskirts of the group, and for a moment they all looked at the pigs in a silence that was only broken by the sound of grunting or the squelch of a sharp hoof in the mire. Rowley turned at last, slowly and ponderously and nobly, as he did everything, and addressed himself to Henry Wimbush.

"Look at them, sir," he said, with a motion of his hand towards the wallowing swine. "Rightly is they called pigs."

"Rightly indeed," Mr. Wimbush agreed.

"I am abashed by that man," said Mr. Scogan, as old Rowley plodded off slowly and with dignity. "What wisdom, what judgment, what a sense of values! 'Rightly are they called swine.' Yes. And I wish I could, with as much justice, say, 'Rightly are we called men.' "

They walked on towards the cowsheds and the stables of the cart-horses. Five white geese, taking the air this fine morning, even as they were doing, met them in the way. They hesitated, cackled; then converting their lifted necks into rigid, horizontal snakes, they rushed off in disorder, hissing horribly as they went. Red calves paddled in the dung and mud of a spacious yard. In another enclosure stood the bull, massive as a locomotive. He was a very calm bull, and his face wore an expression of melancholy stupidity. He gazed with reddish-brown eyes at his visitors, chewed thoughtfully at the tangible memories of an earlier meal, swallowed and regurgitated, chewed again. His tail lashed savagely from side to side; it seemed to have nothing to do with his impassive bulk. Between his short horns was a triangle of red curls, short and dense.

"Splendid animal," said Henry Wimbush. "Pedigree stock. But he's getting a little old, like the boar."

"Fat him up and slaughter him," Mr. Scogan pronounced, with a delicate old-maidish precision of utterance.

"Couldn't you give the animals a little holiday from producing children?" asked Anne. "I'm so sorry for the poor things."

Mr. Wimbush shook his head. "Personally," he said, "I rather like seeing fourteen pigs grow where only one grew before. The spectacle of so much crude life is refreshing."

"I'm glad to hear you say so," Gombauld broke in warmly. "Lots of life: that's what we want. I like pullulation; everything ought to increase and multiply as hard as it can."

Gombauld grew lyrical. Everybody ought to have children—Anne ought to have them, Mary ought to have them—dozens and dozens. He emphasised his point by thumping with his walking-stock on the bull's leather flanks. Mr. Scogan ought to pass on his intelligence to little Scogans, and Denis to little Denises. The bull turned his head to see what was happening, regarded the drumming stick for several seconds, then turned back again, satisfied, it seemed, that nothing was happening. Sterility was odious, unnatural, a sin against life. Life, life, and still more life. The ribs of the placid bull resounded.

Standing with his back against the farmyard pump, a little apart, Denis examined the group. Gombauld, passionate and vivacious, was its centre. The others stood round, listening—Henry Wimbush, calm and polite beneath his grey bowler; Mary, with parted lips and eyes that shone with the indignation of a convinced birth-controller. Anne looked on through half-shut eyes, smiling; and beside her stood Mr.

Scogan, bolt upright in an attitude of metallic rigidity that contrasted strangely with that fluid grace of hers which even in stillness suggested a soft movement.

Gombauld ceased talking, and Mary, flushed and outraged, opened her mouth to refute him. But she was too slow. Before she could utter a word Mr. Scogan's fluty voice had pronounced the opening phrases of a discourse. There was no hope of getting so much as a word in edgeways; Mary had perforce to resign herself.

"Even your eloquence, my dear Gombauld," he was saying—"even your eloquence must prove inadequate to reconvert the world to a belief in the delights of mere multiplication. With the gramophone, the cinema, and the automatic pistol, the goddess of Applied Science has presented the world with another gift, more precious even than these—the means of dissociating love from propagation. Eros, for those who wish it, is now an entirely free god; his deplorable association with Lucina may be broken at will. In the course of the next few centuries, who knows? the world may see a more complete severance. I look forward to it optimistically. Where the great Erasmus Darwin and Miss Anna Seward, Swan of Lichfield, experimented—and, for all their scientific ardour, failed—our descendants will experiment and succeed. An impersonal generation will take the place of Nature's hideous system. In vast state incubators, rows upon rows of gravid bottles will supply the world with the population it requires. The family system will disappear; society, sapped at its very base, will have to find new foundations; and Eros, beautifully and irresponsibly free, will flit like a gay butterfly from flower to flower through a sunlit world."

"It sounds lovely," said Anne.

"The distant future always does."

Mary's china blue eyes, more serious and more astonished than ever, were fixed on Mr. Scogan. "Bottles?" she said. "Do you really think so? Bottles. . . ."

Mr. Barbecue-Smith arrived in time for tea on Saturday afternoon. He was a short and corpulent man, with a very large head and no neck. In his earlier middle age he had been distressed by this absence of neck, but was comforted by reading in Balzac's *Louis Lambert* that all the world's great men have been marked by the same peculiarity, and for a simple and obvious reason: Greatness is nothing more nor less than the harmonious functioning of the faculties of the head and heart; the shorter the neck, the more closely these two organs approach one another; *argal* ... It was convincing.

Mr. Barbecue-Smith belonged to the old school of journalists. He sported a leonine head with a greyish-black mane of oddly unappetising hair brushed back from a broad but low forehead. And somehow he always seemed slightly, ever so slightly, soiled. In younger days he had gaily called himself a Bohemian. He did so no longer. He was a teacher now, a kind of prophet. Some of his books of comfort and spiritual teaching were in their hundred and twentieth thousand.

Priscilla received him with every mark of esteem. He had never been to Crome before; she showed him round the house. Mr. Barbecue-Smith was full of admiration.

"So quaint, so old-world," he kept repeating. He had a rich, rather unctuous voice.

Priscilla praised his latest book. "Splendid, I thought it was," she said in her large, jolly way.

"I'm happy to think you found it a comfort," said Mr. Barbecue-Smith.

"Oh, tremendously! And the bit about the Lotus Pool—I thought that so beautiful."

"I knew you would like that. It came to me, you know, from without." He waved his hand to indicate the astral world.

They went out into the garden for tea. Mr. Barbecue-Smith was duly introduced.

"Mr. Stone is a writer too," said Priscilla, as she introduced Denis.

"Indeed!" Mr. Barbecue-Smith smiled benignly, and, looking up at Denis with an expression of Olympian condescension, "And what sort of things do you write?"

Denis was furious, and, to make matters worse, he felt himself blushing hotly. Had Priscilla no sense of proportion? She was putting them in the same category—Barbecue-Smith and himself. They were both writers, they both used pen and ink. To Mr. Barbecue-Smith's question he answered, "Oh, nothing much, nothing," and looked away.

"Mr. Stone is one of our young poets." It was Anne's voice. He scowled at her, and she smiled back exasperatingly.

"Excellent, excellent," said Mr. Barbecue-Smith, and he squeezed Denis's arm encouragingly. "The Bard's is a noble calling."

As soon as tea was over Mr. Barbecue-Smith excused himself; he had to do some writing before dinner. Priscilla quite understood. The prophet retired to his chamber.

Mr. Barbecue-Smith came down to the drawing-room at ten to eight. He was in a good humour, and, as he descended the stairs, he smiled to himself and rubbed his large white hands together. In the drawing-room someone was playing softly and ramblingly on the piano. He wondered who it could be. One of the young ladies, perhaps. But no, it was only Denis, who got up hurriedly and with some embarrassment as he came into the room.

"Do go on, do go on," said Mr. Barbecue-Smith. "I am very fond of music."

"Then I couldn't possibly go on," Denis replied. "I only make noises."

There was a silence. Mr. Barbecue-Smith stood with his back to the hearth, warming himself at the memory of last winter's fires. He could not control his interior satisfaction, but still went on smiling to himself. At last he turned to Denis.

"You write," he asked, "don't you?"

"Well, yes—a little, you know."

"How many words do you find you can write in an hour?"

"I don't think I've ever counted."

"Oh, you ought to, you ought to. It's most important."

Denis exercised his memory. "When I'm in good form," he said, "I fancy I do a twelve-hundred-word review in about four hours. But sometimes it takes me much longer."

Mr. Barbecue-Smith nodded. "Yes, three hundred words an hour at your best." He walked out into the middle of the room, turned round on his heels, and confronted Denis again. "Guess how many words I wrote this evening between five and half-past seven."

"I can't imagine."

"No, but you must guess. Between five and half-past seven—that's two and a half hours."

"Twelve hundred words," Denis hazarded.

"No, no, no." Mr. Barbecue-Smith's expanded face shone with gaiety. "Try again."

"Fifteen hundred."

"No."

"I give it up," said Denis. He found he couldn't summon up much interest in Mr. Barbecue-Smith's writing.

"Well, I'll tell you. Three thousand eight hundred."

Denis opened his eyes. "You must get a lot done in a day," he said.

Mr. Barbecue-Smith suddenly became extremely confidential. He pulled up a stool to the side of Denis's arm-chair, sat down in it, and began to talk softly and rapidly.

"Listen to me," he said, laying his hand on Denis's sleeve. "You want to make your living by writing; you're young, you're inexperienced. Let me give you a little sound advice."

What was the fellow going to do? Denis wondered; give him an introduction to the editor of *John o' London's Weekly,* or tell him where he could sell a light middle for seven guineas? Mr. Barbecue-Smith patted his arm several times and went on.

"The secret of writing," he said, breathing it into the young man's ear—"the secret of writing is Inspiration."

Denis looked at him in astonishment.

"Inspiration ..." Mr. Barbecue-Smith repeated.

"You mean the native wood-note business?"

Mr. Barbecue-Smith nodded.

"Oh, then I entirely agree with you," said Denis. "But what if one hasn't got Inspiration?"

"That was precisely the question I was waiting for," said Mr. Barbecue-Smith. "You ask me what one should do if one hasn't got Inspiration. I answer: you have Inspiration; every one has Inspiration. It's simply a question of getting it to function."

The clock struck eight. There was no sign of any of the other guests; everybody was always late at Crome. Mr. Barbecue-Smith went on.

"That's my secret," he said. "I give it you freely." (Denis made a suitably grateful murmur and grimace.) "I'll help you to find your Inspiration, because I don't like to see a nice, steady young man like you exhausting his vitality and wasting the best years of his life in a grinding intellectual labour that could be completely obviated by Inspiration. I did it myself, so I know what it's like. Up till the time I was thirty-eight I was a writer like you—a writer without Inspiration. All I wrote I squeezed out of myself by sheer hard work. Why, in those days I was never able to do more than six-fifty words an hour, and what's more, I often didn't sell what I wrote." He sighed.

"We artists," he said parenthetically, "we intellectuals aren't much appreciated here in England." Denis wondered if there was any method, consistent, of course, with politeness, by which he could dissociate himself from Mr. Barbecue-Smith's "we." There was none; and besides, it was too late now, for Mr. Barbecue-Smith was once more pursuing the tenor of his discourse.

"At thirty-eight I was a poor, struggling, tired, overworked, unknown journalist. Now, at fifty . . ." He paused modestly and made a little gesture, moving his fat hands outwards, away from one another, and expanding his fingers as though in demonstration. He was exhibiting himself. Denis thought of that advertisement of Nestlé's milk—the two cats on the wall, under the moon, one black and thin, the other white, sleek, and fat. Before Inspiration and after.

"Inspiration has made the difference," said Mr. Barbecue-Smith solemnly. "It came quite suddenly—like a gentle dew from heaven." He lifted his hand and let it fall back on to his knee to indicate the descent of the dew. "It was one evening. I was writing my first little book about the Conduct of Life—*Humble Heroisms*. You may have read it; it has been a comfort—at least I hope and think so—a comfort to many thousands. I was in the middle of the second chapter, and I was stuck. Fatigue, overwork—I had only written a hundred words in the last hour, and I could get no further. I sat biting the end of my pen and looking at the electric light, which hung above my table, a little above and in front of me." He indicated the position of the lamp with elaborate care. "Have you ever looked at a bright light intently for a long time?" he asked, turning to Denis. Denis didn't think he had. "You can hypnotise yourself that way," Mr. Barbecue-Smith went on.

The gong sounded in a terrific crescendo from the hall. Still no sign of the others. Denis was horribly hungry.

"That's what happened to me," said Mr. Barbecue-Smith. "I was hypnotised. I lost consciousness like that." He snapped his fingers. "When I came to, I found that it was past midnight, and I had written four thousand words. Four thousand," he repeated, opening his mouth very wide on the *ou* of thousand. "Inspiration had come to me."

"What a very extraordinary thing," said Denis.

"I was afraid of it at first. It didn't seem to me natural. I didn't feel, somehow, that it was quite right, quite fair, I might almost say, to produce a literary composition unconsciously. Besides, I was afraid I might have written nonsense."

"And had you written nonsense?" Denis asked.

"Certainly not," Mr. Barbecue-Smith replied, with a trace of annoyance. "Certainly not. It was admirable. Just a few spelling mistakes and slips, such as there generally are in automatic writing. But the style, the thought—all the essentials were admirable. After that, Inspiration came to me regularly. I wrote the whole of *Humble Heroisms* like that. It was a great success, and so has everything been that I have written since." He leaned forward and jabbed at Denis with his finger. "That's my secret," he said, "and that's how you could write too, if you tried—without effort, fluently, well."

"But how?" asked Denis, trying not to show how deeply he had been insulted by that final "well."

"By cultivating your Inspiration, by getting into touch with your Subconscious. Have you ever read my little book, *Pipe-Lines to the Infinite?*"

Denis had to confess that that was, precisely, one of the few, perhaps the only one, of Mr. Barbecue-Smith's works he had not read.

"Never mind, never mind," said Mr. Barbecue-Smith. "It's just a little book about the connection of the Subconscious with the Infinite. Get into touch with the Subconscious and you are in touch with the Universe. Inspiration, in fact. You follow me?"

"Perfectly, perfectly," said Denis. "But don't you find that the Universe sometimes sends you very irrelevant messages?"

"I don't allow it to," Mr. Barbecue-Smith replied. "I canalise it. I bring it down through pipes to work the turbines of my conscious mind."

"Like Niagara," Denis suggested. Some of Mr. Barbecue-Smith's remarks sounded strangely like quotations—quotations from his own works, no doubt.

"Precisely. Like Niagara. And this is how I do it." He leaned forward, and with a raised forefinger marked his points as he made them, beating time, as it were, to his discourse. "Before I go off into my trance, I concentrate on the subject I wish to be inspired about. Let us say I am writing about the humble heroisms; for ten minutes before I go into the trance I think of nothing but orphans supporting their little brothers and sisters, of dull work well and patiently done, and I focus my mind on such great philosophical truths as the purification and uplifting of the soul by suffering, and the alchemical transformation of leaden evil into golden good." (Denis again hung up his little festoon of quotation marks.) "Then I pop off. Two or three hours later I wake up again, and find that inspiration has done its work. Thousands of words, comforting, uplifting words, lie before me. I type them out neatly on my machine and they are ready for the printer."

"It all sounds wonderfully simple," said Denis.

"It is. All the great and splendid and divine things of life are wonderfully simple." (Quotation marks again.) "When I have to do my aphorisms," Mr. Barbecue-Smith continued, "I prelude my trance by turning over the pages of any Dictionary of Quotations or Shakespeare Calendar that comes to hand. That sets the key, so to speak; that ensures that the Universe shall come flowing in, not in a continuous rush, but in aphorismic drops. You see the idea?"

Denis nodded. Mr. Barbecue-Smith put his hand in his pocket and pulled out a notebook. "I did a few in the train today," he said, turning over the pages. "Just dropped off into a trance in the corner of my carriage. I find the train very conducive to good work. Here they are." He cleared his throat and read:

"The Mountain Road may be steep, but the air is pure up there, and it is from the Summit that one gets the view."

"The Things that Really Matter happen in the Heart."

It was curious, Denis reflected, the way the Infinite sometimes repeated itself.

"Seeing is Believing. Yes, but Believing is also Seeing. If I believe in God, I see God, even in the things that seem to be evil."

Mr. Barbecue-Smith looked up from his notebook. "That last one," he said, "is particularly subtle and beautiful, don't you think? Without Inspiration I could never have hit on that." He reread the apophthegm with a slower and more solemn utterance. "Straight from the Infinite," he commented reflectively, then addressed himself to the next aphorism.

"The flame of a candle gives Light, but it also Burns."

Puzzled wrinkles appeared on Mr. Barbecue-Smith's forehead. "I don't exactly know what that means," he said. "It's very gnomic. One could apply it, of course, to the Higher Education—illuminating, but provoking the Lower Classes to discontent and revolution. Yes, I suppose that's what it is. But it's gnomic, it's gnomic." He rubbed his chin thoughtfully. The gong sounded again, clamorously, it seemed imploringly: dinner was growing cold. It roused Mr. Barbecue-Smith from meditation. He turned to Denis.

"You understand me now when I advise you to cultivate your Inspiration. Let your Subconscious work for you; turn on the Niagara of the Infinite."

There was the sound of feet on the stairs. Mr. Barbecue-Smith got up, laid his hand for an instant on Denis's shoulder, and said:

"No more now. Another time. And remember, I rely absolutely on your discretion in this matter. There are intimate, sacred things that one doesn't wish to be generally known."

"Of course," said Denis. "I quite understand."

F. L. Lucas

I include this as an example of scholarly wit. It is marked, at its best, by a wealth of amusing reference, pointing to a cogent generalization; by impeccable style; and by a faint reek of stale briar pipes. F. L. Lucas is a Cambridge Don, very learned in all literatures, and an active participant, it appears, in the current war.

FROM SENSE TO SENSIBILITY

Unfortunately men [in the eighteenth century] were trying to be more reasonable than it is reasonable to try to be. In life, their ideal was not ignoble: but it was impossible. And in literature, it is not the best ideal for verse that it should be "as fine as prose." Like the boy in the story, who was coated all over with gold paint for a pageant, the human spirit stifled. Poetry tended to grow too like this passage from the *Reflections upon Theatrical Expression* of 1755: *"In Astonishment* and *Surprise* arising from *Terror* the *left leg* is drawn back to some distance from the other: under the same Affection of the Mind, but resulting from an *unhop'd for Meeting* with a beloved Object, the *right leg* is advanced to some distance before the left. *Impatience* and *Regret* at being detected in an iniquitous Design may be heightened by shuffling the *Feet* without moving from the *Spot."*

There is indeed little to add to Prior's picture of one besetting malady of his century, the very opposite to the malady of the century that followed it.

> Nor Good, nor Bad, nor Fools, nor Wise,
>   They would not learn, nor could advise;
> Without Love, Hatred, Joy, or Fear,
>   They led—a kind of—as it were:
> Nor Wish'd, nor Car'd, nor Laugh'd, nor Cry'd:
>   And so they liv'd: and so they dy'd.

How significant, behind its banter, is Gray's letter to Nicholls in 1769! —"And so you have a garden of your own and you plant and trans-

plant, and are dirty and amused; are you not ashamed of yourself?
Why, I have no such thing, you monster; nor ever shall be either dirty
or amused as long as I live." The eighteenth century produced the
garden of Candide, as its common-sense substitute for the garden of
Eden; but it remained, for the most part, too urban, as well as too
urbane, to cultivate even gardens very freely. And what a bleak desert
their formal walks could grow! " 'Tis ridiculous to judge seriously of
a poppet-show," writes the disillusioned old age of Lady Mary Wort-
ley Montagu. "I have never yet seen anything serious that was not
ridiculous," echoes Horace Walpole. "*Ah!*" repeats Mme du Deffand,
who has passed a bored and passionless life only to fall in love, when
blind and decrepit, with one who might have been her son, "*je le
répète sans cesse, il n'y a qu'un malheur, celui d'être né. Quelle
cruauté de se marier, tirer des individus du néant! Tout ce qui existe
est malheureux, un ange, une huître, peut-être un grain de sable; **le**
néant, le néant, voilà ce qui vaut le mieux!*" "*Quant à moi,*" echoes
Mme de Staal-Delaunay, as spring returns, "*je ne m'en soucie plus; je
suis si lasse de voir des fleurs et d'en entendre parler, que j'attends avec
impatience la neige et le frimas.*" And he is no isolated figure, that
pessimist of Thomson's *Castle of Indolence* who had found that the
towers of Idlesse, like the gates of Reason, could not bar out the thin
ghost of Ennui—

> Ne ever utter'd word, save when first shone
> The glittering star of eve—"Thank Heaven! the
> day is done."

Thus the natural Adam began to chafe under these silver chains
of good sense and good taste. He longed to dream again. Enthusiasm
—what the eighteenth-century peer who survived in Byron derided as
"entusy-musy" and Landor, in this respect Byron's spiritual cousin,
called "the hot and uncontrolled harlotry of a flaunting and dishevelled
enthusiasm"—was, after all, too deep a natural need. It broke out from
beneath the foundations of eighteenth-century sanity, as it has broken
out again from under the foundations of nineteenth-century science
and freedom of thought. First of all, the need to feel and express feeling showed itself in the growth of sentimentalism.

"You must not exhibit your feelings," said the code of *l'honnête
homme*. "It is egotistic: *le moi est haïssable.*" Thus a gentleman will
be amusing; but he will not display his own amusement by a guffaw.

Lord Chesterfield tells his son he cannot remember laughing since he had the use of his reason. "Do you never laugh, M. Fontenelle?"— *"Non, je ne fais jamais Ah-ah-ah."* Fontenelle never laughed, nor ran, nor wept; took to sitting on a stool without a back when he found himself stooping, towards ninety-eight; and died at a hundred, observing calmly—*"Je ne sens autre chose qu'une difficulté d'être."* But ordinary human nature could not live up to such standards. Men began to feel a chronic *"difficulté d'être."* Repression bred hysteria. The pocket-handkerchief was raised as the first banner of revolt—cautiously and whimsically at first by Sterne, who drops a single tear, as Recording Angel, to blot out Uncle Toby's oath; then wipes his Maria's streaming eyes; then finally howls aloud through the *Journal to Eliza.* "Check not," says Sir Charles Grandison to the weeping bride, "check not the kindly gush." And after that the deluge. Madame de Francueil, for example, reads Rousseau's *La Nouvelle Héloïse* and weeps all day. An ill-dressed little man enters the room. She divines it to be the author himself; more tears—in which Rousseau partakes. Her husband tries heroically to make a jest; as well strike a match to dry the Atlantic; he too bursts into tears. And so for decades to come. "Tell dear George," writes Lady Granville of Byron's latest work, "that I think *Cain* most wicked, but not without feeling or passion. Parts of it are magnificent and the effect of Granville reading it out aloud to me was that I roared until I could neither hear nor see." A young man meeting Lamartine, so the poet himself relates, feels ill with emotion and sinks choking with tears into a chair. The young Victor Pavie describes meeting Victor Hugo and rushing into his arms—*"Ici une lacune d'environ cinq minutes, pendant laquelle je parlai sans me comprendre, sanglotant d'enthousiasme et riant de grosses larmes."* It would be interesting to discover at what point in the nineteenth century the waters really receded.

[From *The Decline and Fall of the Romantic Ideal*]

D. B. Wyndham Lewis

See note on J. B. Morton (ante, *p. 615*). *D. B. Wyndham Lewis's* Weltanschauung *resembles that of Morton and of Gubbins. Lewis brings a daily message to the two or three million readers of the* Daily Mail. *He also has written a number of serious books, including a fine one on François Villon. These have not had a circulation of two million.*

A BALKAN LYRIC

(From the Szlo-Molczchakian of Smorko Kssykvcs.)

To a woman who had slighted him by refusing to acknowledge the gift of a rose in the market-place at Czchbrvcs.

It was, then, you?
You!
Gschzzslc!

THE CASE OF THE VILLAGE BLACKSMITH

The Smithy at St. Mary Cray, in Kent, which (they say) inspired Mr. Longfellow, that poet, to verse, is about to disappear in the rebuilding of the High Street. The chestnut tree was destroyed some time ago. As for the poem, I recited it the other day to a man who thought it was the work of Mr. Drinkwater. Hence, I think, it is only right to celebrate the passing of the smithy by some brief appreciation of the Poet and his Message. The more awful literary reviews will probably follow my example shortly; but I doubt if you will understand a word of it. In any case I doubt if they will tell the real story of the Village Blacksmith; which is all the more reason why we should nip in before them now with some exclusive facts which we owe to the research work of Professor Bodger.

It is well known that Mr. Longfellow was first induced to visit the village by Eliza Cook, the poetess, with whom he was very friendly;

and no doubt when he passed the forge and saw the honest blacksmith the poet's first thought was "How he perspires!" and his second, "I must make a poem about this." Next day the poet passed in the morning, and observed that the honest fellow had just begun making a horseshoe; and at evening Mr. Longfellow returned and found that the task was finished.

"Something attempted, I see," said the poet heartily. "And something done."

"Ay, ay, sir," returned the honest blacksmith, touching his forelock respectfully. "It do earn a night's repose."

Mr. Longfellow, struck by this thought, paced slowly home. In the morning the idea for a new poem was practically roughed out; and he said as much to his hostess at breakfast.

"Nothing indelicate, Wadsworth, I hope?" said Miss Eliza Cook, smoothing her black bombazine gown with a nervous hand.

"Certainly not," said Mr. Longfellow sharply. "Why?"

"You will remember," said Miss Eliza Cook, blushing faintly, "that I had to take exception to one stanza of your 'Wreck of the Hesperus,' in which you dwelt so regrettably on the physical charms of the skipp—"

"No sugar, thank you," said the poet coldly.

"I am also," said the lady, averting her gaze, "thinking of your 'Excelsior!' where—correct me, Wadsworth, if I am wrong—a young female is so far lost to modesty and propriety as to invite a passing stranger of the male sex to lay his head upon her breast." And Miss Eliza Cook, a warm wave of colour rushing over her neck, hid her head behind the tea-urn.

"Allow me," said Mr. Longfellow, coughing, "to recite to you a little of my poem." Whereupon, taking a paper from his pocket, the poet began:

> "Under the spreading chestnut tree
> The village smithy stands—"

reading slowly and enunciating each syllable with the greatest care, while Miss Eliza Cook beat time with a teaspoon. She listened with rapt attention, only interrupting to beg him to alter

> "His brow is wet with honest sweat"

to

> "Though it transpires he oft perspires"

which (as she justly observed) was equally euphonious and more genteel. Mr. Longfellow politely agreed, and pretended to alter the line in pencil.

"Otherwise," said Miss Eliza Cook, "it is a poem of great beauty and profound philosophy, and entirely free from anything objectionable or licentious. Its influence on English poetry will, I think, be incalculable."

"Baby," said Mr. Longfellow simply, "you said it."

He stayed in England a few weeks longer, hoping to be asked to become Poet Laureate, and then went home to America.

As for William Bashing—known in the village as Honest William —the blacksmith, he continued in his modest way to set an example to his fellow men. Toiling, rejoicing, sorrowing, onward through life he went; each morning saw one task (and no more) begun, each evening saw its close. He was, however, no longer compelled in church on Sunday mornings to wipe away his tear with a hard, rough hand, for a wealthy sympathiser supplied him with handkerchiefs for that purpose; and although his daughter's habit of singing high and shrill above the rest of the choir lost her many friends in the village, it brought many visitors. As the Vicar observed, in the wonderful scheme of Providence there is no evil without some attendant good.

There came to the village one day, when public interest in Honest William seemed to be slackening, a gentleman with an American accent, who walked briskly to the forge and held a short conversation with its pious occupant.

"What's it worth?" said Honest William at length.

"Loud sobs," replied the American gentleman, "two and a half per, sales above 1,000. Soft sobs, one per, sales above 5,000. Twice a Sunday. Double if you mention the poem. Get that?"

Honest William stretched out a large and sinewy hand.

The American gentleman's contribution was in pamphlet form, and ran:

You Have Heard the Village Blacksmith Sob.

Now Buy the Poem.

Say "Henry Wadsworth Longfellow" to Your Bookseller.

It's Worth It.

I admit that it has not the pep, the zip, the punch, the verve of modern specimens. But you must remember that publicity was practically in its infancy then. It served its purpose, at any rate, and Mr. Bashing was able to retire much sooner than he expected.

MAINLY MUSICAL

In which we consider the Hardships undergone by Golden-haired Girls in Orchestras, and make the acquaintance of Mr. Reginald Dinchumser, a Writer of Lyrics. We also discuss Publicity and Song-Writing.

MY DEAR BILL,

It is not surprising that military bandmasters have told the Southend (or somewhere) Council that three performances a day entail too great a strain on the musicians. Any one who has observed an orchestra at work knows what a strain it is; and unfortunately in a mixed band the burden and heat of the day seem to fall on the women. I once studied a famous orchestra playing (I think) some of the "Ring" music. There was a golden-haired girl (one of many) among the first violins who aroused my pity; she was so young, so frail, and her bow arm was whizzing so madly that it looked as if it were worked by steam. But for the vicious tightening of her lovely mouth one would never have guessed the ordeal she was undergoing.

And at the same time there were strong, healthy brutes among the brass who did nothing save an occasional "tumpity," or perhaps a "grumph" now and again. One in particular made me furious—a stout fellow who attended to the casual noises. After a single ping or a pong the fellow would lean back and close his eyes with a fine air of indifference.

I took my card and wrote on it: *"Are you not ashamed of yourself? Look at the little girl—golden hair, snub nose, third from the left, second row first violins"*—and was going to have it passed up to him, when the music stopped. Happily in the next piece the conductor detected him and got him into the open among the drums, where he had to work like a galley-slave. Things like these are comforting to a lover of justice.

Some light, by the way, seems to be thrown on the great lyric question by an interview with a lyric writer which I read yesterday. This gentleman confessed that the inspiration for one set of song-words came to him in the bath, and that for another set he was indebted to a bilious attack. This seems to disprove the theory (held by many thinking men) that the words of the common or Queen's Hall lyric are written deliberately and intentionally, and to back up the opinion of another school of thought that they are epidemic and occur in cycles.

In order to get at the truth finally I called to see my friend Reginald Dischwasser yesterday. Mr. Dischwasser is, of course, one of our foremost lyrists. Who does not know his "Heart o' Dreams," "Dreams o' Mine," "Rose o' Dreams," "Bless Your Dear Heart," and the other exquisite lyrics from his pen? I asked Dischwasser why he wrote "Dear Brave Soul o' Mine," and he said quite frankly that he did not know. I pointed out that there *must* be some reason for it. He then looked up his diary, and finally said, "Indigestion."

I said quickly, pressing his hand, "My dear fellow, there is only one thing for you. Go to ——," and I gave him the name of my own masseur. He was much agitated, and muttered, "Thank you, friend o' mine," at the same time mechanically feeling for a pencil. I urged him to lose no time, and went away.

You know "Dear Brave Soul o' Mine," Bill, of course?

> Dear (pom, pom), brave (pom, pom)
>   soul o' mine,
> Heav'n's sunshine on you shine,
>   Dearest, for aye!
> Roses your path bestrew,
> Sweet as the heart o' you.
> God send me back to you,
>   Dear Soul o' Mine!

Ah, well.

Apropos of lyrics, Bill, I was very much interested in the case of some publicity agent or other who lost his case against a club yesterday. There is a romantic glitter about publicity which attracts me like a moth, and I think I should have done pretty well if Providence had been pleased to make me a booster. Let me say at once that my ideas on the subject are of the grandiose, magnificently Napoleonic kind. Suppose, for instance, that I were engaged by Mr. Drew Hermsky, the great music publisher. You figure the scene in my office one morning:

MR. HERMSKY: Look here, I want you to boost my new song, "Cut Out the Sob-Stuff, Honey."

MYSELF (*briskly, to my secretary*): I want 10,000 men with red noses in Trafalgar Square this afternoon to sing "Cut Out the Sob-Stuff, Honey," from three to six without stopping. See to it at once.

MY SECRETARY: Very good, sir. (*Sees to it at once.*)

MYSELF (*snappily*): And the next thing, Mr. Hermsky?

And there you are. Remark that touch of genius as to the red noses. That is how you distinguish the Man Who Gets It Done from the ordinary publicity agent. A good secretary is rather essential, too.

That, broadly, is my style. Other ideas occur to me equally naturally, such as disguising a menial as an old lady from Piddinghoe and having her run over in the Strand. "Can I do anything for you, madam?" inquires a kind-hearted policeman. "Yes," says the old lady, clearing her throat. "You can Cut Out the Sob-Stuff, Honey"—and she bursts straightway into song. No fashionable wedding would be complete without one of my hired bravoes in a shining topper; there would be another (in a turned down collar and a pious expression) at the National Liberal Club, and another (with whiskers) at the British Association. And so on. Before the end of a week all London would know the song. No wonder that the niggling methods of the ordinary agent make one tired.

You will be glad to hear, by the way, that Dischwasser is hard at work on a new song-cycle. His new songs include "Dear Heart O' Mine, the Rose that is Your Smile," "Rose-Time in Your Heart," "God Send Me Back the Rose that Made You Mine," "You Gave Me Roses, Dear, but Ah! Where is your Heart?" and a very charming thing called "Roses." I called at Dischwasser's flat yesterday, and found him at work on the first verse of the song which will complete the cycle.

Personally I consider it one of the sweetest things Dischwasser has yet written. It is called "?," and goes:—

?

> Someone came at twilight to my window,
>   Someone plucked a rosebud wet with dew,
> Someone set my heart a-beating wildly—
>   Was it you?
>   (Ah!)
>   Was it you?

I objected at once. "But surely she *knew?*" He said irritably, "No, she didn't. It's a Queen's Hall lyric." I said, "Well, it's a pretty senseless question to ask now. She could easily have leaned out at the time and said, 'Is that Mr. Snooper-Sharpley?' Suppose," I said triumphantly, "it was only William Blurge, the undergardener?"

Dischwasser gave an impatient gesture and said that he could not find any inspiration for the second verse. He said it must be passionate and throbbing, but not too much so, for Queen's Hall audiences would not stand anything.... Yes, quite.

I leaned back and closed my eyes, and after a moment or so I was able to write down this:—

> Someone stood beside me throbbing madly;
> Someone swiftly took a last adieu;
> Someone gnawed my eyebrows pretty badly—
>   Was it you?
>   (Ah!)
>   Was it you?

To my astonishment the fellow declined it. I told him what I thought of him and went away.

I have entered, by the way, for a lyric writing competition. I have not studied the style of Dischwasser and other front-rank song writers of the day for nothing. I may tell you that as soon as I heard of this competition, I dashed to my desk and wrote three songs at once. They will, I fancy, compare favourably with anything of the kind on the market. One is a rather sweet ballad for a stout contralto, the second is one of those cheery country songs for a bald baritone, and the third is one of those rousing Cavalier songs for a thin tenor in pince-nez.

However. Personally I consider the ballad (No. I.) the best: though I rather like the country song (No. II.), and the Cavalier song (No. III.) appeals to me tremendously. I call my ballad—

I

SOME TIME ("YOU WILL COME BACK TO ME.")

Sometimes when the dusk is falling and the lights begin to glow
I can hear your soft voice calling from the days of long ago.
Sometimes in my heart there waken memories of joy and bliss.
Do you ask me what I murmur? I will tell you. It is this:—

REFRAIN

Some (pom, pom) time, some (pom, pom) how
You will come back to me.
With your dear smile—
Just for a while—
You will love me, dear, and I will love thee.
The ways may be long and dreary,
It may be then or now,
But soon will come rest, and God knoweth best.
Some time, somewhere, somehow!

The country song we will call:

II

UP TEW BURPLE VAIR

O! As I were wamblin' down-along,
　　A' takin' of the air,
A' singin' of a drumbled song
　　I seed a maiden vair.
(Ho! Ho!)
　　I seed a maiden vair.
Sez I, "Young maiden, be yew wed?"
She didden say nowt, but she turned 'er 'ed.
I velt me vaice goo mortal red.
Ho! Ho! Diddle-iddle-dee!
Dub-a-dub-a-doompling, riddle-iddle-ree.
　　Up tew Burple Vair!

That is rather fine. But I like the Cavalier song better because of
all the Cavalier words I have worked into it. Here it is:

III

CAVALIER SONG

Horse, boot, and saddle, and give it a rouse!
Leap to the gaskins and swing at the chouse!
Look to the surcingle, tighten the rein,
Pause at the postern and gallop again!

REFRAIN

King Charles (Ha! Ha!)
King Charles (Ho! Ho!)
To hell with the Parliament men and their snarls!

A firkin of wine ere we gallop away,
We'll be up to the buskins in bloodstains today.
King Charles!
(Ho! Ho! Ha! Ha!)
King Charles!

That is all for today, I think, Bill.

Your affectionate Uncle,

HENRY

William Gerhardi

William Gerhardi is an Anglo-Russian. In his early novel, The Polyglots, *he tells how he was sent to the Far East, at the end of the first World War, in company with the remarkable Major Beastly. The novel deals mostly with his adventures with his astounding relatives in Harbin, Manchuria. It all sounds perfectly truthful and incredible. If not truth, or even if truth, it is art of a very high order.*

THE VANDERFLINTS AND THE VANDERPHANTS

We stepped out at Tokio as though it were Clapham Junction, and repaired to the Imperial Hotel. Tokio, too, seemed a weird city. The houses were weird; men, women and children moved about on weird bits of wood like some mechanical dolls. The sun was blazing hot as we stepped into our rickshaws and drove in search of my aunt's house.

As we drove up round the corner, I saw an apparition of short skirt, dark-brown curls and ruby lips moving on seductive legs. There was a soft smiling look in her eyes, which had a violet glint in the sun. Her head slightly bent, she flitted past us—with her brogues unlaced—and disappeared round the corner.

I guessed that it was Sylvia—perhaps on an errand to a shop across the way. I had seen one or two not very good snaps of her, and there was something queer about her mouth that made me recognise her in a flash. How she had grown! What a "find," to be sure! You read of such in novels by Miss Dell, but you did not often come across them in real life. But what had always rather stirred my blood, long before I ever saw her picture, was that she bore this lovely name—Sylvia-Ninon.

We were first received by a thin middle-aged woman, on the heels of whom followed a somewhat stouter edition of the first, who called out, "Berthe!"—the thin one turning round at this word. As we were shown into the little sitting-room, in came a girl and curtsied in the Latin way, followed by number two (*révérence*), obviously of the same brood. Here, I could clearly see, was a family—mother, sister and daughters.

"Your aunt will be down in a few moments," said the elder of the ladies, who was called Berthe. And while we conversed in French— *"monsieur, madame,"* with the usual complimentary allusions—I heard a rustle, the door opened, and a tall, slim, grey-haired lady with a greyish moustache stooped into the room, and—"Well, well, here you are, here you are at last, George!" she said in a deep drawling baritone which reminded me of my father. I kissed and was kissed by her in turn, feeling how her moustache tickled my cheek.

"My friend," I introduced, "Major Beastly."

"Major *who?*" asked my aunt.

"Beastly."

To suppress the impulse to laugh she looked round quickly. "This is my nephew George," she said vaguely. "Mme Vanderphant and Mlle Berthe. Madeleine and Marie. We all came over from Dixmude together—what is it?—four years ago now."

"Yes, we Vanderphants and Vanderflints have been getting on very well together, as though indeed we were one and the same family— *n'est-ce pas, madame?"* said Mme Vanderphant, smiling pleasantly.

Aunt Teresa at once assumed a presidential attitude towards the people in the room. When she spoke I visualised my father, but in most other particulars she differed from her brother. Aunt Teresa's eyes were large, luminous, sad, faithful, like a St. Bernard dog's. Thick on her heels was a very small gentleman in a brown suit, with a waxed moustache—plainly Uncle Emmanuel. He came up to me, somewhat shyly, and fingering the three "pips" on my shoulder, slapped me approvingly on the back. "Already a captain! *Ah, mon brave!"*

"I owe my recent promotion," I said, "to having, at a psychological moment, slapped a certain War Office Colonel on the shoulder: just as his ego had touched the height of elation. Had I slapped him a second too early or a second too late, my military career would have taken a different course altogether. I am sure of it."

Uncle Emmanuel did not take in what I said, but generalising the topic into a human attitude, murmured: *"Que voulez-vous?"*

"Yes, I wouldn't be here but for that."

"After a big war there are always little wars—to clear up," said Uncle Emmanuel, shrugging his shoulders.

"We sailed three days before the armistice."

"We were in mid-Atlantic," said Beastly, "when the armistice broke out. We did have a binge!"

"*À Berlin! à Berlin!*" said my uncle.

A novel is a cumbersome medium for depicting real people. Now if you were here—or we could meet—I would convey to you the nature of Major Beastly's personality in the twinkling of an eye—by visual representation. Alas, this is not possible. At my uncle's remark, as indeed at all remarks, Beastly screwed up his eye and gave a few slow heavy nods and guffaws, as though the thing—the Germans, the Allies, my Uncle Emmanuel, nay, life itself—confirmed his worst suspicions.

Then the door opened, and Sylvia sidled towards us, with her eyes on the floor. I looked at her closely and noticed that her upper lip was somewhat longer than is usual, which sometimes gave her a guileless look, like a rabbit's. She had the same St. Bernard eyes as her mother, only perhaps of a younger St. Bernard in the act of wagging his tail.

Having greeted me, she went over to the sofa and began playing dolls by herself—a little insincerely, I thought, perhaps out of shyness. Then: "Oh, where's my *Daily Mail?*" She got up to get it, spread it out on the sofa, and began to read.

Uncle Emmanuel stood pensive as though meditating before giving utterance to his thoughts.

"Yes," he said, "yes."

"Today, after the Big War, the world is in as childish a state of mind as before," I pursued. "I do not even vouch for myself. If tomorrow these silly bugles went off again, calling the manhood of Britain to arms, inviting us to march against some imaginable enemy, and tender girls said, 'We don't want to lose you, but we feel you ought to go,' and loved us and kissed us and white-feathered us, I should find it hard to overcome the fascination of donning my Sam Browne belt. I am like that. A born hero."

Irony was not a strong point with them, I noticed. Uncle Emmanuel again did not take it all in, but, with a gesture indicating "*Que voulez-vous?*" he murmured these words.

While I spoke I was conscious all the time of Sylvia—short-skirted and long-legged, in white silk stockings—playing dolls on the sofa. For my own part, I know of nothing so secretly exhilarating as the first meeting with a good-looking cousin of the opposite sex. The rapture of identifying our common relatives, of tracing the life-blood bondship between us. When I looked at her I felt it was enchanting, amazing that this stripling girl of sixteen summers with the wide-awake lustrous hazel eyes, though with a slightly frightened look, should be my cousin, that she should call me by the second pronoun singular, be intimate with the details of my childhood. I felt that I should like to dance with her in a crowded ball-room which would throw into relief the intimacy of our movements, gestures, murmurs, looks; that I should like to float away with her down the sleepy river on a Chinese house-boat, or better still, fly away with her to some enchanted island and drink of her, to satiation. What I would ultimately do on such a desert island did not, of course, occur to me.

Aunt Teresa had just got up out of bed on purpose for me, as she explained. Great exertion! And Uncle Emmanuel enquired at intervals if it was not too much for her, if the talk was not tiring her. No, she would stay with us a little longer. In fact, we would sit out on the terrace.

It was too hot to move; so we sat still all day until evening, staring before us with a kind of semi-intelligent look, as we sat in big soft leather chairs on the open veranda, impotent after a heavy lunch, unfit for anything in the heat but day-dreaming.

And so we sat and looked into the garden, and beyond the garden into the street, and all around us seemed weird and unreal. Weirdness, an unearthly charm, cast a spell over the place. And as I dreamed I fancied that these moving statuettes and weird-coloured landscape were merely a scene from some ballet or a Japanese screen: so unreal they seemed. Even the trees and flowers seemed artificial trees and flowers. Some strange birds or insects made a weird continuous sound. But there was not a breeze, and even the leaves on the trees were motionless, listless with enchantment, lost in unreality.

"Today the air is soft and tender as in spring, and haunts one as in spring; but the cherry blossoms are over." Aunt Teresa as she spoke looked at me with a long, sad, silent gaze. Let me say at once that I'm good-looking. Sleek black hair brushed back from the forehead, lips—and something about the mouth, about the eyes, something—an indefinable something—that appeals to women. You think I'm conceited? I think not.

"You're very much like Anatole," said Aunt Teresa. "Neither of you is good-looking, but both have pleasant faces."

At that I am frankly astonished. I must take an early opportunity to re-examine my face in the looking-glass.

"And you're the same age. I remember so well when Anatole was born and we were thinking of a name for him, your mother writing to me and telling me they had decided to christen you Hamlet."

"But he's called George!" said Sylvia.

"Georges Hamlet Alexander—those are my names. A certain sense of delicacy, I suppose, prevented my people from actually calling me Hamlet. Instead they call me Georges."

"But why Georges and not George?" asked Sylvia.

"I really can't tell," I confessed. "Not after Georges Carpentier, I hazard, for he could not have been many years old when I was born."

"In Tokio!" Aunt Teresa gaily exclaimed, looking round at the Vanderphants. *"Mais voilà un Japonais!"*

"Tiens!" said Mme Vanderphant.

"At the Imperial Hotel. An unlooked-for diversion during my people's pleasure trip in the Far East, I fancy."

"But you're a British subject, so you've nothing to complain of," said my aunt.

"I suppose I am lucky."

"Yes, names are a great trouble," said my aunt, looking round again at the Vanderphants. "My daughter was christened Sylvia because when she was born she was perfectly fair and looked like a fairy. Eventually her hair has turned darker and darker, and is now, as you see, almost black—with gold-brown lights in it."

"And light brown after it has been washed," Sylvia said.

"Is it really?" I asked with genuine interest.

"Or take the names of my brothers," said Aunt Teresa, turning to Mme Vanderphant. "Our mother wanted girls at the time, but the first two born happened to be boys: so she christened one of them Connie, and the other Lucy."

"Tiens!" said Mme Vanderphant.

"Connie—his father"—she pointed to me—"was near-sighted, and Lucy very deaf. And how well I remember it when they took us for a trip on the Neva in a steam-launch. Connie, as blind as an owl, was at the steering-wheel, and Lucy, stone-deaf, down below attending to the engine. And when Connie shouted down the speaking tube to Lucy to back engines, Lucy of course could not hear a word, and Connie, who could not see a thing, landed us right into the middle of the Liteiny Bridge. How well I remember it! And then they shouted,

shouted at each other, nearly bit each other's heads off. It was awful. Your mother was on the launch"—she turned to me. "I think they were just engaged."

And as we plunged into reminiscence I took the opportunity of asking Aunt Teresa to enlighten me concerning my paternal ancestors. Whether what she said was fact or partly fiction I cannot truly vouch. I learnt, however, that originally, centuries ago, our fathers sprang from a Swedish knight who came to Finland to introduce Christianity and culture to the white-haired race; that subsequently he betrayed his stock and went over to the Finns and was disowned by his own clan without ever really being assimilated by the Finns, who, because of his forbidding looks, suspected him of being the devil's envoy and called him old *Saatana Perkele,* which name—von Altteuffel—he adopted as he strayed into Estonia and joined the missionary Teuton knights, I daresay in sinister extravagance, perhaps in evil irony, a dark romantic pride—who knows?—and chose two devils with twisted interlocking tails as his new coat-of-arms. His son, a Finn, but domiciled in northern Italy, had changed his name from Altteuffel to Diabolo. *His* son, an Italian born, but persecuted on account of his Lutheran faith, had fled to Scotland, where *his* son, a Shetlander by birth, to make the name appear more Scottish, added a "gh" ending to it, after the manner of MacDonogh—"Diabologh," to give it a more native air, but only succeeded in so estranging it from its original philology that it was neither fish nor flesh nor good red herring. So much so that when I, a distant offspring (born in far Japan), was joining up a Highland regiment to fight in the World War (for the freedom of small nationalities), the recruiting sergeant looked at it, and looking at it looked at it again, and as he looked at it he looked—well—puzzled. His face began to ripple, changed into a snigger, developed into a grin. He shook his head—"*Gawddamn,*" he said. Just that—and then no more. I took the oath and the King's shilling—which then was eighteenpence. My grandfather, who had been born in London and was of a restless disposition, after travelling in Spain, Holland, France, Denmark and Italy, settled in Siberia, where he had bought a large estate in the vicinity of Krasnoyarsk, where later he developed a successful business in exporting furs. In his diary there are curious references to the bull fights which he saw in Barcelona, where he also met his future wife, a Spanish lady who, after marriage, followed him to Manchester where, prior to settling on the Krasnoyarsk estate, she gave birth to my father,

Aunt Teresa, Uncle Lucy, and half a dozen other offspring. My grandfather, who outlived his wife, provided in his will that the Krasnoyarsk estate (known by the Russian rendering of our surname—"Diavolo") should be equally divided among his many children. "But your father could not get on with your Uncle Lucy," Aunt Teresa told me, "and he withdrew his share of money and set up his cotton-spinning mills in Petersburg. And, of course, he has also done very well." And as she spoke, I saw myself as a child back in the magnificent white house overlooking the Neva and contrasting strangely with the desolating quay on which it stood. Outside the snow was falling. The wind sweeping across the quay was hard, defiant. The ice-chained Neva looked cold and menacing. And looking at me, Aunt Teresa said, "You, George, are not a business man, you're"—she made gestures with her blanched bejewelled hand toward the heavens—"you're a poet. Always in the clouds. But your father—ah, he was a business man!" And Aunt Teresa, to uphold her personal prestige among her friends from Belgium, gave it to be understood that both her brothers had been rich as mischief. "If you went to Petersburg," she said to Berthe, "and asked for the works of Diavolo, why, any cabman would take you to my brother Connie's place at once."

"*Tiens!*" said Berthe, with a very conscious look of reverence for the prestige of Connie coming on her face.

"And now we've lost everything!" she sighed, "in the revolution!"

"*Courage! Courage!*" said Uncle Emmanuel.

My aunt was very proud of the achievements of her clan, and exaggerated a little when talking to strangers. Mme Vanderphant at this point intervened to say that an uncle on their mother's side also had big works in the vicinity of Brussels, and incidentally, a lovely house in the capital. But Aunt Teresa dismissed her lightly. That was nothing, she implied. Mme Vanderphant should have seen Connie's house in Petersburg! As if talking to me, but really to impress the audience, in a deep contralto voice she said:

"Your father's house in Petersburg. Ah, that was a palace! And now, alas, all gone, all gone."

"*Courage! Courage!*" said Uncle Emmanuel.

While Aunt Teresa talked of the glorious past, the Vanderphants, with their own thoughts far away, assumed a polite interest; Mme Vanderphant feigned to attend, with an unconvincing smile of humility on her face. Berthe, half-closing her eyes, listened to what I said

and exchanged frequent glances with Aunt Teresa—little nods of intimate reminiscence, of warm approval and understanding. She could
not have shared these memories, but in this assumption lay the secret
of a personality too kind and sensitive even to think of chilling us with
any attitude to our memories less intimate than our own.

"Sylvia! Don't blink!" said Aunt Teresa sternly.

Sylvia made an inhuman effort—and blinked in the doing.

"Of course, your father is independent of us," said Aunt Teresa,
"and we can't expect him to be sending us any remittances. But your
Uncle Lucy has been our trustee ever since our father died, and is obliged to see that we receive our dividends as they are due to us."

"And has he managed well?"

"Well, yes," she said. "I must confess that he has been very generous.
Very, very generous. Only lately—"

"Lately—?"

"Lately he hasn't been sending us any dividends."

"Oh?"

"It's very strange," she said.

"Of course, his business is paralysed by what is going on in Krasnoyarsk," said I.

"Quite. But we can't be living on nothing. And in Japan where
everything is so dear! Sylvia's convent alone eats up half of my money.
It's over two months overdue. It's very strange," she said. "We've
waited, waited..."

"All things come to him who waits," said Uncle Emmanuel.

"Emmanuel," said my aunt, "you will go tomorrow morning to the
General Post Office, and enquire if our telegram has been received by
Lucy."

"Very well, my angel."

Aunt Teresa's way of speaking to her husband reminded me of
regimental orders: "B Company will parade. 3rd Battalion will em-
bark." It was neither strenuous nor bullying; it quietly assumed the
thing done (in the future), it simply did not consider the possibility of
non-compliance.

"*Emmanuel, tu iras. Emmanuel, tu feras.*"

"*Oui, mon ange.*" And he went. And he did.

When Aunt Teresa went up to her bedroom to lie down before dinner, Uncle Emmanuel told us that he would be able to procure the
autograph of a famous French marshal for anyone who chose to con-

tribute twenty thousand francs to the French Red Cross; and my uncle took the opportunity to ask us if we knew of any possible buyers or, perhaps, of an auction or a war charity where such a bait would prove attractive. "Zey askèd me to do it," he was telling Major Beastly, with propitiatory gestures, "and I takèd it; I tellèd dem: I doèd what I can."

"I know a chap," said Beastly, "an American called Brown, who knows everybody who is anybody. I'll tackle him, and I am sure he'll take it on. But"—he held out a warning forefinger—"no bunkum, you know."

"Please?" asked my uncle, not understanding the word.

"No bunkum!" warned Beastly, who was suspicious of "foreigners." My uncle did not deign to reply.

[From *The Polyglots*]

L. A. G. Strong

THE BREWER'S MAN

Have I a wife? Bedam I have!
But we was badly mated:
I hit her a great clout one night,
And now we're separated.

And mornin's, going to my work,
I meets her on the quay:
"Good mornin' to ye, ma'am," says I;
"To hell with ye," says she.

JESSE WELCH

Here be the bones of Jesse Welch,
Who died of keeping back a belch:
Which same did in his pipes expand
And blew him to the Heavenly Band.

Anthony Armstrong

One of the favorite devices of the humorist is to pretend to be dumb, helpless, incompetent, beating ineffectual flippers against the cement walls of civilization's tank. The device becomes tiresome, and I have included few examples of it here. But Anthony Armstrong's account of his descent into New York's Avernus may rank with Virgil's picture of the underworld. Anthony Armstrong is one of Punch's stalwarts; he is now writing a series from the Army camps.

AT GRIPS WITH THE SUBWAY

For a long while after my first experience with the New York subway I avoided the thing like Prohibition, and would sheer off nervously from any corner where I saw a subterranean entrance leering at me. Then I got on my mettle about it. Why should I be laughed at by a cheap New York subway, a mere five-cent automatic subway—I, who could take an eightpenny ticket in a London tube without turning a single stile? I must get to grips with the damn thing—and at once.

So I determined I would use it to visit a friend who lived up on Twenty-fourth Street at the corner of Fourth Avenue. I chose him because I was then down on the extreme south point of Manhattan Island, and so felt that at least I couldn't help *starting* in the right direction. Moreover, I was only twenty yards from a subway station called South Ferry, which seemed a good starting-point.

So using South Ferry as a base, I decided, after intense business with a map outside, that I must somehow get on a line that ran up north underneath Fourth Avenue, and thus come to the Twenty-third Street station. Possessing, as I do, a good bump of locality, I had a shrewd idea I would then be quite close to Twenty-fourth Street.

So I went down, a lone British dare-devil, into the New York subway system and the irrevocable turnstiles closed behind me.

There are three things about the New York subway which discourage the stranger. First, there are no officials from whom to ask your way (except a harassed subway guard who, though pressed for time,

667

can yet pause to be as rude as the next man). Secondly, there are no maps on the platforms and only a few incomplete ones in the trains themselves, so that you can't tell whether you are going wrong till you have done it. Thirdly, there is an express train service, which plays old Harry with your preconceived ideas of where you are going to get out. Otherwise it's easy.

I got into a train. It was not crowded. Only two flappers, a negro, and an Italian woman got in too. Then we went off. The next station was called Bowling Green. Two Jews got in; the Italian woman and the negro and the two flappers got out. Then the flappers looked at me sitting there, giggled, and got in again. I blushed and tried to appear high-minded. The train moved off.

At the next station the two Jews got out, but the flappers remained. They were still giggling at me. The name of the station was South Ferry. For a moment I thought it was the same one, till I remembered that in New York very often two subway stations had the same name.

We moved off again. The next station was Bowling Green, and, by now a little distrait, I had to admit that the name seemed familiar. The flappers, however, who must have been going somewhere, did not get out, so I too stayed tight. The train moved off.

The next station was South Ferry. I crossed myself secretly, and looked round for a map. At this one of the flappers asked me if I wanted to get anywhere. I said a trifle haughtily that I was going to Twenty-third Street, and they retorted that I'd never make it at that rate, as I was merely on a shuttle railway between Bowling Green and South Ferry. I ventured to point out that I'd have realised that sooner if I hadn't seen them staying in it. They replied they had just been waiting to see what in hell I thought I was doing anyway. We then all got out at Bowling Green and the party broke up.

After an interval of wandering in passages I got pushed into a train which, under the title of "Lexington Avenue Express," volunteered to take me up Fourth Avenue, but for some while it only looked in at places like Wall Street, where I happen to own some shares that used to go up and down, and now just go down. Then to my joy we suddenly stopped at Fourteenth Street.

"Getting near Twenty-third," I murmured encouragingly to myself, adding: "A nine point rise will do it," for my thoughts were still on Wall Street.

The next station, however, called itself by the imposing name of

Grand Central, and before I could remember what number street it was on, we were off again.

The next stop staggered me. It was Eighty-sixth Street. And I thought we hadn't reached twenty. I leapt out like a bear operator caught short, as the express whizzed off, *en route* for a new high. If I hadn't I don't doubt I'd have been well beyond par by the next stop.

Feeling that I'd better travel on a falling market this time, I got in a return train. This one, calling itself a local, dropped my street stock carefully from 86 to 77 to 68 to 59 to 51, and then I was at Grand Central again. At this I shuddered and got out, although I hadn't intended to close the deal till 23. But I had learnt already that Grand Central had a queer effect on trains. They seem to get all funny after looking in at Grand Central. If I'd stayed in that train I'm certain that before I knew where I was I'd have found myself at First Street with the bottom out of the market.

So, resolved now to speculate with caution, I began to explore Grand Central. And I just got lost.

Grand Central is a fine place to get lost in, for, in addition to being an indefatigably conscientious subway station, it is a proper railway station and a shopping centre and hotel into the bargain, and as it is one of the only two real railway stations in Manhattan it is a big one. In fact, it is bigger than that. I wandered about till I was tired, getting into subway trains here and there to look at the maps in the carriages and getting out and into others, and I could not get away from Grand Central. At last I found myself in Times Square subway station. I don't know how I got there, but personally I think it is also part of Grand Central.

Here I clambered, tired but joyful, into a train that had Fourth Avenue on it, and wonderful as it may seem, the next stop was at Thirty-fourth Street. I scarcely dared breathe in case the next might take it into its head to be Third or 180th.

To my annoyance it was called Union Square, which put me right out. I am pretty safe on numbers, but I cannot follow these names. The next was Canal Street, which had a familiar ring, but when I came after a ten-minute run to a station named DeKalb Avenue I felt I had had just about enough. I climbed out and found our first porter.

"I want Twenty-third Street," I said. He told me I meant Twenty-fifth, five stations away. I didn't argue about it. On most of the sub-

way maps I had been able to glance at a number might be anything—
and probably is.

I was at Twenty-fifth Street station in six minutes. It was still daylight, I remember, when I came above ground. But I could not locate
our friends in Twenty-fourth Street....

I had quite a crowd round me before I was made to realize the truth
of the saying, "New York is not America," and that I had got to
Twenty-fourth Street, *Brooklyn*. I took a taxi back over the East
River to Manhattan and went to bed. I have promised myself never to
touch another subway as long as I live.

Eric Knight

In general we have avoided in this volume excesses of dialect wit. Dialect as seasoning is very tasty, but dialect for dialect's sake disagrees with those who have not been brought up on it. The injudicious use of the same North-country wit which Eric Knight handles so agreeably is to be seen in a little volume of which the title-page reads: "Sondnukkur's ryde fro Ratchda to Manchistur: iz visit to Manchistur Mechaniks Hinstitushun sho; wi o full okeawnt o whot hee seed un wheer he went, wi o iz adventurs. By Sam iz sel. Manchester, 1857."

THE FLYING YORKSHIREMAN
(Selection)

The conviction that he could fly didn't come over Sam Small gradually. It just hit him all of a sudden.

That night he and Mully had been down to Los Angeles to hear Sister Minnie Tekel Upharsin Smith at the Temple. First off Sam hadn't wanted to go, but before it was over even he agreed that it was quite a bit of a do, and Mully had as rare a time as she'd had in all her born days.

Sister Minnie sang a hymn she had written herself, which started:

"Won't you buy my violetsss—m'dam?"

When that was over she had all the people who were from California stand up and turn round and shake hands with the people who were sitting and who weren't from California, and say: "God Bless you, Brother or Sister," as the case was.

Sam felt right funny what with a stranger pumping his hand, but Mully began to warm up to the whole thing; so that when Sister Minnie asked the people from foreign lands to get up and say where they were from, Mully kept nudging Sam to stand on his legs like a man and put their ha'porth in. But Sam wasn't having any. People got up and shouted that they were from Germany and Italy and China and Hawaii and Mexico and Canada. There was even one chap from India.

Finally Mully couldn't stand it any longer, so she tied her bonnet tight under her chin and got up and shouted at the top of her lungs:

"Mr. and Mrs. Sammywell Small, Powki'thorpe Brig, near Huddersfield, Yorksha', England."

Then she sat down with her face all flushed, while everybody applauded and the woman next to her, who was from the city of Ioway, struck up acquaintance with her, and Mully decided that California was the right nicest and friendliest place they'd struck since they'd started on that trip around the world.

Sam tried to make out as if he didn't think much to it all, but even he got interested when Sister Minnie tore into her sermon.

It was entitled: "Faith Will Move Mountains," and a rare champion thing it was too, all full of quotations and rhetoric and little halts to give the people chance to applaud, and big halts where everyone sang the chorus of a hymn and clapped their hands to keep time. During these long pauses Sister Minnie would work up another store of energy and come out for the next round fresh as a daisy.

Everything depended on Faith, she said, and for her part she believed in it so much that she just *knew* that if the 5000 or so Brothers and Sisters present tonight, Praise be to God, were to head right out of that Blessed Temple and drive down to San Bernardino, she would bet you right now that if they would have Faith together they could make Mount Baldy shift ten feet toward the sea. The only thing that stopped her from putting it all into execution, she said, was that her legal advisers had told her it would cause too many possible suits for damages; because naturally, if you moved a mountain ten feet there was going to be a lot of disturbance. There'd be a ten-foot gap on one side, like as not running down through a lot of good real-estate developments, and on the other side there'd be a churning and a whortling of the earth that wouldn't be too good for California. People with spiteful tongues were ready enough to talk about earthquakes anyhow, even when you could call up the Chamber of Commerce and find out it was never a thing at all but the Battle Fleet off San Diego in firing practise that was making the ornaments on the mantelpiece sound like Fred Astaire in the introduction part of the Packard hour on the radio.

But nevertheless, as she was saying, Faith was a very, very wonderful thing, in fact, a marvellous thing, and if the Sisters and Brothers believed in our Dear Lord Jesus and believed in the power of Faith there was nothing they couldn't do. Nothing!

That was the sermon on Faith, and everybody applauded and clapped their hands in rhythm, being not only pleased with Sister Minnie's faith, but her evident faith in their faith, and her clever explanation of why they were not going to have to drive ninety miles on a chilly evening to do anything about demonstrating it.

That was about the end of the do. They closed up with some more hymns, one half the audience singing and then the other half to see who could be loudest; then the women singing and after them the men all by themselves, to see who could be loudest. And then it was over and everybody streaked for the doors.

Mully had had a good time, and there was no two ways about that. When she and Sam had pushed out through the crowd and were standing on the corner, waiting for the Wilshire Boulevard bus, she got enough words together to say:

"Well, Ah don't knaw how tha feels about it, Sammywell, but Ah've had a rare good time, and Ah think this is the right nicest place us has struck in all our travels."

Sam didn't doubt that she'd enjoyed it, but he knew, too, her remark was all part of the campaign to keep him in California. Neither Mully nor Lavinia, their daughter, ever missed a chance to put in a good word about Southern California. Vinnie wanted to stay so's she could have a bit of a dab at becoming one of these cinema stars; and Mully wanted to stay partly because of Vinnie and partly because she could never get over it that palm trees really grew in a white man's land. On top of that, there was no doubt about it that Sam had given the women quite a turn with the bad attack of bronchitis he'd had when they were visiting Vancouver.

So, of course, they never missed any opportunity now to keep after Sam about how good California was for his chest, and how that since he now was retired and a chap of independent means as you might say, there was no use leaving this sunshine to go dashing right back to England.

Now Sam knew all about the way the women were working on him, and he knew why they were doing it. He knew, too, that it wasn't over sensible to battle with them because probably they'd wear him down in the end. But still and all, a chap can't help putting his ha'porth in once in a while. So he blew his nose and said:

"Aye, taking the rough with the smooth, this ain't a bad place—for Yankeeland, o'course. But still and all, Ah'd give ten quid, Ah would, reight now, to be sitting back hoam i' t' Spread Eagle wi' ma chums on either side o' me and a good pint o' Guinness's in front o' me and a nice gert big coal fire to warm ma behind on."

Mully snorted.

"Sammywell," she said, "didn't Ah tell thee to put a clean henkercha' in thy pocket afore tha coomed out toneight?"

Sam knew he was licked if he got drawn away from the subject into any minor skirmishes. Everyone's cock on their own midden tip, and he wasn't off to argue about handkerchiefs, where Mully was on her own ground. So he just jammed his shameful bandana into his pants pocket and kept quiet. Mully kept on giving him a little bit of hell—the way a woman will; and finally Sam stopped listening to her —the way a man will.

And while she barneyed on, his mind went floating away in a hazy sort of manner and settled on two things. First he began wishing the bus would hurry up and come so Mully would stop talking; second he got to thinking about Sister Minnie's sermon. He began wondering if there was anything to it all—this Faith business. He began wondering if a whole bunch of people, all having Faith together with a sort of yo-heave-ho effect, really could move a mountain—if only for a matter of an inch or two.

He thought about it a long time, and decided that if a chap was going to do anything with Faith, he'd be smart if he picked on something rather easy at first and progressed gently to stubborn things like mountains.

Now all the time Sam had been thinking that, he'd been standing there waiting for the bus—and it gets rare chilly in California when the sun goes down. And that was what put the bus idea in his head. He said to himself that if a chap decided to try moving things by Faith a bus would be a champion thing to begin on—it having wheels which, as you might say, would aid the whole proposition.

It was no sooner thought than done, because, as Sam said to himself, it doesn't cost a chap a ha'penny to have Faith. Even if it doesn't work out, what have you lost?

So Sam shut his eyes and said to himself: "Ah have Faith that by t' time Ah open ma ee's that so-and-so bus will have arrived."

And by gum, he had no sooner said it than Mully was poking him in the short ribs and saying:

"Wakken up, gormless!"

And he opened his eyes, and there was the bus standing there.

Now naturally Sam was both surprised and pleased. As he said to himself, it might have been just a bit of coincidence, but still and all, it fair gave a chap something to think about. The best thing to do about it, he decided, was to give it a good thinking over. So when he got himself settled nicely on the bus he started putting his mind to thinking about Faith, and kept at it all the way home, being only interrupted once as the bus went past the Beverley-Wilshire and Mully said she saw Nelson Eddy coming out of the Brown Derby.

After that Sam got back to his thinking and kept right at it until they got to the end of the line. Then he and Mully got off right by the statue of Santa Monica on the Beach Drive palisade, and walked slowly and wearily along the palisade toward their boardinghouse.

They were both quite a bit played out after their exciting evening, and they went along slowly, arm in arm. Mully always liked that good night walk along the alameda, because it was peaceful and romantic and so tropical. Bordering the gravel walks there are no less than *three* kinds of palms: date palms, royal palms and palmettoes. Then, too, it's on a cliff high up over the shore, and as you walk along you can look out over the rustic wood railing and see far out to the ocean, or you can look straight down on the shore and see all the beach castles of the movie stars. They are all very splendid and big, but the biggest and most splendid one belongs to Marion Davies. It is such a sight that the tourist buses always stop by that palisade and all the sightseers get out and have a five minute stop to look down on the very home that Marion Davies lives in sometimes.

Mully never tired of looking down from that palisade. She never liked to go to bed without a sort of good night look at it; because she always thought that some night she might see a light in an upstairs window, and that would be Marion Davies going to bed, perhaps.

So when Sam and Mully got up by Marion Davies' house, they stopped and looked over the rail. There was Mully, full up of the awe of standing underneath a real palm tree and looking at a real cinema star's palace, and never aware of what Sam was thinking. For Sam, now he'd stopped walking, was able to think again. He had his pipe going good, and there he stood, looking far out over the ocean to where the fifty-cent all-night fishing barge lay, lit up and festooned with lights so that it looked like a twinkling diamond brooch of a ship.

And it was there and at that moment, that he first got his amazing conviction. Perhaps it came from being so high up, together with the sermon and the upsetting episode of the bus coming by Faith. No matter what it was, he got the conviction as surely as ever a man had one. What he felt was that he could fly. That was the conviction he had. He had it so strongly that he couldn't keep quiet about it.

"Mully," he said. "Tha knaws, sometimes Ah hev a feeling that a chap could put out his arms and launch himself off of here and fly— if he nobbut hed Faith."

"Aye, If!" Mully retorted. "And if thy aunt hed of hed you-know-whats she'd ha' been thy uncle."

In spite of her determination to live up to the position of wife of a rich retired man, Mully could be quite Yorkshire at times. And her last remark wasn't calculated to help a chap who wanted to talk things over. Not things like Faith and really moving mountains.

It really made Sam a bit mawngy. But there's one thing about a Yorkshireman. The madder you make him, the more determined he gets. And as Sam got undressed that night he couldn't help feeling stubborn.

"Well, at that," he said to himself, "Ah'll bet a chap *could* do it— if he hed Faith enow."

He kept thinking that after he got into bed. He felt he'd like to fly, just to show Mully that she wasn't right all the time. And as he lay there, he had Faith, and had Faith, and then his hair almost stood on end. For he could feel his body lifting, and lifting, until it was completely clear of the bed beneath him.

It was so amazing that he could hardly believe it himself. So, cautiously, he passed his hand under his body. It was true! As far as he could reach, he was free of the bed. It was so staggering that he had to drop back into bed to think it over. He must have been quite clear of the bed, because when he dropped back the mattress squeaked, and Mully said, snippily:

"Ba gum, Sammywell, if tha doesn't stop jiggling this bed Ah'm bahn to get up and sleep on t' sofa."

But Sam hardly heard her. He was too upset at his discovery. He decided to wait until Mully was surely asleep and try it again, but unfortunately he fell asleep himself.

In the morning when he awoke, his first thought was to tell Mully of his wonderful discovery. But, somehow, it didn't seem too easy in the daylight, sitting there at the breakfast table, with the California sunshine spanking down on the tablecloth and on the tea pot and muffins and marmalade and porridge and eggs and a little rasher of ham and cold steak-and-kidney pie and two or three nice bloaters that Mully had bought down in a Scotch bakery and grocery shop she'd run across down by the Santa Monica pier.

Moreover, Lavinia came in to breakfast, and it's hard for a chap to talk about imaginative things like flying of his own accord when right across the table there's his own daughter with her face all cold cream and her body wearing silk lounging pajamas that start a chap wondering if she's really brazen enough to be walking around without her corsets on, even if it is your own daughter.

So all Sam said was: "Tha knaws, it's funny, Mully; but Ah dreamt last night Ah were really flying around. Ah were floating i' t' air like one o' them bloody Zeppelins what come ovver i' t' wartime."

"Hmmm," said Mully. "What was it that tourist office lad said we maun ax for in this country when us wants brimstone and treacle?"

"Sulphur and molasses, mother," Lavinia said.

"Nay now, it ent ma blood that's off," Sam protested. "This were a varry real and onusual dream, so much so Ah still think Ah were awake."

"Oh, fawther," Lavinia said. "There's nothing unusual about it at all."

"Nowt onusual abaht a chap believes he were flying?"

"Of course not. It's one of the most common of dreams. It's a prenatal memory that's left from the time when you were a foetus swimming and floating in fluid inside your mother's womb."

"Here, here, young lady," Mully said. "What kind o' talk is that to be using at the breakfast table? Ah hear thee speak like that ony more, cinema star or no cinema star, Ah'll smack thy bare backside for thee. The idea! And of your Pa's own Ma, too; dead though she may be. Now thee eat thy breakfast and hurry about it, too. We've got to see t' casting director at Selznick International i' Coolver City by ten o'clock."

Sam said nothing more about flying; but he determined that the minute he was alone he would try it again. He had quite a wait, because the minute Mully and Lavinia were gone, the maid came in to clean up the apartment. There was the maid, dusting and sweeping and humming to herself in a come-day, go-day, God-send-Sunday sort of California way, and Sam thought she'd never be through.

But at last she was. Sam shut the door, tapped out his pipe and got ready. He lay on the sofa and willed and willed, and almost before he could catch his breath there he was floating in the air with the greatest of ease. For a while he just lay there, suspended in space, and amazed at this wonderful new power. He turned his head and looked down. He was fully a foot above the sofa. Very gently he floated to one side, where he was a good three feet above the floor. There could be no mistake about it. Amazed at himself he floated back to the sofa.

"Well, Ah'll be a monkey's ooncle!" he breathed to himself. "That Ah will indeed! Why, even Ah can scarcely believe it's so."

To prove it to himself he tried it again. This time he floated up in the air, then drifted out clean into the middle of the room. He felt quite uncomfortable, somehow, but he thought that only natural.

Then he turned over to look down at the floor. Very slowly he began revolving his body. And the minute he did that all feeling of awkwardness left him. Once he was face-downward toward the floor, a new and tremendous feeling of security and power seized him.

"Why, of course," he said to himself. "Ah were upside down—like a burd trying to fly on its back. This maun be the right way up."

So now, imbued with a new and very great confidence, he stretched out his arms and zoomed down toward the sofa. A foot from it, he banked with his palms, brought his body upright, and lit on his feet as gently as a thrush.

"Well, if this ain't a do!" he breathed.

He spread his arms again, pushed gently with the tips of his toes, and took off again. He soared along like a glider, making a complete circle of the room about a foot below the ceiling. As he did so he was seized with a tremendous exhilaration. All hesitation now was gone, and he used his new power with a fierce joy. He found flying took almost no physical effort whatsoever. Nor did he need any conscious mental effort in controlling himself; that is to say, he did not have to *think* how to do things. When he came to a corner the muscles of his body and the delicate distribution of his weight adjusted themselves by some instinct so that he banked perfectly.

The world became a new place to Sam Small. To us who merely walk, the world is a two-dimensional place; but to Sam it was now three-dimensional.

The room in which he flew thus took on aspects unknown to us who could only know it from a monotonous five-foot eye-level. He could see the tops of doors and of cupboards and could get a bird's-eye view of the chairs and table—which looked very silly pieces of furniture indeed from that angle. He noted, too, that while the room might be clean down below, it certainly wasn't up where he was. There were cobwebs over a closet and dust galore atop every door.

"Ah'll just hev Mully give that maid a good talking-to," he resolved.

Then he gave himself over to the beautiful pure joy of flowing and effortless flying. He swooped around the room, landing lightly as a feather where he would, taking off again with the merest preliminary drive of his toes. He practised landing in awkward corners, to test the range of his new abilities.

Unfortunately he was so occupied that he didn't hear Mully and Lavinia come back; and when they walked into the room, there he happened to be, perched atop a highboy.

"Well, Ah'll go to Helifax," Mully snorted. "Sammywell Small! What in the name o' God is ta laiking up theer for? Coom dahn here afore tha breaks thy bloody neck!"

Sam was so surprised and upset by being discovered that he forgot about flying and jumped down in quite an ordinary, mortal sort of way. He landed with a horrible crash that nearly drove his spine up into his back teeth, and of course there was quite a bit of do about it. Mully rubbed Sam's back with a little Elliman's Embrocation and sailed into him so hard that Sam got stubborn and wouldn't have told her about his new accomplishment even if he had got a chance to get a word in edgewise.

"Sammywell Small," Mully said. "Heaven knaws Ah've swallered a lot o' things since Ah married thee; but this caps the bloody climax, it does. Ba gum, lad, if tha goas on like this, folk'll begin to think tha's balmy i' t' crumpet. Eigh, sometimes Ah rue the day we took out a licence."

"Aye?" Sam came back. "Well, it cost me seven and sixpence. Ah could ha' got a dog licence for t' same price."

"Aye, and there's soom days Ah wish tha'd bowt a dog," Mully rebutted. "And today's one on 'em."

Walter Carruthers Sellar
and
Robert Julian Yeatman

1066 and All That was very popular in this country, which is quite a triumph, for of course it is much funnier to people who studied English history in English schools. I have put in also a superb poem by this remarkable pair. To admit it I have had to break my rule against parody. But their poem isn't exactly a parody, at that; it is rather an improvisation on a theme by Browning.

1066 AND ALL THAT
(Selections)

CHAPTER XXIX
CAUSE OF THE TUDORS

During the Wars of the Roses the Kings became less and less memorable (sometimes even getting in the wrong order) until at last one of them was nothing but some little princes smothered in the Tower, and another, finding that his name was Clarence, had himself drowned in a spot of Malmsey wine; while the last of all even attempted to give his Kingdom to a horse. It was therefore decided, since the Stuarts were not ready yet, to have some Welsh Kings called Tudors (on account of their descent from Owen Glendower) who, it was hoped, would be more memorable.

The first of these Welsh Kings was Henry VII, who defeated all the other Kings at the Battle of Boswell Field and took away their roses. After the battle the crown was found hanging up in a hawthorn tree on top of a hill. This is memorable as being the only occasion on which the crown has been found after a battle hanging up in a hawthorn tree on top of a hill.

HENRY VII'S STATECRAFT

Henry VII was a miser and very good at statecraft; he invented some extremely clever policies such as the one called Morton's Fork. This was an enormous prong with which his minister Morton visited the rich citizens (or burghlers as they were called). If the citizen said he was poor, Morton drove his Fork in a certain distance and promised not to take it out until the citizen paid a large sum of money to the King. As soon as this was forthcoming Morton dismissed him, at the same time shouting "Fork Out" so that Henry would know the statecraft had been successful. If the burghler said he was quite rich Morton did the same thing: it was thus a very clever policy and always succeeded, except when Morton put the Fork in too far.

Chapter XXX

LAMBERT SIMNEL AND PERKIN WARBECK

English history has always been subject to Waves of Pretenders. These have usually come in small waves of about 2—an Old Pretender and a Young Pretender, their object being to sow dissension in the realm, and if possible to confuse the Royal issue by pretending to be heirs to the throne.

Two Pretenders who now arose were Lambert Simnel and Perkin Warbeck and they succeeded in confusing the issue absolutely by being so similar that some historians suggest they were really the same person (i.e. the Earl of Warbeck).

Lambert Simnel (the Young Pretender) was really (probably) himself, but cleverly pretended to be the Earl of Warbeck. Henry VII therefore ordered him to be led through the streets of London to prove that he really was.

Perkin Warbeck (the Older and more confusing Pretender) insisted that he was himself, thus causing complete dissension till Henry VII had him led through the streets of London to prove that he was really Lambert Simnel.

The punishment of these memorable Pretenders was justly similar, since Perkin Warmnel was compelled to become a blot on the King's skitchen, while Perbeck was made an escullion. Wimneck, however, subsequently began pretending again. This time he pretended that he had been smothered in early youth and buried under a stair-rod while pretending to be one of the Little Princes in the Tower. In order to prove that he had not been murdered before, Henry was reluctantly compelled to have him really executed.

Even after his execution many people believed that he was only pretending to have been beheaded, while others declared that it was not Warmneck at all but Lamkin, and that Permnel had been dead all the time really, like Queen Anne.

POYNING'S LAW

Henry VII was very good at answering the Irish Question, and made a law called Poyning's Law by which the Irish could have a Parliament of their own, but the English were to pass all the Acts in it. This was obviously a very Good Thing.

AGE OF DARING DISCOVERIES

The reign of Henry VII marks the end of the Middle Ages. These were succeeded by an age of daring discoveries, such as when Caprornicus observed the Moon while searching the skies with a telescope, thus causing the rotation of the Earth, crops, etc. Emboldened by this, Caprornicus began openly discussing the topic of capricorns, for which he was unanimously put to death.

The greatest of these discoveries, however, was St. Christophus Columba, the utterly memorable American, who, with the assistance of the intrepid adventurers John and Sebastian Robot, discovered how to make an egg stand on its wrong end. (Modern History is generally dated from this event.)

Chapter XLIV

THE BOSTON TEA-PARTY

One day when George III was insane he heard that the Americans never had afternoon tea. This made him very obstinate and he invited them all to a compulsory tea-party at Boston; the Americans, however, started by pouring the tea into Boston Harbour and they went on pouring things into Boston Harbour until they were quite Independent, thus causing the United States. These were also partly caused by Dick Washington who defeated the English at Bunker's Hill ("with his little mashie," as he told his father afterwards).

The War with the Americans is memorable as being the only war in which the English were ever defeated, and it was unfair because the Americans had *the Allies* on their side. In some ways the war was really a draw, since England remained top nation and had the Allies afterwards, while the Americans, in memory of George III's madness, still refuse to drink tea and go on pouring anything the English send them to drink into Boston Harbour.

After this the Americans made Wittington President and gave up speaking English and became U. S. A. and Columbia and 100%, etc. This was a Good Thing in the end, as it was a cause of the British Empire, but it prevented America from having any more History.

Chapter XLV

THE FRENCH REVOLUTION

Soon after America had ceased to be memorable, the French Revolution broke out (in France). This, like all other Revolutions, was chiefly due to Liberty, Fraternity, Equality, etc., but also to the writings of Madame Tousseau, the French King's mistress, who believed in everyone returning to a state of nature and was therefore known as *la belle sauvage*.

The French Revolution is very interesting and romantic; quite near the beginning of it Dante and Robespear, the revolutionary leaders (or *Jacobites* as they were called), met in the beautiful and historic Chamber of Horrors at Versailles and decided to massacre every one in September. This was called the *Glorious First of June* and was done in accordance with a new *National Convention*. Memorable amongst those who were massacred were Robespear himself, who was executed in his own gelatine, and Marat, who was murdered in his bath by Madame Tousseau.

Chapter XLVI

NAPOLEON

The English were disgusted by this new French Convention and so decided to go in for The War again, thus causing Nelson and the Duke of Wellington. The War was now called the Napoleonic War, after Napoleon, a Corsican, whose real name was Bonuapart, and who had cleverly made himself First Consort by means of a *whiff of grape-nuts*. (This is called the Napoleonic Legend.)

The French Revolution caused great loss of life, liberty, fraternity, etc., and was, of course, a Good Thing, since the French were rather degenerate at the time; but Napoleon now invented a new Convention that the French should massacre all the other nations and become top nation, and this, though quite generate, was a Bad Thing.

HOW I BROUGHT THE GOOD NEWS FROM AIX TO GHENT

(or Vice Versa)

I sprang to the rollocks and Jorrocks and me,
And I galloped, you galloped, we galloped all three.
Not a word to each other: we kept changing place,
Neck to neck, back to front, ear to ear, face to face:
And we yelled once or twice, when we heard a clock chime,
"Would you kindly oblige us, *is that the right time?*"
As I galloped, you galloped, he galloped, we galloped, ye galloped, they
    two shall have galloped: *let us trot.*

I unsaddled the saddle, unbuckled the bit,
Unshackled the bridle (the thing didn't fit)
And ungalloped, ungalloped, ungalloped, ungalloped a bit.
Then I cast off my buff coat, let my bowler hat fall,
Took off both my boots and my trousers and all—
Drank off my stirrup-cup, felt a bit tight,
And unbridled the saddle: it still wasn't right.

Then all I remember is, things reeling round,
As I sat with my head 'twixt my ears on the ground—
For imagine my shame when they asked what I meant
And I had to confess that I'd been, gone and went
And *forgotten* the news I was bringing to Ghent,
Though I'd galloped and galloped and galloped and galloped and
    galloped
And galloped and galloped and galloped. (Had I not would have been
    galloped?)

ENVOI

So I sprang to a taxi and shouted "To Aix!"
And he blew on his horn and he threw off his brakes,
And all the way back till my money was spent
We rattled and rattled and rattled and rattled and rattled
And rattled and rattled—
And eventually sent a telegram.

Bruce Marshall

CONVERSATION IN AN EDINBURGH BAR

That same night at half-past six Andrew Gillespie, the Bishop's Bad Brother, leaned across the counter of a very popular bar near the Waverley Steps.

"Winnie," he said to the young lady on the other side, "what's on at the Garden tonight?"

Winnie, who was a pretty young girl with the same philosophical outlook as the Dean of Saint Paul's, smiled a smile which contributors to popular magazines would describe as "displaying two pearly rows of even, white teeth."

"Eh don't kneow, Mr. Gillespie," she answered in the dreadful English affected by Edinburgh young ladies who wish to appear more *de famille* than they really are. "But they say that the chirus from the Aimpire is geowing to be thaire and that it's a lit night."

"A late night, is it?" The Bee Bee Bee nodded his head in that slow up-and-down manner which, because the deliberateness of the nodding suggests that the nodder is reviewing the whole range of the higher mathematics and physics, has won for Caledonians the reputation of being one hundred times as intelligent as they really are. (A Scotsman nods his head for the same reason as a puppy chases its tail and, expressed in terms of pure thought, the nodding equals the chasing.) "A late night, is it?" he asked again, returning from the higher mathematics and physics which he hadn't visited. "Och, well, Ah s'pose Ah'd be'er dander along. The bit lass'll be pleased tae see me."

His last sentence was almost inaudible, partly because he spoke in that thick, guttural tone which prideful Picts imagine to be as attractive as the Irish brogue and which, in reality, resembles nothing so much as a horse with a cold in the head, partly because the bar was crowded with young gentlemen in chatty golfing suits who were discussing loudly what various teams had been doing with various sorts of balls during the afternoon. But the Bee Bee Bee didn't care. He spoke as much for the benefit of his own soul as for Winnie's; and, if Winnie

686

didn't hear, his own soul did, down beneath the padding of his woolly waistcoat. So he said it again, this time for the exclusive benefit of his own soul (Winnie was now up at the other end of the bar serving a purple-faced stockbroker): "The bit lass'll be pleased tae see me."

His soul and the bar kept getting more golden and glorious and jolly. Indeed, as the gin and Italian vermouth dissolved into vapour inside him, he found it increasingly difficult to tell which was his soul and which was the bar, so much at one with these hearty, healthy, friendly men did he seem. For the Bee Bee Bee was a low-brow, not of the aggressive my-boy-is-a-duffer-at-Greek-but-by-Gad-he-plays-for-his-school type, but of the genial beery brand whose critics say, according as charity gives them utterance, that they are "dull but good-hearted" or "good-hearted but dull." And all around him were low-brows: golfing low-brows, footballing low-brows, low-brows who liked to watch other low-brows footballing, biscuit-making low-brows, all the great plus-foured mindless who, getting their names in the papers only when they were hatched, matched, or despatched, did more to mould contemporary Caledonian thought than all the professors, authors, and bigwigs that the country had ever produced. He himself belonged to the second hierarchy of Caledonian low-brows, to those who wore a mental kilt and were all for Rabbie Burns whom they never read and for the Church of Scotland which they never attended; but he bore no ill-will to his superiors of the first hierarchy who preferred, or had had preferred for them, Kipling and the nice clean white surplices of what was known by those Scots who didn't belong to it as the English Church. For, among low-brows of the first hierarchy or among low-brows of the second hierarchy, he was among his ain folk, among the noble army of average men who, by their common sense and breadth of vision, had raised profound thinkers like Vilma Banky and Warwick Deeping to the platform from which, nobody saying them nay, they dispensed their sooth to a world which had poisoned Socrates and burned Savonarola. So his soul, surrounded by other souls with the same image and superscription upon them, expanded, like a balloon into which gas is pumped, into a golden orb of sleek content.

"Aye," he said again, "the bit lass will be pleased tae see me." The words were uttered to nobody in particular, as Winnie was still serving the purple-faced stock-broker, but they spiralled up none the less surely into the haze of alcohol and tobacco and passed with them into the great limbo of things said, smelt, and tasted. And as they swung upwards they were heard by a lanky egg merchant who had just finished his second.

"Wimmen," said the egg merchant sententiously and rolling the word round his mouth as though it were a cough lozenge, "wimmen are fair hellish."

The Bee Bee Bee turned and nodded his head quite seven times before he replied.

"Aye, laddie. But there's wimmen and wimmen, mind. Aye, there's wimmen and wimmen." His eyes moistened ginnishly as he thought of Bubbles and her golden hair and of how she snuggled up to him in taxicabs. "Aye, there's wimmen and wimmen, mind. And mine's as bonny a wee bit hen as ever cried cock-a-doodle-doo."

"But hens don't cry cock-a-doodle-doo," said the egg merchant, who, *de par sa profession,* knew something about the matter. "Hens don't cry cock-a-doodle-doo. Cocks, old man, cocks. You've got the blanket the wrong way up."

The Bee Bee Bee laughed noisily.

"Good for you, Jock," he said. "Hen's don't cry cock-a-doodle-doo. Anyway, ye ken what Ah mean. Ah've got a dandy wee bit lassie and no mistake. She teaches dancing down by at the Garden of Eden."

"Is that a fact?" said the egg merchant.

"Yes. And Ah've just been asking Winnie here what's on down by tonight and she tells me that there's going to be fine high carryings-on. A late night, you know, and all the lassies from the Empire waggling their wee bit beam-ends. Ah wouldn't miss it for worlds. Bubbles— that's my lassie's name—doesn't expect me, but Ah'm thinking that Ah'll just be giving her a surprise." The alcohol he had consumed and the general brotherly atmosphere common to all bars made him feel that the egg merchant was a man in whom confidences could be safely deposed. "Ah may be on the wrong side of forty, but Ah've got young ideas." He laughed as though the phrase and the feeling were original. "Yes, Ah've got young ideas all right."

The egg merchant, his whiskey lapping in a yellow tide up the side of his glass, leaned nearer.

"Nice piece, is she?" he asked, with a look which showed that he was fully prepared to take a vicarious pleasure in her niceness and in her piece-ness.

The Bee Bee Bee winked cheerfully.

"I should say that she is. She's only twenty and she has got legs with muscles like a racing champion's. All yon dancing, Ah s'pose."

The egg merchant rolled his eyes lugubriously.

"Aye, all yon dancing as you say." He stared across at the tiers of bottles on their shelves as though reading on the labels of the Erastian Johnny Walkers and the Ultramontane Benedictines the foretelling of a doom yet to come. "As you say, all yon dancing." His eyes gradually lost their Calvinistic gloom and he continued briskly and with every appearance of taking pleasure in what he was saying: "Ah hope Ah'm not offending you, mister, but perhaps a word in season mightn't do any harm. Mind you, no offence meant. But seeing as you and me are standing here pally like and talking away as if we'd known each other all our lives and seeing as you have honoured me with your confidence Ah might as well tell yew that in my opinion all yon dancing is dee-moralising and is making the lassies o' Bonnie Scotland no better than a lot o' koantanental baggages. Mind you, Ah'm no a great boy for the kirk, but there's something in what the meenisters say about dancing turning little white vurgins into scarlet primer donners. And it's not just hearsay, mind yew. Ah kent a bit of goods in Glasgow..."

The Bee Bee Bee said with what he imagined to be simple dignity: "Scarlet primer donners be damned. Ma wee Bubbles is as innocent as the sunlight on her hair. As innocent as the sunlight on her hair, Ah tell you."

The egg merchant took a gulp at his whiskey and continued lusciously:

"Aye, they're all as innocent as the sunlight on their hair until they're caught napping." He nodded with the aggravating self-assurance of a man who knows human frailty too well ever to do business or make love on trust. "As Ah was saying, Ah kent a bit of goods in Glasgow. Proper little pink-and-white angel she was, and to look at her you would have said that butter wouldn't melt in her mouth. Real pally with a friend of mine in the motor trade, she was. Said she loved him and all the usual yarn. Loved him!" He laughed loudly and harshly. "Perhaps she did. But she loved his money more. And one day he found out that she'd been up to all sorts of high jinks with medical students when he wasn't there. He was a middle-aged gentleman like yourself."

His last sentence discomfited the Bee Bee Bee who, being a neat and pseudo-military forty-five, did not like to be termed "middle-aged."

"Ah'm on the wrong side of forty," he admitted again, but heavily this time and despondently as though it were another ten years that he was acknowledging. "But that's not middle-aged."

The egg merchant, who was a youthful thirty-eight, emptied his glass.

"The half of three-score years and ten is thirty-five," he said maliciously. "And yewth to yewth, that's the trewth. Lassies are all very well and patting a pair of young knees does us old lads good. Makes us younger than we are and more sympathetic to the clarion call of Progress," he declaimed, misquoting the leading article in the current issue of his favourite technical journal. "Ah, well, must love you and leave you, Ah s'pose. The missus, you know. Doesn't like to be kept waiting. So long, old scout. No harm meant. Liked the looks of you and just thought Ah'd like to tip you the wink. Cheerio!"

And with a wave of the hand he allowed himself to be caught into the whirlpool of the swing door and was whisked into the Leith tram and non-existence.

[From *Father Malachy's Miracle*]

James Laver

A STITCH IN TIME, OR PRIDE
PREVENTS A FALL

Belinda—for I filch that pretty name
Already dear to Letters, and to Fame,
And seek to decorate my modern page
With some few graces of a former Age,
A happy Age, ere jest or drink was thin,
Or ever wit went out, or cant came in,
And gallantry was only—half a sin.
Blest eighteenth century, propitious clime,
Enchanted island in the Sea of Time!
Goal of fastidious poets who would flee
The modern bard's suburban ecstasy;
Elysian fields beneath unchanging skies,
Where Garrick lives, and Queen Anne never dies,
Where Burke and St. John, Sterne and Congreve meet—
The period's all one to Wardour Street.
In *talons rouges* the veriest dwarf looks big,
And wit, when bald, should steal a periwig.
For flavouring a play, a tale, a song,
With *settecento* sauce, you can't go wrong;
And borrowed elegance may oft atone
For wanton fancies that are all your own.

Belinda, then, was modern—with an air,
This age's joy, her grandmama's despair,
She had, like many maidens of her kind,
A perfect *flair* for sailing near the wind;
Assumed a vice, although she had it not,
Concealed *no* blemish with a beauty spot,
And, lest mere Nature should the beaux offend,
Called the cosmetic arts their aid to lend,

To give unneeded whiteness to her nose
And to her cheek a quite superfluous rose.
In dazzling, swift succession, shy and bold,
Pure as an icicle, but not so cold,
Her morals still Victorian, although
Her manners were distinctly rococo—
She would adventure in the street alone,
And go to plays without a chaperone,
From cigarette set cigarette alight,
And drink a dozen cocktails every night;
Hold, with ambiguous smile, each gallant's hand,
And laugh at tales she did not understand,
Still tempting, as a godless wit might say,
Not only Providence, in every way.

But what of that?—though censure of the Age
Echoes diurnal in each scribbling page;
And "Old Etonian," writing to "The Times,"
Bemoans the mounting tale of sins and crimes;
Though pulpit prudes unendingly abuse
The harmless, empty, uncomplaining pews;
And see, in each Manhattan that goes down,
A tarnished maidenhood, and lost renown—
Such slanders still the wise will disbelieve,
Nor let appearances too much deceive.
Though life moves faster than it moved of yore,
And primrose paths are all asphalted o'er,
Though Pleasure bears an e'er-increasing load,
And broader still is broad Destruction's road,
Not yet is every pillion in the land
Bound straight for Brighton and the Paphian strand,
And nymphs there are, like several I have known,
Who sup at two, but always sleep alone,
As chaste as those who with the Family dine,
And kiss papa, and go to bed at nine.
And such was she, one of that fairy band
That, e'en in this mechanick time and land,
Sometimes the happy eyes of men may see,
Strayed from their merriment in Arcady.

Creatures of Twilight, children of the Moon,
Who dance all night, and go to sleep at noon,
Whose step and spirit is as light as air,
And their accustomed garments, gossamer;
Beyond their day and generation wise,
Yet with a spark of folly in their eyes,
Of malice empty, yet of mischief full,
And—till you touch them—hardly tangible.
But when you do, no pale, dissolving form
Of cloud or wraith, but vital, human, warm,
As fragrant as ripe apples on the tree,
Of sun and sap a mingled mystery,
Perfect in savour, texture, hue and shape,
And more intoxicating than the grape.

But to our theme; and think me not too bold
To ape a tale more delicately told.
For though I cannot write as Pope might do,
Fame's Sun may rise on my Belinda too.
The bright beams, gliding o'er the narrow sill,
Revealed the maiden wrapped in slumber still.
So deep entranced she lay, she might have been
The unkissed form of that enchanted Queen
Who, to content a jealous goblin's bale,
Slept for long ages, in the fairy tale,
Yet smiled in sleep, as though not unaware
Of her deliverer's step upon the stair.
Even the Sleeping Beauty woke at last;
And Phoebus, seeing that the day was past,
Perplexed and angry at his power denied,
Cast with disdain the obscuring clouds aside,
Put the last arrow to his gleaming bow,
And loosed it at the unconscious nymph below.
Swift as a beam of light it cleft the sky,
And brushed the corner of Belinda's eye,
Then, caught within the tangle of her hair,
Forgot its speed, and rested, quivering, there.
For one brief moment motionless she lay,
Stunned with surprise, and shrinking with dismay,

Then started from her pillow, at the shock,
And cried, "My God! It's nearly four o'clock."
Swift from her brain the mists of slumber fled,
She rose, like Venus, from her billowy bed;
And suddenly, obedient to her will,
Her *robe de nuit,* although reluctant still
To leave the form it knew and loved so well,
Sighed silkily, and round her ankles fell;
And, at the end of its unwilling fall,
Formed round her feet a plinth or pedestal,
Such as whereon was Aphrodite viewed,
Of old, by an adoring multitude,
Or Artemis, chaste Goddess of the Moon,
Naked, and out of pure Carrara hewn.
But something vital in her aspect shone
Which quite forbade the cold comparison,
No sculptor could have matched the living hue,
That scarce a master-colourist could do;
And to portray such piquancy were hard
Even for Boucher or for Fragonard.

Long time the nymph before her *armoire* stood,
Looked on God's work, and found it very good.
An *amorino,* perched aloft, surveyed
The slender white perfections of the maid,
And, deep ensconced within his stucco bower,
Reflected much upon Reflection's power,
That multiplying such a form by two,
The mirror did what Nature could not do.
But even sweets can weary, being too sweet.
E'en woman tire of her own counterfeit.
Belinda, who had sought her couch at dawn,
Stretched her lithe limbs, and half concealed a yawn.
Then suddenly remembered Damon's voice—
Damon the dancing partner of her choice—
Who, as he kissed her hand at break of day,
Had asked her to partake a dish of tea.
With a small party, in his little flat,
At half-past four—"But it's already that!"

The prettiest women sometimes feel regret
A pleasant invitation to forget;
And strive to recollect, in every score,
One assignation made the night before;
And, if the promised pleasure's very great,
Will be, perchance, but twenty minutes late.
Her hasty toilet then the maid began,
For Damon was a rather nice young man.
Her swift ablutions done, she open drew
The mirrored portal, and displayed to view
Her splendid battle-harness, row on row,
Her armoury of frill and furbelow;
And, in a sliding tray, her eye could see
A royal repertoire of *lingerie*.
Belinda rummaged, but she could not find
A panoply just suited to her mind.
A white, a mauve, a pink were thrown aside,
Until at last, oh rapture! she descried
An airy something, delicately green,
Of triple ninon or of *crêpe-de-chine*.
(Such fortune more than paid her for her pains.)
Its shoulder-straps were little silvered chains,
And, as along the margin of a bay
The green, translucent water breaks in spray,
So, to complete that dainty garment's grace,
Around its edge rippled a froth of lace.
Her sparkling orbs with satisfaction shone,
But as, too hastily, she slipped it on,
Alas! a sudden tearing sound she hears—
Oh, Atropos: oh, Fate's abhorréd shears!—
In the frail web a dreadful rent appears.
Belinda sees, and tears of anger start
To those bright eyes, and anguish wrings her heart.
"Did ever breathe a more unfortunate maid?
I'd set my soul on wearing just that shade."
Hastily seizing needle, thimble, thread,
She sits down petulantly on her bed,
And too distracted by her haste to try
To find a thread of just the proper dye,

Takes the first hasty reel that Fortune sends,
And darns the rent, as sails a sailor mends.
The finished task made e'en Belinda blink,
The garment green, the staring stitches pink,
"And yet what matter," she exclaims, "to me?
No human eye but mine will ever see."
The angelic hosts, in highest heaven arrayed,
Applaud this resolution of the maid;
And she, this time, with new-instructed care,
Puts on the green chemise, without a tear.
Her other garments then she donned in haste,
A pliant girdle nestled round her waist;
(Although Belinda was not one of those
Who need such aid, save to suspend her hose:)
And, with a single gesture, she assumes
The mingled product of a thousand looms.
A comb's caress, her close-shorn head is curled,
And she is all prepared to face the world.

The times are gone when ladies needed quite
An hour to get their corset-lacing right.
And modern vestments—let no cynic scoff!—
Are easy to put on as to put off.
Our grandmamas, when tempted, were afraid
That they could never dress without a maid;
And girls were fearful to discard their stays,
Who'd make no bones about it now-a-days.

Belinda, armed against the wintry breeze,
Her bosom bare, her skirts about her knees;
Shoes delicate as rose-leaves, and as thin,
Transparent stockings that revealed the skin,
And each imperfectly protected charm,
To chill herself, and keep spectators warm,
Snatches her bag, and dabs upon her nose
Three hasty grains of powder as she goes;
Outruns the stride of Time with flying feet,
And adds the final touches in the street.

How negligent was Venus not to send
Her dove-drawn car Belinda to befriend!
And Sol, she sure had found an aid in him;
But he was now below the ocean's rim.
So, as no supernatural aids appear,
She hailed a taxi that was cruising near.
A page-boy oped the portal with a grin,
She murmured the address, and bounded in.
Swiftly she leaped, yet might a sharp eye see
A gleam of stocking, far beyond the knee.
And a young haberdasher, passing by,
Gave one quick look, then staggered home to die.
The page-boy's eyes went lastingly askew,
An old archdeacon felt his blood renew
Its pulsing youth in every shrivelled vein,
And a blind beggar found his sight again.
Oh then, how swiftly had Belinda flown,
Had she but wheels, or pinions of her own!
But Pleasure's whim, nor Desperation's need,
Can urge the London taximan to speed,
Who, to his five-mile limit staunchly true,
Crawls to a funeral, or a rendezvous,
And when the tardy traveller pants to pay,
Gropes for his change, and fumbles time away.

Belinda left him more than he had earned,
And swiftly in beneath the archway turned;
Pressed, in a hall discreeter than the grave,
The bell that summoned Levitation's slave.
And in the twinkling of an eye was seen,
Swooping to earth, the god in the machine
(Although this modern deity, I doubt,
Gets men in trouble, but ne'er gets them out,)
Who to her timid query, soft replied:
"The second floor, Miss. Will you step inside?"

But oh! that some wise counsellor, betimes,
Or old magician, deep in Runic rhymes,
Moon in eclipse, or meteorite ablaze,

Or Endor's Witch or Bond Street's latest craze,
Or nightmare shapes that moan, and cry "Alas!"
Or crossed fish-knives, or broken looking-glass,
Palmist, or sorcerer, or Sibyl black,
Or weather chart, or Old Moore's Almanack,
Had warned Belinda of her threatening Fate.
But Prophecy ne'er speaks, or speaks too late,
For as she stepped out on the second floor,
Her light footfall brought Damon to his door
(Opened in vain so many times before).
She smiled, and shook his hand, and in she passed,
And the quiet portal shut behind her fast.

The maiden stood at gaze, her roving eyes
Swept the apartment with a pleased surprise,
And comprehended in one searching glance
The jars of China, and the silks of France,
The walls jade-green, the tasselled hangings red,
(His flat was very nice, Belinda said.)
The tea-things set, a cake with marzipan,
Eclairs, and *marrons glacés,* strawberry flan,
Chocolate-liqueurs, and what was more than these,
The sense of haven after stormy seas,
Of languor after hurry, peace from strife,
Rest from the rigours of our modern life,
Three downy cushions in a deep armchair,
The drowsy breath of blossoms in the air—
But there was nobody but Damon there.

Her swift, apologetic host explained,
An aunt, who should have come, had been detained.
His other friends were ill, or working late,
So that his party is—a *tête-à-tête.*
Belinda pales to find herself immured,
But at his smile is partly reassured,
And while she swears she must at once return,
The faithful Charles brings up the steaming urn.
Half in a dream she hears the gallant say:
"You can't go off without a dish of tea.

You will stay, won't you? Oh, Belinda, do!"
And she replied with, "Sugar? One or two?"

And now begins the old strategic game;
Its methods vary, but its end's the same.
Now doth the foe—for mere politeness' sake—
Hover about her as he cuts the cake.
Nor doth the base philanderer omit
To brush her sleeve, by chance, in passing it.
And in his easy talk, contrives to weave
A web of war, disguised as make-believe,
Striving with hidden jest, and double sense,
To undermine the walls of the defence,
And tell of madcap pranks, that had no consequence.

For well he knew that doubtful pleasures please
The purest minds, presented by degrees;
And many a maid discovers, to her cost,
Who laughs at Virtue is already lost.
Things best undone are better left unsaid—
This scouting party Innuendo led,
And watched her cheek, which gave no hint of red.
The enemy then took a bolder line,
But still the chaste Belinda gave no sign;
And he, concealing his fell purpose yet,
Proffered the heedless maid a cigarette,
And, as he held the match, their fingers met.
But oh! that those who Virtue's crown desire
Would learn 'tis dangerous to play with fire,
That smoke implies a corresponding flame,
And tea for two is oft a risky game!
Too late Belinda sees within his eyes
The furious floods of heady Passion rise;
Too late essays his purpose to withstand,
For now he prisons her defending hand,
And she, too horrified to raise a cry,
And all uncertain, or to stand or fly,
Starts to her feet in terror and despair,
Staggers, retreats, then sinks upon a chair;

And, as she trembles at her peril dire,
A battery of kisses opens fire.
The first went wide, the second fell more near,
The third exploded just beneath her ear.
The fourth, a lock of hair blows right away,
And then, with paralysing ricochet,
Along her brow and cheek rebounds and skips.
The fifth lands full on her protesting lips,
And shakes the fortress to its finger-tips.
How may the maid this furious siege repel?
For this was no old-fashioned citadel,
Framed, in despite of any tyrant's rage,
By some more military Middle Age,
Buttressed by bombazine, secure, remote,
Entrenched behind a seven-fold petticoat.
For these weak walls, for peaceful seasons made,
No whalebone stiffened, and no stuffing stayed,
No complicated garment guards her knees,
No line of pins form a *chevaux de frise,*
No bastioned bodice keeps the foe at bay,
And poor Belinda seems an easy prey.

Then, in the inmost chamber of the keep,
Old Conscience stirred from his uneasy sleep,
Peeped o'er the battlements and scanned with fear
The army of besiegers thronging near.
And seeing the furious foe so hardly stayed,
Bemoans his power, insulted and decayed,
And seeks to muster all the force he can,
To check the martial ardour of a Man.

He blows his trumpet, and anon appears
A motley troop, unmobilised for years,
Her mother's Counsels, solid, old and wise,
But rheumatick from lack of exercise;
Her Nurse's Warnings, full of truth and zeal,
But somewhat out-at-elbow, down-at-heel,
And, for the service of a modern state,
Their weapons just a little out of date.

"But where," cried Conscience, "oh! unhappy day!
The Cohorts of *Religion,* where are they?
These had been mighty to repel the foe,
But were, alas! disbanded long ago."

Still his two loyal regiments, alone,
In spite of opposition, held their own.
And all had yet been well, but now arose
All her interior and forgotten foes—
Loose, idle dreams, those cankers of the soul,
No maid can banish, and no state control,
A revolutionary army led
By Passion, with a red cap on his head—
Who now, throughout the poor beleaguered town,
Formed their wild ranks, and shouted Conscience down,
Pouring so swiftly in from every side,
That soon his Bastille doors were standing wide,
And each imprisoned, vagabond desire
Rushed madly forth, and set her heart on fire.
Her fell besieger, though she strove to hide
The flame within, this through her eyes espied,
And deemed already gained the expected bliss,
The fortress conquered, and the treasure his;
And raised a shout of triumph, loud and clear,
That all the maid's defenders shrank to hear.

Assailed from out the walls, within betrayed,
Poor trembling Conscience, ever more dismayed,
Seeks any aid, before it is too late,
To save Belinda's virtue, and the State.
And looking wildly forth, while on the walls
A red-hot shower of oaths and kisses falls,
Whom, by good fortune, should he chance to see
But that fantastic fellow Vanity?
Twirling his beard, his hat upon one ear,
A cross between a Spaniard and Mounseer,
He stalked indifferent by, his head in air,
As who should say, "This isn't my affair."
By turns with terror white, and red with shame,

Old Conscience calls the gallant by his name,
And, as the coxcomb negligently stays,
He half upbraids him, and half humbly prays.
"How can you, even you, stand idly by,
When from these walls our last defenders fly?
When all beset with terrors and alarms,
Belinda is, against her will, in arms?
When burst is every lock and bar and bolt,
And half our population's in revolt;
When fast a scaling party of our foes
Climbs by a treacherous ladder in her hose,
And hostile scouts with stealthy steps repair
To throat, wrist, ankle, breast, and God knows where?
So close invested, moat and tower and wall,
This virgin fortress is about to fall,
Lost if she yield, yet powerless to withstand,
Will soon lie open to a tyrant's hand,
And of the direful consequence afraid,
I sink my pride, I stoop to beg your aid."

Old Conscience ceased; a smile sardonic, slow,
Wrinkled the handsome features of the beau.
"My lord," he said, "although in days gone by
We have not always seen things eye to eye;
And often, to my sorrow and surprise,
You've shown a tendency to tyrannise,
Yet we must give our private feuds a rest;
In war-time coalitions are the best,
And for the State alone, if not for you,
I'll take a hand, and see what I can do."
Then, gazing on his troops' depleted ranks,
Old Conscience murmured his uneasy thanks.
And Vanity, who held Belinda dear,
Climbed to her brain, and whispered in her ear:
"To rule your conduct I do not pretend,
But listen to the counsel of a friend.
I am no priest, be vicious if you please,
But not, Belinda, in a darned chemise!
Had it been merely torn, you then might say

That his own fury rent the lace away.
Had it been merely mended, it might be
Your maid had mended it too hastily.
But from your curious botching, I'm afraid,
It will be plain you do not keep a maid,
Since never maid, however lax, I think,
Would dare to darn a green chemise with pink."

Thus far the beau, and none too soon he spoke,
Belinda heard, and all her virtue woke.
Within her breast the clang of battle died,
And turned again tempestuous Fortune's tide.
With outraged dignity her body shook,
She quelled her adversary with a look.
"You *Gothic* boor," she cried, "barbarian churl!
You should have known I'm not that kind of girl."
With virtuous indignation justly fired,
She spurned the foe, and then herself retired,
While Damon knew his trap prepared in vain,
Vanity smiled, and Conscience breathed again.
Then down the staircase to the street she sped,
And praised the gods that she had kept—her head;
Reflecting, as again she gained her home,
A joy resisted is a joy to come;
And she who is assailed, and runs away,
May live to fight, and fall, another day.

Ye British nymphs, that still, free-hearted, rove
With chaste Belinda, in Diana's grove,
Yet would not have Diana's grove to be
A hopeless, cold perpetual nunnery;
Who search the sky each night for love's bright star,
Who travel fast, but never go too far,
Who run a straight, if not a godly race,
Avoid the kill, yet quite enjoy the chase;
The natural prey of all with eyes to see,
But whose own heart is your worst enemy—
Scorn not a lesson from the halting pen
Of one who understands the wiles of men;

And who would beg you, though himself a man,
At least to be as careful as you can.
So be not over-hasty to expel
One poor meek devil from your heart's warm cell,
Lest you be forced to welcome back the elf,
With seven friends, more wicked than himself.
But let the story of Belinda show,
A little fault is sometimes *à propos*.
For they are not the hardest to assail,
Who put their trust in flawless coat of mail,
Nor most immune from dangers such as these,
Who wear an irreproachable chemise.
And, when you too are into ambush led,
And all *your* virtue hangs upon a thread,
When men entrap you, and the gods forget;
One touch of vanity may save you yet.

And so my little moral tale I call
A Stitch in Time, or Pride Prevents a Fall.

Noel Coward

WEATHERWISE
A Comedy In Two Scenes

LADY WARPLE ⎤
MONICA ⎥
CYNTHIA ⎥ Her daughters
VIOLET ⎦
THE REV. HAROLD BASSET—Monica's husband
REGGIE WHISTLER
BUTLER
DR. TWICKENHAM—A Psychoanalyst

The action takes place in the Library of Warple Manor in the County of Leicestershire.
One week elapses between Scenes I and II.

SCENE I

(When curtain rises, it is late afternoon, after tea. LADY WARPLE is knitting by the fire—she is a dignified and slightly austere-looking old Lady. REGGIE WHISTLER, CYNTHIA and VIOLET are seated about smoking.)

CYNTHIA: And, my dear—they went up and touched him and the body was still warm!

VIOLET: What a perfectly horrible story—it gives me the creeps—ugh! *(She shudders.)*

REGGIE: You don't seriously believe in it though, do you?

CYNTHIA: Of course I do.

VIOLET: Don't you scoff, Reggie, there are more things in heaven and earth than are dreamt of in man's something or other.

705

REGGIE: I'm not scoffing, but I must say I think this psychic business has been rather overdone lately.

VIOLET: It's sometimes very useful; Gloria Frimpton found out all about her first husband through a fortune-teller.

REGGIE: Only because he happened to be living with the fortune-teller at the time.

CYNTHIA: Not living *quite*—just visiting occasionally, but still it only shows—

LADY W.: I fear, Violet dear, that you have not placed before Reggie's doubting mind a really convincing example of the marvels of Psychic Research. You have both witnessed, in my presence, the most amazing demonstrations—I cannot imagine why you have not quoted them to prove your point. Take for instance our wonderful conversation with your dear Auntie Clara only last Thursday. We actually heard her voice, did we not?

CYNTHIA: Yes, Reggie, we did honestly.

REGGIE: I don't see how; if she's nothing but a spirit I doubt if she even has a larynx.

VIOLET: I don't believe one speaks with one's larynx, anyhow.

REGGIE: Auntie Clara *always* did, it was one of her greatest charms.

LADY W.: Even though you are an old friend of the family, Reggie, it is hardly nice of you to be facetious on such a subject.

REGGIE: But are you quite certain that you weren't all thinking of her so hard that the sound of her voice was a sort of subconscious suggestion?

LADY W.: Quite certain. But if you're determined not to believe in a thing, of course you won't. Nothing can ever be proved without Faith.

CYNTHIA: You're being very tiresome, Reggie.

REGGIE: Not at all, I want to be convinced frightfully badly.

VIOLET: Nonsense, you laugh at everything.

LADY W.: I read a dreadful story in the Psychic Herald the other day, about a woman who refused to believe—and one evening when they were doing a little table turning after dinner—she went off into a trance.

REGGIE: I frequently go off into a trance after dinner.

CYNTHIA: Don't interrupt, Reggie.

LADY W.: I repeat, she went off into a trance, and when she came to, she was found to be possessed by an evil spirit.

VIOLET: Mother—you never told us that.

CYNTHIA: What did it make her do?

LADY W.: I couldn't possibly repeat it out loud—bend forward.

    (CYNTHIA *leans forward and* LADY WARPLE *whispers in her ear.*)

CYNTHIA: How appalling!

VIOLET: You must tell me, Cynthia.

    (VIOLET *bends forward and* CYNTHIA *whispers in her ear.*)

    I suppose they had to dismiss the butler in sheer self-defence.

LADY W.: Yes, but with a handsome compensation.

VIOLET: Naturally.

LADY W.: To my mind there's something absolutely terrifying in the thought of being possessed unconsciously possessed by an alien spirit.

CYNTHIA: Didn't she know anything about it?

LADY W.: Not until afterwards when they told her, then she went mad and imagined she was Charlotte Corday— It was all very awkward as they had a Cabinet Minister staying in the house at the time and she kept trying to get into his bathroom.

VIOLET: Poor dear, how awful!

LADY W.: Eventually she had to be sent away, that sort of thing is so likely to be misconstrued—especially in Leicestershire.

REGGIE. That theory does account for a lot though. Sophie Flotch was behaving in a most peculiar way in the Ritz last week, I think her possessive spirit must be an emu, or something equally unbecoming.

CYNTHIA: Oh, mother, do let's do the Ouija board for a little while, I feel wonderfully eerie inside—we might get thrilling results.

REGGIE: What is a Ouija board?

VIOLET: My dear, don't you know? They're marvellous things.

CYNTHIA: Like Planchette; you must have seen them.

REGGIE: How many can do it at the same time?

VIOLET: Only two, but one has to sit by the side and write down the answers.

LADY W.: It would be absurd to attempt it with Reggie in the room.

REGGIE: No it won't—I'm absolutely serious—do get it, Violet.

VIOLET: All right, pull the blinds down—it's here I think.

    (*She goes over to desk and searches.* REGGIE *proceeds to pull the blinds down.*)

REGGIE: Surely if it's pitch dark we shan't be able to see anything at all.

CYNTHIA: It's not going to be pitch dark, there'll be firelight—very ghostly and effective—draw up the chairs closer, Reggie.

VIOLET: Here it is—any one got a pencil?

REGGIE: Yes.

*(They assemble round a small table by the fire—*CYNTHIA *takes* REGGIE's *pencil and balances a Bridge marker on her knee.)*

CYNTHIA: You and Violet had better begin, mother—it always starts more quickly for you than anyone else.

LADY W.: I don't feel well enough today, dear,—I'll just sit here and listen.

VIOLET: Come along then, Reggie, rest your hands quite lightly on it, and for heaven's sake don't sneer, because it's frightfully unlucky. Can you see to write, Cynthia?

CYNTHIA: Yes, but I'm not going to write all the time, I want to work the thing too.

REGGIE: We'll take it in turns.

LADY W.: If it starts to say rude things like it did to Fanny Belton, you'd better stop immediately.

VIOLET: Don't press so hard.

REGGIE: I'm not.

VIOLET: What shall we ask it?

CYNTHIA: You'd better find out if it's there first.

VIOLET: All right. *(Whispering mysteriously.)* Is any one there?

(There is a slight pause, then the board begins to move.)

REGGIE *(looking carefully)*: It says "No."

CYNTHIA: That's absurd.

VIOLET: You pushed it, Reggie.

REGGIE: I did not push it.

CYNTHIA: Ask it again.

VIOLET: You, this time, Reggie.

REGGIE *(obediently)*: Is any one there?

(The board moves again.)

CYNTHIA *(looking)*: No.

REGGIE: This is ridiculous—there must be some one there to say "No."

VIOLET *(with superiority)*: It often behaves like this at first—one must have patience.

REGGIE: Never mind if it's there or not, let's ask it a question.

VIOLET *(to the board)*: Are you an Elemental?

(The board moves.)

CYNTHIA (*looking*): No!

REGGIE: The thing's stuck.

VIOLET (*perseveringly*): Who are you?

CYNTHIA (*spelling out*): Q U E E N   V I C T O R I A.

REGGIE: My hat!

VIOLET: Shut up, Reggie— (*To board.*) Have you a message for us?
     (*The board moves.*)
     You pushed it then, Reggie, I saw you.

REGGIE: I did *not* push it.

CYNTHIA: If you go on quarrelling over it, you can't expect it to answer.

REGGIE: She was probably pushing it herself and trying to put the
     blame on me.

VIOLET (*hotly*): Reggie, how *can* you tell such lies!

CYNTHIA: Oh, for goodness' sake ask it what its message is.

VIOLET (*to board*): Have you got a message for us?
     (*The board moves.*)

CYNTHIA (*looking*): Yes.

REGGIE (*to board*): What is it?
     (*The board moves.*)

CYNTHIA (*spelling out*): W E   A R E   N O T   A M U S E D. It's
     Queen Victoria all right.

REGGIE: That's because we quarrelled—I suppose we'd better apologise
     —(*To board*) We're awfully sorry.

VIOLET (*to board*): Have you any other message for us?
     (*The board moves.*)

CYNTHIA (*looking*): Yes.

REGGIE (*intensely*): What is it?
     (*The board moves.*)

CYNTHIA (*spelling out*): B O W — B O W.

VIOLET: Reggie was pushing—I felt him all the time.

REGGIE: I wasn't—I swear I wasn't—Queen Victoria really meant Bow-
     wow.

VIOLET: Look out—it's moving again—
     (*The board moves quickly.*)

CYNTHIA (*spelling out*): W H A T — D R E A D F U L —
     W E A T H E R — W H A T — D R E A D F U L —
     W E A T H E R — O H — D E A R — O H — D E A R
     — B O W — B O W.

(*Enter* MONICA, LADY WARPLE's *eldest daughter, with her husband, the* REV. HAROLD BASSET. *They turn up lights.*)

MONICA: What are you all doing in the dark?—We've been for a splendid tramp, right through the village and round.

VIOLET: Oh, Monica—you've ruined our séance.

REV. BASSET (*confidingly to* CYNTHIA): Yes, right through the village and round, we went—most delightful—such a holiday for me after my parish work in Shadwell.

MONICA: Not that absurd thing again, Violet—really you are ridiculous—it would have done you all more good to be out in the fresh air—we've had a ripping walk.

REGGIE: Right through the village and round?

MONICA: Yes.

REGGIE: I thought so.

MONICA (*quietly to* CYNTHIA): You know perfectly well I asked you not to encourage mother in all this spiritualistic nonsense, she takes it seriously and it's very bad for her.

REV. BASSET: If it had been intended that we should communicate with the other world, it would have been made easy for us.

REGGIE: Nothing could be easier than sitting here with a Ouija and talking to Queen Victoria.

CYNTHIA: Look at mother, what's the matter with her?

VIOLET: She's asleep.

MONICA: That will mean a headache all the evening. (*She goes over to* LADY WARPLE.) Wake up, mother.

(LADY WARPLE *remains quite still.*)

Wake up, mother!

VIOLET: Something's happened—she's not asleep—look at her eyes, they're open. (*She rushes to* LADY WARPLE *and shakes her.*) Mother—mother—wake up!

MONICA: Feel her heart, quick.

(VIOLET *does so.*)

VIOLET: It's beating all right.

MONICA: Fetch some brandy, Harold, at once.

(*The* REV. HAROLD *departs hurriedly into the dining-room.*)

CYNTHIA: Brandy's no use—don't you see—she's in a trance!

MONICA: A trance?

CYNTHIA: Yes, and it's our fault for conjuring up evil spirits. Oh, what are we to do, what are we to do?

REGGIE (*with a certain amount of relish*): Burn feathers under her nose—that always brings people to—
> (*He seizes a large brocade cushion and having set light to it, brandishes it about over* LADY WARPLE.)

MONICA: Reggie, that was one of the best brocade cushions.

REGGIE (*waving it about*): Of course, brocade smoke is much more pungent than the ordinary kind.
> (*Re-enter the* REV. HAROLD *with brandy and a glass.*)

REV. BASSET (*excitedly*): Here you are—here's the brandy.

MONICA (*taking complete command of the situation*): Give it to me.
> (MONICA *tries to make* LADY WARPLE *swallow some brandy.*)

CYNTHIA (*suddenly*): My God!

MONICA: What is it?

VIOLET: What's the matter?

CYNTHIA: Violet—Reggie—don't you remember—a trance—the woman who thought she was Charlotte Corday—

VIOLET: You mean mother might be— Oh, dear, oh dear!

MONICA: What on earth are you talking about?

CYNTHIA (*breathlessly*): There was a woman who went off into a trance and they told her afterwards and she thought she was Charlotte Corday, and she tried to get into the bathroom with a Cabinet Minister and—

REGGIE: Well, we needn't worry about that yet—the nearest Cabinet Minister is twelve miles away at Warborough.

MONICA: Are you all stark staring mad—what do you mean?

VIOLET: I'll explain. You see, when people go off into trances there's always the fear that when they come to they may be possessed by some alien spirit. Mother read about a woman in the *Psychic Herald* who— (*She whispers in* MONICA'S EAR.)

MONICA: Great heavens! But how could she do it in the time?

REV. BASSET: I'm sure that a dutiful Christian woman like your mother could never be possessed by anything unpleasant—the disembodied spirit of some noble heroine perhaps—working for the good of mankind—

REGGIE: Well, let's all hope it doesn't turn out to be Joan of Arc; think how embarrassing it would be if she persistently rode to hounds in shining armour.

MONICA: Look—look—she's coming to—

CYNTHIA: Don't tell her she's been in a trance *whatever* happens.

LADY W. (*drowsily*): What a dreadful smell of burning.

MONICA: Here, mother dear—sip some of this.

LADY W.: How can you, Monica, you know perfectly well I hate brandy; what are you all looking so frightened for?

MONICA: Well, mother—you see—you've just fainted and we—

LADY W. (*crossly*): Fainted! What nonsense—I've never fainted in my life—good gracious! One of my best cushions—who did this? (*She holds it up furiously.*)

REGGIE: I did—I think it saved your life.

LADY W.: Have you all taken leave of your senses? Where's my dinner?—I want my dinner.

CYNTHIA: It isn't quite time for it yet, mother dear.

REGGIE (*softly to* VIOLET): It's all right, she's only been possessed by a hearty appetite.

LADY W.: I want my dinner.

VIOLET: We're all going up to dress in a moment.

LADY W.: I must go out soon.

CYNTHIA: Go out? Why—where?

LADY W.: Don't all jump at me like that every time I say anything; surely there's nothing extraordinary in wanting to go out?

REV. BASSET: It would have been quite understandable this afternoon— but now it's simply pouring—really you never know where you are with the English climate—

LADY W. (*growls softly*): Grrrrr! Grrr!

REV. BASSET: I beg your pardon.

MONICA: What did you say, mother?

LADY W. (*ferociously*): Grrr—Grrr—Grrrrrr!!!

CYNTHIA: Good heavens—what's she doing?

> (LADY WARPLE *suddenly takes a flying leap from her chair and, growling and barking furiously, proceeds to career round the room on all fours— Everybody shrieks.* MONICA *makes an effort to stop her but is severely bitten for her pains.* CYNTHIA *and* VIOLET *jump on to the sofa and* REGGIE *takes refuge on the club fender.* MONICA, *weeping with pain and fright, clambers with her husband on to the writing-desk.* LADY WARPLE *with yaps and growls of delight seizes the remains of the cushion in her teeth and worries it round the room, occasionally sneezing playfully and tossing the feathers in the air.*)

REGGIE (*from the fender—soothingly*): Down, sir; down, sir, down!
(LADY WARPLE *crouches on the rug more or less quietly and
continues to tear the cushion with less ferocity but great
concentration.*)

CYNTHIA (*from the sofa*): It's a dog—a dog—mother's been possessed
by a dog.

REGGIE: Yes—and I *think* it must be a bull terrier.

MONICA (*furiously*): Surely this is no time to discuss the breed.

REGGIE: It's always better to be accurate—then we shall know what to
say to the authorities.

VIOLET (*in tears*): Authorities—authorities—you don't mean—? Oh,
this is horrible—horrible.

REGGIE: It's not the slightest use getting hysterical—we must keep
quite calm and think things out—she'll probably get dangerous
again when she's finished that cushion; perhaps we'd better ring
for a bone or something—

MONICA: Don't you dare—we must get her up to bed without the
servants knowing. (*Ingratiatingly to* LADY WARPLE.) Here then—
here then—good dog—good ole doggie—
(LADY WARPLE *snarls and shows her teeth.* REGGIE *jumps down
fearlessly from the fender, pats* LADY WARPLE's *head, and then
pats the seat of her armchair insinuatingly. With a little
snort she ambles across and jumps up into it, then with all
the family breathlessly watching she straightens out her legs
and settles herself into an ordinary human position with her
eyes closed.*)

REGGIE (*in a hoarse whisper to everybody*): For heaven's sake don't
mention the weather—that's what does the trick.

VIOLET: That's what the Ouija meant when it said, "What weather—
bow-wow!"

REGGIE: Exactly.

CYNTHIA: Oh, this is too frightful for words—poor, poor mother.

VIOLET: I wish it had been Charlotte Corday now, or even Lucrezia
Borgia—they were quiet!

REGGIE: Shhhh!!!
(LADY WARPLE *slowly opens her eyes and looks round absently.*)

LADY W.: Has any one seen my knitting?

QUICK CURTAIN

One week later.

(*When curtain rises,* MONICA, CYNTHIA, VIOLET, *the* REV. HAR-
OLD, *and* REGGIE WHISTLER *are all standing near the door back
centre—in rather strained, listening attitudes.*)

REGGIE: Unless she breaks out and does something violent he'll think
we've been lying.

VIOLET: Perhaps he hasn't mentioned the weather yet.

MONICA: Didn't you tell him to?

VIOLET: No, somehow I felt that it sounded so silly.

MONICA: My dear Violet, it's sheer stupidity to try to hide anything
from a doctor, specially a Psychoanalyst—he must know every
symptom if he is to cure her.

CYNTHIA: So far he's done nothing but question her about her childhood—I can't think why.

REV. BASSET: I believe it is in order to discover the roots of her com-
plexities—I've heard the subject discussed—very interesting indeed.

REGGIE: He seemed awfully upset when she answered the hoop question.

CYNTHIA: I didn't hear that—what did she say?

REGGIE: Well, apparently she was a year later than the average child
in bowling her first hoop—which made her correspondingly backward with her doll's perambulator.

VIOLET: Did he attach any awful significance to that?

REGGIE: He shook his head gravely and asked her if she'd ever broken
a slate at school.

MONICA: Yes, I heard him—I'm sure it's all rubbish.

REGGIE: Not at all—I believe in it all implicitly—of course it's bound
to take time—going through every small incident of her childhood
—these Psychoanalysts are marvellous—they always find something in the end.

CYNTHIA: She was possessed last Tuesday by that beastly dog, and
nothing will convince me to the contrary, whatever he says, it was
all our fault—she'll be wanting to go out sooner or later, and
think what will happen if any one comes up and says, "What a
fine day it is" or something—she'll fly at them and bite them.

REV. BASSET: Have you tried prayer?

CYNTHIA: Yes, and without the slightest effect.

VIOLET: What are we to do if he can't cure her?

REGGIE: Well, it depends if she gets better or worse—I should refrain from chaining her up in the yard for as long as possible.

MONICA: Shhh! Here comes the doctor!

> (*Enter* DOCTOR EVERARD TWICKENHAM, *the eminent Psychoanalyst—he has spectacles and a rather supercilious expression.*)

MONICA: Well?

DOCTOR: There is no cause for alarm.

REV. BASSET: God be praised.

DOCTOR (*breathing on his glasses and polishing them*): For a long while I delved unsuccessfully in the slightly complicated psychology of her childhood—then suddenly I hit—quite by accident —upon the root of the evil.

VIOLET: What was it?

DOCTOR (*complacently*): Your mother's nurse—I gather from her descriptions rather a gaunt woman—upon her fourth birthday, snatched from her hand a small woolly dog on a stand—recently given her by her Auntie Jessie—and in a moment of anger struck her sharply on the head with it. This thoughtless act in due course formed a complex in the child's mind, the active results of which you have all witnessed.

REGGIE: They were certainly active.

MONICA: Are you sure that that was the cause, Doctor Twickenham?

DOCTOR: Quite convinced of it, my dear Mrs. Basset.

VIOLET: I have a sort of confession to make, Doctor.

DOCTOR: Well, well, well, what is it?

VIOLET: I told you the story of the Ouija board and Queen Victoria and everything, but I omitted one fact—

DOCTOR: Yes?

VIOLET: You haven't seen mother during one of her attacks, have you?

DOCTOR: Unfortunately not—but it is of no vital consequence.

VIOLET: Well, I never told you the actual cause of her outbreaks.

DOCTOR (*testily*): Surely I mentioned that I've discovered the cause for myself.

VIOLET: But you haven't—I mean—you never discussed the weather with her at all, did you?

DOCTOR: No, but all this is beside the point.

VIOLET: It *isn't* beside the point—because the weather is what makes her bark.

DOCTOR (*smiling pityingly*): My dear Miss Warple—please forgive me —but really—it's too absurd.

REGGIE: It's the truth, Doctor.

DOCTOR (*severely*): Perhaps you will allow me to know best, young man. I have made a thorough examination and I'm perfectly satisfied that—providing you carry out my instructions—your charming hostess will be her normal self by this evening. It is all extremely simple, I have worked it out psychologically. The only thing required to cure her completely is a sudden shock, and what is more, a shock possessing some relation to her present mental condition.

MONICA: How do you mean, Doctor?

DOCTOR (*consulting his watch*): It is now nearly four-thirty—in a few moments tea will be brought in, will it not?

CYNTHIA: Yes.

DOCTOR: Excellent—that is by far the best time.

REGGIE: The best time for what?

DOCTOR: Control your impatience, young man, and attend carefully. Miss Warple, your mother—being unaware of the peculiar malady from which she is suffering—will come down to tea as usual—I too will be present and we will all talk and laugh in an ordinary manner. Suddenly I will blow my nose loudly like this—(*he does so*)—then, having claimed your undivided attention, I shall say "bow-wow" softly. At this signal you will instantly proceed to emulate the manners and habits of dogs, making as much noise as you can. The unexpected sound of everybody barking and growling will undoubtedly restore the old lady's mind to its normal condition, and the canine complex will—by sheer force of con- centrated suggestion—be completely exorcised.

CYNTHIA: Is that the only way?

DOCTOR: Absolutely.

MONICA: I suppose it wouldn't do if we got Rover in and hid him under mother's chair?

VIOLET: Rover's bark is beautifully piercing.

DOCTOR: That would not be sufficient—concerted effort is essential.

MONICA (*unhappily*): Very well—you'd better ring for tea at once, Reggie, and we'll get it over.

(*She goes out.* REGGIE *rings bell.*)

MONICA: Forgive our apparent lack of enthusiasm over your suggestion, Doctor—but we have all been in an exceedingly nervy state during the last week—what with trying to keep everybody off the subject of the weather, and trying to hide the truth from the servants—it's all been very, very uncomfortable.

CYNTHIA: Only this morning mother had an outbreak all by herself and disappeared—I think she must have been reading the forecast in the *Daily Mail.*

DOCTOR: Where did she go to?

CYNTHIA: We discovered her on one of the upper landings tearing the cook's bedroom slippers to pieces.

MONICA: That sort of thing is so dreadfully difficult to explain; of course we told cook it was Rover, but she looked awfully suspicious. She'll probably give notice soon.

REV. BASSET: And on Sunday evening we found out that—(*He whispers to the* DOCTOR.)

DOCTOR: What on earth did you do?

REV. BASSET: We said it was Rover!

(*Enter* BUTLER *with tea things, which he arranges round fire, and exits.*)

REGGIE: You won't say Bow-wow until I've had at least three hot cakes, will you, Doctor?

MONICA: Don't be so selfish, Reggie—you know we want to cure mother as soon as possible.

CYNTHIA: How long are we to go on being dogs?

DOCTOR: Until I shout Bow-wow a second time, then you must all run out of the room, and leave me alone with your mother.

MONICA: I do hope the Dermotts won't call—we should never hear the last of it.

(*Enter* LADY WARPLE *leaning on* VIOLET's *arm.*)

LADY W.: Ah, Doctor, I'm so glad you're staying—so far everyone refuses to tell me what is the matter with me—perhaps tea will make you a little less reticent on the subject; I know it can't be anything really serious because I feel so extraordinarily well.

MONICA: It's nothing to worry about in the least, mother dear—come and sit down.

(LADY WARPLE *is installed in her usual chair*—MONICA *proceeds to pour out the tea, while* REGGIE *hands round the cakes.*)

LADY W.: Hand me my knitting, will you, Violet dear—it's on the window seat.

VIOLET (*gives her knitting*): Here it is—you've nearly finished it.

LADY W.: It's been a terrible nuisance—I get so tired of these depressing sales of work.

DOCTOR: Have you always been a parish worker?

LADY W.: Now he's going to ask me some more embarrassing questions—I never know what to answer.

REGGIE (*with tea-cup*): Here's your tea, Doctor.

DOCTOR: Thank you so much.

LADY W.: As if I could possibly remember Burglar Bill.

CYNTHIA: Burglar Bill?

LADY W.: Yes, I recited it at my school concert when I was six.

DOCTOR: Never mind, we jogged your memory a bit, didn't we?

LADY W.: Only to the extent of my saying, "Wat's oo doing, Mr. Wobber." I'm sure that couldn't have conveyed anything to you.

DOCTOR (*jovially*): Ah well—I'll explain my methods at more length another time.

CYNTHIA (*softly, in answer to a whispered question from* VIOLET): No, I shall just whine—that's all.

LADY W.: What did you say, Cynthia dear?

CYNTHIA (*airily*): Nothing, mother—nothing particular—

REGGIE (*to the* DOCTOR *in a hoarse voice*): You can go ahead now, I've eaten four.

LADY W.: I wish you'd all stop whispering to one another—it's exceedingly irritating.

REGGIE: I'm sorry.

LADY W.: When I was eight and a half I can remember quite distinctly being sharply slapped for whispering.

DOCTOR: Ah!

LADY W. (*reminiscently*): I was in the schoolroom at the time— Elizabeth Spoopin had come to tea with me—fancy—her daughter had twins only last week, how time flies—

(*The* DOCTOR *with a look at every one blows his nose loudly.*)

LADY W. (*jumping*): My dear man, what a start you gave me.

DOCTOR (*austerely*): Bow-wow!

LADY W. (*astonished*): I *beg* your pardon.

> (*With a howl*, CYNTHIA *jumps on to the sofa, where she begins to scratch excitedly, whining loudly all the time.* MONICA *and the* REV. HAROLD *leap on to the hearthrug on all fours— yapping hideously, where they proceed to worry mythical bones.* REGGIE *with a loud bark chases* VIOLET *round the room on all fours, then he catches the hanging edge of the tablecloth in his teeth and pulls everything to the ground— then he and* VIOLET *nuzzle the cakes along the carpet with their noses. The concerted noise is deafening. The* DOCTOR *stands in the background with a watch in his hand.* LADY WARPLE *looks startled for a moment and then bursts out laughing.*)

LADY W. (*weakly*): Absurd creatures—how ridiculous you are!

> (*She proceeds with her knitting, laughing fondly. The family make renewed efforts to rouse her but with no success; at last the* DOCTOR *steps forward.*)

DOCTOR (*loudly*): Bow-wow!—(*Nobody hears him at first, so he has to bellow at the top of his voice.*) BOW-WOW!!

> (*The family all make a dive for the door—still yapping and barking and growling—leaving the* DOCTOR *and* LADY WARPLE *alone.*)

LADY W.: Have you ever known anything so ludicrous—really I'm surprised at Harold—the children have always loved practical jokes and booby traps, but he never seemed to have enough spirit for that sort of thing until today.

DOCTOR: Lady Warple—I want you—if you don't mind—to look straight into my eyes.

LADY W. (*putting down her knitting*): Must I?

DOCTOR: If you please.

LADY W. (*staring into his eyes*): Is that right?

DOCTOR: Thank you—yes—I am now perfectly satisfied you are now completely and absolutely cured.

LADY W.: I'm so glad, and I'm sure you've been awfully clever, but would you be so kind as to tell me what has been the matter with me?

DOCTOR: Just a slight nerve complex, that's all. You must go on being comparatively quiet and take as much fresh air as possible without overtiring yourself—luckily the cold snap is over and the weather has become delightfully mild again—

(*Before he has time to defend himself,* LADY WARPLE *with a fearful growl makes a spring at his throat—in a moment she gets him on to the ground and worries him like a rat—snarling ferociously. He gives one loud cry which brings all the others rushing into the room.* MONICA *with a shriek pulls* LADY WARPLE *off him, and* REGGIE *bends down and feels his heart. Then he gets up.*)

REGGIE (*shaking his head sadly*): He's quite quite dead! Now we shall have to destroy Rover!

CURTAIN

"Sagittarius"

"Sagittarius" has successfully kept his incognito, though I have heard it said that he is a woman. He, or she, contributes deft and witty verse to the New Statesman. *Most of his/her work deals with politics, and therefore soon becomes incomprehensible. But the date of the enclosed will explain it, I think.*

THE LION ROARS

(Endymion, bombed and sunk, Jan. 31, 1938.
Alcira, bombed and sunk, Feb. 4, 1938.)

General Franco's a sahib we know,
He gave us the Calpe Hunt
Where our Army johnnies can ride to hounds
In sight of the Spanish battlegrounds.
But when Franco's bombers get out of bounds
Our language is pretty blunt.

General Franco safeguards our trade,
He's the friend to British firms.
Back in Bilbao our fleet stood by,
But if his pirates again let fly
The British Government will reply
In no uncertain terms.

He had rotten bad luck at Teruel,
(Though he's got the scrap in hand)
But our Government's not afraid to state
The sinking of British ships and freight
Is something we will not tolerate
And are not prepared to stand.

The Nyon Patrol is wide awake
Round Spain's blockaded shore,
And if merchant vessels are seen attacked
It will rank as a most unfriendly act,
And General Franco will know in fact
Just what he is asking for.

General Franco's a sahib right through
And the great white hope of Spain;
But we warn him here, if he won't play ball,
Our Tokyo Note he had best recall,
And he'd better not do it again, that's all,
He'd better not do it again.

Jan Struther

One kind of humor may be classified as Proustian. It enlarges an experience nine diameters; it reveals in the experience many organisms invisible to the average naked eye. It does not depend on incongruity or the ridiculous; it depends on a recognition of concealed meanings. Women do this sort of humor best, and no one does it better than Jan Struther.

THE EVE OF THE SHOOT

Every year without fail Mrs. Miniver received an invitation written in a sloping Victorian hand on lavishly stout cream-laid. The right-hand top corner was embossed in heavy black Gothic with the address "Chervil Court, Crampton." On the left were three tiny formalised sketches—a telegraph-pole, an upright telephone, and a railway engine of the Stephenson period, stocky and high-funnelled—followed respectively by the words, "Great Yettingford," "Buntisley 3," and "Slape Junction." The letter began with old Lady Chervil's unvarying formula:

My dear Mrs. Miniver,
    Chervil and I shall be delighted if you and your husband will stay with us from Friday 19th to Monday 22nd November.

(She would have gone to the guillotine sooner than use the expression "week-end.")
    Mrs. Miniver tossed the letter over to Clem. There must, he remarked, be an air-port near there by now, and sketched in under the other pictures a little pre-War biplane, single-engined and very short in the wing, followed by the words, "Market Bumbleton." There was no need for them to discuss whether they were going to accept the invitation. They always went to Chervil. The shooting was excellent, the food beyond praise; and it was soothing, for a short time, to slow oneself down to the pace of its old-fashioned ritual, and to spend three days in inverted commas.

723

"And what," said the Colonel, turning to Mrs. Miniver at dinner on the night of their arrival, "is your opinion ... ?"

She had been afraid of this ever since, over the *vol-au-vent,* that woman in the wrong shade of green, on being asked whether she was coming out with the guns tomorrow, had shut her eyes and ever so delicately shuddered: thus plunging everybody around her into what was bound in that company to be a tedious and unprofitable discussion. Tedious because neither side possessed any currency but clichés, and unprofitable because it was clear from the outset that neither side was going to budge an inch. Besides, what a hare to start at a shooting-party! You might with as much sense and propriety get up at a Lord Mayor's banquet and give a harangue on vegetarianism. If you felt as strongly as that, the only thing to do was to have 'flu and stay away.

It raged, if such a stale controversy could be said to rage, all through the quail, the ice-pudding, and the mushrooms on toast. Well-worn coins rang in Mrs. Miniver's ears. "After all, the birds get a sportin' chance...." "Animals may not have *souls,* but still ..." "Now take huntin'..." "Oh, *bull*-fightin'—that's *quite* a different kettle of fish. ..." Italics bred italics. Dropped g's fell as thick as confetti. Sooner or later the tide of argument was almost certain to reach her end of the table, but she made up her mind that she would not be drawn in. She had been through it all too many times before, and even in circles where one could speak freely the subject had become too hackneyed to be borne. Her own attitude, she knew, was unethical but honest. She did not happen to be personally squeamish, which was merely a matter of chance. She enjoyed any display of skill; she enjoyed bare trees, rimy pastures, breath made visible by frost, the smell of dead leaves, and the intricate detail of winter hedgerows; above all, she enjoyed that element of woodcraft, that sense of "playing Indians," which games fail to supply and which the detractors of hunting, shooting, and fishing so often mistake for bloodlust. And although she admitted that all shooting was cruel and that all cruelty was wrong, it seemed to her that to abolish shooting before you had abolished war was like flicking a speck of mud off the top of a midden.

For the moment the conversation on either side of her had flowed away, leaving her on a blessed little island of peace and silence. She had time to study the heraldic beauty of the pineapple (for they had now reached dessert), to speculate on the second footman's private life (he had a studious, enigmatic face and probably read philosophy), and to reflect how unpleasing, musically, is the sound of a pack of upper-class English voices in full cry.

Lady Chervil, however, was a watchful and tidy-minded hostess of the old school, who regarded a dinner-party as a quadrille and disapproved of islands. With a masterly verbal tweak she readjusted the guests who had got out of step. "And what," said the Colonel, turning to Mrs. Miniver, "is *your* opinion of all these blood sports?"

"I think they are indefensible, but irresistible," she answered. She had found through long experience that this remark usually closed the subject pretty quickly. It left very little to be said. Besides, she meant it.

"Ha!" said the Colonel. She noted with delight that he really did say "Ha!" This made a valuable addition to her collection. She had lately acquired a "Humph!" and two "Whews!" but she was still waiting in vain for a "Pshaw!"

"Tell me," she said, "weren't you with an uncle of mine in Singapore—Torquil Piggot?"

"Piggy!" exclaimed the Colonel, beaming gratefully, and plunged into reminiscence. Thank God for colonels, thought Mrs. Miniver; sweet creatures, so easily entertained, so biddably diverted from senseless controversy into comfortable monologue: there was nothing in the world so restful as a really good English colonel. She nailed her smile to the mast and reverted to the pineapple and the second footman. Clem caught her eye across the table. It seemed to her sometimes that the most important thing about marriage was not a home or children or a remedy against sin, but simply there being always an eye to catch.

———

CHRISTMAS SHOPPING

One of the minor arts of life, thought Mrs. Miniver at the end of a long day's Christmas shopping, was the conservation of energy in the matter of swing doors. With patience and skilful timing it was very seldom necessary to use your strength on them. You could nearly always follow close behind some masterful person who had already done the pushing; and if you were too late for that and the door had begun to swing towards you, then it was well worth pausing for a second until it swung away again and needed only a gentle encouragement. This seemed obvious enough; but there was an astounding number of people who seemed to glory in taking the line of most resistance, hurling themselves against an approaching door and reversing its direction by brute force, as though there were virtue in the act. They must lead, she reflected, very uncomfortable lives.

Placing herself neatly in the wake of a bull-necked woman in tweeds, she slipped out of the shop. There was a raw wind; sleety rain was beginning to fall, blurring the lamplight; the pavements were seal-sleek; it was settling down into one of those nasty wet evenings which the exiled Londoner longs for with a quite unbearable nostalgia.

She tumbled all her parcels into the back of the car, slid, happy but exhausted, into the driving-seat, and set off for home. The double screen-wiper wagged companionably, uttering over and over again the same faint wheedling word, which she could never quite make out. It was a dissyllable, something like "receive" or "bequeath." She was glad, at any rate, that they now had a screen-wiper which moved at a constant speed. Their last had been one of those which work off the induction: lively and loquacious when you are at a standstill, sulky and slow as soon as you get going and really need its help—like the very worst type of human being.

She felt a little guilty: it was the first time she had caught herself comparing the beloved old car unfavourably in any way with the usurping new one.

Getting home was evidently going to be a long job. The usual six o'clock home-going stream was in spate with Christmas crowds, and Oxford Street was a solid jam. It was her own fault, she had to admit, as she sat back and waited for the lights to change. Every year the same thing happened. At the beginning of November she made up her mind that this time, for once, she would get her Christmas shopping done early. She went as far as writing out a list—and there, for several weeks, the matter rested. At intervals she tried to pretend that Christmas Day fell on the fifth of December, or, alternatively, that all her friends and relations lived in South Africa and that she had to catch an early mail; but it was no use. The feeling of temporal urgency cannot be artificially produced, any more than the feeling of financial distress. The rich young man who determines to work his way round the world may gain many things, but the experience of poverty is not one of them. He knows that in the ultimate emergency he can always cable home for funds; and Mrs. Miniver knew perfectly well that Christmas was not until the twenty-fifth of December, and that all the people on her list lived in England.

(The screen-wiper wagged steadily. "Sea-green ... sea-green ..." Perhaps that was nearer the mark?)

Besides, successful present-choosing depends very largely upon the right atmospere, upon the contagious zest of crowds, upon sudden inspirations and perceptions, heightened rather than otherwise by a certain sense of pressure in space and time. To do it cold-bloodedly, in a half-empty shop, without any difficulty or competition, is as joyless as a *mariage de convenance.* So perhaps it was just as well, she told herself consolingly, that she had, as usual, left it till the middle of December.

("Wee Free ... Wee Free ..." Warmer. She'd get it yet.)

The lights changed. She put the car into bottom gear, paused, then let in the clutch. It occurred to her as she did so that it was not only people's physical reactions to those three colours that had become automatic but their mental ones as well. Red, yellow, green—frustration, hope, joy: a brand-new conditioned reflex. Give it a few more years to get established, and psychiatrists would be using coloured rays, projected in that sequence, for the treatment of melancholia; and to future generations green would no longer suggest envy, but freedom. In such haphazard ways are symbolisms born and reborn.

At the next crossing, red again. Frustration—but somehow one accepted it without resentment, simply because it was not imposed by a human hand. One could be annoyed with a policeman, but not with a tin hollyhock. The same was true of automatic telephones: ever since the dialling system had come in, the world's output of irritation must have been halved. It was an argument for the mechanisation of life which had not previously struck her.

She got home at last. Clem was already in, with his legs stretched out in front of the fire.

"Successful?" he asked, seeing her festooned with parcels.

"Look here," she said, "that screen-wiper—I *think* what it says is 'Beef Tea.'"

"My goodness," said Clem. "I believe you're right."

[From *Mrs. Miniver*]

John Collier

THE FROG PRINCE

Two young men were discussing life. Said the richer of them to the poorer, "Paul, you had better marry my sister."

"That is a very strange thing to say," said Paul, "considering I have told you all about my debts."

"I am not worldly," replied Henry Vanhomry. "I should prefer my sister to marry a clean, decent, and kindly fellow like yourself, than some rich but blasé roué, cynic, near-man, sub-man, or half-man."

"I am certainly not blasé," said Paul. "On the other hand, I had not the pleasure of meeting your family when I was in Boston."

"I am very fond of my sister," said Henry, "in a way."

"How delightful! No doubt she was a mother to you when you were small. A little mother!"

"No. No. She is ten years younger than I am, only twenty-eight, in fact."

"Aha! She would have come into her fortune just in the rockiest year of our financial history."

"Fortunately it is well invested, and yields her an income of forty thousand dollars."

"An objection occurs to me. We are men of the world, Henry. If we were of the other sex, we might also make mistakes. Fond as I am of children—"

"That would be a matter entirely for you to decide."

"Henry, your sister sounds charming. Tell me more about her. She is not by any chance a *teeny* little woman?" And Paul held his hand some thirty inches from the floor.

"Quite the reverse."

"*Quite* the reverse, eh?"

"My dear Paul, I do not mean that she is six feet four."

"Six feet three, perhaps?"

"And a half. But perhaps I should tell you she is rather plump. Disproportionately so, in fact."

"Upon my word! I hope she is good-tempered."

"Angelically. You should hear her petting her dolls."

"Pardon me, Henry, but is she at all—backward?"

"A matter of opinion. She reads and writes admirably."

"How delightful. We could correspond, if I happened to be away."

"I will be frank with you, Paul: her letters to famous boxers are quite amazingly expressive, though by no means perfect in orthography."

"Henry, she is capable of hero worship; she has an affectionate nature."

"Almost embarrassingly so. It appears from these letters of hers, which we censor, that she would make a devoted wife. However, my family are old-fashioned, and the boxers are cowardly brutes. I should like to see her married."

"But, as yet, if I understand you, she is pure as the driven snow? Charming!"

"Hers has been a cloistered girlhood. Yet there is something romantic in her nature which causes me alarm. Supposing one of the boxers responded. He might not treat her politely."

"I, on the other hand, would write her the most devoted letters, and bow, with old-world courtesy, whenever we met. Hm! All I fear, to be perfectly candid, is that a certain confounded coldness, a defect of my nature, might be a cause of pain, dissatisfaction, or longing."

"Well, my dear Paul, that is hardly a matter for me to speculate upon. I can only remind you that faint heart never won fair lady."

"Very well, Henry. I will at least come with you and see your sister."

"I am afraid I cannot accompany you. You forget that I am off to Europe next week. However, I'll give you a letter of introduction to the family."

All this being arranged, our good Paul took leave of his friend, and after walking about for a little with an air of distraction, he paid a visit to the apartment of another friend of his.

"My dear Olga," he said, after a time, "I'm afraid I have some very ridiculous news for you. I am going to be poor no longer."

"Tell me only one thing, Paul. Is she beautiful?"

"Not very, it seems. I have not seen her, but she is over six feet three, and disproportionately fat."

"My poor Paul! She is simply bound to have hair on her face. What will become of you?"

"Besides all this, she is not very bright, I hear."

"And, now I come to think of it, what will become of me?"

"She has forty thousand a year, my dear Olga."

"Paul, we women are given to incredible follies when we are jealous. I might refuse everything. I find myself capable of jealousy."

"But, on the other hand, are you, or am I, capable of living any longer without a little of that forty thousand a year?"

"Or some other."

"But what other, my dear Olga? Where is another forty thousand?"

"It is true, Paul. Am I right in believing that your gigantic bride-to-be is mentally nine years, or is it twelve years, old?"

"Seven, I should think, by all that Henry told me of her. She has an exuberant innocence. She writes to boxers, but caresses dolls."

"Really? That is very interesting. Dolls are so featureless. Now, is there any great hurry, Paul? I have still that bracelet you found at Palm Beach. It would provide us with a few last weeks together."

"I was going to suggest, as a matter of fact, that it should be my present to the bride, for I like to do things in good style. However, something may turn up. I admit that I love you."

"You shall promise me not to go near Boston for at least a month. I shall be busy, I have decided to wear my hair short, but at least we shall meet at week-ends. In between, you may say farewell to all your bachelor life."

"Yes, that is true, Olga. I shall have to do that, I suppose."

Everything being agreed, this young couple spent the next month or so as Olga had suggested, and at the end of it, she saw him off to Boston, with a restraint that he found almost too admirable.

He arrived at Boston, presented his letter of introduction, and was very well received by old Mrs. Vanhomry.

They got on admirably. "You are still a bachelor?" she asked.

"I cannot," he replied, "bring myself to regard the modern girl as a true mate. Those clipped locks, that flat masculine figure, that hardness, that ultra-sophistication! Where are the curves, the innocence, the warmheartedness of yesteryear? But why am I telling you all this—?"

"You would have liked our dear Ethel. Such a big, healthy, affectionate, old-fashioned girl! You must meet her, and her fiancé. Perhaps you will come to the wedding?"

"Nothing could be more delightful. Unfortunately, I have to return to New York almost immediately."

On his return, Paul called at once on Olga, but found that her flat was locked up. She had left no address; you may depend he sought her everywhere.

He saw in the papers an account of the wedding of Miss Vanhomry to a Mr. Colefax: it appeared that the happy pair were on their way to the Ritz-Carlton.

"I really must go and sit in the lobby," said he, "and console myself with a peep at the disadvantages attached to that forty thousand a year."

Very well, he sat in the lobby. Before very long, he saw the enormous form of what was evidently the happy bride crossing from the elevator.

"Upon my word!" he thought. "There is a great deal to be said for the simple life after all. One at least preserves one's individuality."

He peered about for the husband. At last he saw a sensitive face in the neighbourhood of the bride's hips. "That must be the husband," he said. "Very charming! Very charming indeed! But surely I have seen him before."

In order to make sure, he edged closer, and was amazed to find that this husband was none other than his own Olga, in male attire.

He at once applied for a private interview. "My dear Olga, this is a very pretty trick you have played on me. And what can your bride— soi-disant—think of it all?"

"You must regard the matter rationally, my dear Paul."

"I am so afraid there may be a scandal. You have no idea what spiteful tongues might make of it."

"You underestimate the innocence of my wife, whose dolls, as I suspected, were very ordinary dolls. And you must admit, Paul, that if either of us is to be in this position, I at least offer less grounds for jealousy. You had better be my secretary."

Paul submitted with a good grace, and for a long time enjoyed his occupation very tolerably. Fortunately, Henry Vanhomry remained in Europe.

On one occasion there was a dinner party at the Colefax home, and a few of the male guests, with Paul the friendly secretary, and dapper little Mr. Colefax, remained smoking together long after the gigantic bride had retired to bed. The conversation turned on women, a subject which the so-called Mr. Colefax enjoyed more than his secretary. They talked of attractions.

"My wife," said this charming impostor, "is disarmingly simple: why try to disguise it? Nevertheless, she has an amazing personality buried, as it were, beneath her *naïveté*. I am convinced it is there, I sense it, and yet I could hardly find an example to describe. How do you account for that?"

"It is very simple, my dear Colefax," said a very eminent doctor. "Your wife, if I may say so, owes her adorable simplicity, as she does her admirably robust physique, to a little glandular maladjustment, which (always supposing you should desire what professionally we should regard as an improvement) could easily be put right. Who knows what she is like underneath?"

"It would certainly be interesting to find out," said her false husband, intrigued.

"She might be slim, vivacious, a positive butterfly," continued the doctor.

"It would be like carving out ambergris from a whale," observed a well-known adventurer who was present.

"Or opening a neolithic barrow," added an eminent archaeologist.

"Or undressing an Eskimo girl at Christmas," put in a notorious Don Juan.

"You might find more than you bargain for," observed Paul, overcome by an inexplicable foreboding.

He spoke too late. Everyone was desperately keen on the experiment.

"You must bring your dear wife to a little home that I have in Paris," said the doctor, "where I have every facility for the treatment."

"We shall come at once. You, Paul, had better remain behind, to deal with everything we shall have to leave unsettled."

Paul, therefore, was left. Ethel and her spouse went on the next boat to Paris, accompanied by the doctor, and, as a matter of fact, by the adventurer, the archaeologist, and the Don Juan as well.

My Dear Paul,

You will be amazed at the result of our experiment, and possibly a little disconcerted, though you were always a connoisseur of poetic

*justice. Under the treatment Ethel has lost no less than a hundred
pounds. The removal of this prodigious quantity of blubber has left
her exposed as a lean, agile, witty, and very handsome man. "How
absurd that I should have been called Ethel so long!" he observed to
me when first he was apprised of this transformation. In order to put
him at his ease, I replied at once, "No more absurd than that I should
have been called your husband." After all, the cat was, so to speak,
out of the bag, and there was nothing else to do.*

*He took it extremely well, saying with a smile, "We must make the
punishment fit the crime." On my part, I was not long in promising
never to deceive him again.*

*We are remaining on this side to avoid gossip, for the situation has a
ludicrous side which we might find painful. But not nearly so ludicrous or painful, my dear Paul, as it might have proved, in all the circumstances, had you had your original wish.*

Once more,

OLGA

NIGHT! YOUTH! PARIS! AND THE MOON!

Annoyed with the world, I took a large studio in Hampstead. Here I
resolved to live in utter aloofness, until the world should approach me
on its knees, whining its apologies.

The studio was large and high: so was the rent. Fortunately my suit
was strongly made, and I had a tireless appetite for herrings. I lived
here happily and frugally, pleased with the vast and shadowy room,
and with the absurd little musicians' gallery, on which, however, I set
my gramophone a-playing. I approved also of the little kitchen, the
bathroom, the tiny garden, and even the damp path, sad with ever-
greens, that led to the street beyond. I saw no one. My mood was that
of a small bomb, but one which had no immediate intention of going
off.

Although I had no immediate intention of going off, I was unable
to resist buying a large trunk, which I saw standing outside a junk-
shop. I was attracted by its old-fashioned appearance, for I myself
hoped to become old-fashioned: by its size, because I am rather small,

by its curved lid, for I was always fond of curves, and most of all by a remark on the part of the dealer, who stood picking his nose in the disillusioned doorway of his shop. "A thing like that," said he, "is always useful."

I paid four pounds, and had the large black incubus taken to my studio on a hand-barrow. There I stood it on the little gallery, which, for no reason, ran along the farther end.

Now I had no money left; I felt it necessary to sublet my studio. This was a wrench. I telephoned the agents; soon they arranged to bring a client of theirs, one Stewart Musgrave, to inspect my harmless refuge. I agreed, with some reserve. "I propose to absent myself during this inspection. You will find the key in the door. Later you can inform me if my studio is taken."

Later they informed me that my studio was taken. "I will leave," I said, "at four o'clock on Friday. The interloper can come at four-thirty. He will find the key in the door."

Just before four on Friday, I found myself confronted with a problem. On letting one's studio, one locks one's clothes in a press reserved for the purpose. This I did, but was then nude. One has to pack one's trunk: I had nothing to put in it. I had bidden the world farewell: here was my studio—sublet—there was the world. For practical purposes there is very little else anywhere.

The hour struck. I cut the Gordian knot, crossed the Rubicon, burned my boats, opened my trunk, and climbed inside. At four-thirty the interloper arrived. With bated breath I looked out through my little air-and-peep-hole. This was a surprise. I had bargained for a young man of no personal attractions. Stewart Musgrave was a young woman of many.

She had a good look around, pulled out every drawer, peeped into every corner. She bounced herself on the big divan-bed. She even came up onto the little useless gallery, leaned over, recited a line or two of Juliet, and then she approached my modest retreat. "I won't open you," she said. "There might be a body in you." I thought this showed a fine instinct. Her complexion was divine.

There is a great deal of interest in watching a lovely young girl, who imagines herself to be alone in a large studio. One never knows what she will do next. Often, when living there alone, I had not known what I would do next. But then I was alone. She thought she was alone, too, but I knew better. This gave me a sense of mastery, power.

On the other hand, I soon loved her to distraction. The hell of it was, I had a shrewd suspicion she did not love me. How could she?

At night, while she slept in an appealing attitude, I crept downstairs, and into the kitchen, where I cleaned up the crockery, her shoes, and some chicken I found in the ice-box. "There is," she said to a friend, "a pixie in this studio." "Leave out some milk," said her friend.

Everything went swimmingly. Nothing could have been more delicate than the unspoken love that grew up between the disillusioned world-weary poet, and the beautiful young girl-artist, so fresh, so natural, and so utterly devoid of self-consciousness.

On one occasion, I must admit, I tripped over the corner of a rug. "Who is there?" she cried, waking suddenly from a dream of having her etchings lovingly appraised by a connoisseur.

"A mouse," I telepathed squeakingly, standing very still. She sank into sleep again.

She was more rudely put to sleep some days later. She came in, after being absent most of the evening, accompanied by a man to whom I took an immediate dislike. My instinct never fails me: he had not been in the studio half an hour before he gave her occasion to say, "Pray don't!"

"Yes," said he.

"No," said she.

"I must," said he.

"You mustn't," said she.

"I will," said he.

"You won't," said she.

A vestige of refined feeling would have assured him that there was no possibility of happiness between people so at variance on every point. There should at least be some zone of enthusiastic agreement between every couple: for example, the milk. But whatever his feelings were, they were not refined.

"Why did you bring me here?" said he with a sneer.

"To see my etchings," she replied, biting her lip.

"Well, then—"

"I thought you were a customer."

"I am. A tough customer." With that he struck her on the temple. She fell, mute, inanimate, crumpled.

"Damn it!" said he. "I've killed her. I've done her in. I shall swing. Unless—I escape."

I was forced to admire the cold logic of it. It was, momentarily, the poet's unreasoning prostration before the man of action, the worldling.

Quickly he undressed her. "Gosh!" he said. "What a pity I hit so hard!" He flung her over his shoulder, retaining her legs in his grasp. He bore her up the stairs, onto the shadowy balcony. He opened the trunk and thrust her inside. "Here is a fine thing!" I thought. "Here she is, in her condition, alone with me, in my condition. If she knew she was dead she'd be glad." The thought was bitter.

With the dawn he went for a taxi. The driver came in with him; together they bore the trunk to the vehicle waiting outside.

"Strewth, it's heavy!" said the driver. "What yer got in it?"

"Books," said the murderer, with the utmost calm.

If I had thought of saying, *"Paradise Lost,* in two volumes," I should have said it, then and there, and this story would have come to an end. As it was, we were hoisted on to the cab, which drove off in the direction of Victoria.

A jet of cool night air flowed through the air-hole. She, whom I had mourned as dead, inhaled it, and breathed a sigh. Soon she was fully conscious.

"Who are you?" she asked in alarm.

"My name," I said tactfully, "is Emily."

She said, "You are kidding me."

I said, "What is your name?"

She said, "Stewart."

I could not resist the reply, "Then I am Flora MacDonald."

Thus by easy stages I approached the ticklish question of my hitherto hopeless love.

She said, "I would rather die."

I said, "In a sense you have died already. Besides, I am your pixie. Or it may be only a dream, and you could hardly blame yourself for that. Anyway, I expect he will take us to Paris."

"It is true," she said, "that I have always dreamed of a honeymoon in Paris."

"The Paris moon!" I said. "The bookstalls on the *quais.* The little restaurants on the Left Bank!"

"The *Cirque Medrano!"* she cried.

"L'Opéra!"

"Le Louvre! Le Petit Palais!"

"Le Bœuf sur le Toit!"

"Darling," she cried, "if it were not so dark, I would show you my etchings, if I had them with me."

We were in absolute raptures; we heard the ticket being taken for Paris. We were registered; it was next door to being married, and we laughed at the rolling of the vessel. Soon, however, we were carried up an endless flight of stairs.

"*Mon Dieu! Mais c'est lourd!*" gasped the hotel porter. "*Qu'est-ce que c'est—dans la malle?*"

"*Des livres,*" said the murderer, with the utmost sang-froid.

"*Paradis Retrouvé, une édition complète,*" I whispered, and was rewarded with a kiss.

Alone, as he thought, with his lifeless victim, the murderer sneered. "H'ya keeping?" said he coarsely, as he approached the trunk.

He lifted the lid a little, and thrust his head within. A rim ran round inside; while yet he blinked, we seized it, and brought the lid down with a crash.

"*La guillotine!*" I said cuttingly.

"*La Defarge!*" observed my adored one, knitting her brows.

"*Vive la France!*"

We stepped out; we put him inside. I retained his clothes. With a sheet from the bed, the bell rope, and a strip of carpet from before the washstand, she made a fetching Arab lass. Together we slipped out into the street.

Night! Youth! Paris! And the moon!

Roy Campbell

HOME THOUGHTS IN BLOOMSBURY

Of all the clever people round me here
I most delight in Me—
Mine is the only voice I care to hear,
And mine the only face I like to see.

ON SOME SOUTH AFRICAN NOVELISTS

You praise the firm restraint with which they write—
I'm with you there, of course:
They use the snaffle and the curb all right,
But where's the bloody horse?

Stella Gibbons

Cold Comfort Farm *is not a parody; it is a burlesque of a whole type of dank novel of the soil.* Gobbets *of* Wuthering Heights *and of the work of Mary Webb, Sheila Kaye-Smith, T. F. Powys, and others, have been put in a large earthen crock with a noisome sort of yeast and allowed to ferment. The result is called* Cold Comfort Farm.

One curious thing about Cold Comfort Farm *is that, while it begins in the mood of burlesque, its characters gradually capture its author, and the story ends almost in the manner of realism. The result is strangely fascinating.*

MORNING IN COLD COMFORT FARM

[EDITOR's NOTE: Miss Gibbons has adopted the method of Herr Baedeker, and has marked her finer passages with one, two, or three stars.]

** Dawn crept over the Downs like a sinister white animal, followed by the snarling cries of a wind eating its way between the black boughs of the thorns. The wind was the furious voice of this sluggish animal light that was baring the dormers and mullions and scullions of Cold Comfort Farm.

The farm was crouched on a bleak hillside, whence its fields, fanged with flints, dropped steeply to the village of Howling a mile away. Its stables and outhouses were built in the shape of a rough octangle surrounding the farmhouse itself, which was built in the shape of a rough triangle. The left point of the triangle abutted on the farthest point of the octangle, which was formed by the cowsheds, which lay parallel with the big barn. The outhouses were built of rough-cast stone, with thatched roofs, while the farm itself was built partly of local flint, set in cement, and partly of some stone brought at great trouble and enormous personal expense from Perthshire.

The farmhouse was a long, low building, two-storied in parts. Other

739

parts of it were three-storied. Edward the Sixth had originally owned
it in the form of a shed in which he housed his swineherds, but he
had grown tired of it, and had had it rebuilt in Sussex clay. Then he
pulled it down. Elizabeth had rebuilt it, with a good many chimneys
in one way and another. The Charleses had let it alone; but William
and Mary had pulled it down again, and George the First had rebuilt
it. George the Second, however, burned it down. George the Third
added another wing. George the Fourth pulled it down again.

By the time England began to develop that magnificent blossoming
of trade and imperial expansion which fell to her lot under Victoria,
there was not much of the original building left, save the tradition
that it had always been there. It crouched, like a beast about to spring,
under the bulk of Mockuncle Hill. Like ghosts embedded in brick and
stone, the architectural variations of each period through which it had
passed were mute history. It was known locally as "The King's
Whim."

The front door of the farm faced a perfectly inaccessible ploughed
field at the back of the house; it had been the whim of Red Raleigh
Starkadder, in 1835, to have it so; and so the family always used to
come in by the back door, which abutted on the general yard facing
the cowsheds. A long corridor ran halfway through the house on the
second storey and then stopped. One could not get into the attics at
all. It was all very awkward.

... Growing with the viscous light that was invading the sky, there
came the solemn, tortured-snake voice of the sea, two miles away,
falling in sharp folds upon the mirror-expanses of the beach.

Under the ominous bowl of the sky a man was ploughing the sloping field immediately below the farm, where the flints shone bone-
sharp and white in the growing light. The ice-cascade of the wind
leaped over him, as he guided the plough over the flinty runnels. Now
and again he called roughly to his team:

"Upidee, Travail! Ho, there, Arsenic! Jug-jug!" But for the most
part he worked in silence, and silent were his team. The light showed
no more of his face than a grey expanse of flesh, expressionless as the
land he ploughed, from which looked out two sluggish eyes.

Every now and again, when he came to the corner of the field and
was forced to tilt the scranlet of his plough almost onto its axle to
make the turn, he glanced up at the farm where it squatted on the
gaunt shoulder of the hill, and something like a possessive gleam

shone in his dull eyes. But he only turned his team again, watching the crooked passage of the scranlet through the yeasty earth, and muttered: "Hola, Arsenic! Belay there, Travail!" while the bitter light wanned into full day.

Because of the peculiar formation of the outhouses surrounding the farm, the light was always longer in reaching the yard than the rest of the house. Long after the sunlight was shining through the cobwebs on the uppermost windows of the old house the yard was in damp blue shadow.

It was in shadow now, but sharp gleams sprang from the ranged milk-buckets along the ford-piece outside the cowshed.

Leaving the house by the back door, you came up sharply against a stone wall running right across the yard, and turning abruptly, at right angles, just before it reached the shed where the bull was housed, and running down to the gate leading out into the ragged garden where mallows, dog's-body and wild turnip were running riot. The bull's shed abutted upon the right corner of the dairy, which faced the cowsheds. The cowsheds faced the house, but the back door faced the bull's shed. From here a long-roofed barn extended the whole length of the octangle until it reached the front door of the house. Here it took a quick turn, and ended. The dairy was awkwardly placed; it had been a thorn in the side of Old Fig Starkadder, the last owner of the farm, who had died three years ago. The dairy overlooked the front door, in face of the extreme point of the triangle which formed the ancient buildings of the farmhouse.

From the dairy a wall extended which formed the right-hand boundary of the octangle, joining the bull's shed and the pig-pens at the extreme end of the right point of the triangle. A staircase, put in to make it more difficult, ran parallel with the octangle, halfway round the yard, against the wall which led down to the garden gate.

The spurt and regular ping! of milk against metal came from the reeking interior of the sheds. The bucket was pressed between Adam Lambsbreath's knees, and his head was pressed deep into the flank of Feckless, the big Jersey. His gnarled hands mechanically stroked the teat, while a low crooning, mindless as the Down wind itself, came from his lips.

He was asleep. He had been awake all night, wandering in thought over the indifferent bare shoulders of the Downs after his wild bird, his little flower....

Elfine. The name, unspoken but sharply musical as a glittering bead shaken from a fountain's tossing necklace, hovered audibly in the rancid air of the shed.

The beasts stood with heads lowered dejectedly against the wooden hoot-pieces of their stalls. Graceless, Pointless, Feckless and Aimless awaited their turn to be milked. Sometimes Aimless ran her dry tongue, with a rasping sound sharp as a file through silk, awkwardly across the bony flank of Feckless, which was still moist with the rain that had fallen upon it through the roof during the night, or Pointless turned her large dull eyes sideways as she swung her head upwards to tear down a mouthful of cobwebs from the wooden runnet above her head. A lowering, moist, steamy light, almost like that which gleams below the eyelids of a man in a fever, filled the cowshed.

Suddenly a tortured bellow, a blaring welter of sound that shattered the quiescence of the morning, tore its way across the yard, and died away in a croak that was almost a sob. It was Big Business, the Bull, wakening to another day, in the clammy darkness of his cell.

The sound woke Adam. He lifted his head from the flank of Feckless and looked around him in bewilderment for a moment; then slowly his eyes, which looked small and wet and lifeless in his primitive face, lost their terror as he realised that he was in the cowshed, that it was half-past six on a winter morning, and that his gnarled fingers were about the task which they had performed at this hour and in this place for the past eighty years and more.

He stood up, sighing, and crossed over to Pointless, who was eating Graceless's tail. Adam, who was linked to all dumb brutes by a chain forged in soil and sweat, took it out of her mouth and put into it, instead, his neckerchief—the last he had. She mumbled it, while he milked her, but stealthily spat it out so soon as he passed on to Aimless, and concealed it under the reeking straw with her hoof. She did not want to hurt the old man's feelings by declining to eat his gift. There was a close bond: a slow, deep, primitive, silent down-dragging link between Adam and all living beasts; they knew each other's simple needs. They lay close to the earth, and something of earth's old fierce simplicities had seeped into their beings.

Suddenly a shadow fell athwart the wooden stanchions of the door. It was no more than a darkening of the pallid paws of the day which were now embracing the shed, but all the cows instinctively stiffened, and Adam's eyes, as he stood up to face the newcomer, were again piteously full of twisted fear.

"Adam," uttered the woman who stood in the doorway, "how many pails of milk will there be this morning?"

"I dunnamany," responded Adam, cringingly; "'tes hard to tell. If so be as our Pointless has got over her indigestion, maybe 'twill be four. If so be as she hain't, maybe three."

Judith Starkadder made an impatient movement. Her large hands had a quality which made them seem to sketch vast horizons with their slightest gesture. She looked a woman without boundaries as she stood wrapped in a crimson shawl to protect her bitter, magnificent shoulders from the splintery cold of the early air. She seemed fitted for any stage, however enormous.

"Well, get as many buckets as you can," she said, lifelessly, half-turning away. "Mrs. Starkadder questioned me about the milk yesterday. She has been comparing our output with that from other farms in the district, and she says we are five-sixteenths of a bucket below what our rate should be, considering how many cows we have."

A strange film passed over Adam's eyes, giving him the lifeless primeval look that a lizard has, basking in the swooning Southern heat. But he said nothing.

"And another thing," continued Judith, "you will probably have to drive down into Beershorn tonight to meet a train. Robert Poste's child is coming to stay with us for a while. I expect to hear some time this morning what time she is arriving. I will tell you later about it."

Adam shrank back against the gangrened flank of Pointless.

"Mun I?" he asked, piteously. "Mun I, Miss Judith? Oh, dunna send me. How can I look into her liddle flower-face, and me knowin' what I know? Oh, Miss Judith, I beg of 'ee not to send me. Besides," he added, more practically, "'tes close on sixty-five years since I put hands to a pair of reins, and I might upset the maidy."

Judith, who had slowly turned from him while he was speaking, was now halfway across the yard. She turned her head to reply to him with a slow, graceful movement. Her deep voice clanged like a bell in the frosty air:

"No, you must go, Adam. You must forget what you know—as we all must, while she is here. As for the driving, you had best harness Viper to the trap, and drive down into Howling and back six times this afternoon, to get your hand in again."

"Could not Master Seth go instead o' me?"

Emotion shook the frozen grief of her face. She said low and sharp:

"You remember what happened when he went to meet the new kitchenmaid. . . . No. You must go."

Adam's eyes, little blind pools of water in his primitive face, suddenly grew cunning. He turned back to Aimless and resumed his mechanical stroking of the teat, saying in a sing-song rhythm:

"Ay, then I'll go, Miss Judith. I dunnamany times I've thought as how this day might come. . . . And now I mun go to bring Robert Poste's child back to Cold Comfort. Ay, 'tes strange. The seed to the flower, the flower to the fruit, the fruit to the belly. Ay, so 'twill go."

Judith had crossed the muck and rabble of the yard, and now entered the house by the back door.

In the large kitchen, which occupied most of the middle of the house, a sullen fire burned, the smoke of which wavered up the blackened walls and over the deal table, darkened by age and dirt, which was roughly set for a meal. A snood full of coarse porridge hung over the fire, and standing with one arm resting upon the high mantel, looking moodily down into the heaving contents of the snood, was a tall young man whose riding-boots were splashed with mud to the thigh, and whose coarse linen shirt was open to his waist. The firelight lit up his diaphragm muscles as they heaved slowly in rough rhythm with the porridge.

He looked up as Judith entered, and gave a short, defiant laugh, but said nothing. Judith slowly crossed over until she stood by his side. She was as tall as he. They stood in silence, she staring at him, and he down into the secret crevasses of the porridge.

"Well, mother mine," he said at last, "here I am, you see. I said I would be in time for breakfast, and I have kept my word."

His voice had a low, throaty, animal quality, a sneering warmth that wound a velvet ribbon of sexuality over the outward coarseness of the man.

Judith's breath came in long shudders. She thrust her arms deeper into her shawl. The porridge gave an ominous, leering heave; it might almost have been endowed with life, so uncannily did its movements keep pace with the human passions that throbbed above it.

"Cur," said Judith, levelly, at last. "Coward! Liar! Libertine! Who were you with last night? Moll at the mill or Violet at the vicarage? Or Ivy, perhaps, at the ironmongery? Seth—my son . . ." Her deep, dry voice quivered, but she whipped it back, and her next words flew out at him like a lash.

"Do you want to break my heart?"

"Yes," said Seth, with an elemental simplicity.

The porridge boiled over.

Judith knelt, and hastily and absently ladled it off the floor back into the snood, biting back her tears. While she was thus engaged, there was the confused blur of voices and boots in the yard outside. The men were coming in to breakfast.

The meal for the men was set on a long trestle at the farther end of the kitchen, as far away from the fire as possible. They came into the room in awkward little clumps, eleven of them. Five were distant cousins of the Starkadders, and two others were half-brothers of Amos, Judith's husband. This left only four men who were not in some way connected with the family; so it will readily be understood that the general feeling among the farm-hands was not exactly one of hilarity. Mark Dolour, one of the four, had been heard to remark: "Happen it had been another kind o' eleven, us might ha' had a cricket team, wi' me fer umpire. As ut is, 'twould be more befittin' if we was to hire oursen out for carryin' coffins at sixpence a mile."

The five half-cousins and the two half-brothers came over to the table, for they took their meals with the family. Amos liked to have his kith about him, though, of course, he never said so or cheered up when they were.

A strong family likeness wavered in and out of the fierce, earth-reddened faces of the seven, like a capricious light. Micah Starkadder, mightiest of the cousins, was a ruined giant of a man, paralysed in one knee and wrist. His nephew, Urk, was a little, red, hard-bitten man with foxy ears. Urk's brother, Ezra, was of the same physical type, but horsy where Urk was foxy. Caraway, a silent man, wind-shaved and lean, with long wandering fingers, had some of Seth's animal grace, and this had been passed on to his son, Harkaway, a young, silent, nervous man given to bursts of fury about very little, when you came to sift matters.

Amos's half-brothers, Luke and Mark, were thickly built and high-featured; gross, silent men with an eye to the bed and the board.

When all were seated two shadows darkened the sharp, cold light pouring in through the door. They were no more than a growing imminence of humanity, but the porridge boiled over again.

Amos Starkadder and his eldest son, Reuben, came into the kitchen.

Amos, who was even larger and more of a wreck than Micah, silently put his pruning-snoot and reaping hook in a corner by the fender, while Reuben put the scranlet with which he had been ploughing down beside them.

The two men took their places in silence, and after Amos had muttered a long and fervent grace, the meal was eaten in silence. Seth sat moodily tying and untying a green scarf round the magnificent throat he had inherited from Judith; he did not touch his porridge, and Judith only made a pretence of eating hers, playing with her spoon, patting the porridge up and down and idly building castles with the burnt bits. Her eyes burned under their penthouses, sometimes straying towards Seth as he sat sprawling in the lusty pride of casual manhood, with a good many buttons and tapes undone. Then those same eyes, dark as prisoned king-cobras, would slide round until they rested upon the bitter white head and raddled red neck of Amos, her husband, and then, like praying mantises, they would retreat between their lids. Secrecy pouted her full mouth.

Suddenly Amos, looking up from his food, asked abruptly:

"Where's Elfine?"

"She is not up yet. I did not wake her. She hinders more than she helps o' mornings," replied Judith.

Amos grunted.

" 'Tes a godless habit to lie abed of a working day, and the reeking red pits of the Lord's eternal wrathy fires lie in wait for them as do so. Ay"—his blazing blue eyes swivelled round and rested upon Seth, who was stealthily looking at a packet of Parisian art pictures under the table—"ay, and for those who break the seventh commandment, too. And for those"—the eye rested on Reuben, who was hopefully studying his parent's apoplectic countenance—"for those as waits for dead men's shoes."

"Nay, Amos, lad—" remonstrated Micah, heavily.

"Hold your peace," thundered Amos; and Micah, though a fierce tremor rushed through his mighty form, held it.

When the meal was done the hands trooped out to get on with the day's work of harvesting the swedes. This harvest was now in full swing; it took a long time and was very difficult to do. The Starkadders, too, rose and went out into the thin rain which had begun to fall. They were engaged in digging a well beside the dairy; it had been started a year ago, but it was taking a long time to do because things kept on going wrong. Once—a terrible day, when Nature seemed to hold her breath, and release it again in a furious gale of wind—Harkaway had fallen into it. Once Urk had pushed Caraway down it. Still, it was nearly finished; and everybody felt that it would not be long now.

In the middle of the morning a wire came from London announcing that the expected visitor would arrive by the six o'clock train.

Judith received it alone. Long after she had read it she stood motionless, the rain driving through the open door against her crimson shawl. Then slowly, with dragging steps, she mounted the staircase which led to the upper part of the house. Over her shoulder she said to old Adam, who had come into the room to do the washing up:

"Robert Poste's child will be here by the six o'clock train at Beershorn. You must leave to meet it at five. I am going up to tell Mrs. Starkadder that she is coming today."

Adam did not reply. And Seth, sitting by the fire, was growing tired of looking at his postcards, which were a three-year-old gift from the vicar's son, with whom he occasionally went poaching. He knew them all by now. Meriam, the hired girl, would not be in until after dinner. When she came, she would avoid his eyes, and tremble and weep.

He laughed insolently, triumphantly. Undoing another button of his shirt, he lounged out across the yard to the shed where Big Business, the bull, was imprisoned in darkness.

Laughing softly, Seth struck the door of the shed.

And as though answering the deep call of male to male, the bull uttered a loud, tortured bellow that rose undefeated through the dead sky that brooded above the farm.

Seth undid yet another button, and lounged away.

. . . .

Adam Lambsbreath, alone in the kitchen, stood looking down unseeingly at the dirtied plates which it was his task to wash, for the hired girl, Meriam, would not be here until after dinner, and when she came she would be all but useless. Her hour was near at hand, as all Howling knew. Was it not February, and the earth a-teem with new-ing life? A grin twisted Adam's writhen lips. He gathered up the plates one by one and carried them out to the pump, which stood in a corner of the kitchen, above a stone sink. Her hour was nigh. And when April like an over-lustful lover leaped upon the lush flanks of the Downs there would be yet another child in the wretched hut down at Nettle Flitch Field, where Meriam housed the fruits of her shame.

"Ay, dog's fennel or beard's-crow, by their fruits they shall be betrayed," muttered Adam, shooting a stream of cold water over the coagulated plates. "Come cloud, come sun, 'tes aye so."

While he was listlessly dabbing at the crusted edges of the porridge-plates with a thorn twig, a soft step descended the stairs outside the door which closed off the staircase from the kitchen. Some one paused on the threshhold.

The step was light as thistledown. If Adam had not had the rush of the running water in his ears too loudly for him to be able to hear any other noise, he might have thought this delicate, hesitant step was the beating of his own blood.

But, suddenly, something like a kingfisher streaked across the kitchen in a glimmer of green skirts and flying gold hair, and the chime of a laugh was followed a second later by the slam of the gate leading through the starveling garden out onto the Downs.

Adam flung round violently on hearing the sound, dropping his thorn twig and breaking two plates.

"Elfine...my liddle bird," he whispered, starting towards the open door.

A brittle silence mocked his whisper; through it wound the rank odours of rattan and barn.

"My pharisee...my cowdling..." he whispered, piteously. His eyes had again that look as of waste grey pools, sightless primeval wastes, reflecting the wan evening sky in some lonely marsh, as they wandered about the kitchen.

His hands fell slackly against his sides, and he dropped another plate. It broke.

He sighed, and began to move slowly towards the open door, his task forgotten. His eyes were fixed upon the cowshed.

"Ay, the beasts..." he muttered, dully; "the dumb beasts never fail a man. They know. Ay, I'd 'a' done better to cowdle our Feckless in my bosom than liddle Elfine. Ay, wild as a marshtigget in May, 'tes. And a will never listen to a word from annyone. Well, so t'must be. Sour or sweet, by barn or bye, so 'twill go. Ah, but if he"—the blind grey pools grew suddenly terrible, as though a storm were blowing in across the marsh from the Atlantic wastes—"if he but harms a hair o' her liddle goldy head I'll *kill* un."

So muttering, he crossed the yard and entered the cowshed, where he untied the beasts from their hootpieces and drove them across the yard, down the muddy rutted lane that led to Nettle Flitch Field. He was enmeshed in his grief. He did not notice that Graceless's leg had come off and that she was managing as best she could with three.

Left alone, the kitchen fire went out.

Patrick Barrington

TAKE ME IN YOUR ARMS, MISS MONEYPENNY-WILSON

Take me in your arms, Miss Moneypenny-Wilson,
   Take me in your arms, Miss Bates;
Fatal are your charms, Miss Moneypenny-Wilson,
   Fatal are your charms, Miss Bates;
Say you are my own, Miss Moneypenny-Wilson,
   Say you are my own, Miss Bates;
You I love alone, Miss Moneypenny-Wilson,
   You, and you alone, Miss Bates.

Sweet is the morn, Miss Moneypenny-Wilson;
   Sweet is the dawn, Miss B.,
But sweeter than the dawn and the daisies on the lawn
   Are you, sweet nymphs, to me.
Sweet, sweet, sweet is the sugar to the beet,
   Sweet is the honey to the bee,
But sweeter far than such sweets are
   Are your sweet names to me.

Oh, bitter, bitter, bitter is the lemon to the fritter,
   Bitter is the salt to the sea,
And bitter, very bitter was my figure to the fitter
   Who fitted this suit on me;
Bitter to the sitter, when the crowds come and titter,
   Must the R. A.'s portrait be,
But bitterer by far than these bitternesses are
   Is your bitter scorn to me.

Moon of my delight, Miss Moneypenny-Wilson,
   Moon of my delight, Miss Bates;
Cold as you are bright, Miss Moneypenny-Wilson,
   Icily polite, Miss Bates;

Hear you not my voice, Miss Moneypenny-Wilson?
  Hear you not my voice, Miss Bates?
Are you deaf by choice, Miss Moneypenny-Wilson?
  Are you deaf by choice, Miss Bates?

Deaf to my cries, Miss Moneypenny-Wilson,
  Deaf to my sighs, Miss B.;
Deaf to my songs and the story of my wrongs,
  Deaf to my minstrelsy;
Deafer than the newt to the sound of a flute,
  Deafer than a stone to the sea;
Deafer than a heifer to the sighing of a zephyr
  Are your deaf ears to me.

Cold, cold, cold as the melancholy mould,
  Cold as the foam-cold sea,
Colder than the shoulder of a neolithic boulder
  Are the shoulders you show to me.
Cruel, cruel, cruel is the flame to the fuel,
  Cruel is the axe to the tree,
But crueller and keener than a coster's concertina
  Is your cruel, cruel scorn to me.

Evelyn Waugh

A VISIT TO AZANIA

[To understand the following selection, you must know that Seth, Oxford graduate and black ruler of the black African empire of Azania, is trying to bring enlightenment to his backward country. Meanwhile a court cabal is planning a palace revolution. William Bland is the amiably incompetent attaché of the British Legation; Basil Seal is a young man of birth but no breeding, who is making a good thing out of Seth and Azania. M. Ballon is the French Minister, very suspicious of the British Minister, Sir Samson Courteney. Azania bears a close resemblance to Abyssinia, which Evelyn Waugh visited as a reporter and described superbly in *They Were Still Dancing*.]

FROM DAME MILDRED PORCH TO HER HUSBAND

S.S. Le Président Carnot
Matodi
March 8th

MY DEAR STANLEY,

I am writing this before disembarking. It will be posted at Marseilles and should reach you as nearly as I can calculate on 17th of the month. As I wrote to you from Durban, Sarah and I decided to break our return journey in Azania. The English boat did not stop here. So we had to change at Aden into this outward-bound French ship. Very dirty and *unseamanlike*. I have heard very disagreeable accounts of the hunting here. Apparently the natives dig deep pits into which the poor animals fall; they are often left in these traps for several days without food or water (imagine what that means in the heat of the jungle) and are then mercilessly butchered in cold blood. Of course the poor ignorant people know no better. But the young Emperor is by all accounts a comparatively enlightened and well-educated person and I am sure he will do all he can to introduce more humane methods, if it is really necessary to kill these fine beasts at all—as I very much doubt. I expect to resume our journey in about a fortnight. I enclose cheque for another month's household expenses. The coal bill seemed surprisingly heavy in your last accounts. I hope that you are not let-

752

ting the servants become extravagant in my absence. There is no need for the dining-room fire to be lit before luncheon at this time of year.

Yours affec.

MILDRED

DAME MILDRED PORCH'S DIARY

March 8th

Disembarked Matodi 12:45. Quaint and smelly. Condition of mules and dogs *appalling*, also children. In spite of radio message British consul was not there to meet us. Quite civil native led us to his office. Tip five annas. Seemed satisfied. Consul not English at all. Some sort of Greek. Very unhelpful (probably drinks). Unable or unwilling to say when train starts for Debra-Dowa, whether possible engage sleeper. Wired legation. Went to Amurath Hotel. Positive pot-house. Men sitting about drinking all over terrace. Complained. Large bedroom overlooking harbour apparently clean. Sarah one of her headaches. Complained of her room over street. Told her very decent little room.

March 9th

No news of train. Sarah disagreeable about her room. Saw Roman Missionary. Unhelpful. Typical dago attitude towards animals. Later saw American baptists. Middleclass and unhelpful because unable talk native languages. No answer legation. Wired again.

March 10th

No news train. Wired legation again. Unhelpful answer. Fed doggies in market-place. Children tried to take food from doggies. Greedy little wretches. Sarah still headache.

March 11th

Hotel manager suddenly announced train due to leave at noon. Apparently has been here all the time. Sarah very slow packing. Outrageous bill. Road to station blocked broken motor lorry. Natives living in it. Also two goats. Seemed well but cannot be healthy for them so near natives. Had to walk last quarter mile. Afraid would miss train. Arrived with five minutes to spare. Got tickets no sleepers. Just in time. V. hot and exhausted. Train did not start until three o'clock. Arrived dinner-time Lumo station where apparently we have to spend night. Shower bath and changed underclothes. Bed *v. doubtful*. Luckily remembered Keatings Durban. Interesting talk French hotel manager about local conditions. Apparently there was quite civil war last summer. How little the papers tell us. New Emperor v. go-ahead. English advisor named Seal. Any relation Cynthia Seal? Hotel man seemed to doubt government's financial stability. Says natives are complete savages but no white slave traffic—or so he says.

March 12th

Awful night. Bitten all over. Bill outrageous. Thought manager decent person too. Explained provisions hard to get. Humbug. Train left at seven in morning. Sarah nearly missed it. Two natives in carriage. I must say quite civil but v. uncomfortable as no corridor and had left so early. Tiring journey. Country seemed dry. Due in Debra-Dowa some time this afternoon. Must say shall be thankful.

Dame Mildred Porch and Miss Sarah Tin were in no way related to each other but constant companionship and a similarity of interests had so characterised them that a stranger might easily have taken them to be sisters as they stepped from the train onto the platform at Debra-Dowa. Dame Mildred was rather stout and Miss Tin rather spare. Each wore a khaki sun-hat in an oilcloth cover, each wore a service-able, washable frock, and thick shoes and stockings, each had smoked spectacles and a firm mouth. Each carried an attaché-case containing her most inalienable possessions—washing things and writing things, disinfectant and insecticide, books, passport, letters of credit—and held firmly to her burden in defiance of an eager succession of porters who attempted in turn to wrest it from her.

William pushed his way forward and greeted them amiably. "Dame Mildred Porch? Miss Tin? How are you? So glad you got here all right. I'm from the Legation. The Minister couldn't come himself. He's very busy just now, but he asked me to come along and see if you were all right. Any luggage? I've got a car outside and can run you up to the Hotel."

"Hotel? But I thought we should be expected at the Legation. I wired from Durban."

"Yes, the Minister asked me to explain. You see, we're some way out of the town. No proper road. Awful business getting in and out. The Minister thought you'd be much more comfortable in the town itself. Nearer the animals and everything. But he particularly said he hoped you'd come over to tea one day if you ever have the time."

Dame Mildred and Miss Tin exchanged that look of slighted citizenship which William had seen in the eyes of every visitor he had ever greeted at Debra-Dowa. "I tell you what," he said. "I'll go and look for the luggage. I daresay it's got stolen on the way. Often is, you know. And I'll get our mail out at the same time. No King's Messengers or anything here. If there's no European travelling it's put in charge of the guard. We thought of wiring to you to look after it and then we thought probably you had the devil of a lot of luggage yourselves."

By the time that the two-seater car had been loaded with the legation bags and the two ladies there was very little room left for their luggage. "I say, d'you mind awfully," said William. "I'm afraid we'll have to leave this trunk behind. The hotel'll fetch it up for you in no time."

"Young man, did you come to meet us or your own mail?"

"Now, you know," said William, "that simply isn't a fair question. Off we go." And the overladen little car began jolting up the broad avenue into the town.

"Is *this* where we are to stay?" asked Miss Tin as they drew up opposite the "Grand Café et Hôtel Restaurant de l'Empereur Seth."

"It doesn't look terribly smart," admitted William, "but you'll find it a mine of solid comfort."

He led them into the murky interior, dispersing a turkey and her brood from the Reception Hall. "Any one in?" There was a bell on the counter which he rang.

" 'Ullo," said a voice from upstairs. "One minute," and presently Mr. Youkoumian descended, buttoning up his trousers. "Why, it's Mr. Bland. 'Ullo, sir, 'ow are you? I 'ad the Minister's letter about the road this afternoon and the answer I am afraid is nothing doing. Very occupied, the Emperor...."

"I've brought you two guests. They are English ladies of great importance. You are to make them comfortable."

"I fix them O.K.," said Mr. Youkoumian.

"I'm sure you'll find everything comfortable here," said William. "And I hope we shall see you soon at the Legation."

"One minute, young man, there are a number of things I want to know."

"I fix you O.K.," said Mr. Youkoumian again.

"Yes, you ask Mr. Youkoumian here. He'll tell you everything far better than I could. Can't keep them waiting for the mail, you know."

"Impudent young puppy," said Dame Mildred as the car drove away. "I'll report him to the Foreign Office as soon as I get home. Stanley shall ask a question about him in the House."

Mail day at the British Legation. Sir Samson and Lady Courteney, Prudence and William, Mr. Legge and Mrs. Legge, Mr. and Mrs.

Anstruther, sitting around the fireplace opening the bags. Bills, provisions, family news, official despatches, gramophone records, newspapers scattered on the carpet. Presently William said, "I say, d'you know who I ran into on the platform? Those two cruelty-to-animals women who kept telegraphing."

"How very annoying. What *have* you done with them?"

"I shot them into Youkoumian's. They wanted to come and stay here."

"Heaven forbid. I do hope they won't stay long. Ought we to ask them to tea or anything?"

"Well, I *did* say that perhaps you'd like to see them sometime."

"Hang it, William, that's a bit thick."

"Oh, I don't suppose they thought I meant it."

"I sincerely hope not."

March 12th (continued)

Arrived Debra-Dowa late in afternoon. Discourteous cub from Legation met us and left Sarah's trunk at station. Brought us to frightful hotel. But Armenian proprietor v. obliging. Saved me visit to bank by changing money for us into local currency. Quaint bank-notes with portrait of Emperor in European evening dress. Mr. Seal came in after dinner. He is Cynthia's son. V. young and ill-looking. Off-hand manner. V. tired, going to bed early.

That evening, M. Ballon's report included the entry: *Two British ladies arrived, suspects. Met at station by Mr. Bland. Proceeded Youkoumian's.*

"They are being watched?"

"Without respite."

"Their luggage?"

"A trunk was left at the station. It has been searched but nothing incriminating was found. Their papers are in two small bags which never leave their hands."

"Ah, they are old stagers. Sir Samson is calling out his last reserves."

March 13th. Sunday

No news Sarah's trunk. Went to Anglican Cathedral but found it was being pulled down. Service in Bishop's drawing-room. Poor congregation. V. silly sermon. Spoke to Bishop later about cruelty to animals. Unhelpful. Old Humbug. Later went to write name in book at Palace. Sarah in bed.

Town very crowded, apparently preparing for some local feast or carnival. Asked Bishop about it but he could not tell me. Seemed unaccountably embarrassed. Asked Mr. Youkoumian. Either he cannot have understood my question or I cannot have understood what I thought him to say. Did not press point. He did not speak English at all well but is an obliging man.

March 14th

Hideous night. Mosquito in net and v. large brown bugs in bed. Up and dressed at dawn and went for long walk in hills. Met quaint caravan—drums, spears, etc. No news Sarah's trunk.

[A conspiracy to dethrone the Emperor Seth and replace him by his uncle is afoot.]

March 14th (continued)

As Keatings obviously deteriorated went to store attached hotel to buy some more. Met native Duchess who spoke English. V. helpful re bugs. Went with her to her home where she gave me insecticide of her own preparation. Gave me tea and biscuits. V. interesting conversation. She told me that it has just been discovered that Emperor is not real heir to throne. Elderly uncle in prison. They have gone to get him out. Most romantic, but hope new Emperor equally enlightened re animals.

March 15th

Better night. Native Duchess' insecticide v. helpful though nasty smell. Received Invitation dine Palace tonight. Short notice but thought it best accept for us both. Sarah says nothing to wear unless trunk turns up.

It was the first time since Seth's accession that European visitors had been entertained at the Palace. The Ministry of Modernisation was called in early that morning to supervise the invitations and the menu.

"It shall be an entirely Azanian party. I want the English ladies to see how refined we are. I was doubtful about asking Viscount Boaz. What do you think? Will he be sober?... and there is the question of food. I have been reading that now it is called Vitamins. I am having the menu printed like this. It is a good, modern, European dinner, eh?"

Basil looked at the card. A month ago he might have suggested emendations. Today he was tired.

"That's fine, Seth; go ahead like that."

"You see," said the Emperor proudly, "already we Azanians can do much for ourselves. Soon we shall not need a Minister of Modernisation. No, I do not mean that, Basil. Always you are my friend and advisor."

So the menu for Seth's first dinner party went to the *Courrier* office to be printed and came back a packet of handsome gilt-edged cards, laced with silk ribbons in the Azanian colours and embossed with a gold crown.

March 15th

IMPERIAL BANQUET FOR WELCOMING
THE ENGLISH
CRUELTY TO ANIMALS

Menu of Foods.
Vitamin A
Tin Sardines
Vitamin B
Roasted Beef
Vitamin C
Small Roasted Sucking Porᴋs
Vitamin D
Hot Sheep and Onions
Vitamin E
Spiced Turkey
Vitamin F
Sweet Puddings
Vitamin G
Coffee
Vitamin H
Jam

"It is so English," explained Seth. "From courtesy to your great Empire."

At eight o'clock that evening Dame Mildred and Miss Tin arrived at the Palace for the banquet. The electric light plant was working that evening and a string of coloured bulbs shone with Christmas welcome over the main doorway. A strip of bright linoleum had been spread on the steps and as the taxi drew up a dozen or so servants ran down to conduct the guests into the hall. They were in mixed attire; some in uniforms of a kind, tunics frogged with gold braid discarded or purloined in the past from the wardrobes of visiting diplomats; some in native costume of striped silk. As the two ladies stepped from the car a platoon of guards lounging on the Terrace alarmed them with a ragged volley of welcome.

There was a slight delay as the driver of the taxi refused to accept the new pound note which Dame Mildred tendered him in payment, but the captain of the guard, hurrying up with a jingle of spurs curtailed further discussion by putting the man under arrest and signified in a few graphic gestures his sorrow for the interruption and his intention of hanging the troublesome fellow without delay.

The chief saloon was brilliantly lighted and already well filled with the flower of Azanian native society. One of the first acts of the new reign had been an ordinance commanding the use of European evening dress. This evening was the first occasion for it to be worn and all round the room stood sombre but important figures completely fitted up by Mr. Youkoumian with tail-coats, white gloves, starched linen and enamelled studs; only in a few cases were shoes and socks lacking; the unaccustomed attire lent a certain dignified rigidity to their deportment. The ladies had for the most part allowed their choice to fix upon frocks of rather startling colour; aniline greens and violets with elaborations of ostrich feather and sequin. Viscountess Boaz wore a backless frock newly arrived from Cairo combined with the full weight of her ancestral jewellery; the Duchess of Mhomala carried on her woolly head a three-pound tiara of gold and garnets; Baroness Batulle exposed shoulders and back magnificently tattooed and cicatriced with arabesques.

Beside all this finery the guests of honour looked definitely dowdy as the Lord Chamberlain conducted them round the room and performed the introductions in French scarcely more comfortable than Dame Mildred's own.

Two slaves circulated among them carrying trays of brandy. The English ladies refused. The Lord Chamberlain expressed his concern. Would they have preferred whisky; no doubt some could be produced? or beer?

"Mon bon homme," said Dame Mildred severely, *"il vous faut comprendre que nous ne buvons rien de tout, jamais";* an announcement which considerably raised their prestige among the company; they were not much to look at, certainly, but at least they knew a thing or

two which the Azanians did not. A useful sort of woman to take on a journey, reflected the Lord Chamberlain, and inquired with polite interest whether the horses and camels in their country were as conveniently endowed.

Further conversation was silenced by the arrival of the Emperor, who at this moment entered the hall from the far end and took his seat on the raised throne which had stood conspicuously on the dais throughout the preliminary presentations. Court etiquette was still in a formative stage. There was a moment of indecision during which the company stood in embarrassed silence waiting for a lead. Seth said something to his equerry, who now advanced down the room and led forward the guests of honour. They curtsied and stood on one side, while the other guests filed past in strict precedence. Most of them bowed low in the Oriental manner, raising the hand to forehead and breast. The curtsy, however, had been closely observed and found several imitators among both sexes. One elderly peer, a stickler for old-world manners, prostrated himself fully and went through the mimic action of covering his head with dust. When all had saluted him in their various ways, Seth led the party in to dinner; fresh confusion over the places and some ill-natured elbowing; Dame Mildred and Miss Tin sat on either side of the Emperor; soon every one was eating and drinking at a great pace.

March 15th (continued)

Dinner at Palace. Food v. nasty. Course after course different kinds of meat, overseasoned and swimming in grease. Tried to manage some of it from politeness. Sarah ate nothing. Emperor asked great number of questions some of which I was unable to answer. How many suits of clothes had the King of England? Did he take his bath before or after his breakfast? Which was the more civilised? What was the best shop to buy an artesian well? etc. Sarah v. silent. Told Emperor about co-education and "free-discipline." Showed great interest.

Dame Mildred's neighbour on her other side was the punctilious man who had prostrated himself in the drawing-room; he seemed engrossed in his eating. In point of fact he was rehearsing in his mind and steeling his nerve to enunciate some English conversation in which ᵇd painfully schooled himself during that day: at last it came up ᵇy.

"ᵐany ox 'ave you?" he demanded, lifting up sideways from

his plate a great bearded face, " 'ow many sons? 'ow many daughters? 'ow many brothers? 'ow many sisters? My father is dead fighting."

Dame Mildred turned to him a somewhat startled scrutiny. There were crumbs and scraps of food in various parts of his beard. "I beg your pardon?" she said.

But the old gentleman had shot his bolt; he felt that he had said all and more than all that good breeding required, and to tell the truth was more than a little taken aback by his own fluency. He gave her a nervous smile and resumed his dinner without again venturing to address her.

"Which of the white ladies would you like to have?"

"The fat one. But both are ugly."

"Yes. It must be very sad for the English gentlemen to marry English ladies."

Presently when the last vitamin had been guzzled, Viscount Boaz rose to propose the health of the guests of honour. His speech was greeted by loud applause and was then done into English by the Court Interpreter:

"Your Majesty, Lords and Ladies. It is my privilege and delight this evening to welcome with open arms of brotherly love to our city Dame Mildred Porch and Miss Tin, two ladies renowned throughout the famous country of Europe for their great cruelty to animals. We Azanians are a proud and ancient nation but we have much to learn from the white people of the West and North. We too, in our small way, are cruel to our animals"—and here the Minister for the Interior digressed at some length to recount with hideous detail what he had himself once done with a woodman's axe to a wild boar—"but it is to the great nations of the West and North, and specially to their worthy representatives that are with us tonight, that we look as our natural leaders on the road of progress. Ladies and gentlemen, we must be Modern, we must be refined in our Cruelty to Animals. That is the message of the New Age brought to us by our guests this evening. May I, in conclusion, raise my glass and ask you to join with me in wishing them old age and prolonged fecundity."

The toast was drunk and the company sat down. Boaz's neighbours congratulated him on his speech. There seemed no need for a reply and indeed Dame Mildred, rarely at a loss for telling phrases,

would on this occasion have been hard put to it to acknowledge the
welcome in suitable terms. Seth appeared not to have heard either
version of the speech. He sat inattentive, his mind occupied with remote speculation. Dame Mildred attempted two or three conversations.

"A very kindly meant speech, but he seems to misunderstand our
mission.... It is so interesting to see your people in their own milieu.
Do tell me who is who? ... Have they entirely abandoned native costume? ..."

But she received only abstracted answers.

Finally she said, "I was so interested to learn about your uncle
Achon." The Emperor nodded. "I do hope they get him out of the
monastery. Such a useless life, I always think, and so selfish. It makes
people introspective to think all the time about their own souls, don't
you think? So sensible of that Earl of wherever it is to go and look
for him."

But Seth had not heard a word.

March 16th

Could not sleep late after party. Attempted to telephone legation. No
reply. Attempted to see Mr. Seal. Said he was too busy. No sign of Sarah's
trunk. She keeps borrowing my things. Tried to *pin down* Emperor last
night, no result. Went for walk in town. V. crowded, no one working. Apparently some trouble about currency. Saw man strike camel, would have
reported him but no policeman about. Begin to feel I am wasting my time
here.

[From *Black Mischief*]

William Plomer

HEADLINE HISTORY

Grave Charge in Mayfair Bathroom Case;
Roman Remains for Middle West;
Golfing Bishop Calls for Prayers;
How Murdered Bride was Dressed;

Boxer Insures his Joie-de-Vivre;
Duchess Denies that Vamps are Vain;
Do Women make Good Wives?
Giant Airship over Spain;

Soprano Sings for Forty Hours;
Cocktail Bar on Mooring Mast;
"Noise, more Noise!" Poet's Last Words;
Compulsory Wireless Bill is Passed;

Alleged Last Trump Blown Yesterday;
Traffic Drowns Call to Quick and Dead;
Cup Tie Crowd sees Heavens Ope;
"Not End of World," says Well-Known Red.

T. H. White

Anachronism is the easiest humorous device. A person totally deprived of a sense of humor can be fairly funny in telling of the discovery of America, for instance, in modern terms. It is T. H. White's distinction that he has used anachronism with rich and unflagging humor. One reason, probably, that his stories are so rewarding is that he is deeply read in medieval literature, legend, and social history. His knowledge of falconry, for instance, is very impressive to ornithologists.

ENCOUNTER WITH A MEDIÆVAL WITCH

One Thursday afternoon the boys were doing their archery as usual. There were two straw targets fifty yards apart, and when they had shot their arrows at the one, they had only to go to it, collect them, and fire back at the other after facing about. It was still the loveliest summer weather, and there had been chickens for dinner, so that Merlyn had gone off to the edge of their shooting-ground and sat down under a tree. What with the warmth and the chickens and the cream he had poured over his pudding and the continual repassing of the boys and the tock of the arrows in the targets—which was as sleepy to listen to as the noise of a lawn-mower—and the dance of the egg-shaped sunspots between the leaves of his tree, the aged magician was soon fast asleep.

Archery was a serious occupation in those days. It had not yet been relegated to Indians and small boys, so that when you were shooting badly you got into a bad temper, just as the wealthy pheasant shooters do today. Kay was shooting badly. He was trying too hard and plucking on his loose, instead of leaving it to the bow.

"Oh, come on," said Kay. "I'm sick of these beastly targets. Let's have a shot at the popinjay."

They left the targets and had several shots at the popinjay—which was a large, bright-coloured artificial bird stuck on the top of a stick, like a parrot—and Kay missed this also. First he had the feeling of "Well, I *will* hit the filthy thing, even if I have to go without my tea until I do it." Then he merely became bored.

The Wart said, "Let's play Rovers then. We can come back in half an hour and wake Merlyn up."

What they called Rovers, consisted in going for a walk with their bows and shooting one arrow each at any agreed mark which they came across. Sometimes it would be a mole hill, sometimes a clump of rushes, sometimes a big thistle almost at their feet. They varied the distance at which they chose these objects, sometimes picking a target as much as 120 yards away—which was about as far as these boys' bows could carry and sometimes having to aim actually below a close thistle because the arrow always leaps up a foot or two as it leaves the bow. They counted five for a hit, and one if the arrow was within a bow's length, and added up their scores at the end.

On this Thursday they chose their targets wisely, and, besides, the grass of the big field had been lately cut. So they never had to search for their arrows for long, which nearly always happens, as in golf, if you shoot ill-advisedly near hedges or in rough places. The result was that they strayed further than usual and found themselves near the edge of the savage forest where Cully had been lost.

"I vote," said Kay, "that we go to those buries in the chase, and see if we can get a rabbit. It would be more fun than shooting at these hummocks."

They did this. They chose two trees about a hundred yards apart, and each boy stood under one of them, waiting for the conies to come out again. They stood very still, with their bows already raised and arrows fitted, so that they would make the least possible movement to disturb the creatures when they did appear. It was not difficult for either of them to stand thus, for the very first test which they had had to pass in archery was standing with the bow at arm's length for half an hour. They had six arrows each and would be able to fire and mark them all before they needed to frighten the rabbits back by walking about to collect. An arrow does not make enough noise to upset more than the particular rabbit that it is shot at.

At the fifth shot Kay was lucky. He allowed just the right amount for wind and distance, and his point took a young coney square in the head. It had been standing up on end to look at him, wondering what he was.

"Oh, well shot!" cried the Wart, as they ran to pick it up. It was the first rabbit they had ever hit, and luckily they had killed it dead.

When they had carefully gutted it with the little hunting knife which Merlyn had given—in order to keep it fresh—and passed one of its hind legs through the other at the hock, for convenience in carrying, the two boys prepared to go home with their prize. But before they unstrung their bows they used to observe a ceremony. Every Thursday afternoon, after the last serious arrow had been fired, they were allowed to fit one more nock to their strings and to discharge the arrow straight up into the air. It was partly a gesture of farewell, partly of triumph, and it was beautiful. They did it now as a salute to their first prey.

The Wart watched his arrow go up. The sun was already westing towards evening, and the trees where they were had plunged them into a partial shade. So, as the arrow topped the trees and climbed into sunlight, it began to burn against the evening like the sun itself. Up and up it went, not weaving as it would have done with a snatching loose, but soaring, swimming, aspiring towards heaven, steady, golden, and superb. Just as it had spent its force, just as its ambition had been dimmed by destiny and it was preparing to faint, to turn over, to pour back into the bosom of its mother earth, a terrible portent happened. A gore-crow came flapping wearily before the approaching night. It came, it did not waver, it took the arrow. It flew away, heavy and hoisting, with the arrow in its beak.

Kay was frightened by this, but the Wart was furious. He had loved his arrow's movement, its burning ambition in the sunlight, and besides, it was his best arrow. It was the only one which was perfectly balanced, sharp, tight-feathered, clean-nocked, and neither warped nor scraped.

"It was a witch."

"I don't care if it was ten witches," said the Wart. "I am going to get it back."

"But it went towards the Forest."

"I shall go after it."

"You can go alone, then," said Kay. "I'm not going into the Forest Sauvage, just for a putrid arrow."

"I shall go alone."

"Oh, well," said Kay, "I suppose I shall have to come too, if you're so set on it. And I bet we shall get nobbled by Wat."

"Let him nobble," said the Wart. "I want my arrow."

They went in the Forest at the place where they had last seen the bird of carrion.

In less than five minutes they were in a clearing with a well and a cottage just like Merlyn's.

"Goodness," said Kay, "I never knew there were any cottages so close. I say, let's go back."

"I just want to look at this place," said the Wart. "It's probably a wizard's."

The cottage had a brass plate screwed on the garden gate. It said:

MADAME MIM, B.A. (Dom-Daniel)

PIANOFORTE
NEEDLEWORK
NECROMANCY

No Hawkers, circulars
or Income Tax.
Beware of the Dragon.

The cottage had lace curtains. These stirred ever so slightly, for behind them there was a lady peeping. The gore-crow was standing on the chimney.

"Come on," said Kay. "Oh, do come on. I tell you, she'll never give it us back."

At this point the door of the cottage opened suddenly and the witch was revealed standing in the passage. She was a strikingly beautiful woman of about thirty, with coal-black hair so rich that it had the blue-black of the maggot-pies in it, silky bright eyes and a general soft air of butter-wouldn't-melt-in-my-mouth. She was sly.

"How do you do, my dears," said Madame Mim. "And what can I do for you today?"

The boys took off their leather caps, and Wart said, "Please, there is a crow sitting on your chimney and I think it has stolen one of my arrows."

"Precisely," said Madame Mim. "I have the arrow within."

"Could I have it back, please?"

"Inevitably," said Madame Mim. "The young gentleman shall have his arrow on the very instant, in four ticks and ere the bat squeaks thrice."

"Thank you very much," said the Wart.

"Step forward," said Madame Mim. "Honour the threshold. Accept the humble hospitality in the spirit in which it is given."

"I really do not think we can stay," said the Wart politely. "I really think we must go. We shall be expected back at home."

"Sweet expectation," replied Madame Mim in devout tones.

"Yet you would have thought," she added, "that the young gentleman could have found time to honour a poor cottager, out of politeness. Few can believe how we ignoble tenants of the lower classes value a visit from the landlord's sons."

"We would like to come in," said the Wart, "very much. But you see we shall be late already."

The lady now began to give a sort of simpering whine. "The fare is lowly," she said. "No doubt it is not what you would be accustomed to eating, and so naturally such highly born ones would not care to partake."

Kay's strongly developed feeling for good form gave way at this. He was an aristocratic boy always, and condescended to his inferiors so that they could admire him. Even at the risk of visiting a witch, he was not going to have it said that he had refused to eat a tenant's food because it was too humble.

"Come on, Wart," he said. "We needn't be back before vespers."

Madame Mim swept them a low curtsey as they crossed the threshold. Then she took them each by the scruff of the neck, lifted them right off the ground with her strong gypsy arms, and shot out of the back door with them almost before they had got in at the front. The Wart caught a hurried glimpse of her parlour and kitchen. The lace curtains, the aspidistra, the lithograph called the Virgin's Choice, the printed text of the Lord's Prayer written backwards and hung upside down, the sea-shell, the needle-case in the shape of a heart with A Present from Camelot written on it, the broom sticks, the cauldrons, and the bottles of dandelion wine. Then they were kicking and struggling in the back yard.

"We thought that the growing sportsmen would care to examine our rabbits," said Madame Mim.

There was, indeed, a row of large rabbit hutches in front of them, but they were empty of rabbits. In one hutch there was a poor ragged old eagle owl, evidently quite miserable and neglected; in another a small boy unknown to them, a wittol who could only roll his eyes and burble when the witch came near. In a third there was a moulting black cock. A fourth had a mangy goat in it, also black, and two more stood empty.

"Grizzle Greediguts," cried the witch.

"Here, Mother," answered the carrion crow.

With a flop and a squawk it was sitting beside them, its hairy black beak cocked on one side. It was the witch's familiar.

"Open the doors," commanded Madame Mim, "and Greediguts shall have eyes for supper, round and blue."

The gore-crow hastened to obey, with every sign of satisfaction, and pulled back the heavy doors in its strong beak, with three times three. Then the two boys were thrust inside, one into each hutch, and Madame Mim regarded them with unmixed pleasure. The doors had magic locks on them and the witch had made them to open by whispering in their keyholes.

"As nice a brace of young gentlemen," said the witch, "as ever stewed or roast. Fattened on real butcher's meat, I daresay, with milk and all. Now we'll have the big one jugged for Sunday, if I can get a bit of wine to go in the pot, and the little one we'll have on the moon's morn, by jing and by jee, for how can I keep my sharp fork out of him a minute longer it fair gives me the croup."

"Let me out," said Kay hoarsely, "you old witch, or Sir Ector will come for you."

At this Madame Mim could no longer contain her joy. "Hark to the little varmint," she cried, snapping her fingers and doing a bouncing jig before the cages. "Hark to the sweet, audacious, tender little veal. He answers back and threatens us with Sir Ector, on the very brink of the pot. That's how I faint to tooth them, I do declare, and that's how I will tooth them ere the week be out, by Scarmiglione, Belial, Peor, Ciriato Sannuto and Dr. D."

With this she began bustling about in the back yard, the herb garden and the scullery, cleaning pots, gathering plants for the stuffing, sharpening knives and cleavers, boiling water, skipping for joy, licking her greedy lips, saying spells, braiding her night-black hair, and singing as she worked.

First she sang the old witch's song:

> Black spirits and white, red spirits and grey,
> Mingle, mingle, mingle, you that mingle may.
> > Here's the blood of a bat,
> > Put in that, oh, put in that.
> > Here's libbard's bane.
> > Put in again.
> Mingle, mingle, mingle, you that mingle may.

Then she sang her work song:

> Two spoons of sherry
> Three oz. of yeast,
> Half a pound of unicorn,
> And God bless the feast.
> Shake them in a collander,
> Bang them to a chop,
> Simmer slightly, snip up nicely,
> Jump, skip, hop.
> Knit one, knot one, purl two together,
> Pip one and pop one and pluck the secret feather.
> Baste in a mod. oven.
> God bless our coven.
> Tra-la-la!
> Three toads in a jar.
> Te-he-he!
> Put in the frog's knee.
> Peep out of the lace curtain.
> There goes the Toplady girl, she's up to no good
> > that's certain.
> Oh, what a lovely baby!
> How nice it would go with gravy.
> Pinch the salt.

Here she pinched it very nastily.

Turn the malt

Here she began twiddling round widdershins, in a vulgar way.

With a hey-nonny-nonny and I don't mean maybe.

At the end of this song, Madame Mim took a sentimental turn and delivered herself of several hymns, of a blasphemous nature, and of a tender love lyric which she sang sotto-voce with trills. It was:

> My love is like a red, red nose
> His tail is soft and tawny,
> And everywhere my lovely goes
> I call him Nick or Horny.

She vanished into the parlour, to lay the table.

Poor Kay was weeping in a corner of the end hutch, lying on his face and paying no attention to anything. Before Madame Mim had finally thrown him in, she had pinched him all over to see if he was fat. She had also slapped him, to see, as the butchers put it, if he was hollow. On top of this, he did not in the least want to be eaten for Sunday dinner and he was miserably furious with the Wart for leading him into such a terrible doom on account of a mere arrow. He had forgotten that it was he who had insisted on entering the fatal cottage.

The Wart sat on his haunches, because the cage was too small for standing up, and examined his prison. The bars were of iron and the gate was iron too. He shook all the bars, one after the other, but they were as firm as rock. There was an iron bowl for water—with no water in it—and some old straw in a corner for lying down. It was verminous.

"Our mistress," said the mangy old goat suddenly from the next pen, "is not very careful of her pets."

He spoke in a low voice, so that nobody could hear, but the carrion crow which had been left on the chimney to spy upon them noticed that they were talking and moved nearer.

"Whisper," said the goat, "if you want to talk."

"Are you one of her familiars?" asked the Wart suspiciously.

The poor creature did not take offence at this, and tried not to look hurt.

"No," he said. "I'm not a familiar. I'm only a mangy old black goat, rather tattered as you see, and kept for sacrifice."

"Will she eat you too?" asked the Wart, rather tremblingly.

"Not she. I shall be too rank for her sweet tooth, you may be sure. No, she will use my blood for making patterns with on Walpurgis Night."

"It's quite a long way off, you know," continued the goat without self-pity. "For myself I don't mind very much, for I am old. But look at that poor old owl there, that she keeps merely for a sense of possession and generally forgets to feed. That makes my blood boil, that does. It wants to fly, to stretch its wings. At night it just runs round and round and round like a big rat, it gets so restless. Look, it has broken all its soft feathers. For me, it doesn't matter, for I am naturally of a sedentary disposition now that youth has flown, but I call that owl a rare shame. Something ought to be done about it."

The Wart knew that he was probably going to be killed that night, the first to be released out of all that band, but yet he could not help feeling touched at the great-heartedness of this goat. Itself under sentence of death, it could afford to feel strongly about the owl. He wished he were as brave as this.

"If only I could get out," said the Wart. "I know a magician who would soon settle her hash, and rescue us all."

The goat thought about this for some time, nodding its gentle old head with the great cairngorm eyes. Then it said, "As a matter of fact I know how to get you out, only I did not like to mention it before. Put your ear nearer the bars. I know how to get you out, but not your poor friend there who is crying. I didn't like to subject you to a temptation like that. You see, when she whispers to the lock I have heard what she says, but only at the locks on either side of mine. When she gets a cage away she is too soft to be heard. I know the words to release both you and me, and the black cock here too, but not your young friend yonder."

"Why ever haven't you let yourself out before?" asked the Wart, his heart beginning to bound.

"I can't speak them in human speech, you see," said the goat sadly, "and this poor mad boy here, the wittol, he can't speak them either."

"Oh, tell them me."

"You will be safe then, and so would I and the cock be too, if you stayed long enough to let us out. But would you be brave enough to stay, or would you run at once? And what about your friend and the wittol and the old owl?"

"I should run for Merlyn at once," said the Wart. "Oh, at once, and he would come back and kill this old witch in two twos, and then we should all be out."

The goat looked at him deeply, his tired old eyes seeming to ask their way kindly into the bottom of his heart.

"I shall tell you only the words for your own lock," said the goat at last. "The cock and I will stay here with your friend, as hostages for your return."

"Oh, goat," whispered the Wart. "You could have made me say the words to get you out first and then gone your way. Or you could have got the three of us out, starting with yourself to make sure, and left Kay to be eaten. But you are staying with Kay. Oh, goat, I will never forget you, and if I do not get back in time I shall not be able to bear my life."

"We shall have to wait till dark. It will only be a few minutes now."

As the goat spoke, they could see Madame Mim lighting the oil lamp in the parlour. It had a pink glass shade with patterns on it. The crow, which could not see in the dark, came quietly closer, so that at least he ought to be able to hear.

"Goat," said the Wart, in whose heart something strange and terrible had been going on in the dangerous twilight, "put your head closer still. Please, goat, I am not trying to be better than you are, but I have a plan. I think it is I who had better stay as hostage and you who had better go. You are black and will not be seen in the night. You have four legs and can run much faster than I. Let you go with a message for Merlyn. I will whisper you out, and I will stay."

He was hardly able to say the last sentence, for he knew that Madame Mim might come for him at any moment now, and if she came before Merlyn it would be his death warrant. But he did say it, pushing the words out as if he were breathing against water, for he knew that if he himself were gone when Madame came for him, she would certainly eat Kay at once.

"Master," said the goat without further words, and it put one leg out and laid its double-knobbed forehead on the ground in the salute which is given to royalty. Then it kissed his hand as a friend.

"Quick," said the Wart, "give me one of your hoofs through the bars and I will scratch a message on it with one of my arrows."

It was difficult to know what message to write on such a small space with such a clumsy implement. In the end he just wrote KAY. He did not use his own name because he thought Kay more important, and that they would come quicker for him.

"Do you know the way?" he asked.

"My grandam used to live at the castle."

"What are the words?"

"Mine," said the goat, "are rather upsetting."

"What are they?"

"Well," said the goat, "you must say: Let Good Digestion Wait on Appetite."

"Oh, goat," said the Wart in a broken voice, "how horrible. But run quickly, goat, and come back safely, goat, and oh, goat, give me one more kiss for company before you go." The goat refused to kiss him. It gave him the Emperor's salute, of both feet, and bounded away into the darkness as soon as he had said the words.

Unfortunately, although they had whispered too carefully for the crow to hear their speech, the release words had had to be said rather loudly to reach the next-door keyhole, and the door had creaked.

"Mother, mother!" screamed the crow. "The rabbits are escaping."

Instantly Madame Mim was framed in the lighted doorway of the kitchen.

"What is it, my Grizzle?" she cried. "What ails us, my halcyon tit?"

"The rabbits are escaping," shrieked the crow again.

The witch ran out, but too late to catch the goat or even to see him, and began examining the locks at once by the light of her fingers. She held these up in the air and a blue flame burned at the tip of each.

"One little boy safe," counted Madame Mim, "and sobbing for his dinner. Two little boys safe, and neither getting thinner. One mangy goat gone, and who cares a fiddle? For the owl and the cock are left, and the wittol in the middle."

"Still," added Madame Mim, "it's a caution how he got out, a proper caution, that it is."

"He was whispering to the little boy," sneaked the crow, "whispering for the last half-hour together."

"Indeed?" said the witch. "Whispering to the little dinner, hey? And much good may it do him. What about a sage stuffing, boy, hey? And what were you doing, my Greediguts, to let them carry on like that?

No dinner for you, my little painted bird of paradise, so you may just flap off to any old tree and roost."

"Oh, Mother," whined the crow. "I was only adoing of my duty."

"Flap off," cried Madame Mim. "Flap off, and go broody if you like."

The poor crow hung its head and crept off to the other end of the roof, sneering to itself.

"Now, my juicy toothful," said the witch, turning to the Wart and opening his door with the proper whisper of Enough-Is-As-Good-As-A-Feast, "we think the cauldron simmers and the oven is mod. How will my tender sucking pig enjoy a little popping lard instead of the clandestine whisper?"

The Wart ran about in his cage as much as he could, and gave as much trouble as possible in being caught, in order to save even a little time for the coming of Merlyn.

"Let go of me, you beast," he cried. "Let go of me, you foul hag, or I'll bite your fingers."

"How the creature scratches," said Madame Mim. "Bless us, how he wriggles and kicks, just for being a pagan's dinner."

"Don't you dare kill me," cried the Wart, now hanging by one leg. "Don't you dare to lay a finger on me, or you'll be sorry for it."

"The lamb," said Madame Mim. "The partridge with a plump breast, how he does squeak."

"And then there's the cruel old custom," continued the witch, carrying him into the lamplight of the kitchen where a new sheet was laid on the floor, of "plucking a poor chicken before it is dead. The feathers come out cleaner so. Nobody could be so cruel as to do that nowadays, by Nothing or by Never, but of course a little boy doesn't feel any pain. Their clothes come off nicer if you take them off alive, and who would dream of roasting a little boy in his clothes, to spoil the feast?"

"Murderess," cried the Wart. "You will rue this ere the night is out."

"Cubling," said the witch. "It's a shame to kill him, that it is. Look how his little downy hair stares in the lamplight, and how his poor ,eyes pop out of his head. Greediguts will be sorry to miss those eyes, so she will. Sometimes one could almost be a vegetarian, when one has to do a deed like this."

The witch laid Wart over her lap, with his head between her knees, and carefully began to take his clothes off with a practised hand. He kicked and squirmed as much as he could, reckoning that every hindrance would put off the time when he would be actually knocked on the head, and thus increase the time in which the black goat could bring Merlyn to his rescue. During this time the witch sang her plucking song, of:

> Pull the feather with the skin,
> Not against the grain—o.
> Pluck the soft ones out from in,
> The great with might and main—o.
> Even if he wriggles,
> Never heed his squiggles,
> For mercifully little boys are quite immune to pain—o.

She varied this song with the other kitchen song of the happy cook:

> Soft skin for crackling,
> Oh, my lovely duckling,
> The skewers go here,
> And the string goes there
> And such is my scrumptious suckling.

"You will be sorry for this," cried the Wart, "even if you live to be a thousand."

"He has spoken enough," said Madame Mim. "It is time that we knocked him on the napper."

> Hold him by the legs, and
> When up goes his head,
> Clip him with the palm-edge, and
> Then he is dead.

The dreadful witch now lifted the Wart into the air and prepared to have her will of him; but at that very moment there was a fizzle of summer lightning without any crash and in the nick of time Merlyn was standing on the threshold.

"Ha!" said Merlyn. "Now we shall see what a doublefirst at Dom-Daniel avails against the private education of my master Bleise."

Madame Mim put the Wart down without looking at him, rose

from her chair, and drew herself to her full magnificent height. Her glorious hair began to crackle, and sparks shot out of her flashing eyes. She and Merlyn stood facing each other a full sixty seconds, without a word spoken, and then Madame Mim swept a royal curtsey and Merlyn bowed a frigid bow. He stood aside to let her go first out of the doorway and then followed her into the garden.

It ought perhaps to be explained, before we go any further, that in those far-off days, when there was actually a college for Witches and Warlocks under the sea at Dom-Daniel and when all wizards were either black or white, there was a good deal of ill-feeling between the different creeds. Quarrels between white and black were settled ceremonially, by means of duels. A wizard's duel was run like this: The two principals would stand opposite each other in some large space free from obstructions, and await the signal to begin. When the signal was given they were at liberty to turn themselves into things. It was rather like the game that can be played by two people with their fists. They say One, Two, Three, and at Three they either stick out two fingers for scissors, or the flat palm for paper, or the clenched fist for stone. If your hand becomes paper when your opponent's becomes scissors, then he cuts you and wins; but if yours has turned into stone, his scissors are blunted, and the win is yours. The object of the wizard in the duel was to turn himself into some kind of animal, vegetable or mineral which would destroy the particular animal, vegetable or mineral which had been selected by his opponent. Sometimes it went on for hours.

Merlyn had Archimedes for his second, Madame Mim had the gorecrow for hers, while Hecate, who always had to be present at these affairs in order to keep them regular, sat on the top of a step-ladder in the middle, to umpire. She was a cold, shining, muscular lady, the color of moonlight. Merlyn and Madame Mim rolled up their sleeves, gave their surcoats to Hecate to hold, and the latter put on a celluloid eye-shade to watch the battle.

At the first gong Madame Mim immediately turned herself into a dragon. It was the accepted opening move and Merlyn ought to have replied by being a thunderstorm or something like that. Instead, he caused a great deal of preliminary confusion by becoming a field mouse, which was quite invisible in the grass, and nibbled Madame Mim's tail, as she stared about in all directions, for about five minutes before she noticed him. But when she did notice the nibbling, she was a furious cat in two flicks.

Wart held his breath to see what the mouse would become next—he thought perhaps a tiger which could kill the cat—but Merlyn merely became another cat. He stood opposite her and made faces. This most irregular procedure put Madame Mim quite out of her stride, and it took her more than a minute to regain her bearings and become a dog. Even as she became it, Merlyn was another dog standing opposite her, of the same sort.

"Oh, well played, sir!" cried the Wart, beginning to see the plan.

Madame Mim was furious. She felt herself out of her depth against these unusual stone-walling tactics and experienced an internal struggle not to lose her temper. She knew that if she did lose it she would lose her judgment, and the battle as well. She did some quick thinking. If whenever she turned herself into a menacing animal, Merlyn was merely going to turn into the same kind, the thing would become either a mere dog-fight or stalemate. She had better alter her own tactics and give Merlyn a surprise.

At this moment the gong went for the end of the first round. The combatants retired into their respective corners and their seconds cooled them by flapping their wings, while Archimedes gave Merlyn a little massage by nibbling with his beak.

"Second round," commanded Hecate. "Seconds out of the ring.... Time!"

Clang went the gong, and the two desperate wizards stood face to face.

Madame Mim had gone on plotting during her rest. She had decided to try a new tack by leaving the offensive to Merlyn, beginning by assuming a defensive shape herself. She turned into a spreading oak.

Merlyn stood baffled under the oak for a few seconds. Then he most cheekily—and, as it turned out, rashly—became a powdery little blue-tit, which flew up and sat perkily on Madame Mim's branches. You could see the oak boiling with indignation for a moment; but then its rage became icy cold, and the poor little blue-tit was sitting, not on an oak, but on a snake. The snake's mouth was open, and the bird was actually perching on its jaws. As the jaws clashed together, but only in the nick of time, the bird whizzed off as a gnat into the safe air. Madame Mim had got it on the run, however, and the speed of the contest now became bewildering. The quicker the attacker could assume a form, the less time the fugitive had to think of a form which would elude it, and now the changes were as quick as thought. The gnat was scarcely in the air when the snake had turned into a toad whose curious tongue, rooted at the front instead of the back of the jaw, was already unrolling in the flick which would snap it in. The gnat, flustered by the sore pursuit, was bounced into an offensive role, and the hard-pressed Merlyn now stood before the toad in the shape of a mollern which could attack it. But Madame Mim was in her element. The game was going according to the normal rules now, and in less than an eye's blink the toad had turned into a peregrine falcon which was diving at two hundred and fifty miles an hour upon the heron's back. Poor Merlyn, beginning to lose his nerve, turned wildly into an elephant—this move usually won a little breathing space— but Madame Mim, relentless, changed from the falcon into an aullay on the instant. An aullay was as much bigger than an elephant as an elephant is larger than a sheep. It was a sort of horse with an elephant's trunk. Madame Mim raised this trunk in the air, gave a shriek like a railway engine, and rushed upon her panting foe. In a flick Merlyn had disappeared.

"One," said Hecate. "Two. Three. Four. Five. Six. Seven. Eight. Nine—"

But before the fatal Ten which would have counted him out, Merlyn reappeared in a bed of nettles, mopping his brow. He had been standing among them as a nettle.

The aullay saw no reason to change its shape. It rushed upon the man before it with another piercing scream. Merlyn vanished again just as the thrashing trunk descended, and all stood still a moment, looking about them, wondering where he would step out next.

"One," began Hecate again, but even as she proceeded with her counting, strange things began to happen. The aullay got hiccoughs, turned red, swelled visibly, began whooping, came out in spots, staggered three times, rolled its eyes, fell rumbling to the ground. It groaned, kicked and said Farewell. The Wart cheered, Archimedes hooted till he cried, the gore-crow fell down dead, and Hecate, on the top of her ladder, clapped so much that she nearly tumbled off. It was a master stroke.

The ingenious magician had turned himself successively into the microbes, not yet discovered, of hiccoughs, scarlet fever, mumps, whooping cough, measles and heat spots, and from a complication of all these complaints the infamous Madame Mim had immediately expired.

[From *The Sword in the Stone*]

John Betjeman

John Betjeman is an architect, or at least he has an unusual amateur's interest in architecture. I recommend his Ghastly Good Taste. *There is another fine poem of his in W. H. Auden's* Oxford Book of Light Verse.

DISTANT VIEW OF A PROVINCIAL TOWN

Beside those spires so spick and span
    Against an unencumbered sky,
The old Great Western Railway ran
    When some one different was I.

St. Aidan's with the prickly knobs
    And iron spikes and coloured tiles—
Where Auntie Maud devoutly bobs
    In those enriched vermilion aisles.

St. George's where the mattins bell
    But rarely drowned the trams for prayer—
No Popish sight or sound or smell
    Disturbed that gas-invaded air.

St. Mary's where the Rector preached
    In such a jolly friendly way
On cricket, football, things that reached
    The simple life of every day.

And that United Benefice
    With entrance permanently locked—
How Gothic, grey and sad it is
    Since Mr. Grogley was unfrocked!

The old Great Western Railway shakes,
    The old Great Western Railway spins—
The old Great Western Railway makes
    Me very sorry for my sins.

Peter Fleming

Peter Fleming is the fellow who took those long solitary journeys through the Brazilian jungle and the Thibetan hinterlands, wearing a pair of worn-out shoes and carrying a gun with a bent barrel. The attached essay, which is the foreword to a collection of his pieces in the Spectator, *makes clear that his later journeys were undertaken as a relief from being a humorist, and were perhaps even a form of penance.*

ADVICE TO THE READER

C'est une étrange entreprise que celle de faire rire les honnêtes gens—Molière

The process known as Going Downhill has always had for me a powerful, though of course a purely theoretical, fascination. In the kind of fiction I like best there is always a character who Goes Downhill. The stages of his descent are never very closely followed (he is a subsidiary character), but in the last chapter, or in the epilogue if there is one, we get a glimpse of him at the bottom. . . .

Old Etonian braces gleam through a match-seller's rags. An Authentics blazer shows for a moment in the noisome portals of an opium den. A beachcomber quotes Horace between hiccoughs.

"Don't look, my dear," says the hero, thrusting his new-won bride into a taxi, or a rickshaw, or a dhow.

"Why not?" she asks (girl-like) as they get under way.

"That was Carruthers," replies the hero, in a husky voice. "I didn't want him to know we saw.[1] Carruthers . . . My God! To have sunk as low as this. . . . He was Captain of the XI," explains the hero, "my first term."

It is most affecting. The degradation of Carruthers never fails to move me. To start as Captain of the XI, and to end as a match-seller, or an opium-pedlar, or a beachcomber—what a falling off is there!

[1] Or "to see we knew."

Could any one—I mean, of course, any one who has been to a public school—sink from such heights so low?

I used to think that they could not. I used to think that opium-peddling and the rest of it marked the ultimate dark bottom of the abyss—that one could go no further downhill. But now I know that this is not so. There are worse fates, greater depths of humiliation. Or, to be quite accurate, there is one. Carruthers might have become a Humorous Writer.

If he had, revulsion would have strangled the pity which we felt for him before, for what is viler or more despicable than a man whose life-work consists in Trying to be Funny? And yet, poor fellow, his claim on our compassion would be stronger than ever. Carruthers' case was pitiful enough already, no doubt: a man who habitually bowled to three slips can hardly have enjoyed selling matches. But as a Humorous Writer his lot would be ten times worse.

As a match-seller, he had at least a niche in the impressive and complicated structure of World Trade; as an opium-pedlar, he satisfied a constant and even (they tell me) an acute demand; while for the existence of a beachcomber there is justification in the thought that, after all, somebody has got [2] to be a beachcomber. But no one can make out any sort of an excuse for the Humorous Writer.

The Humorous Writer is a superfluous monster, an unhappy freak. There is enough humour about the place already without adding to the world's stock by making black marks on a bit of paper. Life is a funny business. The road winds uphill all the way, but it is covered, as Nietzsche pointed out, with banana skins. To publish humour in a literary form is indeed to do mankind a disservice; for it breeds in them a neglect for the raw humour of life, and they keep their laughter for *Punch* as they keep their piety for church. The Humorous Writer is an anti-social pest.

His genesis was accidental. Humorous writing started in England in the ninth century A.D., and it started by mistake. What happened, if my memory serves me right, was this:

The King of Wessex, Hrogswith the Ineffectual (not to be confused with his son, Hrogswith the Good, or his uncle, Hrogswith the Filthy-Minded: not to be confused with any one, in fact—it's not fair on

---

[2] For proof of this necessity, see Professor R. W. V. Farbetter's monograph on "Occupational Misfits in Polynesia," and also Miss Stamina Tells' more sympathetic "Leisure at the Helm."

him)—well, the King of Wessex wanted an ode composed in honour of his wife, the beautiful Stoppa of Northamptonshire. A young poet called Hacklefroth (or, as we should say today, Hacklefroth) got the job, and turned out 504 verses of very decent stuff indeed. Professor Wind, of Cincinnati University, says that verse 2 is much the best, but I can't help feeling that is because he didn't get any further than verse 2; all the verses look good to me.

They all looked good to Hrogswith, too. The thing was a best-seller for those days. The King ordered no less than eight copies to be made, and the Queen said she really must learn to read one of these days, if only she could find the time.

Then a most unfortunate thing happened. Two of the monks (their names were Hodda and Staotun) who were at work on one of the copies made a misprint. They were frivolous young fellows, who ought never to have gone into the Church at all, and instead of getting another sheepskin and starting their copy again they deliberately let the misprint stand. It was a particularly unfortunate one; in verse 89, line 3, Hodda had written down *byngorlichthan* (which means a wissel-throde) as *byngorlochthan* (which means a sney, or flinge). The passage, you will scarcely need to be reminded, is one in which the poet is comparing the Queen's nose to a number of beautiful things, among them the dainty wissel-throde; the misprint—which made it appear as if the analogy drawn was with a sney, or flinge—rendered the whole verse not only nonsensical but slightly obscene. One would have thought that only to people with very depraved minds, or to foreigners, could the consequences of this distortion appear laughable; but Hodda and Staotun were so tickled by the humorous possibilities of their initial blunder that they began to misprint words deliberately. That is why one of the three extant copies of Hacklefroth's ode amounts to nothing better than a lampoon, which, as *lèse majesté*, reaches its culminating point in verse 492, where Stoppa is likened, not to the moon sailing in the sky, but to a young badger gorging itself on worts.

The discovery of their elaborate and disgraceful joke provided one of the court scandals of the day, and Hodda and Staotun fled to East Anglia. They knew that it was unlikely that they would ever be asked to copy anything out again; but the new vice had fast hold of them, and it was not long before they realized that it was in their power to satisfy, unaided, their insatiate craving for what a later age was to describe as literary compositions of a humorous nature. Soon they were hard at it, turning out Light Verse and Occasional Essays whenever they could get hold of a sheepskin. A new influence had been born in English literature; and you can judge what sort of an influence it was from the fact that Professor Wind calls Hodda "an East Anglian Elia" and Staotun "the Milne of the Middle Ages." Humorous writing had started.

Since then it has raged practically unchecked: an unnatural practice, superfluous, degrading, in every way to be deplored. Those who can do anything, however small, to stamp it out are public benefactors; and I therefore appeal to the reader of these words to buy up all the available copies of this book and burn them. If the publisher brings out another edition, buy that up, too. Go on till he stops. It's practically a duty, when you come to think of it.

R. A. A. Robertson

KULTUR

Typical englisch Conversations for nordic Students
(Made in Germany)

I. Horseflesch

(The Scene is at the Horseflesch-market.)

Lord Smith: I would buy a nag.*

The Vendor: Certainly, milord. I have horses of all colours, of all sizes and of all shapes for dirty track racing, hacking, leaping or the fox-chase. Examine, pray, the yellow dun.

Viscount Brown: Make it go at a foot-pace, in trot, in galop and with loose rains.

Lord Robinson: It is a good ambler, by Jove.*

Lord Smith: It takes frights. It walks rudely. It jolts.

Viscount Brown: It jumps both ways.

The Vendor: No, indeed, milord, what ho. It is the cat which jumps both ways altogether, according to our englisch folk proverb saying.

(All shake their sides with tittering. It is a choke.)

Lord Robinson: Ho Ho Ho! I am so tikled!* I am so tikled! Ho ho ho!

Lord Smith: Perchance we shall purchace the nag. But first we shall examine the others, great Scot! *

[They depart, talking shops.]

The Vendor: Aha! They talk shops.* We Englisch are a nation of shoptalkers. Aha!

* Sehr idiomatisch.

786

(This too is also a choke as well. Englisch chokes are quite peculiar. Students are advised to chortle, for it is polite.)

II. Society.

LORD SMITH: I am going into society. Are you also invited as well?

VISCOUNT BROWN: Always I am invited.

(They go into society.)

LORD SMITH: Let us commence a conversation with these lords.

VISCOUNT BROWN: Consider what you are about. One would think you no gentleman. Dear me! You have to be introduced by the lady of the house.

LORD ROBINSON: There are beutiful ladies here, splendid toilets.

LORD SMITH: It is hot. The air is so thick, one can hardly see each other.

VISCOUNT BROWN: Take some sherbert—some limonade.

LORD ROBINSON: Thanks. I can be without it.

LORD SMITH: I perceive champagne.

VISCOUNT BROWN: Good egg!

LORD ROBINSON: Let us all swallow the champagne!

(All swallow.)

ALL: Ah! The topping englisch society!

III. Sporty Talk

LORD SMITH: Let us televone some of the best people and brobose a party at cricket, foutbal, tennice, rogger, sogger, pingping, horse-polo or le croquet.

LORD ROBINSON: I pooh-pooh the idea. It rains cat and dog, with thunder. Besides, my hat, there is snow, I hear! Too bad!

VISCOUNT BROWN: I too pooh-pooh the idea. Let us therefore commence a conversation of a sporty species. Eh what?

LORD SMITH: Are we all sporty public schoolers?

LORD ROBINSON *and* VISCOUNT BROWN *(together)*: Indeed of course we naturally attended the very best establishment every day.

Lord Smith: Not only gained I a bosition in the first fivdeen of Rogby sports but also one at the same time in the segond.

Viscount Brown: I played the part of the man who defends the sticks. The goalbird.

Lord Robinson: Pay attention! Lo! it shines. Let us go a-hunting.

(They go and a-hunt.)

Lord Smith: Halloo! Whoopee! Oscar has found something; he stands. Peace! It is a partridge!

Viscount Brown: I perceive many braces.

Lord Robinson: Let us enter the spot where they have perched.

Lord Smith: Alas! my birdshot passed the partridge by and entered the beater while he bended. Dear, dear!

Viscount Brown: He squeals.

Lord Robinson: That is enough sport for today. Let us carry him into the house.

A Servingman: Milords, the lunchion awaits!

The Sporty Lords: We will at once munch the lunch. Let us bang off our guns before entering.

The Servingman: How sporty are the milords!

The Beater: Would that I had not bended!

IV. At Meat

Lord Smith *(the host)*: The gong has banged. Let us set to.

Viscount Brown: First let us grace.   *(They grace.)*

Lord Smith: Do not sup the broth so. It is not-done. It is putrid bad form.

Lord Robinson: It is putrid bad broth.

Lord Smith: What? Eh, I say! But no, I see what! You are pulling me by the legs,* eh? Well, I am not one of those fellows who grumble when they are pulled by the legs. I can laugh it off at myself ever so merrily.

(Laughs at himself.)

*Englisch custom.

VISCOUNT BROWN: What a fish! Scrumptious! I smack my lip* with love for this tasty dish of fresh, fried fish. I beg, please pass the salt-box.

LORD SMITH: There is now chops and juggled hare.

(All lick their chops.*)

LORD SMITH: Pray, the chops I hope are not overdone?

LORD ROBINSON: Nay. This one is quite undone, I assure you.

VISCOUNT BROWN: Shall I dine wisely or twice as well?

LORD ROBINSON: It is the same thing. Aha! How I am a funny choker! Ho! ho! It is good to make chokes, while at meat, as a digestive.

(All choke together.)

LORD SMITH: What fun!

VISCOUNT BROWN: Quite first-hole!

LORD SMITH: May I help you with the gravy?

LORD ROBINSON: Thanks, no. There is already a sufficiency in my spoon.

LORD SMITH: Pray chew some slices of this sweetie. It is Rolly-Polo.

VISCOUNT BROWN: Nay. I always pass the pudding by. It distresses my within.

LORD SMITH: Then sample this dessert fruit or pastry cake.*

VISCOUNT BROWN: Thanks. I shall take the cake.*

LORD SMITH: Here is porto and cigars. Let us drink ourselves under the table.*

*Englisch custom.

(They do so.)

Nathaniel Gubbins

Nathaniel Gubbins is the chief humorist of the Sunday Express. *His real name is Nathaniel Gubbins. There was obviously only one course open to him.*

FUN IN A NURSING HOME

If you read what I have written here (and as I am in bed feeling as if I had just taken part in an "all-in" wrestling match, I don't care twopence if you read it or not) you must forgive me if you discern occasionally a certain vagueness of statement, an incoherence of thought or kind of whimsical rambling, which, if written by Sir James Barrie, would have set his admirers simpering and whimpering with joy.

If there is anything strange or wild in what is to come, you must not blame me, but the following diet upon which I have subsisted for the past week:

MONDAY

Aspirin varié
Œufs au lait à la Maison
Grand Injection Morphine
L'eau froid

TUESDAY

Aspirin varié
Œufs au lait Maître d'Hôtel
Grand Injection Heroin
L'eau chaud

WEDNESDAY

Same as Monday

THURSDAY

Same as Tuesday

FRIDAY

Aspirin varié
Consommé mystérieuse
Œufs au lait Bonne Femme
L'eau

SATURDAY

Same as Friday

SUNDAY

Aspirin varié
Mouth-Wash Angleterre
Injection spéciale au docteur
Tonic 'Orrible
Œuf au lait disgoosting
Café terrible

* * *

12 midday: I am sitting alone in my little room at the nursing home waiting to be called to the operating theatre. They have given me an injection and a copy of *Punch*. What more could I want?

12:05 P.M.: I am still waiting. The matron, smiling the forced, fixed, eternal, irremovable, come-let-us-be-cheerful smile worn by all matrons in front of all patients, says, "How do you feel?"

"Like a rat in a trap," I reply.

The matron, shocked, but still smiling, goes out.

12:15 P.M.: I begin to wonder if I have been reprieved by the Home Secretary. Perhaps I shall only get twenty years' penal servitude. Life seems sweet in these last few moments.

After all I never meant the girl any harm.... What girl? ... What am I saying? ...Am I in a nursing home or a condemned cell? Am I a convicted murderer? I cannot be.

Convicted murderers have what they like for breakfast on the last morning. Here they would not give me any breakfast. I must be in a nursing home.

12:30 P.M.: There is a tap on the door.

Is it the priest and the prison governor? No, it is the nurse. She says, "They are ready for you. And the trolley is waiting outside." I fling *Punch* out of the window. The first ordeal is over.

12:35 P.M.: I refuse to travel on the trolley. I am not a cripple. I am not even ill—yet. So I push the trolley myself. The nurses laugh. When I arrive in the theatre pushing my trolley, the surgeons and the doctors laugh. Patients must be humoured. Brightness is everything.

12:40 P.M.: I am lying on my back with a little cage over my nose and mouth. The anaesthetist is allowing drops of chloroform to saturate the cage.

"Count after me," he says. "One." "One," I reply. "Two." he says. "Two," I reply. "Three." "Three."

We reach the thirties, and I am beginning to think I am rather clever to answer back.

"Thirty-two," he says. "And the same to you," I reply.

"Thirty-three." "Two for tea."

"Thirty-four." "And a sock on the jaw...."

"That's very clever of you," says the anaesthetist.

"It's——clever," I shout back.

"All right," says a faraway voice, "it's——clever."

5 P.M.: I am back in my bed, and the nursing-home cabaret is on. The room has been transformed into a Honolulu beach scene. Seventeen nurses, their arms and faces stained brown with iodine, are dancing the Hula-hula, and the matron, in the foreground, is prancing up and down singing:

> Whatever you have the matter with you—
> A boil, or carbuncle, a bunion or two,
> Or even a bout of the gout or the 'flu,

> Paint it with iodine,
> Paint it with iodine,
> Paint it with iodine,
> Do!

THE CHORUS OF SEVENTEEN NURSES:

> Paint it with iodine,
> Paint it with iodine,
> Paint it with iodine,
> Do.

THE MATRON:

> Perhaps you have toothache or tic douloureux?
> Perhaps you have something entirely new?
> Perhaps you're in love or perhaps you feel blue.

> Paint it with iodine,
> Paint it with iodine,
> Paint it with iodine,
> Do.

THE CHORUS:

> Paint it with iodine,
> Do.

A YOUNG SURGEON: Hello, girls, let's all go to Monte Carlo. What do you say?

THE CHORUS: Oo-o, let's. Hooray. Hooray.

THE MATRON: Certainly not.

THE CHORUS: Why not?

THE MATRON:

> We have patients in the home
> None of whom are fit to roam,
> And what is more important still,
> Each must pay his weekly bill.

THE CHORUS:

>Each must pay his weekly bill,
>It is costly to be ill.
>Special medicines and dressings,
>Cotton wool and other blessings.

The young surgeon suddenly draws his knife and rushes at the matron, shouting:

>"The time has come," the surgeon said,
>>"To take out many things,
>Your tonsils and appendices,
>>And swabs and curtain rings."

The matron runs screaming past my bed with the surgeon following. The Hula-hula chorus race after him, and as the last one is passing I grab her by the arm.

"Little brown girl love big, bald white man?" I ask. "Big, bald white man he heap plenty money. Make little brown girl very happy."

5:05 P.M.: The Honolulu beach scene has been replaced by the bare walls of my room, and instead of holding a slim brown wrist I am clinging desperately to a starched white cuff.

"Drink this," says the ex-Hula-hula girl, "and you will feel better."

[From *The Diary of a Worm*]

Daniel Pettiward

CORRESPONDENCE OF A CENSOR

DEAR MRS. BOLEWEEVIL,

In the course of my duties as a censor of letters I can't help noticing, since you devoted some three pages to the subject, that you were a martyr to tired feet. Now I know what it is to suffer in this way, so I feel that I must write and tell you of the benefit which I have derived from bathing the affected members in a solution of bread-crumbs and barley-water. I am afraid I was compelled to delete the instructions which you sent your sister for knitting a pullover suitable for our fighting forces. My wife tried to follow the instructions during the fortnight that your letter was with us, and since her efforts seemed to be heading unmistakably towards a tea-cosy I felt I was justified in assuming that you had inadvertently chosen the wrong pattern to send. We were unable to believe that you were genuinely desirous of providing the Forces with tea-cosies, even supposing they could discover some outlet for the arms and head.

Yours very truly,

HERBERT CLAMM

P. S.—I loved your description of the moonlight over the downs and your graphic account of the anti-aircraft guns peeping out of the heather "like giant sticks of liquorice," though I wasn't able to follow all the technical details you supplied.

DEAR MRS. JAMES,

In a letter from a Mrs. Tightfit to a Mrs. Peahen which recently came into my hands officially I was interested to find mention of your husband, Chutney James, my old school friend. James came to Cadminster in the hard winter of '03 and early made his mark as a deadly adversary with the bread pellet. I was shocked to learn that he was beating you, though not surprised when I recall what a stern disciplinarian he was—ready in his last years to pounce on and ruthlessly stamp out the slightest hint of inefficiency on the part of any of his fags. I would suggest that if he starts beating you again you might try saying, "What became of Clamm's batting gloves?" in a sinister voice. I hope that you still find a use for the fish-slice which I believe I presented to Chutney on the occasion of his wedding.

Yours sincerely,

Herbert (Fishy) Clamm

Dear Mr. Drill,

The remark which in your letter to Mrs. Homingpin you claim to have been made by your little niece was actually first made by my Uncle Redgrave when, as a child of three, he was taken to the Great Exhibition. I have taken the liberty of mentioning this in a footnote and also altering the ending slightly in a way which I am sure you will agree is an improvement. The story now runs as follows:

Great-Aunt Rosa (*to her son* Redgrave): Now, Redgrave, say "Good-bye" to Canon Corker.

Uncle Redgrave: Shan't.

Canon Corker: Come, now, say "Good-bye," you little ruffian.

Uncle Redgrave (*to* Canon Corker, *resignedly*): Good-bye, you little ruffian.

I am sorry to hear your parsnips have not repaid the confidence you placed in them.

Yours, etc.,

H. Clamm

P. S.—Do you honestly think you spell manoovers "manoeuvres"?

Dear Mrs. Beamend,

With reference to your letter to a Miss Handcart declaring your affection for a Mr. Freebooter, I have, curiously enough, had to deal with some of Mr. Freebooter's correspondence and am in a position to tell you that it is not a bit of use you running after him because he is in love with a certain Miss Claplow. Perhaps it would be kindest in the end to tell you that when Mr. Freebooter has occasion to bring up your name he more often than not refers to you as the "not very merry widow." I was sorry to hear that you were finding the long winter evenings dull and that your little dog is off colour. I may be passing through your neighborhood next Tuesday, and as I have made rather a study of dogs' ailments perhaps you would not take it amiss if

I were to drop in to offer a little advice and (who knows?) encouragement.

Yours in antic.,

HERBY CLAMM

MY DEAR COUSIN,

I must apologise to you that in my capacity as a censor I was forced to delete so much of my sister's letter to you, but the censored passages could not have been of the slightest interest to you and merely dealt with private affairs of mine which Jane had no right whatsoever to divulge. I regret also that the snapshot (taken by me) of Jane and her baby is not included as I do not consider it anything like my best work, as it gives Jane a quite erroneous appearance of good looks. I have substituted a snapshot of my dog Gregory which I consider much more tasteful. I am thoroughly enjoying my new job and find it far more exhilarating than my work as a photograph tinter.

Yours ever,

COUSIN CLAMMY

DEAR MR. MAPLEDURHAM,

Forgive my apparently butting into your affairs, but I couldn't help observing in your letter to Mr. Dimple which came to my notice recently that you claimed to have come to an understanding with a young person called Bubbles. If by any conceivable chance it turned out to be Bubbles Pinkerton-Jones, I strongly advise you against continuing the attachment, as I was engaged to her once myself and discovered that among other things she wears a wig and has a husband in the Federated Malay States. If, as I hope, it is quite another Bubbles I can only wish you the very best of luck in your venture.

Yours truly,

HERBERT CLAMM

Angela Milne

ENTERTAINING IN WAR-TIME

One of the more unimportant aspects of the war in this country is the lack of effect it has had on entertaining. To put it more plainly, people still visit other people, as often as not when there is a meal going, and on the whole the other people are no gladder or sorrier to see them than they were before. Then these other people are asked, in return, to have meals with the people who had meals with them, and *those* people are no gladder or sorrier either. You see how it all is. It would take more than a war to stop it.

There are, of course, two kinds of entertaining, according to whether you live in London or the country, and I shall ignore the first kind because nowadays it is nearly always the same. People ring up to say they are in London and are coming round for a drink. Then they come round for a drink.

But in the country it is more involved. The first thing that happens is that there is a ring at the front door (unless the bell has a strip of sticking-plaster over it, when there is a knock), and the people in the house have to be pretty quick thinking what to do about it. Not that thinking helps, because the reactions of some one in a house who hears some one else at the door are purely instinctive. People trapped in a drawing-room with the front door between them and the rest of the house instinctively tidy the room. They do it in curious ways. If they are playing halma they ram the lid on the box and push it under the sofa. It is as if some primal urge in the human conscience had been telling it all the time not to play halma and in this unguarded moment has got the upper hand. Again, people eating chocolates hide the chocolate box. This is easier to analyse.

People scattered over the house and garden also react instinctively. If in the garden, they instinctively work out which bush or tree will put them out of sight from the house and move behind it. If they are in the house their instinct takes them up to their bedrooms. But the funny part of all this is that when it turns out to be a tradesman who didn't know there was a side door, everyone is instinctively disappointed.

It is not usually recognised, by the way, that visitors waiting for a door to open feel just as bad as the people inside. They wish they had never come. If there are several of them they say so among themselves, but very quietly, because if one side knew that it knew what the other side was thinking the whole thing would fold up. The people inside, if they hear the murmur of voices on the door-step, think the people outside the house are telling each other how happy they are.

But all this is nothing to what happens when the visitors get *inside* the house. The people who were already in it find themselves doing and saying the most extraordinary things. They run downstairs or in from the garden. They say they are glad to see them, even if they are not, and it has seemed ages since they last saw them, even if the time has gone by in a flash. One minute of this will so tie up both sides—for the visitors are just as bad—over what is true and what isn't that they will often agree it is a lovely day when it is pouring. You see what a maze of subterfuge and self-deception it all is.

Now for the actual *entertaining*. As you know, this means meals. While it is true that in war-time the people who used to come to a house only to eat and drink have had one or two setbacks, visitors still expect meals. The meals people usually come to are tea, dinner, and lunch. No one comes to breakfast. People are not awfully pleased about people coming to lunch because there is an idea behind their minds that it makes them too important. They have to get themselves tidy, and they feel let down in the middle of the afternoon. People like people coming to dinner because there is not time afterwards to feel let down, and they like them coming to tea because it means there is more to eat than there ordinarily would be.

Remember, by the way, that when you cut bread and butter the slices will get thinner and thinner as you get your eye in, and then thicker and thicker because the end of a loaf is difficult to hold. So don't put the slices on the plate as you cut them; arrange them afterwards with the thin ones on top. There is still a chance that your visitors will get the thick ones, but you will have done your best, and these details mean a lot in entertaining. Another detail is not to cut a cake before you ask your visitors if they want any; with any luck they will say No, they would rather have a chocolate biscuit. They think you want to keep the cake whole but they think you don't know they think so. *You* think they don't know you want to keep the cake whole, so you give them a chocolate biscuit and everything is all right.

Remember that very few people ask their visitors when they are going. They wait for them to make the first move. If a visitor asks if a clock is right, they either say it is or it is a bit fast. If a visitor burns a hole in an armchair with a cigarette they deliberately say it doesn't matter. The result of all this is of course that the visitors feel they are in a false position. They can only get straight again by returning the invitation and having *their* armchairs burnt. So, as I was saying, you see how it is.

Angela Thirkell

Part of Angela Thirkell's charm derives from the fact that she does not particularly love humanity. This, in a time when love and hatred are prescribed on a national basis, is very piquant. Miss Thirkell is cruel to men, and more cruel to women; and she has even the courage to dislike children. (Of course, I recognize that in private life she has a heart as big as a watermelon.)

EVACUEES IN BARSETSHIRE

When the question of receiving children from danger zones was first discussed, Mrs. Miller, who had taken on the ungrateful job of Billeting Officer, had been inspired to put all the children—luckily not a very large number, for Pomfret Madrigal was a small village with a very small Church school—into cottagers' houses. Here the eight shillings and sixpence a week provided for the evacuees by a grateful if bewildered country were extremely welcome and the London children, apart from their natural nostalgia for playing in dirty streets till midnight and living on fish and chips, settled down almost at once into the conditions of licence, dirt, overcrowding and margarine to which they were accustomed. The special Paradise, much envied by such children as were billeted elsewhere, was Grumper's End, the congested district of Pomfret Madrigal, and in that Paradise the most longed-for house was the Thatchers'. Here Mr. and Mrs. Thatcher, with eight children of their own, found no difficulty in housing four more, and to their hospitable kitchen, where cups of strong tea and bits of tinned salmon were almost always to be had for the asking or the taking, most of Pomfret Madrigal's twenty evacuated children gravitated. As they only went to school in the morning, the afternoon being kept for the village children, they had played, screamed, fought, made mud pies, or fallen into a little pond covered with green slime for four blissful weeks and all called Mr. and Mrs. Thatcher Daddy and Mummy. As for Percy and Gladys Thatcher, the children of shame of the two eldest Thatcher girls, they had never enjoyed themselves so much in their very young lives. Pulled about in an old soapbox onto which Ernie Thatcher their young uncle by shame had fixed wheels, stuffed with the sweets which all the evacuee children bought with postal orders sent every week by their parents, carefully instructed in all the latest bad words fashionable in the select locality round King's Cross Station from which St. Gingolph's (C. of E.) School had been evacuated, they became so overbearing that Mr. Thatcher said more than once that he'd have to take the stick to them, while Mrs. Thatcher, feeling that with so many children about everything was all right, went out charing from morning to night, so that what with the money she earned and the money that Edna and Doris, the mothers of the children of shame, were earning as daily helps at the Cow and Sickle, which was doing very well owing to officers' wives who wanted to be within reach of Sparrowhill Camp, Mr. Thatcher was able to lose more on the dogs than ever and was later to lose in the Football Pools an amount of money that earned him the deep respect of every one in the Cow and Sickle Tap.

As for the really difficult children, Mr. and Mrs. Miller, who were as good as gold, had taken them into the Vicarage and though Mrs. Miller had not the faintest hope of reforming them (for she was a very sensible and practical woman) she managed to keep her eye on them to that extent that they found it less trouble on the whole to do what the Lady said. All the jobs she found for them in house or garden were cunningly chosen to include dirt or destruction in some shape, and after a Saturday on which they had helped Cook (of whom they were in as much awe as their natures permitted) to clean out the flues of the kitchen stove, had helped the gardener to fetch a load of pig manure from a neighbouring farm, and to empty the septic tank near his cottage, they all burst into tears at the sight of their parents who came down on Sunday for the day to see them, hit at their mothers, used language to their fathers which surpassed anything that St. Gingolph's had yet produced, and said they would never go home.

The most beautiful autumn that any one could remember now spread its mantle over Barsetshire and the rest of England. The evacuated children, who were by now all dressed by the hand of charity in coloured woolen frocks arted up at the neck, and coloured woollen coats of no particular shape or cut, not to speak of nightgowns and dressing-gowns and underclothes, looked fatter and pinker every day. Owing to the vigorous efforts of volunteer workers there was now not a lice-infested head among them, except when one of them was taken back to London by its parents for a week, cried all the time, and was returned to start the whole thing all over again. The primitive Wessex speech of the country children was being rapidly overlaid with a fine veneer of Cockney. As far as bad words went neither side had the advantage and the grosser names of Barsetshire were bartered against the more up-to-date obscenities of the evacuated areas. In writing, however, the London children had a distinct advantage. Maturing more early than the children of the soil, quicker if shallower witted, more bad language was written on the walls of Southbridge owing to their efforts in ten weeks than had been seen since Roman soldiers inscribed facetiae on the clay tiles of the Roman villa whose foundations had lately been excavated near Northbridge.

Lydia Keith, after a single-handed fight with Palmer about tea-cloths in which she scored heavily, went off on foot to Northbridge village with a large flowered overall in a bag. As most of the neighbourhood was Cathedral property, and the firm of Keith and Keith had for many years done much of their legal business, Mr. Keith had been able to put gentle spokes in the way of building development, and even bully the Barsetshire County Council into building quite presentable houses for the working classes well away from the delightful village street, of which no fewer than fourteen different views, including the church, the brick and stone houses of the gentry and the remaining plaster and thatch houses of the cottagers can be got at any picture postcard shop in Barchester. Next to the Hollies, a pleasant Georgian house standing back behind its shrubbery, was a plain-faced stone house that had been vacant for some time owing to a death and an entangled will. As soon as the threat of evacuee children had become a near menace, the Women's Institute, headed by Mrs. Turner who lived at the Hollies and her two nieces who lived with her, had given an entertainment followed by a whist drive and dance by which they earned enough money to start a Communal Kitchen. The trustees had consented to the use of the large kitchen quarters of the empty house, the money from the entertainment had been used to install a new gas cooker and buy a quantity of cheap tables and forms, some very cheap cutlery and various cleaning materials. Volunteers had supplied cooking utensils, dish cloths, crockery, and other necessities. The possessors of vegetable gardens and hens had promised weekly supplies according to their means. Mrs. Turner from her own purse bought a part share in a pig whose owner was on the dole and had no intention of coming off it, and supplied a pig bucket, on the understanding that the pig's owner would fetch the bucket daily and make over certain portions of the pig to the Women's Institute when it was killed.

With a great burst of gladness and relief nearly all the hostesses of the evacuated boys and girls sent them up to the Kitchen, paying three-pence a head for an excellent and substantial meal. It is true that almost in the same breath they said that threepence was too much, but Mrs. Turner took no notice at all. Under her truculent despotism a number of ladies undertook to do the cooking, the serving, and the washing-up in rotation, and it must be said to the credit of North-bridge that very few had defaulted. What with her mother and the house and the Red Cross and the estate and working parties, Lydia had not much time to spare, but she helped to serve the lunches one day a week and, as we have seen, did not allow anything to interfere with it.

The church clock was striking twelve as Lydia went into the house by the side door and down a long stone-flagged passage to what were called by the estate agent the commodious offices. Here Mrs. Turner was hard at work superintending the preparation of great saucepans of rabbit stew and potatoes. She had been at the Kitchen since ten o'clock that morning and would be there till the last helper had gone, and this she did every day except Saturdays and Sundays. By her instructions the gas cooker had been installed in the scullery, so that the washing-up could go on under her eye. The kitchen itself with its wasteful range and huge dresser was not used, and the servants' hall had been turned into a dining-room. In it Mrs. Turner's nieces were laying a knife and fork and a spoon and fork and a china cup fifty times over on the bare deal tables. Lydia put on her overall and seizing two large tin loaves cut them up into small hunks, two plates of which she put on each table. She then filled a large jug with water and poured some into each cup, repeating these actions till all the cups were half-full; for if they were any fuller the children always slopped them at once.

"That's right," said Mrs. Turner, as she prodded a large saucepan of potatoes to see if they were done. "How is your mother, Lydia?"

"Pretty all right," said Lydia. "What's the pudding?"

"Stewed pears and synthetic custard, and plain cake baked in meat pans," said Mrs. Turner. "Where's my colander, Betty?"

"Ackcherly," said Betty, who was Mrs. Turner's elder niece, "it's on the hook. I'll get it."

Mrs. Turner took the colander and began turning out her potatoes, of which a dozen large dishes were put on a long table near the door of the servants' hall, together with piles of plates. At the same moment the younger niece opened the door into the stable yard and fifty children, rushing clumping into their dining-room, formed up in a rough, pushing, gabbling queue. The well-known smell of children and stew filled the air and Lydia wished for a moment every one were dead. The other helpers, who though extremely good and conscientious are too dull to mention, lifted great fish kettles of stew from the stove onto the serving-table and the ritual began.

"Who's doing the veg?" asked Lydia, getting behind the table.

"Well, ackcherly it's me," said Betty, "but you can if you like. I'll do the rabbit. I hope they didn't leave any eyes in."

Betty stationed herself behind a kettle of rabbit and with an iron ladle half filled a plate with a luscious stew. To this Lydia added potatoes and handed the plate to the child at the head of the queue. The other helpers served in the same way and each child carried its plate to its own seat. No sooner were they all served than a dozen or more came back, carrying their plates, with expressions of fastidiousness and insolence that Lydia tried hard not to see.

"Miss, I don't like rabbit."

"Miss, there's something nasty on my plate. Dorrie says it's kidneys."

"Miss, the lady didn't give me any gravy."

"Miss, Gracie's got a bigger bit than me."

"Miss, mother wrote to me not to touch rabbit."

"Miss, can't I have some more rabbit? I don't like potatoes."

"Miss, Jimmy Barker took three bits of bread and I ain't got none."

"Miss, I don't like rabbit. I want fish and chips."

Gradually the plaints subsided. Lydia went round the dining-room with the jug of water replenishing mugs. Already the tables were slopped with water, gravy, rabbit bones and splashings of potato. The smell of children and stew became thicker. The children themselves looked remarkably healthy and were well and warmly dressed. Lydia recognised some of the arted-up frocks from her working party and a couple of boys' jerseys that had belonged to her brother Robert's little boy Henry. The children filed back with their plates which the helpers rapidly emptied into the pig bucket. What with those who didn't like rabbit and those who didn't like potato and those who didn't like gravy and those who had taken three pieces of bread and only messed it about, and those who had eaten so many sweets already, bought with postal orders sent to them by their starving parents, that they could not eat at all, the bucket did very well.

The helpers now stationed themselves behind the serving table and dealt out stewed pears and custard, with a strip of cake to each. A number of children raised plaintive cries for or against these different articles of food, but the plaints, owing to fulness, were less violent. As soon as they had finished they rushed shrieking into the stable yard and so out into the street, and quiet fell.

[From *Cheerfulness Breaks In*]

Eliot Crawshay-Williams

This final selection (dated February 22, 1941) may not seem very mirthful. But to me it takes the place of many a long essay on the nature of British humor.

BOMBED

The telegram ran: *Residence bombed advise you to come.* So of course I went.

The end of the road was blocked, and over opposite was a notice DANGER: UNEXPLODED BOMB. But people were passing and repassing; and, leaving the taxi, I got out and walked on. Round the corner I should see! With a curious, slightly sick feeling I went to the corner and looked round. Round the corner wasn't there. It had just disappeared. Instead, there was a great gap in the row of houses, as if (I foolishly said to myself) it had lost a tooth.

Here was a view I had never seen in all those twenty-seven years during which I had walked up to that corner; a view of the backs of other houses, which had now a clear prospect of the river. I had not been prepared to find my home had *gone,* gone altogether.

One hardly noticed the grim heap of debris where the building had been; a heap, it surprised me to see, to a great extent formed, apparently, of earth. I said to one of the demolition men, "That earth, is it from some bomb-crater?" "No, sir," he told me, "that's the building." Earth! It had turned to earth.

I looked stupidly round. I looked vaguely up. And there, hanging above me in mid-air, I saw something I recognised.

A picture hanging on a wall, four storeys above. Even at that distance I recognised the picture. It was mine—one of Walter Greaves' engravings of Old Chelsea. And the wall was the wall of my flat. And there was my bath, projecting over the abyss.

But—I tried to adjust myself—it all looked so odd. Where was the rest? The door? The stairs?

It took a moment or so to realise that the flat had been sliced sideways; the east part had gone—with the landing and the stairs—and half my kitchen-dining-bathroom was left. And—*and*—the inner room! With my bookcases and bed. And my piano!

There was no glass left in any of the windows; the end of the flat stood open to the sky, like a doll's-house with the front removed; but almost certainly most of the furniture inside must be, if not intact, at all events existent.

I looked vacantly over the shapeless mound on which I was standing. A draggled envelope met my eye. I stooped and looked closer: *Eliot Crawshay-Williams, Esq.* In a writing now almost forgotten. I took up the envelope and dejectedly threw it down again.

There were still five bodies under that mass of bricks and earth and human possessions. The demolition gang were trying to get them out; though, of course, no hope remained that any living thing lay buried there. The foreman of the gang came up. I found it difficult to talk at first. Apart from other things, I felt a curious sort of shyness, seeing bits and scraps of my things lying there. Almost as if I myself were indecently exposed.

He was a genial soul, with a pungent sense of humour.

"Gets some surprises, we do, in this 'ere business," he told me. "I was diggin' for a little boy an' girl the other day, an' I come across an old chap of eighty."

He let me go up the somewhat tottering staircase of the next block of flats (evacuated), and over the roof right to the place where that roof abruptly ended. I had thought I might drop down on to the window-sill of my flat, get in through the smashed window, and see what things looked like inside. I had done it before, when I'd locked myself out, I explained.

"It's at yer own risk," he said, "an' it's nothing ter me what becomes of yer. But don't yer go comin' down on the 'eads of any of my chaps 'ere."

But when I got up I found I just couldn't do it; even if I could have got down, I could never have got back. And it was all pretty shaky.

Down at the bottom again, I found my friend had dragged out of the mess a cardboard target registering one or two shots, none of them very near to the bull.

"Not much of a shot, was you?" he remarked, holding the target in front of him and looking at it scornfully.

Suddenly, I remembered—dimly, yet with conviction—what it was.

"I didn't fire those shots," I said. "They were fired by the girl I was going to marry, at Earl's Court exhibition, nearly forty years ago. You remember Earl's Court Exhibition?"

"Don't I!" he said, with a dry smile. " 'Savage South Africa!' They was run in over that in the end. An' that was a good bit ago; when these young chaps," turning to the, considerably less mature, rest of the gang, "was in a fluid state."

"Or a twinkle in their fathers' eye," was my more modest suggestion.

He smiled approval, and pulled a hat-box out of the general chaos. "This yours?"

It was. I opened it. An old top hat—undamaged—and a Gunner cap from the last war.

"You can have 'em," I said.

"No, guvnor," he remonstrated. "Keep the army 'at—fer luck."

"All right," I said, and took it out.

Then, asking him to do his best for me, I turned to go.

"Well, guvnor," were his parting words, "you've 'ad a damn good spring clean, anyway."

•

Authors and Titles

12115